LADY HOPE

The Life and Work of Lady Hope of Carriden

Elizabeth Lady Hope

Born Hobart, Tasmania, 9 December 1842

Died Sydney, Australia 8 March 1922

Engraving from *The Methodist Temperance Magazine*

Vol XVII (1884) page 127

LADY HOPE

The Life and Work of Lady Hope of Carriden

L. R. Croft

ELMWOOD

First published in Great Britain by Elmwood Books in 2017.
Elmwood Books, 11, Ambleway, Walton-le-Dale, Preston,
Lancashire PR5 4JF

A copy of the British Library Cataloguing in Publication Data is
available from the British Library.

ISBN   978-0-9568089-5-0

Printed and bound in the United Kingdom.

Contents

Introduction

IF ONE LOOKS today at a map of India, one finds just off the coast east of Kakinada in the Bay of Bengal a small tadpole-shaped island. This small island provides a natural barrier that protects the port of Kakinada from cyclones and tidal waves, so making it one of the safest harbours in India. This small place has been, for many years, the home of a few fishermen and their families. However it has now begun to attract a significant number of tourists on account of its natural beauty and tranquillity. It is called - somewhat appropriately - 'Hope Island' and is thought to have been named after Lady Hope the subject of this biography. Nearby is the great Godavari River, sacred to many Indians, which has built across it the 'Arthur Cotton Dam' which is named after her father. Thus in this part of the world both father and daughter are permanently remembered.

The life of Lady Hope is not only a story of a remarkable daughter of the British Empire, but it is also very much the story of the daughter of a remarkable father. The father was General Sir Arthur Cotton, a member of the aristocratic Stapleton-Cotton family whose ancient home was Combermere Abbey in Cheshire. As will be seen later in this book, both father and daughter gained the admiration and respect of Florence Nightingale. She referred to General Cotton as 'a great friend' and 'the most perfect master' in connection with his work in India.

Sadly Arthur Cotton has long been forgotten in England, however, in India, where he worked for some four decades, his memory is very much alive. Indeed he is venerated to the extent that he is worshipped very much like a semi-god. There are literally hundreds of statues of him throughout Southern India around which celebrations are held each year on the anniversary of his birth. It is claimed that he is the only Englishman who has had a statue erected to his memory since Independence. There is also a Sir Arthur Cotton museum in the State of Andhra Pradesh and the recently constructed dam across the Godavari River has been named in his honour. In addition to all these honours, the Jawaharlal Nehru Technological University has recently made a documentary film of his life and work. All this is in contrast to how he has been largely forgotten in England. However things may change, for only recently the author has noticed that his marble bust has been dusted down and moved from the basement of the National Portrait Gallery, and placed in the Eminent Victorians Gallery. It is now housed in the same room as Florence Nightingale and positioned between Baden Powell and Scott of the Antarctic. However, unlike these British heroes, there has only ever been one biography of Arthur Cotton, and that was written shortly after his death in 1899, by his daughter, Lady Hope. From Lady Hope's illuminating biography it is very appropriate that his portrait should now be alongside that of Florence Nightingale, for they were great friends, and collaborated together on numerous projects. Miss Nightingale greatly admired General Cotton, as she did his daughter, for her social campaigning and for highlighting the dreadful social depri-vation that existed in the Empire's capital city.

Lady Hope's story is therefore very much a story of her father. She was his only surviving child and he had a great influence on her. They came to have similar religious beliefs. Although in practice he was an Anglican, he recognised all denominations and gave them all equal respect. And this was how Lady Hope also lived her Christian faith. Both were evangelical but with a very practical 'hands-on' form of Christianity. This is not altogether surprising as he was by training an engineer. As an engineer he was remarkably inventive, as was his daughter, for she also patented at least one invention. For a woman of her generation this was something quite exceptional. Furthermore, both father and daughter had a keen interest in technological developments. General Cotton was one of the first engineers to harness steam power and use it in irrigation. He also invented a steam rotary engine and experimented with early bicycles, and his daughter was one of the first women in Britain to own a phonograph as well as a motorcar.

As a soldier General Cotton had distinguished himself in action. In the face of danger he was fearless and this is evident from his military record. His daughter also was a brave and courageous individual, as we will discover in the forthcoming pages, notably when she was faced with possible death at the hands of a brutal thug who held a pistol to her head. He ordered her not to scream, whereupon she responded by telling him in no uncertain terms, that she was not the sort of woman to scream.

Then when she was challenged to take her Christian message to the mean dark streets and alleyways of 'Outcast London'; she never hesitated. So for several years she worked alone in the filthy slums of Central London, among an underclass of humanity. Here she ventured down alleyways where even policemen feared to go, so as to take the gospel message. It was here she entered not only the world we know now from the writings of Charles Dickens, but also the world of 'Jack the Ripper'. This was an area of central London populated by hundreds of prostitutes, so for a woman to venture alone was extremely dangerous. But she had left behind a comfort-able life as the 'lady of the manor' at her Scottish estate and now lived a new life alongside the poor and destitute. For an aristocratic woman to do this at this period in time, indicates not only of her strength of character, but also a measure of her Christian faith.

What does become clear when one studies Lady Hope's life is just how much she was a daughter of the Empire. She had been born in Tasmania and as a child had lived in India, where she travelled extensively following her father as he engaged in various projects. There followed a stay in Mauritius and then Australia, and then back to India. She later stayed on St Helena, as Charles Darwin had done some years before. In England the family moved around and then they settled in Ireland for some three years. On her marriage she lived at Carriden in Scotland and then after her husband's death, it was back to London. Over the following years she travelled extensively in Europe, and following her second marriage she visited South Africa and Egypt. Then in the last decade of her life she lived in North America, first in Canada, then New England and finally California and just before she died, she returned to Australia. There can be few Victorian women who had seen so much of the world.

But it is not just her travel experience that is so exceptional. What is remarkable is the variety of eminent Victorians she had encountered during her lifetime. To list them would be a 'Who's Who' of the nineteenth century. However, to name just a few one would include: David Livingstone, Florence Nightingale, General Gordon, Queen Victoria, Queen Mary, the Duchess of Teck, Charles Darwin, Lord Shaftesbury, Earl Cairns, Dwight Moody, William Booth, Agnes Weston, Baroness Burdett-Coutts, Dr. Barnardo and so one could go on.

The story that is now told is a remarkable one, and it is one that is told for the very first time. It relates how a young aristocratic woman highlighted the dreadful conditions of an entire underclass living in London, the capital city of the greatest empire the world had ever seen. The manner in which she did this reads more like fiction than it does fact. But it is a story that until now has not been told. Lady Hope, herself told nobody, and left no documents, other than a somewhat disguised account. The reason was that if she had made known the facts it would have scandalised Victorian society and she had no wish to do that, and neither did she wish to gain self-aggrandisement for her work.

Then there is a second remarkable story which is also now told for the very first time. It is how her trusting and generous nature was taken advantage of by probably the most notorious conman of all time. This story goes to the very heart of the Empire and involves the highest elite, together with the world's wealthiest man.

However old memories die hard, and the story for which Lady Hope is best remembered today involves her relationship with Charles Darwin. The Darwin family have always been adamant that she had never met Darwin, but the consensus among historians and biographers today is to give them the benefit of the doubt and suggest that they were simply mistaken, or at best, suffered from injured pride. I leave the reader to judge as to who might be telling the truth as the evidence is unfolded in the pages that follow.

For many years the identity of the woman who claimed to have interviewed Darwin shortly before his death was lost in the mists of myth and legend. Darwin biographers, even as late as 1989, were reporting that this woman could not be identified and that the story was just a myth. Even Professor James Moore of the Open University, an eminent biographer of Charles Darwin, had to confess that even after studying this particular incident for some twenty years, he could not pin-point who exactly the woman was. All this changed in 1989, when I published my biography, *The Life and Death of Charles Darwin*, in which I correctly identified the woman to be Elizabeth Lady Hope, daughter of General Sir Arthur Cotton. Now that her identity was established, it was for writers and biographers to turn their pen to denigrating her character. So we read in books from such reliable publishers as Oxford University Press and those of the universities of Harvard, and John Hopkins, that not only was Lady Hope a fraudster, but that she was a down-right liar. Sadly many of the individuals who have made these mischievous claims have failed to do even the most basic of background research.

This being so, my main purpose in writing this biography is to make available the results of my research, and to correct much of the misinformation that has been published. In addition to this my aim has been to attempt to illuminate the remarkable character of Elizabeth Lady Hope, and in so doing to obtain for her that respect and recognition which she so justly deserves.

## CHAPTER 1

Family Background

THE SUBJECT OF this biography was born Elizabeth Reid Cotton on 9 December 1842 in Hobart Town, Tasmania, the first child of Arthur Thomas Cotton (1803-99) and his wife, Elizabeth, née Learmonth (1814-1907). In later life she became Lady Hope, however, throughout the rest of this book she will be referred to simply as Elizabeth. At the time of her birth, Arthur Cotton was an officer with the Royal Engineers and was in the colony on sick leave as a consequence of exhaustion following prolonged work on the construction of anicuts (dams) across the Cauvery and Coleroon rivers in the Madras Presidency of Southern India (now the modern state of Tamil Nadu).

Captain Arthur Cotton was to become one of the most outstanding men of the Victorian Age. In the National Portrait Gallery his portrait is now between that of Baden Powell, and Scott of the Antarctic. He had been born into an aristocratic military family that could trace their roots back to the twelfth century, with the ancestral home at Combermere Abbey in Cheshire. His cousin was General Sir Stapleton Cotton who at the time of Elizabeth's birth was Viscount Combermere, whose statue now stands outside Chester Castle.

Arthur Cotton had been born in 1803, at Woodcote, in Oxfordshire, the tenth son of Henry Calveley Cotton and his wife Matilda (née Lockwood). At the age of 15 he entered the Addiscombe Military College near Croydon, which was the military college of the East India Company. In 1819 after a distinguished career at the college, he was commissioned in the Madras Engineers.

Then in September 1821, after a short spell with the Ordnance Survey in Wales, he joined the office of the Chief Engineer in Madras. His first posting was to survey the Paumben Pass (Adam's Bridge) the sea channel between the southern tip of India and the island of Sri Lanka. He later served in the 1st Burmese War (1824-26) and was involved in the capture of Rangoon, and Donabew, and took part in the jungle fighting at Paghammew that ended the war. During this time he demonstrated exceptional bravery and courage and was mentioned in dispatches.

Following the Burmese War he returned to Madras. It was during the voyage that he experienced a religious conversion that completely changed his life, and he became a deeply committed evangelical Christian.

On his return to Madras he was appointed the Superintendent Engineer, and in 1828 he was given the task of improving and extending the irrigation of southern India, particularly the construction of anicuts (dams) across the Cauvery and Coleroon Rivers. However, in early 1830 he suffered a breakdown in his health and he returned to England on sick leave. During his recuperation he assisted his brother, the Reverend Richard Cotton, vicar of Denchworth, in carrying out parish work. In the autumn of 1832, after his health improved, he returned to India by an overland route. This journey was by way of Baghdad where he encountered the missionary, Anthony Groves. At the time the population of Baghdad had been devastated by plague which was still present in the city. Unfortunately he contracted the disease and was near to death, so much so, that his grave was prepared. However he miraculously recovered and in later life he would rejoice at being one of the few people who had actually visited their own grave. It was during this illness that he spent time learning the Arabic language and some years later he published a book on the subject which is still in use today.

On his return to Madras he continued with the work of building the two anicuts across the Coleroon and Cauvery rivers. What was notable in his work was his clear ability to understand the technical demands necessary to build dams on an unstable sandy river bed. When the dams were completed in the winter of 1835-36, it became immediately apparent that they would be of immeasurable benefit to the local population by ensuring that widespread famine could be avoided.

However the work had exhausted him; resulting in a further breakdown in his health. On this occasion he was allowed to go to Tasmania to recover. So on 12 December 1838 he arrived at Hobart aboard the *Guillardon* and for a time he lived in Hobart Town. Here he was invited to stay with Captain Beecher, of the Bengal Native Infantry, and it was while he was with Beecher that he was introduced to a young lady who would later become his wife. She was Elizabeth Learmonth, the daughter of Thomas Learmonth, an Australian landowner. At this time he also cultivated a friendship with Sir John Franklin, the governor of the island, and he had the opportunity of visiting the ships, *Erebus* and *Terror*, while they were in Tasmanian waters during the 1839 expedition to the Antarctic.

It was during this period that he experimented with a centrifugal steam engine, a primitive form of steam turbine, which he had built himself and which he hoped might be useful in his irrigation work. The Madras Government acknowledged his work on this invention in an official citation published in October 1838. Unfortunately due to inadequate parts the machine exploded and he suffered serious injury. For many weeks after this accident he lay dangerously ill, all alone in his hotel room, until a local Christian family learnt of his plight and they took him in. After much tender care, at their home in Longford on the Norfolk Plains, he recovered from his dreadful injuries. What is striking from this incident is the lack of concern he had for his own well-being. He was at death's door but to him the most important thing was how many revolutions per minute his machine had achieved.

This accident made additional sick leave necessary and it was during his extended convalescence that he courted his future wife, and towards the end of 1839, they became engaged. However, the proposed marriage was not encouraged by Miss Learmonth's family who thought that his health was so poor that it was unlikely he would live very long. (How wrong this turned out to be as he was to live for another sixty years!)

His fiancée Elizabeth Livingstone Learmonth had been born on 1 June 1814 at Polmont, near Stirling, the daughter of Thomas Learmonth (1783-1869) and Christian Donald. (The middle name of Livingstone, was derived from her maternal grandmother, Margaret Livingstone, heiress to the Parkhall estate in Stirlingshire.) The family had moved to Tasmania some years earlier when her father had established himself as a successful merchant in Hobart Town. He later became a large land owner in Australia and had business interests in wool, and tallow production in Geelong, near Melbourne as well as in India.

The Livingstone Learmonths were an ancient Scottish family that could trace their roots back as far as Thomas of Ercildoune, also known as 'Thomas the Rhymer' (1220-1298). Thomas the Rhymer features in early Scottish literature and is believed to have been the inspiration for Washington Irving's *Rip Van Winkle*. Today there remains in the Border country, near Earlston, an old ruin known as 'Rhymer's Tower' which at one time was the ancestral home of the Livingstone Learmonths. Indeed, Thomas Learmonth's sons, Thomas, and Somerville who became wealthy landowners in Australia, incorporated a stone from Rhymer's tower in their mansion 'Ercildoun' which they built at Buninyong, near Geelong in Victoria. It is of some considerable interest, in the light of what follows in this account, that Thomas the Rhymer was reputed to have powers of prophecy, and was known as 'True Thomas' as he was incapable of telling a lie.

In October 1840 Arthur Cotton returned to Madras. His return proved to be premature as on arrival he was found to be deemed unfit so he was promptly sent back to Tasmania for further recuperation. He landed at Launceston on board the *Nerio* on 6 October 1841. This extended convalescence enabled him to continue his relationship with his fiancée and on 29 October 1841 they were married. The marriage took place at the bride's home at Kempton (Green Ponds) and was officiated by the Reverend John Lillie. Kempton, at this time, was a small settlement some 49 km north of Hobart, just off the main highway. It had originally been known as Green Ponds, but the name was changed in 1838 to Kempton after Mr Antony Kemp a soldier–merchant who owned substantial land there. Later the newly married couple settled in a small cottage on the Norfolk Plains where he spent more time building another steam engine which he used to irrigate his garden. However, Captain Cotton was still suffering considerable ill-health. We know this from an article he published, at this time, in the first volume of the *Tasmanian Journal of Natural Science* in which he made an extraordinary statement to be included in a scientific article, namely: 'my state of health is such that I find it impossible to give due attention to anything...' This being so he was nonetheless very happy with his new wife as they had much in common, particularly their religious views. She was a Scottish Presbyterian and very much also an evangelical Christian. This marital happiness was further increased when on 9 December 1842 their first child was born, and christened Elizabeth, after her mother. Then in early April 1843, his health having sufficiently improved, the Cotton family left Tasmania for India. Some five years later they returned to this colony but stayed only for a short time before moving on to Victoria.

## CHAPTER 2

An Indian Childhood

IN THE APRIL of 1843, the Cotton family returned to India. On their arrival it was decided that as Captain Cotton was still not fully recovered he would be assigned 'lighter' duties. This involved a posting to Vizagapatam in the Madras Presidency and entailed a crossing of the Bay of Bengal in a small vessel. While they were at sea they were caught up in a major cyclone, which caused immense devastation with many ships being wrecked. Elizabeth at this time was just a small baby some three months old; but years later her mother described to her the terrible journey and told her how throughout the hurricane her father had remained calm, trusting in God, and how they came through safely. On arrival her father's duties involved the building of a church at Waltair, and in the construction of sea defences along the coast. Two years were spent here, and during this period another child was born in 1844. The boy was christened George Michael, but sadly he died soon after birth.

When Arthur Cotton was back to normal health he returned to the work on the construction of irrigation schemes in the Godavari delta. The Godavari is one of the great sacred rivers of India, along with the Ganges and the Indus. It rises in the mountains some 70 miles north-east of Bombay (Mumbai) and runs in a south east direction, when after some hundred miles it falls into the Bay of Bengal, about 250 miles north of Madras (Chennai). It is a massive river with a discharge some three times that of the Nile and almost 200 times that of the Thames. At the time the Godavari region was in a desperate state, as there had been several famines when millions of people had died of starvation. Captain Cotton's task was to investigate the possibility of constructing a huge anicut across the river, to conserve the water and provide irrigation to the land. This was an immense project as the width of the river was almost four miles. He was appointed in charge of the project and the family settled on the bank of the river several miles from the town of Rajahmundry. They pitched tents and erected a rough building of Palmyra posts and thatched it with Palmyra leaves. Shortly afterwards another baby was born. Her mother recalled that the child was, 'a sweet babe, who was her father's delight' but the baby sadly died at about twelve months old and was buried at Rajahmundry, in a little graveyard looking down to the river.

Then in 1847 work began in earnest on the construction of the anicuts. At first the family lived near the construction site adjacent to the river but they soon found the place liable to flooding. On one occasion the family returned home to find that the river had flooded and the waters had entered the house and was sweeping away all their belongings, including Captain Cotton's parade hat in its tin box, and a favourite book, which was particularly cherished. This was the autobiography of the French Christian mystic, Madam Guyon. For them to watch their special book floating down the river was just too much, so they got a boat and rescued the volume. Many years later, Elizabeth reflected on this incident and recorded that the book had in fact been retrieved and at the time of her writing, it was in pride of place on her own bookshelf.

This experience led the family to move to a residence on higher ground. Their new home was an isolated bungalow at the top of a hill and was known as 'The Dolphin's Nose'. By this time, Arthur Cotton had been promoted to Major Cotton. Then in 1847 work began in earnest on the construction of the anicuts. It was an ambitious project as special techniques were needed to construct the dam on the sandy river bed. In particular it was necessary to construct an enormous aqueduct to carry water across the tidal part of the river. An enormous quantity of rock was needed and thousands of local people were employed as labourers. It was exhausting work and the immense pressure on Major Cotton proved too much and he had a further breakdown in health. When the Governor of Madras was informed of his ill-health he arranged for him and his wife to have a sabbatical in Bangalore, while another married officer looked after their children.

At this time child mortality in British Army families stationed in India was extremely high and Elizabeth's mother had gone through several pregnancies only to lose her babies. Indeed, India was not the best place for Europeans to bring up children, as there was much disease. Furthermore, the climate was extreme, and the housing was usually in makeshift tents that were completely inadequate. There were also the hazards of poisonous snakes and other wild animals. In particular, for a soldier's family travelling alone through isolated and lonely regions, as the Cotton family frequently did, was particularly hazardous. On one occasion while Mrs Cotton was travelling alone with Elizabeth, through a remote area they stopped at a rest bungalow to shelter from the extreme heat only to find that there was no food available. They were desperate, so much so, that Elizabeth's mother offered up a short prayer. Then within a short time a servant appeared immaculately dressed, as if he had just arrived from England. He entered their shelter and informed them that his master had just pitched his tent nearby and had heard that an English lady and her children had stopped to shelter. He enquired as to whether they would like food and drink. They gladly accepted and the gentleman sent over an abundance of delicious fresh food, yet they never actually met the man, nor even knew his name.

On another occasion Elizabeth's health suffered and she was seriously ill, the precise nature of this illness is not recorded. It was possibly cholera as she was so badly affected that she almost died. She was saved by the fact that the doctor who was called to attend to her, had had much experience of treating this disease gained in a London hospital during the cholera epidemic of 1849.[1] There is no record as to the doctor's name but some twenty years later Elizabeth met him again while they were both working as hospital visitors in a London hospital. Although he was now much older, with white hair, she nevertheless immediately recognised him. It was a thankful reunion. They talked about life in India and recalled the previous occasion of their meeting, when he told her of how near to death she had been. In return she expressed her gratitude to him and thanked him for what he had done to save her life.

It is possible that this was the occasion when part of her treatment was to shave off all her hair. In her autobiography of her childhood, *Sunny Footsteps, or When I was a Child*, published in 1879, she tells of the time when all her hair was shaved off. Shortly afterwards she was travelling by palanquin, carried by several servants, when during a rest break in the heat of the day, the curtains were pulled apart and several dark faces peered in, somewhat mystified to see a white child with a bald head.

Besides disease there were other hazards, such as prowling tigers and poisonous insects and snakes. As they lived near to the quarry where the rock was obtained for the building of the anicuts, occasionally the blasting disturbed the snakes and they would take refuge in their house. On one occasion she recalled that the nanny had seen a large cobra glide through an open window into the children's bedroom. The nanny immediately warned the servants but after a search they could not locate the creature. But as the nanny was putting the children to bed in the evening it was again observed. Fortunately her father was at home and after being called, he shot the creature with his rifle. However, the snake was not killed outright. Although it was fatally wounded, it raised up its head, with its hood fully extended and in its rage spat venom at those present. Eventually one of the servants killed it, but this incident must have been a terrifying experience for Elizabeth and her small brother to witness.

There were many other hazards. As they lived near the quarry they would occasionally go and watch the blasting of the rock, always standing at a safe distance away. But on one occasion the explosive had been badly placed and fragments of rock blasted in their direction. There was no time to take cover and they were showered with sharp pieces of rock. Fortunately, no one was injured, but she recalled that her straw sunhat had received a direct hit with a sharp splinter of rock passing cleanly through it. It was indeed another near miss for her.

Then there were the hazards in travelling. Usually they would follow her father around and on many occasions they would travel by sea. On one occasion when she was travelling with her mother, they had been at sea for some two days when they were hit by a severe hurricane. The ship was battered by the wind and the waves swept across the vessel. The storm was so severe that the sea broke the port-hole of their cabin and washed the cabin fittings against the door making it impossible for them to get out. The situation became desperate but no matter how loud they shouted they couldn't be heard above the roaring of the gale. Eventually the storm died down and they were rescued by the ship's carpenter cutting an opening in the cabin wall through which they made their escape. They were then given the captain's cabin, but the sea remained rough and they didn't reach their destination of Madras for some two weeks after setting sail.

Towards the end of the year 1848, on account of her father's health he was again advised to seek recuperation and the family sailed for Australia. At the time the only route possible was by way of Mauritius, which had been a British colony since 1810. After a pleasant voyage they arrived at the capital, Port Louis, in what she recalled as 'lovely moonlight'. The harbour was packed with sailing ships, and amongst them was a large British man-of-war. When their vessel was recognised as being British the ship's band played the national anthem for them. The next day they ventured ashore and explored the town and took advantage of the shops. They then sought accommodation in the small village of Cure Pipe, situated in the central plain of Mauritius, where the climate was more agreeable than on the coast. Their little cottage was called 'Curepeep' and it was here they stayed for some eight weeks, while they waited for a ship to take them on to Australia. Young Elizabeth and her brother soon made friends with other children of the village and they would enjoy riding on the back of a giant tortoise that lived in the area. Many years later she was reminded of this animal, when she read a biography of Admiral Keppel in which the same tortoise was described. Although giant tortoises are today a major tourist attraction in Mauritius, the particularly large species described by Elizabeth in her memoir is now extinct.

Early in 1849 they set sail from Mauritius aboard the sailing ship, *Martha*, bound for Australia. Some weeks later they arrived in Melbourne, which was then just a small town of some 10,000 inhabitants, having been founded just ten years before. Here they stayed with her uncle in the Geelong district, some 45 miles south west of Melbourne, where the Learmonth brothers had sheep farms, as well as a large tallow factory.

Geelong was a small port on Corio Bay in the State of Victoria where wool products were exported. It had a warm pleasant climate and was ideal for her father's recuperation. At the time Elizabeth was just six-years-old and was able to accompany her father on his many country rambles in the nearby Australian outback. She found her father to be a good companion as he took great trouble to interest her in the notable features of the landscape, and to the natural history of the area. Of a morning they would go in search of 'manna', a white, deliciously sweet, natural product (presumably a form of honeydew) that could be found lying on logs, or blades of grass. They would collect it and take it home to eat for breakfast. When they were out in the heat of the day they would occasionally take refuge at a remote hostelry which was called '*The Squeakers*'. It had a notorious reputation and was usually frequented by ex-convicts and other desperadoes. One wonders what these men would have thought of this frail and delicate-looking Englishman and his small daughter when they arrived in search of shelter from the heat.

Overall it was a pleasant time for the Cotton family, and with the agreeable climate and the days of relaxation, Captain Cotton's health improved and they were soon able to return to India. However, shortly after they left Australia, gold was discovered in the Ballarat district of Geelong and in a short time the place witnessed a gold-rush stampede which became known as the 'Victoria gold rush'.

On their return to India, Captain Cotton continued with his work on the construction of the giant anicuts across the Godavari River. Young Elizabeth continued to grow up in a very loving environment and during these formative years she was greatly influenced by her parents' religious convictions. Her father was a devout Anglican, and when travelling in India he would often take the services himself if there was no church or mission nearby. He had little time for sectarianism, and had the greatest regard for all Christian mission-aries, no matter what denomination they represented. To him they were all the Lord's servants and that was good enough.

One can see how this religious background influenced young Elizabeth. Besides the teachings she received from her parents, she received instruction from local missionaries, and when she was no more than eight-years-old, she would travel alone on horseback, at least once a week, over what she recalled as 'beautiful hills' to a local mission station, 'a lovely cottage covered in jessamine and roses'. Here she would receive Bible teaching. On other occasions she would meet missionaries that her father had invited home, one in particular, impressed her. He was a German missionary, and her father informed her that he had a reputation as being a very brave and courageous preacher of the Gospel. Unfortunately, she failed to record his name, however the memory of him remained with her for the rest of her life.

CHAPTER 3

This England

Towards the end of 1854 Colonel Cotton's health was again of concern so that his medical advisers recommended that he should return to England with his family. At the time his wife was again pregnant, so they waited until after she had given birth in the February of the following year. The new addition to the family was a little girl who was christened Ann Lynch. Shortly afterwards on 8 March 1855, the family set sail from Madras for England. The family now consisted of, Colonel Cotton and his wife, Elizabeth, together with four children, young Elizabeth, the eldest child now just twelve years old, two brothers, Alfred aged five and Arthur Stokes aged three, and baby Ann Lynch. They faced a long voyage of some four months by way of Cape Town - the shorter route by way of the Suez was not opened until 1870. Their vessel was the *Earl of Hardwicke*, a traditional sailing ship with auxiliary steam engine and paddle wheels. The *Earl of Hardwicke* had been launched in 1838 and worked on the London-India route. She was a reasonably large vessel of some 850 tons and 170 feet long and 36 feet in breath. Her captain was Robert Dawson Crawford (1814-1902). He had been born at Chelsfield Court Lodge, Kent in 1814, the same year as Elizabeth's mother. He was a religious man, having been brought up in an Anglican home, as well as having a brother who was an Anglican priest. With this background he got on well with Colonel Cotton. However as a very down-to-earth man who had previously captained convict ships to the penal colonies of Australia, he was concerned, as to how a man with Colonel

Cotton's exceptionally active mind was going to cope with the monotony of a long voyage. In the event his concerns were unfounded for as soon after setting sail, Colonel Cotton approached him with the proposal of organising Bible study and prayer meetings in the saloon lounge after breakfast each day. Although sympathetic to this suggestion the captain refused permission on the grounds that the saloon was the only public area of the ship and that to occupy it in this way would be unfair to other passengers that might not hold his religious views. This rebuff did not affect their friendship and Colonel Cotton soon found himself a quiet corner of the ship where he could hold his religious meetings and on occasions Captain Crawford himself attended.

In June, the *Earl of Hardwicke* reached the South Atlantic island of St Helena, which had been a British colony since 1834. For young Elizabeth the approach to the island was a spectacular experience. In years to come she recalled how they sailed into Jamestown harbour with the steep mountain sides towering above their vessel, and how a small boat took them ashore, when they had to scramble up the rock face on scaling ladders so as to reach the land above, in much the same way as Charles Darwin had done some nineteen years before.

Following breakfast on their first day on the island, young Elizabeth and her father travelled on mules and ponies to Longwood, where Napoleon had been imprisoned in 1815, and where he had died in 1821. They found his tomb to be surrounded by iron railings, and under the shade of a large weeping willow. Overall it was a very isolated and peaceful place that left her feeling somewhat melancholy. Later they were able to take a tour of Napoleon's house, which again gave her a feeling of sadness, just as it had done to Darwin. In his journal Charles Darwin had complained as to how changeable the weather was, on the island, and how frequently it rained. This was also Elizabeth's experience for she recalled how in the morning it had been fine and sunny, but in the afternoon on their journey back to the town, there was heavy rain and her clothes became soaked through. Then on the following day as they set sail from St. Helena she complained to her mother that she felt unwell and remained so for the remainder of the voyage. This must have been a particularly anxious time for her parents as there had already been serious illness on board with an outbreak of smallpox which had caused panic amongst the passengers. By the time they came in sight of the English coast some fourteen passengers had died including a number of invalid soldiers who were returning home from India.

On Monday 2 July 1855 they docked at Gravesend and young Elizabeth was able to step ashore for the first time on to the solid ground of England, a place she had heard and read so much about. It was exceptionally hot that July with temperatures well in the 90s. However besides the temperature, her parents found England remarkably changed since they were last in the country some decades before. In particular, they found London to be a very different place to how they remembered it. They also found the country to be involved in a major war with Russia in the Crimea.

Although Colonel Cotton had family he could have stayed with, he decided to take his family to the home of an old friend. So they travelled the short distance to Penge, near Beckenham in Kent, where Colonel Cotton's friend Frederick Chalmers was the vicar. Some thirty-six years before, the Reverend Chalmers had served in India and had fought alongside Colonel Cotton in the Burmese War. Now he was the vicar of Beckenham. Being an evangelical it was his practice to have open-house religious meetings at noon each day. If the weather permitted this meeting would be held in the rectory garden. On this particular occasion as the weather was so hot, the meeting was held in the cooler drawing room with the French doors left open. So when the Cotton family arrived they found the small group of worshippers praying, so they slipped in at the back unannounced. It was only when it came to repeating the Lord's Prayer that Colonel Cotton's voice was recognised. It had been some 36 years since the two men had last seen each other and now they were able to renew their friendship and introduce their family members.

After many years in India, and the long voyage home the Cotton family found the hospitality at Beckenham to be a great blessing. Colonel Cotton was still quite ill, and his wife had three children and a small baby to care for. At Beckenham they received the encouragement and uplift they all needed. In particular, it gave the family much spiritual renewal. For years they had lived in make-shift homes in a tropical climate with irregular contact with mainstream Christianity. Now at the Beckenham rectory they were at the powerhouse of the evangelical movement in Britain. It was here that they were introduced to the minister's father-in-law, the Reverend William Marsh D.D., the noted evangelical author whose writings had influenced Jane Austen. They also met Catherine Marsh, the minister's sister-in-law, who is now recognised as one of the five great evangelical Catherines of the nineteenth century.[2]

Indeed at this date Catherine Marsh was at the peak of her success as an evangelical author. Her book, *Memorials of Captain Hedley Vicars* was one of the literary blockbusters of the Victorian Age. It had sold some 78,000 copies in its first year, as it had captured the mood of the day. It was a book that told in emotive terms the life of a brave Christian soldier who had died at the battle of Sebastopol (Sevastopol). Thus the meeting with Catherine Marsh was highly significant to young Elizabeth's religious development. As she was on the verge of her teenage years, it was to have an important influence upon her. Indeed, this short period at the Beckenham rectory was to have a significant effect also on the entire Cotton family.

Following their stay at the Beckenham rectory they moved on and rented a house in Tunbridge Wells. However, Colonel Cotton's health was still very fragile and he found that the place was too busy, making it difficult for him to get the rest he most needed. As winter approached they sought a warmer climate and moved to Weston-super-mare where they settled for the winter of 1855. Then they moved to a small cottage in Nailsworth, in the Cotswolds. For an Anglo-Indian family this little haven was an indescribable paradise. It was an old-fashioned cottage, with clean fresh water and surrounded by a beautiful flower garden and orchard. This was the England that young Elizabeth had only read and dreamt about. The pleasure she had in living in such a peaceful and beautiful place was to give her a lasting love for this country that would never leave her. Sadly, as this account will reveal, in her old age she was forced to leave the country and live in a foreign land, however that was to be in the future.

Living in such an idyllic place had a beneficial effect on her father's health and he soon became restless and wanted to return to public life. In order to be nearer to the heart of things they decided to move to London. However this turned out to be a disastrous decision.London in the 1850s was not as Colonel Cotton remembered it from the early part of the century. It was now an overcrowded industrial city. The air and water were greatly polluted, and the sanitation, where it existed, was completely inadequate. It was grossly over-populated and an extremely unhealthy place to live. Some years earlier, in September 1842, Charles Darwin had found this to be the case and had wisely moved his family to live some 17 miles south of the capital in the small rural village of Downe in Kent.

So in early 1856 the Cotton family took up residence at 17 Wimpole Street, in Marylebone. Not long afterwards the entire family went down with whooping cough, with the exception of young Elizabeth. Colonel Cotton was particularly badly affected and it was a major set-back to his recovery. Then worse was to follow; when her little sister, Ann Lynch, just 12- months-old fell victim to the disease, and died on 11 February 1856. The death certificate records the sad details. The child had suffered for some five weeks, and the cause of death was stated as being a result of

'Pertussis' (whooping cough) and 10 days of convulsions. This was a particularly tragic blow for the family. Young Elizabeth, many years later, mentioned the family's 'great grief' at the loss, and mentioned 'the great blank' that had been left in her life after losing her little sister.

Towards the end of the year the family decided to move out of London to a healthier place, yet within easy reach of the capital. They decided on the village of Hadley Green, on the outskirts of Barnet in North London. Soon afterwards the missionary David Livingstone and his family arrived to be their neighbour. He had only just returned from his exploration of Central Africa having been re-united with his family on 9 December 1856. Although, Elizabeth's grandmother's maiden name had been Livingstone, they were not related to the famous explorer, however, the two families were soon acquainted and became firm friends. This was particularly strong as they all worshipped together at the parish church. Years later, Elizabeth recalled how she had attended a missionary meeting in the local schoolroom when David Livingstone gave a lecture on his travels. She noticed in particular that he had great difficulty in finding the right word to express himself, on account of the fact that he had been away from English-speaking people for so long. However, during informal meetings with him, she found that he could greatly entertain them with vivid accounts of his travels and adventures.

Another neighbour who befriended the Cotton family was Wilbraham Taylor, whose residence, Hadley Hurst, was a large red brick Georgian manor house that remains an impressive landmark in Hadley today. Mr Wilbraham Taylor was an eminent London solicitor, who acted as usher to Queen Victoria. He was also secretary of the Church Protestant Defence Society. His daughter, Janetta Mary, had much in common with young Elizabeth, particularly their religious convictions, so they soon became firm friends. She would later become a noted hymn writer under her married name of Trench. As Anglicans, the Cotton family attended worship at Christ Church, in Hadley village. This church had been built about ten years before on the generous donation of Captain Trotter of Dyrham Park. Its first incumbent had been a converted Jew, Alfred Moritz Myers. His successor was the Reverend William Pennefather (1816-1873) who was to have a profound effect on the religious development of young Elizabeth.

Pennefather and his wife, Catherine (1817-93) were passionate evangelicals. Catherine Pennefather had an aristocratic background and was the daughter of Admiral James King and granddaughter of Robert King, the Earl of Kingston. The couple were to make a major contribution to the religious revival of the mid-Victorian period. In 1856 Pennefather started an annual missionary conference which became known as the Mildmay Conference. Its object was to increase the personal holiness of those who attended, and as such it was very much a precursor of today's Keswick Convention. The first meeting was held in June 1856 when some 120 individuals attended, but this greatly increased over the following years to many thousands, and it had a major effect on Christianity in Britain. In 1869 the Mildmay conference hall was opened in the East End of London, which could accommodate some 3000 people for the annual conference which was usually held in the last week of June. During those years young Elizabeth attended regularly and in later years she became a well-respected conference speaker.

Catherine Pennefather was an equally active Christian worker as her husband. In 1858 she became the President of the Association of Female Workers, a charitable organisation that had its headquarters at Mildmay. Here she established the Mildmay Institution to train women as deaconesses to work in the community. Mildmay was also used for other good causes. There was a widows' sewing class, and a flower mission, where floral displays were made and distributed freely to sick people across the city. During the cholera epidemic of 1866 these women became known as 'angels' on account of their distinctive uniforms, and they would work in the most deprived areas of the city. Catherine Pennefather later founded a charitable hospital which remarkably survived until 1982 when it was closed. However, following a local campaign it was re-opened in 1985. It then became the first hospital in Europe to care for AIDS patients and it was here that Princess Diana famously shook hands with an AIDS sufferer, so removing much of the stigma associated with this disease.

Probably the Pennefathers' greatest legacy to Christianity in this country is the crucial role they played by inviting an unknown American preacher to Britain. Unfortunately, the Reverend Pennefather never lived to witness the spectacular religious revival that followed, however his widow did. She saw how the whole nation became galvanized by the man. The unknown American was Dwight L. Moody. And it was Moody who would open the door for young Elizabeth to find a role as an evangelist, but this was some time in the future.

What was to shake Britain to the core in 1857, was not religious revival but serious disturbances in the Empire, particularly India. Although trouble had been brewing for some time in India, it was not until 10 May 1857 that the so-called Indian Mutiny started. This began at Meerut where sepoys massacred Europeans and then occupied Delhi, with the insurrection quickly spreading to other areas. Colonel Cotton was immediately recalled to India and he left soon afterwards. For his family this proved to be a period of great uncertainty. Communication with India was a lengthy process and news would filter across continents very slowly. During this time families only heard occasional fragments of incidents that usually horrified them, fuelling their sense of anxiety and foreboding. Indeed some families were known to have rejoiced when they received the news that a loved one had died of cholera, rather than at the hands of the rebels. Elizabeth's mother later referred to this period as "those terrible weeks". However, her husband fortunately missed most of the troubles as in the Madras Presidency there was little unrest. On his arrival he was made the assistant to General Sir Patrick Grant, when his duties were to inspect various stations where trouble might possibly break out.

On account of this uncertain future, before he left England, Colonel Cotton asked the Reverend Pennefather to look after his family. In particular, he asked that he pray and support them. This he did, for Elizabeth's mother later wrote: 'the dear pastor's visits and prayers were a support for which I can never thank God enough.' During this time Elizabeth's younger brother Arthur became much attached to the minister, and although only six-years-old, the little boy, would listen intently to the minister's Bible readings and sermons. Sadly, the little boy died shortly afterwards, and it was only some years later that his mother could allow herself to reflect on an incident that revealed the child's innocence and faith. It happened around the boy's seventh birthday, when he had received small amounts of money as gifts for him to spend in the local toyshop. At the time the little boy had heard that the minister was planning a mission to neighbour-ing parishes, so when he received the money he carefully divided it up and allocated two shillings for the Reverend Pennefather's mission. As a consequence the boy secured a special place in the minister's heart, so when the minister heard the news that the boy was seriously ill, he rushed over to be at his bedside. This was during the second week of May 1859. It appears to have been croup, probably brought on by an acute infection such as influenza or diphtheria. Then on 11 May the little boy died. The death certificate recorded the bleak facts: 'Croup 4 days' and was certified by a doctor. There was nothing anyone could have done. There was great sadness and tears in the Cotton family that summer. Since arriving in England young Elizabeth had lost her only sister and now her youngest brother. Although ever close to her mother, she particularly missed her father at this time, when his absence was most keenly felt.

By the summer of 1859 the emergency in India had been resolved and Colonel Cotton was able to resume his position as Commandant of Engineers and adviser to the government in the Madras Presidency. He also took on the role of adviser on irrigation projects throughout the whole of India. His projects included irrigation in the Province of Orissa, the supply of water to Calcutta, and a new project on the Ganges Canal. His reputation was now assured and he was recommended for a knighthood for his work on Indian irrigation and was allowed to return to England to receive this honour. So on Monday 4 February 1861, he attended Buckingham Palace where he was presented to Queen Victoria, whereupon she bestowed on him the honour of a knighthood.

Two weeks later, on 20 February, a public banquet was held in his honour at the Willis's Rooms in King Street, St James, London. It was a grand affair, with some two hundred eminent people gathered together to recognise his achievements. The Earl of Shaftesbury, who presided, declared that they were gathered together to celebrate Sir Arthur Cotton's forty years of dedicated service to the people of India. What he had achieved was unparalleled in the history of the British Empire. He had been able to bring hundreds of thousands of acres of land into productive cultivation and had prevented famines thereby saving millions of lives. Shaftesbury then had to apologise for having to say so many good things about Sir Arthur, so much so, that he confessed he felt like the judge who commented to the man in the dock: 'My good man, it's your fault, you have brought it upon yourself'. This comment brought immediate laughter from those assembled.

When it came to the reply Sir Arthur was extremely modest and after a brief summary of his work he indicated how further success might be achieved. When the newspapers the following day reported on the occasion they referred to how exceedingly fatigued he appeared. They were correct, for once again Arthur Cotton was exhausted and broken in health. His health advisers once again recommended rest in a warm sheltered location. This time they decided on north-west Devonshire. However, when the family arrived at Barnstable in search of a suitable property to rent, he was completely unable to set about the task. For a few days they remained at a hotel and then a friend arrived with information about a suitable residence, but he couldn't find the energy to make the effort to view it. In the event his wife took a carriage and travelled herself to view the property. To her surprise she found it to be a delightful house surrounded by pleasant gardens, and ready to move into, with fires burning in all the rooms and with a charming drawing room, furnished with the best Chippendale furniture. She immediately returned to her husband with the good news and they immediately took possession of the property. Many years later, young Elizabeth recalled that she would never forget how grateful her father was for his wife.

The family remained in Barnstable for about a year, during which time Arthur Cotton officially retired, however he was asked to return to India as a special adviser to the Behar irrigation project in the Sone river valley. This change meant they were on the move again and the family returned to Tunbridge Wells where they waited for his return. In early 1864 he returned from India. This would be his last home-coming. He would not leave Britain again.

## CHAPTER 4

Ireland and a Deeper Faith

THE COTTONS, NOW complete as a family and settled in Tunbridge Wells, sat at breakfast on the morning of Saturday, 12 March 1864, when an urgent telegram arrived that would get them on the move again. It was from a government minister requesting that General Cotton immediately proceed to Sheffield where a dreadful flood had occurred during the previous night with much loss of life.

Young Elizabeth recalled that on receipt of this communication not only was her father's bag quickly packed, but also her own, for she was to accompany him to act as his assistant. Their carriage was called and they made their way to the station where they caught the next train to London. Then at St Pancras station they met up with four other civil engineers that included Sir Robert Rawlinson (1810-1898) the chief engineering inspector to the local government board, who had worked closely with Florence Nightingale at Scutari during the Crimean War. They secured a first-class carriage and were soon on their way to Sheffield. It was a journey young Elizabeth would never forget, as she was fascinated as she listened to the discussion of these down-to-earth engineers as to what may have been the cause of the catastrophe. However, nothing could have prepared them for the scenes of horror and devastation that met them on their arrival at Sheffield.

What had occurred during the previous night was an appalling flood resulting from the Bradfield Reservoir bursting its embankment to engulf the city of Sheffield. Indeed, what young Elizabeth witnessed that morning was the worst civilian disaster to occur during the whole of the Victorian era.

The Bradfield Reservoir, also referred to as the Dale Dyke Reservoir, had been constructed by the Sheffield Waterworks Company some four years previously at Bradfield some eight miles north west of Sheffield, and covered an area of about 78 acres. The present Dale Dyke Reservoir has been built several hundred yards further up the valley, with just a stone marker in place indicating where the original dam wall existed. During the days leading up to the disaster there had been persistent heavy rain and the reservoir over-reached its safe capacity. The strain on the retaining embankment reached such a critical level in the early hours of Saturday morning, that it suddenly gave way. The result was the liberation of a vast body of water that rushed down the steep-sided valley as a gigantic torrent and with such immense force that it washed away everything that was in its path. Unfortunately as the disaster occurred in the middle of the night when people were in bed; many were drowned, or swept away in their sleep. As the enormous surge of water rushed down the valley towards the centre of the city, it washed away the Malin Bridge, and swept through Hillsborough and through the city centre. Eye witness accounts spoke of the body of water sounding like the roar of the heaviest thunder. Many people in their cottages instantly perished as there was little chance of escape.

When later in the morning, Elizabeth and her father arrived on the scene the waters were still roaring through the city, and they stood horrified as they watched parties of men pulling out dead bodies from the water and laying them out on higher ground. Many years later, recalling the scene she referred to it as 'a terrible sight' and said she could not find words that were adequate to describe what she had witnessed. Substantial buildings, bridges and workshops had been washed away and only ruins remained. In the waters she could see the remains of complete houses, haystacks and farming equipment, and amongst all the wreckage were the bodies of the unfortunate people who had been swept away, most of them still in their nightclothes.

Over the following days Elizabeth accompanied her father as he inspected the devastation, and examined the dams to determine the likely cause. When he had completed his work Elizabeth helped him prepare his report, which was then submitted to the government minister.

With their work completed they left Sheffield by train for Liverpool. Here they took the ferry to Belfast as they had been invited to stay with the Earl of Roden. Robert Jocelyn, (1788-1870) was the third earl and he had married Arthur Cotton's cousin, Maria Stapleton. Both the earl and his wife were fervent evangelicals and their home at Tollymore Park, near Newcastle in County Down, had become a haven for evangelical Christians.

Sir Arthur Cotton had now served some forty years in tropical India, and was still not completely recovered from his physical exhaustion. Thus their invitation to stay at Tollymore was welcomed. Indeed, it was the perfect place for him to convalesce. Tollymore House was situated some two miles north-west of Newcastle, and was in the shadow of the Mourne Mountains, where the majestic golden eagle could often be seen gliding high in the sky. The house itself was surrounded by beautiful parkland and delightful forests, through which flowed the Shimna River, which was rich in salmon and sea trout. In the grounds was an outstanding arboretum containing many rare species such as Monterey pine trees, Himalayan cedars, cedars of Lebanon, and many fine specimens of Douglas fir, together with stately beech trees and large silver fir trees. This was the perfect place for Sir Arthur to recover his health and vigour.

Tollymore House was particularly important to the Cotton family as it gave them the opportunity to meet many of the leading evangelical figures of the period. Among the frequent visitors was Catherine Marsh, whom they had known from their stay at the Beckenham Rectory some years before. There was Sir Arthur

Blackwood (1832-1893), one of Catherine Marsh's early converts, who was later to become head of the Post Office, also Lord Roden's daughter, the Countess of Gainsborough, who was Queen Victoria's lady-in-waiting. Meeting these distinguished evangelicals had a significant effect on young Elizabeth. It gave her inspiration to find some way in which she also could be of similar service to others.

On most mornings she would accompany her father on his walks in the nearby mountains, when he would visit isolated farms and cottages and distribute religious tracts and books, and offer Bible readings to the occupants. On these ventures he was always welcomed and given a very friendly reception. On many days they would have relaxing walks in the Tollymore parkland and enjoy the extensive network of paths that meandered through the forest grounds. They could admire the numerous ancient follies that had been built many years before, and walk across the ancient bridges over the Shimna river. Occasionally they would stop at an enormous granite boulder. It is still there today between the Foley's Bridge and the Old Bridge. On the rock Lord Roden had engraved the verse from John 1.3 ('All things were made by Him, and without Him was not any thing made that was made.'). Following this biblical quotation were engraved the words: 'Stop, look around and praise the name of Him who made it all.'

On one of these walks, when they were accompanied by Lord Roden, he gave them a potted history of each of the bridges that crossed the river. Then on reaching a certain point he stopped and pointed to the river below and explained that at that particular point they had never been able to construct any sort of bridge. On hearing this Elizabeth's father jumped to the challenge and offered to design a bridge for this particularly difficult location. He immediately drew up plans and engaged workmen to prepare the wood and before long Lord Roden was delighted to find he had a new wooden chain suspension bridge across the river. For many years afterwards this bridge remained in use until it was eventually demolished in 1936, however even today there are some remnants of it to be found at that place.

The Cotton family later moved into their own property on the Tollymore estate. It was in the small village of Bryansford, adjacent to the Gothic entrance to the park, and situated about one and a half miles from the sea at Newcastle. It was a large picturesque rambling residence, fully furnished, which was known as 'The Nest'. It was a delightful place with Tudor arch doorways and mullioned windows, and a coach house, with stables and a harness room, together with beautiful gardens and orchard.[3]

Elizabeth's time in Ireland was not all serious as she made friends with other young people, and enjoyed joining in with their activities. She also appreciated the beautiful countryside and would enjoy long walks in the mountains and forests, as well as walks along the beach when she admired the changing colours of the sea. But beneath her youthful urges she had a deep spiritual longing that at times troubled her. On one beautiful summer's day she had gone with some friends to bathe in the sea, but on their arrival at the beach she changed her mind and decided to walk along the beach on her own. She later recalled that her heart was 'very heavy'. One presumes she meant by this that she was troubled about her relationship with God. This being so she walked on alone beneath the rocks, with the playful sounds of her friends disappearing in the distance. And then she noticed an old man walking towards her with his head bent forward and apparently deep in thought. Where they lived was only a small place and by now she knew most people by sight, but this man she had never seen before, so she wondered who he was. As he passed her, he looked up and spoke: 'Young lady, do you love the Lord?' She looked at him somewhat surprised, whereupon he gave her a little card that had on one side a verse of a hymn and a text of scripture on the other. Having given her the card the old man continued on without further speaking. She stood still being completely taken aback, and then when she had recovered from her surprise, she plucked up courage and followed him until she had caught up with him. 'I wish I could have a talk with you,' she said. At which the old man nodded but as she began to ask him a question she observed that her coachman had returned with their carriage and her friends had gathered together for their journey back to the village. As she turned to join them, the old man told her that he was to hold a meeting, 'to tell the people of Heaven and of God's great love to mankind in Christ Jesus.'

Where was this meeting to be held, she enquired. The old man smiled. 'A long way from here,' he replied as much as to say that it was too far away for her to attend. But she insisted and he gave her the details as to where the meeting was to be held, 'some five miles off, in a little shed – a very rough place by the road-side.' She asked him again as to its exact location as she was determined to hear what he had to say, for the old man's few words had touched her heart and she wanted to learn more. She had met many religious teachers and preachers before, but there was something different about this strange old man. She wasn't sure what it was, but she felt a resonance between them. She had to learn more. As to what ensued it is best described in her own words written some thirty years later.

'After luncheon, the rain began to come down as heavily as it can in those mountain regions. All the afternoon it continued; still I was bent on going to this little meeting at seven o'clock. I went out to our coachman, who was always kind and helpful, and I asked him to go to my father and tell him that he wanted to take the carriage out at six o'clock; and if any questions were asked, he was to say that I was going in it to a meeting.

He did so, and my father came to inquire of me what my object was on going out on such a night.

I told him that I had set my heart on hearing this old man speak, and that the coachman had no objection to drive me there.

So it was settled, and I went to the appointed spot. I shall never forget that strange, weird place. It was a very rough shed, with large holes in the roof through which the rain was falling in little streams, so that the earthen floor was all muddy; and there were a couple of common benches in it, where in a few minutes, some ragged boys took their places, and one or two men and women – in all, I think our congregation consisted of eight people.

Then the old man arrived. His face bore the stamp of Heaven upon it. He began to preach on the 89th Psalm, 'Mercy shall be built up for ever; Thy faithfulness shalt Thou establish in the very heavens.'

He grew more and more animated as he enlarged on this passage, speaking with marvellous eloquence and increasing earnestness... I think I see him now, as he stood with a rapt look upon his face, pointing up to the miserable roof of our shed, and saying, 'This is a poor place, but tonight it may be the gate of Heaven to some soul here.'

For a long time he spoke, and every sentence was filled with power and originality; and his closing prayer was singularly impressive; in fact the whole occasion was one never to be forgotten. I cannot describe the effect it had upon my own soul;- it was the means in God's hands of chasing the clouds and darkness away, which seemed to have surrounded me.

I remember shaking hands with him when the meeting closed, and thanking him for all he had said; and his earnest entreaty to me to work for God while there was time, and to tell every sinner of the love of Christ Who has power to save.

I drove home again through the pouring rain, but there was sunlight in my heart now, and I always feel grateful to that old man for his message that night."[4]

This experience may be seen as a major turning point in her life. She was now convinced that her future lay in serving God and following in the footsteps of the Christian women she had encountered, such as Catherine Marsh and Catherine Pennefather. It was Christian evangelism with a practical dimension, but exactly how she was going to do this was, at that moment, unclear.

CHAPTER 5

Dorking and Mission Work

IN 1867 AFTER some three years in County Down, Sir Arthur Cotton's health had improved sufficiently for him to feel confident enough to enter public life again. On Monday, 24 June he gave a presentation to the Royal Geographical Society in which he proposed a line of land communication between Burhampooter in Assam and Yang-tze-kiang. Then in September he participated at the British Association conference, which that year was held in Dundee. On each of these occasions he was accompanied by Elizabeth, when she acted as his assistant. This gave her the opportunity of meeting many of the leading men of science.

The previous year her father had been promoted to Major General and made a Knight Commander. He had also been awarded the prestigious Most Exalted Order of the Star of India. This was the most illustrious decoration awarded to those who have served in India. He was accordingly a man of some eminence and consequently attracted around him a circle of equally prominent men.

Now completely recovered, General Cotton believed he could contribute to society and felt that he could do this more effectively if he moved nearer to the heart of things in the city of London. So towards the end of 1868 the family moved to the small town of Dorking in Surrey. Dorking offered a pleasant healthy environment in which to live, yet was within easy reach of London by rail. On first arriving in the town they rented a small cottage, while they engaged a builder to build them a new house on the outskirts of the town in an area known as 'Tower Hill'. In 1870 the new house was completed and they moved in giving it the name of 'Woodcot', after the village in Oxfordshire, where General Cotton had been born. It was a substantial three-story residence, with nine bedrooms and a spacious entrance hall with an elegant staircase and beautifully wood-panelled rooms. A particular feature was the wide spacious landing area on the upper floor which was flooded with light from the skylights above. The house is still in existence today, although it has been converted into a residential home and its original name changed. It is now known as 'Garth House'. [5]

Elizabeth was now approaching her thirtieth birthday, an age when most women of her generation had long since married and started families. However, if one looks at her life up to this point one may see that the family had never settled very long in any one place, so it is understandable that she had never married. Her father's decision to settle in Dorking proved to be a turning point. It was the first permanent home she had known. However, now settled for the first time, rather than seeking a husband, she began the evangelical work that would occupy her for the rest of her life.

In the early 1870s, Dorking was a small Surrey town of some 5000 inhabitants. On account of the opening of the London to Brighton railway line the town was undergoing a period of rapid population growth, particularly with the influx of numerous middle-class residents who were now able to commute easily to the capital. As a consequence there were many substantial villas built in the outskirts, largely in the Rose Hill district, which had become a very desirable area to live. By the early 1870s this area of development extended up into Tower Hill where numerous Italianate and Tudor style villas could be found, together with many fine mansions that had been built for wealthy individuals from the city. It was in this district that General Cotton's house was situated.

Dorking, at the time of the arrival of the Cotton family, was not a particularly religious place, despite the fact that it was not short of places of worship. The principal parish church was that of St Martin's just off the High Street. The church had been built around a medieval chancel, its consecration having taken place some two years before the Cottons arrived in Dorking. The foundation stone for the tower and spire had been laid by Bishop Wilberforce in May 1873, shortly before he was killed in a riding accident. This is the same bishop who just a few years before had challenged Huxley in the notorious evolution debate at the British Association at Oxford.

St Martin's church had been built in an elaborate and sumptuous style. It was very much High Church, and as such it had little appeal to the working classes, so consequently attendance rates were poor. (It was probably on account of this, that some years before, the incumbent the Reverend W.H. Joyce, had refused to complete the religious census.) However, there was another Anglican church in the town. This was in the Tower Hill district, and it was here that Elizabeth worshipped. It had been designed by the architect, Benjamin Ferry and built of Bath stone and flint, and consecrated in 1857. It was dedicated to St Paul, and was very much in the Low Church tradition. Indeed, right from the beginning it tended towards the evangelical wing of the church community, as it does today.

Non-conformists were also well represented in the town. There was a Baptist chapel in Junction Road which had been completed in 1876. Today it is known as the Crossways Community Baptist Chapel. There was also a Congregational chapel, having a fine Italianate frontage in West Street that had been opened in 1860. It is now the United Reform Church. Methodism was also strong in the town. John Wesley had preached in the district on many occasions and a chapel in the town had been opened by him in the November of 1772. Today the Methodists have joined up with the Anglicans and hold their services at St Martin's Church. The Quakers were also established, their first meeting house having been opened around 1709. They are also very active today and have their meeting house in Butter Hill. There was also an Open Brethren gospel hall in Hampstead Road that had been built around 1863. This is now an independent chapel. Finally, in this brief survey of the churches in Dorking, one would not omit to mention the arrival of the Salvation Army in the late 1880s. Their arrival led to some controversy regarding the manner of their street missions, which resulted in several of their members being imprisoned in Wandsworth jail.

It is against this background that the Cotton family arrived in Dorking, and Elizabeth commenced her work as an evangelist. By the time the 1871 census was taken in the April of that year, the Cotton family had settled into their new home. The census return indicates that the Woodcot household consisted of General Sir Arthur Cotton 67, his wife, Elizabeth 56, and daughter Elizabeth 28, together with son, Alfred aged 21. Also recorded were the resident servants, Angelina Leeming and Mary Ann Gates, aged 44 and 23 respectively.

As General Cotton's health had now recovered he threw himself into various projects and activities. In particular, he kept up-to-date with changes taking place in India, and this led him at this time to collaborate with Florence Nightingale on various projects. He was also active in the Church Missionary Society and addressed their meeting at Winchester in May 1872, and during the following year he addressed meetings of the British and Foreign Bible Society.

He was also active as an inventor. Around this time he began work on a safety bicycle and invented a tricycle for which he obtained a patent. He was also working on a new form of cycle-braking system. At this time cycles were awkward and dangerous machines. It would be another ten years before the first safety bicycle was invented. Elizabeth recalled how one day when she was returning home she saw her father coming down Tower Hill at tremendous speed on his tricycle, so much so, that he lost control of the machine and crashed into a hedge. When she ran over to rescue him, she found him to be in a terrible state, covered in cuts and bruises, but all he was concerned about was whether his machine had survived intact. The upshot was that Lady Cotton became so concerned about his activities with his cycle inventions that she persuaded him to give them away.

At this time General Cotton had lost four of his six children. As Elizabeth, was his first born, she held a special place in his affection, and she clearly meant everything to him. In her semi-autobiographical novel, *A Maiden's Work*, the principal character, Geraldine, tells the reader that her father, Mr Grayson, 'doted on her'. One can be sure that this is how General Cotton treated her. Father and daughter shared many notable characteristics. In looking at their lives one can recognise similarities between them, however, as she was female, it was very difficult for her to follow in his footsteps. She could not join the army nor have any sort of career. As a Victorian lady her role in life was to find a suitable husband. She was very much aware of this, yet to describe her as a 'feminist' would miss the mark. That said, many feminists would today be sympathetic to the outburst she gave her fictional character Elline in her novel, *Golden Lines*:

> 'What nonsense!...when one has no outside world, how can one expand one's self upon it? The thing is absurd. Men have splendid openings and grand careers. They can look forward to the battlefield or diplomatic service – India, Africa, the colonies, or even the law courts; there is always something for them-'

However her father had progressive views about the role of women in society. Indeed, he very much believed there should be equality of the sexes. In her biography of her father she wrote: 'One of my father's strongest characteristics was his admiration and support of women's work!' This is slightly understated, for there is evidence that he would positively encourage her to be active in society, and not to sit around waiting for the right man to appear. 'Do something my girl; do something,' he would tell her. 'Never be idle for a single minute. Remember, Time is short. Eternity is near.' Taking this advice this is exactly what she did.

She began to do Bible readings in cottages in the town, and visited sick patients in the Cottage Hospital, just like Mrs Ranyard's Bible women were doing in London. The Dorking Cottage Hospital had been opened in 1871, and was located in South Terrace not far from the Cotton home. It was largely supported by voluntary contributions and was only small; just seven beds and three cots. The nurse in charge, according to Elizabeth, was 'a very formidable character'. The only other place for sick people in the town was the Dorking workhouse. This was also situated not very far from her home in Tower Hill. Like many other similar institutions in the country, the Dorking workhouse had a dreadful reputation. But this did not deter Elizabeth from visiting patients there.

At the time Elizabeth was not alone in this activity, as Catherine Tait, the wife of the Archbishop of Canterbury, had recently established the Ladies Diocesan Association in London. This philanthropic organisation was exclusively for aristocratic women, who had to be invited to join. They were then given a specific workhouse to visit; the Marchioness of Ailsa, for instance, was allocated to the City Road Workhouse.

Whether Elizabeth was aware of this organisation is unclear, but she was probably acting completely independently out of her own deep concerns. Some years later she described visiting a young man who had attended her Bible class in the town. She recalled the dark grim corridors that led to the sick wards. When she entered the ward she found herself in a long room filled with narrow beds. Besides the window the young man 'a fine handsome fellow' lay on a rough bed with his head thrown back. He was suffering from a high fever and was clearly in great pain. 'His sheets and pillows were brown with dirt', she recalled. The blazing summer sun was shining full into his face as there were no window blinds, and he was covered in flies. She fanned away the flies then placed a newspaper against the window to shield him from the blazing sun. When she bent down close to him and spoke gently to him, the tears rolled down his cheeks. 'I am sorry,' she said, and then he sobbed outright. For a while she read to him some passages from the Bible. Afterwards she said a short prayer, and then just at that moment she was startled by a terrible groan from an adjoining bed. She turned around and there in front of her, stood a man in dirty rags with a matted beard. He stood glaring wildly at her and stretched out his hand in a menacing manner. She was at first alarmed but then one of the other inmates told her the man was harmless enough although he was a nuisance as he made awful groans day and night. It was a sickening sight, she recalled, made worse when the 'nurse' in the establishment appeared and with a voice, 'like a door on its unoiled hinges' screamed at the man, 'Hold yer tongue, and be quiet will yer?' Writing, some years afterwards, she commented that this work-house had a good reputation as being one of the very best of its kind in the country, with good men on the board of management. If so, what were the others like?

One has to remember that one of Florence Nightingale's greatest achievements was the introduction of trained nurses into the dreaded workhouse infirmaries. Miss Nightingale's work in this area began around this time. Before her improvements were introduced the 'nurses' were women inmates employed by the managers, not to care for the patients but to keep some sort of order. In many cases they were tough formidable characters who would spend their wages on drink. What Florence Nightingale campaigned for, at this time, was for trained women to take on this role. It is clear from this episode that Elizabeth and Florence Nightingale shared a similar compassion towards the sick, and that they both felt that there was much work to be done.[6]

Some years later Florence Nightingale came to greatly admire Elizabeth. They became acquainted by way of her father. In the 1870s Miss Nightingale became concerned about the desperate conditions of the people in India during periods of famine and she began a long-term friendship with Elizabeth's father. When Miss Nightingale first approached General Cotton to ask his advice, he was delighted and replied: 'If fifty years of hard work and contempt had produced no other return but a letter from you, it would be an honour beyond what I deserve. The plot is now rapidly thickening and I have not the smallest doubt that your having taken up this great subject will turn the scale.' This was the start of a long collaboration between them. Today amongst the Florence Nightingale papers in the British Library there is a manuscript written by Miss Nightingale in 1874 on irrigation in India, entitled: *'The Zeminder, the Sun and the Watering Pot as Affecting Life or Death in India'*. This original manuscript is heavily annotated in pencil by General Cotton. Although it was never published she did have several copies privately printed in which she prefaced the text with a 'Dramatis Personæ'. In this she listed General Cotton as 'The most perfect master of the water question living'.

It is clear that like Florence Nightingale, Elizabeth was a young woman with a deep compassion for others. At a time when most women in her social position were interested in only one thing, namely a 'good-marriage', Elizabeth Cotton was driven by a different passion. Like the Booths she wanted to improve the lives of others not only by revealing to them the gospel story, but by giving them a helping hand. This is best illustrated in the role she adopted towards the Rowland brothers, both of whom worked for the Dorking post office as telegram boys.

The story begins one cold January morning in the year 1872, when a telegram boy arrived at Woodcot to deliver her a telegram. His name was Arthur Rowland and he was aged fifteen. As the telegram required an immediate reply, she asked the boy to wait until she had written it. The boy had called on previous occasions in the course of his employment, but on this occasion she noticed that he looked unwell. 'Is anything the matter?' she enquired, but the boy failed to reply. 'You don't look well,' she continued, as she stepped closer. At this the boy took out his handkerchief, which was covered in fresh blood. The sight of the blood caused her to look somewhat shocked. The boy then explained that he had this terrible cough and that having to walk up the hill to the house had caused him to cough up all this blood. At this he began to cry, and he had to wipe away his tears on the sleeve of his uniform.

She knew, well enough, what this meant. At the time it would have been known as consumption, or 'phthisis', today we know it as tuberculosis. It was extremely common at this time accounting for about 15% of all deaths. Although it was invariably fatal, a small proportion of victims did survive if they had improved living conditions and convalescence. So this was her immediate suggestion. 'You must rest,' she said, 'you are not fit for work.' At this the boy cried again and told her that he couldn't stop work as his mother was a widow and needed his wages of five shillings a week to pay the rent. There was little more that she could say, so the telegram boy returned to his duties. But he wasn't forgotten.

Within the hour she had put on a warm coat and made her way over to the boy's home in East Street, Dorking, where she spoke to his mother. Just as the boy had told her, his mother Sarah Rowland was indeed a widow with eight children to support. On entering the little cottage, Elizabeth explained the purpose of her visit, namely her concern over the woman's sick boy. Mrs Rowland, looked somewhat surprised, as it was not everyday she had someone from one of the large mansions enquiring after her children. 'But which one do you mean?' she asked, 'I have two boys that are ill.' Elizabeth Cotton looked puzzled, and then she remembered that she had seen the two brothers standing together outside the door of the post office. At this the mother called the two brothers in to meet their unexpected visitor. There was Arthur, whom she had just encountered, but there was also one of his older brothers, William Edward, who was seventeen. She could see that as they stood beside their mother they both showed all the symptoms of advanced consumption. They must stop work and rest immediately, she insisted. Better still, they should move away to a better climate, and she suggested a place where they could go. But the brothers would have none of it. They wanted to stay with their mother in their own home. Reluctantly Elizabeth accepted this, and in parting, she told the mother that she would visit the post office and arrange for the boys to be given sick leave.

Over the following weeks, Elizabeth paid daily visits to the two boys. On the earlier visits she would find the brothers sitting in front of a fire, propped up with pillows, but as the disease progressed they took to their bed in the upstairs bedroom. One day when Elizabeth visited she found the mother to be upset, as William had overheard the doctor comment that they would never get better. She immediately made her way up the narrow staircase to the bedroom and sat down at the bedside. The younger brother was asleep, but on seeing her William covered his face with his hands and told her as to what he had overheard the doctor say to his mother. He then asked her to kneel down and pray for them to get better. This she did, and afterwards she gently spoke to him of the love of God in his Son, Jesus Christ, and before she left they prayed together.

Each day she would make her way over to the Rowland household and talk to the brothers, and read passages from the Bible, and then pray with them. On the bedroom wall, opposite the bed, was a 'Silent Comforter' and she would read the biblical text for the day. This gave the boys immense comfort. On Friday, 23 February, it was the last occasion she saw William alive, and he asked her to read the text for the day. It was, 'In all their afflictions He was afflicted, and the angel of His presence saved them.' They prayed together and afterwards as she left she could hear his feeble voice repeating the text. That Saturday morning she was away in London and on her return to Dorking that evening, she met the boys' older brother, James Rowland, who broke the news to her that William had died during the night.

She was distraught with grief, but instead of returning home she made her way to East Street to visit the sorrowing family. It was a typical Saturday night in Dorking and as she made her way along the High Street, she paid little attention to the crowds of rowdy men that congregated outside the doors of the public houses. At that moment her thoughts were with poor Arthur. The rough drunken men would be for another day. On arriving at the house she immediately made her way up to see 'little Arthur', and for some minutes she sat alone with him and then he asked her a favour. Would she allow him to stay in her house while they take away William?

Later, on recalling the incident, she referred to him affectionately as 'the child', she wrote: 'The child, as he lay there propped up with pillows, his breath so laboured, his white hand hanging feebly over the coloured dressing jacket, which covered his wasted shoulders, did not look able for a journey; and yet I had hardly the courage to give even a doubtful answer.'

For several more days Arthur lingered on. On the afternoon of Monday, 26 February, she visited again. However, Mrs Rowland, wiping away a tear, told her that her boy would probably not recognise her. Elizabeth gave her a hug, then made her way up the stairs to the bedroom and sat beside the bed. The boy was unconscious and near to death. She knelt down and prayed for a while and then slowly read aloud the words of the Silent Comforter. 'I know that my Redeemer liveth, and that He shall stand at the latter day upon the earth.' She leaned forward bending over the boy and whispered in the boy's ear, 'now so nearly closed to earthly voice', the words, 'I know that my Redeemer liveth'.

The following day Tuesday, 27 February 1872, had been declared to be the country's Thanksgiving Day and was a Public

Holiday. This day of National Celebrations had been given because the Prince of Wales had recovered from a serious illness. The church bells rang out across the country and there were grand processions to the services held at St Paul's and other churches. But Elizabeth's feelings were not on these celebrations as her 'heart ached for the little sufferer'. Amidst all the celebrations, in deep sadness, she made her way across the town to the Rowland's cottage. On her arrival she was met by the weeping mother with the news that little Arthur had died earlier that morning. At a loss for words to convey her grief, Elizabeth hugged the woman, and they wept together.

In her account, published about two years afterwards, Elizabeth described the boys' grave in the Dorking cemetery, 'overlooking the Mickleham valley' where a little gravestone had been erected to mark the place. On it were inscribed their names alongside the verse: 'In all their affliction He was afflicted, and the angel of His presence saved them: in His love and in His pity He redeemed them.'

This very sad story tells us a great deal about Elizabeth Cotton. One has to consider that here we have a young attractive woman, still in her twenties, from a very prosperous home, and well educated. But instead of doing what other women in her position were doing, she was visiting the homes of the poor and needy. The telegraph boy was a stranger - yet she dropped everything to go and see his mother. She arranged for the brothers to have sick leave and one wonders whether she compensated the employers for this herself. In her account she makes no mention as to what medicines or other gifts she gave to the brothers, but it is likely she did not arrive empty-handed. And as the mother needed Arthur's five shillings a week to pay the rent, it seems unlikely that the family had enough money to pay for a headstone. One therefore feels that it is likely Elizabeth paid for this, particularly as it was her biblical text inscribed on it. However, these are trivial concerns, the real insight we get from this account is that

Elizabeth Cotton had a deep love for other people less fortunate than herself. In particular, she must have known that tuberculosis was highly infectious and that by visiting the brothers she was risking her own health. But this fits a pattern repeated throughout her life, and we will see it again, when she seems to have little regard for her own personal safety.

CHAPTER 6

'My Heart Ached'

O N ANOTHER OCCASION she had been busy visiting the sick in their homes and doing Bible readings. It was summer and it had been very hot all day. She had promised to meet a friend at Dorking station who was arriving on the six o'clock train, to stay with her for a few days. At the last cottage she had visited she had miscalculated the time it would take her to get to the railway station, so she had been forced to hurry in order to get there on time. When she arrived there she was flushed and with the heat her face was covered with droplets of perspiration. Fortunately, the train was a little delayed, so she was able to recover her composure and taking out a neatly-folded handkerchief she wiped her brow. There were a number of other people waiting on the platform for the train to arrive. As she stood there, a young well-dressed gentleman came up and spoke to her. At first she failed to recognise him, but he knew her.

'You have been hurried in trying to get here on time,' he said.

She smiled at him. 'Yes', she said. 'I have been very busy, for several hours amongst the people, visiting from house to house.'

He knew this already, as indeed he knew that she was the daughter of General Cotton, however she still didn't recognise him. 'You are always busy, are you not?'

'Oh!' she replied. 'I am always busy and my life is so full of interest. It is such a joy to be able to take to the people the message of Christ's love and mercy.'

He then shook his head. It was now some ten years since Charles Darwin had published his theory on the origin of species.

49

He had bought one of the first copies of the book from the bookstall at Waterloo station and had read it with great satisfaction. Then at medical school he had attended lectures given by Professor Huxley that had completely shattered any remnants of his faith. 'You believe in Him?' he asked.

She smiled at him. 'Believe in Him!' she said. 'Do you not believe in him?' She hesitated then looked into his eyes. 'He is all in all to me.'

He turned slightly away and in a hushed voice said: 'I am not sure of anything. I have no beliefs at all now, for I do not know what is true and what is not true. Life is an entire mystery, and a very sad one, I think.'

The truth was he had come to the railway station not to meet any friend, but to end his life by throwing himself beneath a train, but on finding so many ladies on the platform he had lost his nerve.

She stepped closer to him and was just about to place her gloved hand on his arm when the train she was waiting for arrived. She turned to look for her friend stepping down from the carriage and for a moment she forgot about the young man. She rushed forward to greet her friend and then on turning she realised that the man had gone.

As they made their way to her waiting coach her friend began excitedly to give her all the recent gossip. For a while she listened to her friend and then on getting into the carriage she thought about the conversation she had just had with the young man. She felt sure she knew him from somewhere, but still she couldn't place him. The carriage jolted as it turned towards the High Street, and then on noticing a large elegant mansion, which she had frequently visited with her father, she remembered where she had seen the man before.

He was a doctor living at that house, which was the country residence of one of her father's friends, a military man whom he had known from his time in India. But now the man was ill and whenever he was in the country he liked to have a doctor living with him in his house. That was where she had seen the young man before.

Soon they were at Tower Hill and on reaching Woodcot they were greeted by her mother. One of the maids then took her friend to one of the guest rooms overlooking their large garden. Elizabeth then told her parents about the conversation she had just had with the young doctor. 'How awful it must be to have no belief,' she exclaimed to them. And then she told them that she intended to visit the young doctor when she would tell him about the good news of the gospel.

It was late the following day that news reached the Cotton household about the tragedy that had happened in the town earlier that day. When Elizabeth heard about it she was so shocked that she almost fainted. Apparently the young doctor had failed to come down for breakfast that morning. They waited for him for some time and then as ten o'clock struck they became anxious and sent a servant up to his room. The servant on his return gave the news that after knocking on the doctor's door there was no reply, even after he had knocked several times, and that the door had been locked on the inside. News of this quickly spread through the house that something must have occurred. The gardener then procured a ladder and climbed in at the window. Then on entering the room to his horror he found that the doctor had drawn a chair up in front of the mirror and deliberately cut his own throat. That it was suicide was clear from the note the doctor had left which confessed that his intention had been to end his life on account of his miserable state of mind and his lack of belief. What made matters worse for Elizabeth was that the note had on it the time that it had been written. It was just three hours after he had spoken to her at the railway station.

This experience had a great effect upon her. For many years afterwards she had great difficulty talking about it as it distressed her so much. She felt tremendous guilt. If only she had spoken to him for a little longer. If only she could have led him to a belief in the Lord Jesus Christ. If only she had prayed with him. But she had missed the opportunity and had rushed off with her friend and left him. The upshot was that she made the resolution that this would never happen again and whenever she had the opportunity she would tell people the joyful news of the gospel.

And it wasn't long before she had an opportunity of doing just that but it was a completely unforeseen event. It was one Sunday evening some weeks afterwards. She would normally attend evensong with her parents, but on this occasion she was feeling slightly under the weather and decided not to go along with them. She felt slightly unhappy at making this decision, as following the service the vicar was going to give an illustrated talk about his recent visit to the Holy Land. Knowing that this would be a very interesting talk she had persuaded her maid to go. This meant that she was left alone in the house apart from the parlourmaid.

Shortly after the family had left for church she went to her bedroom to change her dress. For a brief moment she stood at her bedroom window and looked at the garden below. It was a beautiful spring evening with the leaves on the trees a beautiful fresh green and the flowerbeds filled with blue and pink flowers.

She then crossed the room intending to go to the library where she was going to finish the book she was reading when she heard a slight noise on the landing outside. Thinking that this must have been the parlourmaid she called out her name, but there was no reply. She then left the room and went on to the landing, but there was no sign of the parlourmaid. She called her name again, but there was no response. Then she noticed that the door of the guest bedroom, which was next to her own, was slightly ajar. This was not usual, so she pushed open the door and walked straight in. Then turning she was horrified to see that standing behind the door was a tall man with a revolver in his hand.

Immediately the man sprang at her, grabbing hold of her arm and dragging her towards himself. He then gave her three blows to the head and pushed the revolver against her forehead. 'If you scream I'll shoot you through the head,' he said.

Having quickly recovered from the initial shock, she looked him in the eye. 'What a coward to strike a woman!' she said. 'Who are you, and what do you want?'

The man pressed harder with the gun. 'I want your money,' he said. 'If you scream. Or try to give the alarm, I'll blow your brains out.'

Elizabeth shook her head. 'I'm not going to scream.'

The man tightened his grip on her arm and pulled her closer. 'Women always scream,' he said.

'Well, I'm not a woman who screams,' she replied. 'Put that pistol away and let go of my arm, you are hurting me dreadfully.'

At this the man let go of her arm, but continued to hold the gun against her head. 'Get me your money,' he said, 'or I'll shoot, the gun is loaded.'

At this the horror of the situation dawned on her and she began to feel faint and had to lean against the bedpost. When she recovered her composure she looked up at the man. 'If you shoot me you'll get hanged,' she said. 'Besides if you shoot me, I can't get you the money.'

She had said the right thing as the thought of being hanged made the man hesitate and he put the gun into his pocket. But this was only done following a further outburst of foul language and demand for money.

The man then walked over to the door and locked it. As he did this she glanced at the bell pulls on either side of the bed, however he noticed her looking at them. 'If you try to ring the bells or call out I'll shoot you,' he snapped.

She then walked across the room to her dressing table and picked up her purse. He immediately snatched it off her. 'I'll have that,' he said ripping it open. He emptied the money out and counted it. 'Four pounds fifteen shillings,' he said. 'Is that all you have?' At this time this was a substantial amount of money, representing several hundred pounds in today's money.

'Yes,' she replied. 'You can have it, but let me have the purse back as it was given to me by my mother. It's no value to you.'

At this he put the money into his pocket and handed the purse back to her. 'Your mother gave you the purse?' he said.

'Yes,' she replied. 'Do you have a mother?'

At this unexpected enquiry he became agitated. 'Yes, and a good one too,' he replied. 'But she died some five years ago.'

Elizabeth now moved towards the man and looked him in the eye. 'What would she think if she could see you now?' She paused. 'Do you believe there is a God, and that he sees you now?'

He turned away. 'Yes,' he replied. 'My mother taught me that.' And then he walked across to the dressing table and picked up a bottle of her 'Jockey Club' perfume. He put it to his nose. 'That's nice,' he said.

This made her feel anxious. 'You can have it,' she said nervously.

He then saw her watch on the dressing table together with some jewellery, but made no attempt to take them. He then picked up a small vase of flowers that her maid had placed on the dressing table earlier that day. 'These are pretty flowers', he said.

Elizabeth smiled. 'Yes, they are from the garden.' She paused thinking how she might get him to think again about his mother again. 'Did your mother like flowers?'

'Yes, yes, she did,' he replied. And then he walked up to her and looked her in the eye. 'I've lived a bad life since she died.'

Suddenly he now seemed so pathetic that she forgot about the earlier violence. 'You know what God says,' she said. 'Though your sins be as scarlet, they shall be as white as snow; though they be red like crimson they shall be as wool.'

'Say that again,' he said.

She repeated it and added. 'I don't know what crimes you have committed, but remember Jesus loves you and died on the cross for your sins.'

At this moment he glanced at the clock on the mantelpiece. 'I must be off,' he said. 'It's a matter of life and death. I'll get nabbed.'

'Go quick,' she said. 'But before you do let us ask God to forgive you.' At this she said a few words of prayer asking God to forgive him and that he might change his ways.

Before leaving he asked her to forgive him for striking and hurting her. He then put on his shoes, which previously had been poking out of his pockets, and left the house by the front door.

When he had gone Elizabeth went over to the window and watched him leave by way of the front gate and make his way towards the open fields. She then turned to ring the bell but the strain had been too much for her that she could not reach it before falling down in a fainting fit.

On recovering she found herself lying on the floor. Had it all been a dream, she thought. And then she saw her empty purse. Then looking at the clock she could see that she had been in a faint for almost three-quarters of an hour. She got herself up and rang the bell. When the parlourmaid arrived she told her what had happened and she immediately gave the alarm to the police station. Shortly afterwards her parents returned from church with the other servants and the house was searched from top to bottom. Later when the police arrived they also searched the house and having not uncovered any clues they left two policemen in the garden on watch all night. The next day an inspector and two detectives came to ask her more questions and made a further search of the house and grounds but nothing was found.

Some days afterwards, while her arm was still in a sling, she was out walking in a nearby lane. It was a beautiful warm day with a slight gentle breeze. As she turned homeward she noticed a tall man leaning on the fence besides the road. At the sound of her approach he turned around and she immediately recognised him as the burglar. But now he was smartly dressed in a dark blue serge suit, a black tie, and black hat with a cane in his hand. She was so astonished that at first she didn't know what to do, as there was no one about. Then quickly she decided she must confront him.

She walked straight up to him and said: 'You! You here! You told me you were going miles away.'

He nodded. 'I did indeed, ma'am. I got to the place and waited some days for a ship, but then a telegram from my sister's husband arrived telling me that Rosie, my twin sister was dying and that she wanted to see me.'

'And did you go and see her?' she asked.

The man nodded. 'Yes, I did and now she is gone. I loved her so much.'

'But how could you venture to come back here in daylight? Do you know that the police are looking for you?'

'I had to come for the funeral this morning and I'm now waiting for the train.' He hesitated. 'I am now so miserable I can't tell you, lady; you know I'll never forget that text you said. I'm now going to be a changed man.'

He then asked her as to whether he had hurt her badly, to which she replied that he had. 'See the sling,' she said indicating her arm. 'It still hurts a good deal and so does my head. You frightened me very much you know that.'

He shook his head. 'I am sorry,' he said. 'I was such a wretch that Sunday evening. I will never do it again.' At this he took off his hat respectfully, and after thanking her for speaking to him, jumped over the fence and was off across the fields.

She later recalled that as she watched the man walking off in the direction of the station, that 'her *heart ached* for him, the poor, miserable, misguided man, with a soft place in his heart, and yet leading such a life.'

When she got home the police were again called but by the time they set about searching for the man he had got away.

It was some weeks afterwards that a letter was delivered to the house addressed to her. It was from the burglar. In it he said how sorry he was for hurting her and how he had now become a changed man. He explained that his wretched behaviour was on account of his having been led astray by bad company. He had now turned over a new leaf thanks to her Christian example. 'You did not despise a wretch like me,' he wrote. 'I had behaved like a brute to you but you spoke words of forgiveness. I now realise that this was real Christianity. I never saw it like that before. You are the bravest woman I ever saw. You never flinched that terrible Sunday evening. Most men dread a pistol: you lady have pluck enough for a hundred men. I never saw any one like you lady. I thought, never, she's so plucky and I did feel a coward and a fool.' He then concluded the letter by promising to return the money he had stolen and asked her to pray for him to keep a changed life.

When she showed this letter to the police, the detective in charge of the case concluded that the letter had been a hoax. 'What object could the man have in writing it?' he exclaimed.

However, Elizabeth believed it had been a genuine letter from the man and continued to pray for him. Then some months afterwards she received another letter in the same hand. In it were five sovereigns. 'I took four pounds fifteen shillings on that terrible night,' the man wrote. 'And your purse was torn. Lady, please buy a new one with the extra five shillings. I'm now leading a changed life. God bless you for making me do so, a scoundrel like me. You are the bravest and pluckiest lady. I'll never forget you lady, you've saved me.'

Now she had no doubt that this was a genuine letter, as no one except the man and herself knew that the purse had been torn.

CHAPTER 7

Our Coffee Room

SHORTLY AFTER THE Cotton family settled in Dorking, Elizabeth opened a Sunday school for girls in the town. It was an immediate success. Then one Sunday afternoon, as she walked down the hill to the High Street where she held the Sunday school, she noticed that there were large numbers of boys hanging around the street corners and generally up to no good. Although she referred to them as 'wild boys', she probably realised that they were just ordinary lads, with time on their hands, and although they got up to minor mischief they were basically good. This being so she began to think seriously about extending her Sunday school to include boys. She mentioned the idea to a couple of her friends but they were shocked at the suggestion and insisted that teaching the likes of these ruffians was not the thing 'a young lady' ought to contemplate. When she mentioned it to her father, although he didn't immediately go along with the idea, he did at least agree with the notion that something ought to be done to give these boys some religious instruction. But, rather than allow his daughter to teach them he decided to employ a male Scripture Reader to take charge of a Sunday school just for the local ruffians. This arrangement worked well at first but after a short time, the man left for a better position, and there was no one to take over the class. At this turn of events, Elizabeth again proposed that she should be allowed to take over the class as it was now leaderless. Her father agreed to this, but on the first Sunday when she turned up to take over the class, the ruffians played up, acting as if they were indeed 'wild boys' so much so, that she was forced to abandon the class and return home. It seemed that her friends had been proved right, and that teaching adolescent boys was not what a young lady should engage in. 'We told you so,' they said on learning of her difficulties. But then on the following Sunday something amazing happened. When the appropriate time arrived, instead of making her way over to the Sunday school room she stayed at home. Then she happened to look out of the drawing room window, and there outside the front door was a crowd of scruffy boys. She called her father and they opened the door to find out what was going on. On meeting her again, the boys pleaded for her to continue with the class, promising never again to misbehave. And this is how her class for the 'wild boys' started, and good to their word, they never again misbehaved.

The boys' class proved a great success, so much so, that the numbers attending increased dramatically and they had to find larger premises. A hall was rented but even this proved inadequate, so her father built them a much larger room on the same site, which became known as 'the Orchard'. He also presented her with a Chappell's Cellestina - a portable musical instrument, like a harmonium - that she could use to accompany their hymn singing. Then she decorated the walls of the room with biblical pictures and texts, installed a cupboard to store Bibles and hymn books, and placed a blackboard at the front.

She was now running three Sunday school classes, one for the girls at 2pm, the second at 3pm for the young boys, and the third at 4pm for the older boys. It was a great success with attendances increasing week by week. But this was not the end of her work for during the week she had a Bible class for women on one afternoon, and during the rest of her time, she continued with her Bible reading in cottages in the town, and visiting the sick.

It was on such a visit that her life was to take a dramatic turn. It happened in this way. On one of her cottage visits, the lady she had gone to see was out and only her husband was at home. She recalled that he was, 'a fine-looking specimen of a navy, head and shoulders taller than most of his fellow workmen'. He invited her in and after telling her he had heard about her Sunday school teaching, and Bible reading to the women of the town, demanded to know why she did not also have a men's meeting. At first she didn't know how to respond. She turned away as if to leave, but then he insisted. She hesitated again, and then turning to face him she said, 'It's because people say it is not right for a woman to teach men.'

'I thought that was it,' he replied, as he thumped the table with his fist, in rather an alarming way.

She stepped back, rather shocked, and at a loss for words. And then he went on to give her instances from the Bible when women had been used by God, and in each case she nodded her head in agreement. After this harangue he concluded by saying, 'And this is what I think, Miss: if a man don' know, and a woman do know, she ought to tell he, and it's very wrong of you not to tell we...' He then went on to explain that it was his conclusion that nobody cared about men.

Writing about this later, she recorded that this last statement had, 'like lead sunk into her heart', so on returning home she discussed it with her parents and it was decided that she would open up her Sunday school room for a men's meeting. To get started she got invitations printed announcing her Bible meeting the following Sunday evening at 7pm in her room in the Orchard.

The first meeting was a great success and was crowded with men all eager to learn about the Bible. Although it would have been a novelty at this time, for them to hear a woman preach and take the lead in any form of worship; it is nonetheless clear from reading the accounts written by some of the men, that she was a very charismatic speaker, with an attractive voice. One of those who attended these early meetings referred to her 'pleasant manner and silvery voice'. She did not attempt to have a formal church service but there would be hymns, a Bible reading and then she would speak to embellish the reading. It would have been much more informal than they would have known in any of the town's churches and it is this that probably made her innovation such an immediate success. Following the service she would mingle with the men and talk to them. It was while she was so engaged that she quickly uncovered the reason why the average working man was so reluctant to adopt the Christian way of life. The hindrance was drink. On coming to this conclusion she wrote, 'It was like the cry of the Israelites in bondage...' In response to this revelation she turned her attention to promoting temperance. At this time the Cotton household was completely alcohol-free as her father was a staunch supporter of the temperance movement and always wore with pride the Blue Ribbon that indicated his commitment to the cause.

The debate about the dangers of alcohol consumption to society was as heated then as it is today. To put it into historical perspective one has to recall that in the eighteenth century there was much drunkenness in England, as it was the era of cheap gin and gin-palaces, dram-shops, and beer-shops all thrived. It was only in the early part of the nineteenth century that a movement began to discourage drinking alcohol. The temperance movement had its origins in the early religious antagonism towards alcohol by the Quakers and the Methodists. However, the problem for the early reformers was that for the working classes, drinking ale was preferable to the then available drinking water, which in the eighteenth and early nineteenth century, was a dangerous source of numerous diseases, such as dysentery, typhoid and cholera. Indeed at the time, many working-class families would brew their own ale at home. So it was only when cleaner water became available that the temperance movement began to succeed in getting the public to turn away from alcohol. A further impetus for the movement was the realisation that alcohol abuse was a major source of serious illness.

The problem facing the early reformers was the belief, particularly in England, that drinking spirits was good for one's health. Indeed as it was thought that a man might die if he were deprived of alcohol; it was the practice in many workhouses to give alcoholic drinks to the inmates. So when John Wesley attempted to curb the drinking of his followers, his main concern was with the consumption of distilled spirits, gin, brandy and whisky, rather than ale. However, it was not until the 1820s that the first serious ideas regarding temperance arrived in England from the United States, where a temperance society had been formed in New York as early as 1808. The first Temperance society in England was not formed until 1830, this being the Bradford Temperance Society. Shortly afterwards a society was formed in Liverpool, following the tragic loss of the steamship *Rothsay Castle*, with large loss of life, due to its drunken captain. It was not long afterwards that others were formed across the country. These societies employed agents to travel around their districts advocating temperance. However, these early attempts to promote temperance were not successful as alcohol abuse instead of declining became more prevalent. One of the main reasons for this is that they advocated moderation rather than complete abstinence.

Advocating complete abstinence, rather than moderation marked a change in the direction of the movement. The reformers argued that moderation didn't work as drinking alcohol always tended to excess. This new movement was started in Preston when Joseph Livesey formed the Preston Temperance Society on 1 January 1830. The idea of complete abstinence soon became known as 'teetotalism', this word being derived from the common Lancashire expression for something final. The earlier movement had attempted to keep men temperate by moderating their consumption of alcohol, whereas the new movement demanded complete abstinence, as being the only way to combat the 'demon drink'. They introduced the idea of signing the pledge - a deliberate act taken to mark a break with the past - and the start of a new life now free of alcohol.

This new approach became much more successful and numerous national organisations were founded. There was the British Temperance League, the National Temperance League, the Methodist Temperance Society, the Band of Hope and the Blue Ribbon Society. The Anglican church however was rather slow at taking up the temperance cause and it was not until about 1873 that the Church of England Temperance Society was formed, however once established it quickly attracted many influential aristocrats.

Elizabeth realized that alcohol abuse was the root cause of many of the problems in society, and that the only answer to it was complete abstinence. However, she knew that this was very difficult for a man to adhere to and that a drunkard would easily backslide into his old ways. Something more was needed. This she believed was faith in the Lord Jesus Christ. Thus for the drunkard to mend his ways it was necessary for him not only to renounce his old ways but he had to turn to Christ for support. Only then would he escape from his addiction. When she first came to this realisation she was anxious to obtain a pledge-book. When she located it she was told that the last man who had signed it was an old drunken shoemaker and that he had signed it some twenty times but on every occasion he had broken his commitment. She asked for the address of this man and resolved that she would commence her temperance work with him. She went to his cottage and there she found him busy at his work repairing shoes and boots. She asked him whether he was prepared to make another attempt at temperance. He replied that it was no use as he had failed so often before. At this she knelt down beside him and prayed while he continued with his hammering away at the shoe he was repairing. Still she continued to pray for him until at last he ceased his work and said to her: 'Miss, I believe there is hope for me'. At this he signed the pledge. Afterwards, she visited him daily to encourage him and he became a steadfast Christian in the town.

This is the message she took to the men who attended her Bible class. But she was aware of one major difficulty. The working men she was now dealing with were in the habit of going to the public house following their day's work and drinking ale. On one occasion she noticed a newcomer to her meetings. He was a big man, much taller than the others, and was dressed in very dirty working clothes. She was told that the man was always in the public house where he drank away all his earnings. She approached him and tried to persuade him to abandon his drinking habit. She recalled: 'His replies when I expostulated with him, were so singularly candid that one could only like the man for his honesty... "You see, Miss" he said, one day looking up at her with the most extraordinary mixture of gravity and satire: "You see, Miss, you never was a coalheaver. Was you, now?"'

At this she was taken aback and for a moment she was off balance, however when she recovered she turned to him and with the same honesty replied: 'Well no...I can't say I ever have.'

This made her very sensitive to the men's way of life. She realized that after a day's work the public house offered everything that their own home lacked. It would be warm with a roaring log fire, with good company and somewhere comfortable to spend the evening. But being there necessitated that they drank the ale. Thus to counteract this attraction she had to offer something similar, but without the alcohol, and so the idea of a coffee room was born.

Coffee Houses had been known from the seventeenth century when they existed right across the country. Although some were respectable, especially in the early days, most were not. With very few exceptions most of the coffee-houses were haunts of dubious characters of both sexes. Many of them although professing to serve only coffee, tea and other light refreshments actually carried on a brisk trade in gin and other spirits, and those that offered nightly lodgings were in fact just brothels.

Elizabeth's idea of a coffee room was for it to be not only a complete alternative to the public house, but also a place of worship. Although she was always an Anglican, like her father, she was conscious of the fact that the Church of England had failed in its mission to the ordinary working man. This being the case, her idea was that the coffee room not only could be a haven for the working man, but that it could also be his place of worship. Although she had her father completely behind her, she was nonetheless facing formidable difficulties. Not least among them was that women, at this time, had no active role to play in furthering the Christian message. It was simply not thought right for women to preach in public. Even women such as Catherine Booth, wife of the founder of the Salvation Army had great difficulty becoming accepted as a preacher. Indeed, only a few years before the American evangelist Mrs Phoebe Palmer had visited Britain and caused outrage amongst the clergy on account of her preaching. At this time, public opinion considered the possibility of female ministry to be scandalous. As for the idea of the twenty-something Elizabeth preaching the gospel to men, this could not only be seen to be outrageous but highly presumptuous. However, unlike Catherine Booth who had a personal struggle with the problem of a woman's right to a Christian ministry, young Elizabeth seemed to simply by-pass the issue. Thus the Coffee Room was formed where working men could obtain non-alcoholic drinks and food, in a warm homely environment, and where she could hold Bible classes and prayer meetings.

The premises was provided by courtesy of her father who arranged for the building to be constructed on land belonging to Job Pledge, of Falkland Road, Dorking, who was the local undertaker and carpenter. It consisted of two rooms, one above the other, each about 30 feet by 20 feet. The ground floor was the coffee room and the upper floor was for the religious meetings. A red lamp was installed over the entrance, with the name of the establishment painted in white. In an opening speech, the General named the building, 'The Beckenham Rooms' after the Beckenham Rectory where the Cotton family had sought spiritual refuge on their arrival in England. Elizabeth later wrote that it had been so named as it was there that she had, 'First learned to care for the souls of the working men and to see for myself the true joy of a devoted Christian life.'

The walls of the coffee room were decorated with pictures of biblical stories. The room itself was furnished with plain tables and benches covered with crimson cushions that had been provided by her father, and towards one end of the room there was a bar for refreshments. Visitors were free to relax, in the warmth provided by a log fire. In his opening speech General Cotton extended a warm invitation to the assembled crowd and announced that all were welcome, between the hours of 5am and 10pm, the only rule being that no alcohol was allowed nor any bad language. A resident manager of the coffee room had been appointed, he was a Mr Gooding, and Adam Brace was appointed as the mission worker with accommodation provided for both of them in adjacent cottages.

A fly-sheet was printed announcing the opening of the Coffee Room which was circulated around the town. It stated the hours of admission, being 5am to 10pm, with coffee, tea, cocoa served with dinners and suppers. A price list accompanied the announce-ment which gave the following prices: Coffee (1d @ cup), and Bread and Butter (2 slices, 1d) and Dinners (8d). However to get the place established all drinks on the first night were completely free. On that night about 50 men turned up but on the following nights of the first week there was an average attendance of about one hundred.[7] Over the following months this gradually increased and it soon became overcrowded. The decision was then made to exclude boys, but this led to so much dissatisfaction, that the only solution was for Mr Pledge to build another similar hall just to accommodate the boys.

Elizabeth's work soon began to attract the attention of church leaders in the town, particularly those clergy who opposed a woman preacher. On one occasion a local clergyman arrived accompanied by a large party of curious individuals to inspect the goings on beyond the red light over the entrance. They were shown the prayer room, with the Bible pictures on the wall and the platform from where she would lead the hymn singing and prayers. Afterwards they sat in the coffee room with some refreshments, and the clergyman turned to Elizabeth and informed her that he approved of all the work she was doing amongst the working people: but only the 'secular' part of the work. He did not approve of her prayer and Bible reading, as this was not for a woman to engage in.

But opposition was not just from the clergy. Many of her own social circle disapproved of her work. After dinner one evening she was criticised by guests who considered her temperance work not to be beneficial to working men. 'A coffee room without beer' they said disapprovingly. It was unfair to deprive a working man of his beer, they contended, as this was his little comfort, his one pleasure. However, Elizabeth believed differently and when she argued her case for abstinence from all alcoholic drink, she had her father's full support.

During these early years Elizabeth left a marked impression on all those she came into contact with. She clearly had a relaxed friendly manner that led people to be comfortable and completely frank with her. On one occasion a stranger visited the Coffee Room. He was a well-dressed young man, and soon Elizabeth was talking to him. He confessed that his life was being ruined by drink. 'It's my curse,' he admitted. He then told her that he felt helpless in not being able to stop his addiction. She then asked him if he would kneel down with her, and she would pray 'for our Father in heaven for His gracious help in this difficulty.' At first the young man hesitated but then he agreed, and they knelt down and prayed together. Afterwards he thanked her and said: 'I am very grateful to you indeed. Nobody ever prayed with me in my life before.' We don't know whether it cured him of his addiction, but certainly her compassionate nature must have left a marked impression on him.

On another occasion when she visited the Dorking Cottage Hospital for Bible reading she was warned by the nurse to avoid one of the patients. 'He's a terrible character,' warned the nurse. 'A very turbulent and disagreeable man, who drank hard and was a great fighter.' However, instead of avoiding him she confidently walked over to him and touched his hand. She sat down beside him and read a passage from the Bible. A few days later, she was visiting the hospital again, when the man was being discharged. The man offered to walk her home up Tower Hill. On reaching her house, he turned to her and announced, 'I want to give my heart to Jesus, When shall I do it?'

'When!' she exclaimed. 'Tonight, to be sure...Now is the accepted time; now is the day of salvation.'

'I should like you to pray with me,' he said, very earnestly.

So she took him into the house, to her sitting room, and they knelt down together and prayed.

Such acts of kindness would have had a marked effect on the working men she encountered. In particular, her sincerity was clear to everyone. An instance that shows the depth of her feelings was her involvement with a young railway guard, whom she had been responsible for his conversion. The man had subsequently fallen victim to tuberculosis and eventually he died. The man's colleagues from the railway company attended the Coffee Room following the funeral for refreshments and a short informal memorial service. But when it came to her to say a few words, she was completely overwhelmed with emotion, so much so, that she had great difficulty in speaking.

William Dinnage was only a small boy when his father took him to Elizabeth's Coffee Room, yet the impression made on him remained with him for the rest of his life. In 1950, some eighty years afterwards, he recorded his visits, describing the coloured pictures on the walls of, 'The Good Shepherd' and other scenes from the Gospels.[8] He remembered the simple religious services she held in the Coffee Room, and recalled that she had an engaging manner, with a pleasing 'silvery' voice.

However, it was not all Bible teaching at the Coffee Room. Elizabeth's mission had a very practical dimension. She introduced a library and encouraged her visitors to borrow books and improve their education. There was also a Penny Bank and a shoe club, where they could save the money they might otherwise have spent on drink. And there was also a lighter side, such as the Whit Monday when she took some thirty working men to the seaside at Eastbourne. For many of these men it had been the first time they had seen the sea. She later recalled: 'The men have often alluded to this delightful Whit Monday, saying it was one of the happiest times they ever spent in their lives.'

On another occasion a group of workmen from a building firm in London had been given a day's holiday and they had gone on a ramble up Box Hill. On their way home they called in at the Beckenham Room for supper, without realising that it was also a mission hall. Elizabeth was there to welcome them and after they had had their refreshments, she handed out some tracts and offered a prayer for God to bless their homes. Writing about the incident later she recalled that the men gave 'a look of amazement'. On overhearing one man whisper to another that it seemed an inappropriate time for prayer, she tackled him about it and a religious discussion ensued as to whether religion was equally for the rich and poor. The upshot being that the majority of the men agreed with her, and when she suggested they sing some hymns they welcomed the idea. Afterwards, the man who had spoken out came up to her and apologised, she recalled: 'we parted the warmest of friends, he accepting a small Bible with maps from me'. But it was not the end of the matter. Some days later she received a letter from the head of the building firm in London, saying that his men had asked him to write on their behalf, thanking her for the interest she had taken on the men's visit to Dorking.

But it was not all serious, for as already mentioned, there was a lighter side to her nature. Indeed, it would not have been possible for her to take some thirty rough-and-ready working men on a trip to the sea-side, and for them to enjoy it, if she did not have a very attractive and charismatic personality, enabling her to always see the lighter side of life. A good instance of this was her visit to the Dorking lime works.

At this time, Dorking boasted the best chalkpits in England. Much of this chalk was converted in large kilns into lime, which was much sought after by London masons and bricklayers. Indeed, Dorking lime had been used to build several of the capital's most important buildings including the Bank of England, Somerset House and London Bridge. The early chalkpits were situated to the north of Dorking at Chalkpit Lane, however later pits were opened up at Brockham some three miles away. On the occasion in question, Elizabeth had promised to visit the men working at the Brockham lime works, during their dinner break, when she intended to distribute tracts together with some of Miss Marsh's little books. She had travelled there in her pony carriage, but on reaching the lane leading to the works she found it so thick with mud, that her pony trap could not negotiate the ankle-deep mud, so reluctantly she abandoned her visit. The fact that she had broken her promise hurt her conscience, so a few days later she made another determined effort to reach the place. This time she was successful and when she made her way into the works a group of men gathered around her to listen to what she had to say. It was no doubt a remarkable occasion for these rough and ready men to have this young aristocratic lady arrive at their works as most of them would have had little respect for religion. Having explained the purpose of her visit, the men replied by telling her that no one cared for the spiritual needs of working men such as themselves. She then opened her Bible and told them that that would be the last time they would make that claim for she would tell them of, 'a Friend that loved them and died for them'. She then continued with her message and the men listened to her 'earnestly'. Then after a prayer many of the men responded with a sincere, 'Amen'. She then asked them to sing a hymn, but at this request they smiled and said, 'We ain't much use to that'. 'But I will teach you,' she replied. At which point she got her small harmonium and began to sing.

Following this first visit she was invited again and she was offered the use of the carpenter's shed for a weekly Bible meeting. The following week there was a good attendance, however she was told that there were some new men that had sloped off to have their lunch in another shed further up the hill. On being told this she went to the shed to invite them to her Bible meeting. 'No', they said and shook their heads. 'Not today thank you, Miss.' She then enquired as to what they thought about all day, to which one big man pointed with a knife to the boarded sides of the shed, which were pasted with crude pictures of 'the lowest description'. 'These are what we talks about' said the big man with a determined air. In the event she succeeded in persuading them to attend the meeting the following week. However, when she arrived, she was accompanied by a friend, and they had brought with them a large pot of paste and brushes, together with aprons. These were put on and they set about pasting over the crude pictures with coloured engravings from the Religious Tract Society. 'We were kindly thanked by the inmates...' she later recalled. Reflecting on this today one is left completely bemused on trying to imagine this extraordinary scene.

Another instance of this side of Elizabeth's personality occurred one Thursday evening in the Coffee Room. Normally she held a simple service, during which there would be a Bible reading, but on this particular occasion she was reading from Bunyan's *Pilgrim's Progress*. In our present age when radio and television are so ubiquitous one might easily forget the hold a good reader could have on an audience, particularly someone with an attractive voice. Elizabeth's public readings were so successful that on occasions she would have several hundred people listening to her. Indeed, some told her that they could listen to her all night. On this particular occasion Elizabeth had her audience entranced as she read the passage from Bunyan that involved the conversation between Faithful and Christian. Up to that point the reading had proceeded normally with just a few smiles and nods from the audience, but then she suddenly came to Faithful's remark about the 'Old Man' who had invited him into his house and then offered him the charms of his 'three unmarried daughters- Lust of the Eyes, Lust of the Flesh, and Pride of Life,' and permitting him to 'marry them all' if he so wished. On reading this the men burst out in raucous laughter which, innocent as she was, took her by surprise. However, she quickly recovered her composure and responded: 'Well, that was a chance for him wasn't it?' This quick-witted reaction only served to double the laughter of the audience; however she took it in good humoured spirit.

The normal routine was that after her readings there would be hymn singing and prayers and when this was over the people would return to the Coffee Room for refreshments. Throughout there was no compulsion, and visitors could please themselves to what extent they entered into the religious side of things. Indeed, she once referred to the Coffee Room, as 'Liberty Hall' as there was complete freedom for visitors to do as they wanted.

As a consequence of Elizabeth's amiable way of running the establishment she became greatly loved by those she encountered. This led to her being given many gifts and tokens of appreciation. Many of these she never recorded as she would have felt embarrassed to do so. Yet there is one that she did record and it was the gift she received from the working men of her Bible Class on Christmas Eve 1874. Just before she retired for the night she happened to glance out of the landing window into the darkness outside. At that time, on account of the elevation of the house, the view from this window would have extended right across the fields towards the town. Today the view is obstructed by the many houses that have since been built, but then there was a clear view across the fields. Although it was completely dark outside, she noticed a little glimmer of light moving slowly along the path that led to the house. For a time she watched it moving slowly up the hill, and then she called her father. They then watched the light getting brighter as it neared the house until it eventually reached their gate when they could see that it was a group of men with lanterns. On going outside to investigate they discovered that it was a group of workmen from her Bible class that had come to leave her a surprise Christmas present. It was a beautifully carved pedestal together with a large vase to hold flowers or climbing plants. As it was dark, the skill and perseverance involved in making the gift was not immediately apparent and it was only on Christmas morning, in daylight, that she appreciated the immense skill and labour that had been involved in creating this charming Christmas gift.

Soon afterwards she introduced a further innovation in the town that of a mobile coffee-stall. Around this time the Church of England Temperance Society had a number of these wagons usually pulled along by a small pony which offered warm temperance drinks to people passing by in the street. On hearing of her temperance work in Dorking Elizabeth was offered one of these wagons, initially on a loan basis, but with the option to purchase it later. When it arrived she was rather disappointed to find that it was in rather a dirty and dilapidated condition. It was painted in an unattractive yellow colour with the words 'Church Temperance Society' on the side in large letters. She was so disappointed with its appearance that she told Mr Gooding, the Coffee Room manager, to hide it from view until it was cleaned up and given a decent coat of paint, and more importantly when reference to the church temperance society was removed. She felt that this was important as these words would serve to turn people away rather than attract them. That same evening she had organised an event in the coffee room and had intended to show off the newly arrived coffee-stall, but in its present state this was not possible. After a few hymns she got up to speak and then gave a very amusing talk that got her audience into fits of laughter. 'I had invited a little friend to come,' she told them. 'But that at present he had on such shabby clothes that I cannot introduce him.' The audience was greatly amused and laughed most heartily, intrigued to know what the mystery newcomer might be. 'But my friend is very shy,' she continued, 'and is afraid of being given the cold shoulder. He is such a nervous little creature...' At this there were shouts of laughter. She eventually revealed that her 'friend' was a Coffee Stall pulled by a pony. This resulted in tremendous applause and approval at the idea. Soon afterwards she appointed a man to operate the stall, which by then had been repainted a rich crimson colour with the words 'church temperance' completely obliterated. This she explained, 'would be as obnoxious to our desired customers as a red flag in the eyes of a bull'. The stall was then situated at the opposite end of the town from the Coffee Room and proved immensely popular with the many men passing that place on their way to work, as well as advertising the presence of the Coffee Room in the town.

Much of her work in the Coffee Room has been documented in her two books, *Our Coffee Room*, and *More About Our Coffee Room*, published in 1876 and 1878 respectively. When these books were published they were well received and went into many editions, including publication in America. Florence Nightingale was particularly impressed with them and commended them in a letter published in *The Times* of 27 March 1878. Miss Nightingale also recommended them in her published writings, 'Coffee Houses,' she wrote, 'the best introduction to them is the series of books by Lady Hope of Carriden.'[9] Her enthusiasm for Elizabeth's writings was such that she began to give copies away at every opportunity. As a collector of Lady Hope's books I have found copies of *Our Coffee Room*, inscribed by Florence Nightingale, turning up all the time. So far the author has identified at least five such copies. There is one at the Florence Nightingale Museum in London, another in the library of the Whatstandwell Coffee House (now in private ownership), a third inscribed to Robert Robinson, drummer boy of the 68th Light Infantry, being one of the soldiers Miss Nightingale nursed during the Crimean War. This was dated, 18 July 1876. A further one is to be found in Australia inscribed to Sir Henry Parkes and dated September 1876. And a fifth one was sent to Miss Margaret Verney: 'I venture to send you,' Miss Nightingale wrote, 'if you have not seen it, "Our Coffee Room" by my dear old friend Sir Arthur Cotton, the Indian irrigation engineer, or rather by his daughter....I have read nothing which has given me so much pleasure since Agnes Jones went 'home'.'[10] Indeed, Miss Nightingale was so enthusiastic about Elizabeth's Coffee Room idea that she opened one herself in the village of Whatstandwell, near Crich in Derbyshire.

A further example of how Elizabeth was appreciated by the men she helped can be illustrated on the occasion when some 4000 men of the Scotch militia arrived in the Dorking district to carry out their summer manoeuvres on the common. Elizabeth on hearing news of their imminent arrival sought advice from her father as to how best they might be able to use the opportunity so as to spread the gospel message among them. At first her father was apprehensive, but she succeeded in talking him around. Then on visiting the proposed camping ground they met the commanding officer who encouraged them with their plans and offered to help them set up a temperance room on the site. They immediately recruited their friend, the Dorking carpenter, Job Pledge, and a large wooden hut was soon constructed. Over the weeks that followed the men of the various regiments found that there was a friendly centre where they could go for recreation in a temperance environment. Elizabeth and her father were there most days and much of their time was taken up in writing letters for the men to send home to their families. During this time they posted some 7000 letters to the men's families in Scotland. There were several highland brigades included in the manoeuvres and Elizabeth found that they were all warm-hearted men. She soon built up a good relationship with them, so that when she visited Perth the following year (in connection with the Moody revival) she renewed her friendship with some of them. She also had a surprise visit from one of them the following year. It was one Wednesday afternoon when she was sitting reading in her drawing room, when the maid announced that she had a visitor. On going to investigate she found it to be one of the Perth riflemen, but he had changed his uniform for a plain grey tweed suit, and instead of a rifle, had in his hand a knotted stick. Despite this change she recognised him as he had been one of her principal helpers, in distributing tracts and booklets to the men in their tents. 'His greeting was warm enough to be worthy of a Highlander,' she recalled. He then told her that he had returned to England with a drove of cattle, and then he had travelled another ninety miles, just so as to thank her and the people he had made friends with at the Coffee Room. Later she learnt that many of Highlanders had changed their ways after attending her Coffee Room and that they were now living changed lives. In his village alone, the man knew of at least ten other men who had been converted and were living new lives. Indeed, it had been noticed by the locals, and they had enquired as to the cause of the change, to which the men had replied that it was on account of them attending the Coffee Room in Dorking. This incident must have been a source of considerable encouragement to both Elizabeth and her father, but to us today, it is clearly an indication of her remarkable charisma.

This charisma was further demonstrated in the July of 1875 when she organised a group of her working men to attend the Moody revival meeting in the Camberwell Green Hall. The group consisted of some 120 men. How she organised them and got them to the meeting is unclear, nevertheless it must have been some achievement for a young woman to accomplish. Although she had probably learnt much from watching her father organise his men, it nonetheless does indicate that she was able to gain the admiration of ordinary working men, so that they became captivated by the unique features of her personality. However, this personal magnetism was not just towards men, for as we will see in the following chapter, which deals with her involvement with the Moody revival, she was equally effective when dealing with those of her own gender.

## CHAPTER 8

With Moody and Sankey

F OLLOWING THE RELIGIOUS movement of John Wesley and his
Methodist followers in the eighteenth century, Britain had
undergone sporadic periods of religious revival. One of the most
significant revivals was that brought about by the American
evangelist, Dwight L. Moody in the last decades of the nineteenth
century. This religious revival took place at a time when religious
belief was under considerable attack from the promotion of new
scientific ideas and the revisionist interpretations of scripture that
had been started by Bishop Colenso of Natal.

Dwight Lyman Moody (1837-1899) was an unlikely religious
figure to bring revival to this country. Not only was he a poorly
educated lay-person, he had been brought up on a simple farm-
stead and had a broad American accent, a disadvantage that was
not helped by his appearance. In his mid-thirties, he was slightly
overweight with a receding hairline, and a beard turning grey.
Most of the contemporary reports agree that he was not an
outstanding orator, but point out that his strength was in his
sincerity. He had been born in Northfield, Massachusetts, on 5
February 1837. On leaving school, having received a very basic
elementary education, he was given a job as a shoe salesman in
his uncle's shop, on condition that he attended the local Congregational Church. It was here that he was converted and he became
a born-again Christian. However, he had good business sense and
proved to be a talented salesman and moved to Chicago where he
hoped to make his fortune in the shoe business. It was in Chicago
that he became involved with the YMCA (Young Men's Christian

Association) and he started a Sunday school for local children in a converted saloon. This proved very successful and it quickly outgrew the premises so that he had to look for larger rooms. He then decided to abandon his business career and work full-time for the YMCA as a city missionary. Soon afterwards when he had gathered together a significant following, he decided to open his own mission hall. This opened its doors in 1864 and is still in existence today. It is known as the Moody Church.

It is curious that although Moody and Elizabeth, shared several common features, such as similar age, and had followed similar pathways in their early Christian ministry, yet they had markedly different backgrounds. They had both started their ministry in their own Sunday school, and from this it had progressed to opening a mission hall for working men. It is somewhat strange that although they had started their early work on entirely different continents, and from vastly different backgrounds, that their paths had somehow converged and eventually crossed. How this came about will now be considered in some detail.

Soon after forming his own church in Chicago, Moody felt called to bring his message to Britain. In preparation for this he made several preliminary visits to assess the religious mood of the country. His first visit had been in the spring of 1867, when he stayed for about three months. During this time he had meetings with George Muller of Bristol, and the Baptist leader, the Reverend C.H. Spurgeon. At this time, he was completely unknown, but on account of his connection with the YMCA in Chicago, he was able to give some talks at the London branch of this organisation. He was also able to visit Edinburgh where he spoke to religious leaders. However, his most important contacts were made in London, when he made the acquaintance of the Reverend William Pennefather, the founder of the Mildmay Conference. Another significant contact was with Richard C. Morgan, the religious publisher of *The Revival* journal which had been first brought out in 1859 (in 1870 its name was changed to

The Christian). Morgan who was also a supporter of the London YMCA, later came to play an important role in the Moody mission to Britain and became the movement's principal publicist. Both these men had been impressed by Moody's enthusiasm, so much so, that they invited him back to England. However, it was not for another five years before he would return. This was in the June of 1872. On this occasion he was able to speak at the Mildmay conference. Pennefather was so impressed with Moody that he proposed a longer evangelical campaign the following year, and together with Cuthbert Bainbridge of Newcastle, promised that they would sponsor him for all his expenses.

On 17 June the following year Moody, and his co-worker, Ira Sankey, together with their families arrived in Liverpool aboard the S.S. *City of Paris*. They later confessed that they had the modest target of winning some ten thousand souls for Christ. In the event they greatly exceeded this target, but it was a slow painful start, as on arrival in Liverpool they were dismayed to learn that both their sponsors had died, and consequently there were no funds to support their proposed mission. Undeterred they proceeded to York. Here they arrived late at night at the YMCA headquarters, where they received a very cool reception, on account of it being the holiday period with many people away and no one there had even heard of them. It was a gloomy start, but not entirely unexpected for as Spurgeon, the Baptist preacher, once pointed out: 'The inhabitants of cathedral cities have never been remarkable for their zeal in the promotion of religious revivals.'[11] Nevertheless they commenced their first meeting with just 50 people attending. Following their usual format Sankey sang a solo before Moody preached; but the meeting was not well received. The following day they held a prayer meeting in the afternoon when only six people turned up. However, on the fourth day things changed when the Reverend Frederick Meyer, a Baptist minister, led the way by opening up his church to them. Others followed and soon Moody was receiving invitations from far and wide (with the notable exception of Durham, where he was told to stay away). After about six weeks in York they moved on to Sunderland and it was here that Sankey's first Song Book was published by Richard Morgan, who had travelled up to the north-east to review Moody's campaign. Moody began to attract enormous crowds with many accepting the invitation to accept Christ as their personal Saviour and very soon Moody's target of reaching ten thousand souls was easily exceeded. With this success he moved on to other towns and cities in the north, ending that phase of the mission at Carlisle in the middle of November. By then news of the revival had reached Scotland and Moody was invited to Edinburgh. The first meeting was held at the Music Hall when some two thousand people attended with a further thousand having been turned away. Over the Christmas period he was invited to stay with the Reverend William Blaikie, of the Free Church College in Edinburgh, and in the New Year he moved over to Glasgow. In the early weeks of 1874 Moody held meetings in many halls and churches of the city. Special services were held for teachers, and children, which were all filled every day. Then in February he held a series of meetings in the Free College Church. The *Glasgow Herald* reported that at one of the meetings Moody informed the congregation that thousands of American Christians were praying for the success of his mission in Scotland. This upset one Scottish minister who wrote to the newspaper complaining that Scotland was not 'a land of Heathen darkness that had not heard the Christian message until the year of grace 1874 when Messrs Sankey and Moody stepped down on our shores'. Despite this most of the newspaper reports were favourable. The *Dundee Courier* of 29 July reported that Moody, was not 'clerical in speech or appearance' and although he spoke with a 'Chicago dialect' he was nonetheless, 'the greatest lay preacher of our times'.

It is probably in Aberdeen that Moody first came across Elizabeth. This was in the June of 1874. The precise circumstance of their meeting remains obscure. It is thought she was sent to Scotland to report on the Moody revival for the periodical, *Times of Blessing*, and the newspaper, *The Christian*, as Richard Morgan, the publisher, was her father's friend. But there is an earlier occasion when she was taken to meet him by her friends, the married couple, Peter and Jane Mackinnon. The author has in his possession an inscribed copy of Elizabeth's first book, *Our Coffee Room*, dedicated to these friends. We don't know when they first met, but it is possible it was on a cruise to Norway around this time. Peter Mackinnon was the cousin of Sir William Mackinnon and they had known General Cotton from a meeting in Calcutta some years before. Sir William Mackinnon had invited the Cottons to join him on a cruise aboard one of his newly launched passenger steamships to the Norwegian Fjords.

Sir William Mackinnon (1823-93) was a Scottish self-made businessman and shipowner. From very humble origins he had founded the British India Steam Navigation Company and the Imperial British East Africa Company. In their time these shipping companies possessed the world's largest sea-going fleet and consequently Mackinnon became very wealthy. Indeed, when he died in 1893 he left one of the largest self-made fortunes in the entire country. But on account of his humble origins he never felt accepted in the higher echelons of British society. As a consequence he tended to seek out influential individuals, such as senior military officers, peers and eminent politicians whom he would invite to take a cruise holiday with him and his family on one of his newly launched steamers. Following this he would entertain them at his mansion at Ballinakill on the west coast of Kintyre. Among those whom he is known to have invited was Sir Arthur Cotton and his family, for a cruise to the Norwegian Fjords. We know also that following the cruise the Cottons remained for some time at Ballinakill, so it is likely that it was here that Elizabeth became acquainted with Jane Mackinnon. In her journal Mrs Mackinnon describes the occasion:

'A trial trip to Norway of one of the B.I. steamers took place. The steamer came into Campbeltown Loch on a Saturday night. On Sunday a number of people came in and had lunch with us after coming from church, and in the evening Miss Cotton came on shore to stay all night. She told me she had been so full of hope and expectancy in coming to Scotland, about getting to see something of the Lord's work in the land, but so far, she had been disappointed.'

On hearing this Jane Mackinnon, who had met Dwight Moody during Moody's time in Edinburgh towards the end of 1873, suggested that they take Elizabeth to Aberdeen to meet the revivalist. She had been completely captivated by Moody's magnetism and the power of revival. She wrote in her journal:

'People were thoroughly roused either to opposition or to sympathy. It was the subject of conversation everywhere, and everyone had a position to take up – for or against. The doors of the places of worship were beset by crowds of people long before they were quite full and overflow meetings had to be provided for.'

She was also motivated at this same time to try and persuade Moody to visit Campbeltown. In the event Mrs Mackinnon succeeded, but only after she had boldly offered Moody the exclusive use of one of the Mackinnon's British India steamers.

As this first encounter with Moody was in the June of 1974, Elizabeth must have returned to Dorking, for at least a couple of weeks, before returning to Scotland. We know for certain that she spent some six weeks with the Moody campaign and that she returned again to Dorking at the beginning of September. It is possible that she had gone, on this second occasion, to cover the campaign for *The Christian*.

However, there is one thing we can be certain about. Moody was impressed by the depth of her Christian faith and her knowledge of Scripture. Moody himself had never had any formal

Bible education, so it must have been a surprise for him to find a young woman as familiar with scripture as any university professor. In her journal Jane Mackinnon refers to Elizabeth as 'a wonderful Bible teacher'. Secondly, he would have been particularly impressed by her public speaking ability. This also would have come as a surprise to him, for it was still generally unacceptable for women to preach in public, particularly to men. Elizabeth, by this time would have had several years experience at public speaking, so she would have spoken with considerable confidence, and with her exceptional 'silvery voice' and aristocratic manner, she would have made an immediate impact on Moody. Jane Mackinnon recalled:

'Miss Cotton's address was beautiful, her voice alone has a pathos and sweetness in it that moves me to tears. I have notes of this, and other later addresses. She certainly has a gift of speaking – a gift of voice and a power of engaging the fullest attention and sympathy of her hearers.'

This had come as a complete surprise to them all. Mrs Mackinnon recalled her sister's first impression of Elizabeth's talk to a group of young ladies:

'She is a devoted worker, but we did not know what her 'gift' was till my sister told us how she had spoken; and everyone at the hospital was transfixed, doctors, chaplains, patients and all.'

Moody first employed Elizabeth to help with the inquiry room, around the middle of July 1874. The inquiry room was for those who had expressed a commitment to Christ and wished to be counselled and prayed with. Moody had found that there were more women coming forward than men and he needed help from someone he could trust and rely on. Mrs Mackinnon recalled that one night Moody approached Elizabeth and said: 'I'll tell you what must be done. There's evidently more work among the women than among the men here. You must stay here and give them a few meetings, and I'll intimate it to-night.' Elizabeth, however was not so sure, as she was due to return home.

84

According to Mrs Mackinnon, Moody then, 'overruled her objections and after a little more talk it was settled that she should stay on.'

Moody soon found that Elizabeth was a dependable co-worker and he gradually gave her more responsibilities. In particular, when he moved the mission on to another town he would leave Elizabeth behind for some days for her to follow-up those women who had committed themselves to Christ.

It is notable that Moody organised his crusade with military precision. On visiting a town he would have a series of meetings during which he would invite those who wished to follow Christ to publicly declare their decision, by either standing up, or moving towards the front of the hall. Following this they would be instructed to go to the inquiry room where there would be prayer. The report in the *Dundee Courier* of 29 July 1874, noted that Moody's strength was in the management of people. This being so, on moving on to another town he would leave behind some of his helpers who would follow up the new converts. Other helpers, in whom he had greater confidence, he would leave to continue the mission with them holding further meetings. One such person was a young theological student, Henry Drummond, who carried on Moody's work in the north-east of England. As we will see in a later chapter the relationship of Drummond with Moody is interesting, and has significance to both his relationship with Elizabeth, as well as Moody's second campaign in Britain a decade later.

Moody's last meeting in Dundee was held on 12 June, when the Kinnaird Hall was packed to capacity. The following day there was a converts' meeting in the Chapelshade Free Church when Moody addressed all the new converts. The campaign then moved on to Aberdeen when the first meeting was held in the Music Hall on Sunday 14 June. The Hall was so packed that a decision was taken to move the meeting to the Links, where some 15,000 people crowded to listen to Moody preach. He then preached in many of the town's churches as their pulpits had been opened up to him. He then went on to Peterhead and later to Montrose before returning for a final three-week period in Aberdeen.

On Monday 28 June the campaign moved to Huntly, where Sankey, accompanied by a choir, arrived first by the 9 o'clock train from Aberdeen. It was a beautiful warm day and there was an open-air meeting in the Lodge Park that was attended by some ten thousand people, many of whom had travelled in from distant towns and villages. Moody didn't arrive until the afternoon when another open-air meeting was held with a larger congregation than the morning service. Afterwards Moody moved on to Inverness. Here on Thursday 16 July he preached to several thousand gathered for an open-air meeting on the Castle Hill. The following Sunday was a remarkable day. Again open air meetings were held on the Castle Hill when some 5000 people listened to his message. Sankey sang the hymn 'Almost Persuaded' with such intensity that it left a deep impression on all those present. The meeting then broke up with the men adjourning to the Congregational Chapel where the follow-up meeting was presided over by Mr Sankey. Whereas the women went over to the session-house, which was soon found to be inadequate in coping with the huge numbers seeking help. It is here that Elizabeth helped in praying with those women who were seeking salvation.

Fortunately, Elizabeth has left a record of Moody's final meetings in Aberdeen. On the afternoon of 31 July, Moody addressed a meeting of the converts. 'A grand discourse it was,' she recalled. 'Confession of the Name by which we are saved' was its theme. In the evening there was a crowded meeting in the Music Hall when Moody preached on John iii, talking about the darkness of Nicodemus and the exaltation of Christ as a crucified and risen Saviour. It was a story 'he so loved to tell'- a simple message of faith resulting in everlasting life. When the meeting was concluded he invited all who wished to be saved to meet him in one of the smaller rooms adjoining the hall. About seventy women were kneeling when Elizabeth entered the room. Moody was already praying with them. Soon afterwards he was obliged to leave for the quay in order to catch the evening ferry to Wick and she remained to supervise the work with the new converts. 'A blessed time it was!' she recalled. 'The Lord drew wondrously near, and healed so gently many sorrowing hearts, whispering to them of peace and love in His promised Word- pardon for today, strength for tomorrow, while many believed and accepted the offered gifts.' At eleven o'clock her work was done, however there was some paperwork to be completed, so that it was almost midnight before she was able to leave the hall for the hotel where she was staying. It was dark outside and raining. She put up her umbrella and began the walk to the hotel alone. She hadn't gone far when she noticed a small figure standing beneath a street lamp. It was a little girl in a print pinafore over her head, her frock dripping wet and with bare feet. At the time, it was a sad but not uncommon sight. (Many children went about with bare feet as shoes were expensive and they grew out of them very quickly.)

As Elizabeth hurried past, the little girl spoke to her. 'Is Mr Moody within?' she asked.

Elizabeth was halted in her tracks and she turned to look at the child. She was familiar with Moody's meetings for young people but was surprised that one so young had been affected by his message. The little girl looked up at her, with eyes that appeared grave and wistful. 'No my child,' she replied, 'he has already left for the quay, to take the steamer to Wick.'

At this information the little child began to cry. Elizabeth leaned forward and took her hand. 'You can give me a message for him,' she said, 'and I will give it to him.'

At this the little girl began to cry and Elizabeth moved closer to her, protecting her from the pouring rain with her umbrella. 'Oh,' said the child, 'thank Mr Moody for coming to Aberdeen, because he has helped me to find Jesus.'

Elizabeth put her arm around the little girl and kissed her and then they parted. However, she had only gone some few steps before she heard the patter of bare feet on the wet pavement behind her. She turned around and the little girl was once more looking up at her.

'Jesus will take care of me, winna He?' she asked.

'He says,' Elizabeth replied smiling, 'I will never leave thee, nor forsake thee. He loves you, dear child.'

'Thank you,' she said turning, and she was gone.

Elizabeth then turned and continued walking towards her hotel. But the little child remained in her thoughts. When she reached the hotel, where it was warm and cosy she thought of the little girl with bare feet and wet clothes. During supper her mind was thinking as to what sort of home the child had come from. Where were her parents? Why was she out in the street at that time of night? These are the thoughts that must have passed through her mind as she lay in bed that night. Jesus did indeed love the child but there must be something she could do as well. It would be several years later before she found the answer to this dilemma.

During the following days she continued with the follow-up meetings with the new converts. Moody meanwhile had travelled further north. Having left Aberdeen on the night ferry he had intended to go to Wick, but they encountered a severe storm that made docking at Wick impossible. As a consequence the ferry was diverted to Thurso from where he took the train to Wick. During the voyage he had been violently sea-sick and on arrival at Wick he was unable to preach. The Free Church had been full to capacity with people having travelled from surrounding areas to listen to him, with the railway companies having put on special trains. In his place Mr Torrance of Chicago preached.

On 13 August Moody travelled further north to John O'Groats and after walking around Duncansbay Head with some sightseeing of local landmarks he returned to John O'Groats where he found a large crowd gathered together where once the old house had stood. All that remained of it was a large mound. This gave him the vantage he needed, so standing on it he preached, taking as his text John 1 v.12. Many in the crowd were so moved that they openly wept.

Towards the end of the month he returned to Inverness to hold farewell meetings and to re-join the workers he had left behind, including Elizabeth. During these meetings, held in the West Church, Mr Sankey could not attend having fallen ill with exhaustion. The final meeting was held on Thursday, 27 August, when some 2,500 people crowded into the church. The following morning they were all up at the crack of dawn to board the paddle steamer, *Gondolier* for the journey to Oban along the Caledonian Canal.

The Caledonian Canal was one of Thomas Telford's greatest engineering achievements. This 62 mile waterway had been opened in 1822 and linked Inverness with Fort William. It had originally been conceived as providing a safer route for shipping between the East and West coasts of Scotland, so avoiding the treacherous seas around Cape Wrath. It had been designed for sailing vessels, but with the introduction of steam powered vessels that were more able to sail in these dangerous waters, the canal never proved profitable. Things however changed dramatically in the autumn of 1873 when Queen Victoria took the paddle steamer *Gondolier* along the length of the canal and the voyage took on the status of a sort of Scottish Grand Tour. From that moment the Caledonian Canal became a major tourist attraction. Even today it still attracts millions of visitors each year and is known as 'the Royal Route'.

The paddle steamer *Gondolier* had been built just seven years before. It was an elegant vessel of 173 tons. It had full width saloons forward, and alleyways round her aft saloon, with a spacious deck. The vessel proved an exceptionally long-lived steamer and continued to sail up and down the Caledonian Canal until 1939 when she was taken over by the Admiralty and scuttled in Scapa Flow, as a blockage to enemy shipping.

Fortunately, Elizabeth has left us a vivid description of her cruise on the *Gondolier*. The party had set off from Inverness at 6 o'clock in the morning. Her account continues: 'A great bell ringing –handkerchiefs waving – good-byes shouted – and a chorus of voices, bass and treble, uttering a volume of parting good wishes. Then the shrill scream from the steamer's whistle, and we are off, and the shores of Inverness are vanishing in the distance!'

She was a member of a small group of workers who were accompanying Moody on his mission. They were heading for Oban where Moody was due to preach that night at the Presbyterian Church in Breadalbane Street. Her account continues: 'It was a special day for our happy party...indeed one day in a thousand...As we steamed through the Caledonian Canal the mountains rose on all sides, sometimes tipped with snow on their highest peaks, sometimes graced with dashing waterfalls which came tumbling down from alarming heights.' When they reached the Fall of Foyers waterfall, the spectacular 140ft waterfall on the River Foyers, that feeds into Loch Ness there appeared an 'exquisite rainbow' that inspired her further. In her party were both friends and some strangers. In the centre of the group was Moody himself. 'The happiest hours' she recalled, 'we spent gathered together for Scripture reading on the deck of the steamer.' At eight o'clock they reached the little harbour of Oban, where a group of friends were waiting for them on the pier. They informed them that the church had been packed for some two hours. It was just a few minutes walk from the pier and they were soon there. Moody preached on the text from Luke xix – 'The Son of Man is come to seek and to save that which was lost.' The *Glasgow Herald* later reported that the church was so crowded that many had been turned away disappointed. Those that had been admitted heard Moody speak for a little over an hour and at the close of the meeting many had committed themselves to Christ. Elizabeth recalled that 'the two vestries were soon filled'. She was to help with the women who had come forward. On entering the room she noticed a woman sitting beside a darkened window, as outside a storm had blown up and the rain was battering against the glass. The woman appeared distressed and was crying. Elizabeth sat down beside her and asked her what was the matter. The woman looked up at her and in broken English she confessed that she was seeking the Lord Jesus but, 'canna find Him'. She then explained that she was from a distant island and had journeyed to the mainland with her husband and sons after hearing news of the great many people being saved after hearing Mr Moody. At this she burst out crying again and said: 'I am more miserable than ever. The meeting is over and I canna find Him...'

They then knelt down together and Elizabeth prayed with her. When they got up Elizabeth pointed out to her the text Moody had used: 'The Son of Man is come to seek and to save...' and that the seeker was already the finder. At this the woman grasped what she meant and she clasped her hands together and there was a great joy upon her face. They knelt down again and prayed, the woman 'in broken words uttered her grateful thanks to the Lord...'

It was now almost eleven o'clock, most of the other people had left, and the doors of the church were being closed. The woman remembered her husband who had gone to the men's inquiry room and made her way over towards it. There inside was her husband dressed in the woven shirt of a boatsman, together with his son of 'ruddy, weather-beaten countenance' in earnest conversation with 'a much loved pastor of a Glasgow church'. On seeing the woman they got up and rushed over and they all embraced. Elizabeth recalled: 'It was a beautiful sight.... a scene I could not describe, but shall never forget.'

'We shall have a happy journey in the boat to-morrow' the woman said turning to Elizabeth. 'We start at daybreak, and we'll talk about Jesus all the way.' And so they departed. But it was not for long. As Elizabeth was retiring for the night at her hotel, the woman and her family turned up again. 'They had come to try and get one more look at the messengers that had been sent to bring them the tidings of peace.' It was past midnight, but now time was unimportant.

The following day the group that had travelled with Moody split up. Moody and a few close friends had been invited to stay with Peter and Jane Mackinnon in Campbeltown. Among this inner circle was Elizabeth. On the morning of Saturday, 29 August, they left Oban on the steamer and headed for the Forth of Clyde. When they arrived at Ardrishaig they were met by Peter Mackinnon, who had a carriage for the ladies and a wagonette for the men. They then set off for the Mackinnon's home, *Ronachan* a three-story mansion overlooking the white sandy bay of Tarbert. By the time they reached their destination it was 10 o'clock and they were all exhausted, particularly little Willie, Moody's son, who was now fast asleep.

During the following days Moody and the others relaxed. They went for walks in the fine countryside and admired the scenery. Moody found time to play with his children, and took them down to the shore to collect crabs. On the following Tuesday they all drove over to Davaar where they all enjoyed a game of croquet and admired the greenhouses. On their return Moody and the other men got out the carriage as he wanted Elizabeth to travel with Mrs Moody and Mrs Jane Mackinnon. By this time the three women were firm friends and they enjoyed a delightful journey back, while the men had to walk. The following day, 3 September, Moody left early for Campbeltown where he took the ferry for Rothesay. He was to preach at the West Free Church, but on arrival he found the church was again full to capacity, with the heat inside unbearable, so much so, that several people had already fainted. He made a snap decision and moved the congregation outside where he held an outdoor meeting on the nearby beach when some 4000 people listened to him preach standing on a table. The following day he left Rothesay early in the morning for Greenock where he took the steamer to Belfast. This was his last day in Scotland in this his first mission. Over the following three months Moody took the mission to Belfast and then on to Dublin. Elizabeth was to join him in Dublin in November when she was accompanied by her father. Mrs Mackinnon recalled that Moody had missed her support and on one occasion had admitted to her that: 'I wish I had Miss Cotton here now.'

One of her responsibilities was to return to Belfast and supervise the work there. Mrs Mackinnon recalled:

'Mr Moody said she was to have a meeting in a certain church, Mr Hanna's in Belfast. We found his large, double-galleried church filled with young women. I never saw more intensely earnest faces than these girls in Belfast had, listening to Miss Cotton. Such intense listening was almost oppressive. We had inquiry work afterwards, and I had the joy of believing that a girl to whom I spoke put her trust in Jesus. One could see how deeply the work had taken hold here, and it was so in many places, after the evangelists themselves had gone. Here in Belfast, there was a large ingathering among young women. How they flocked round Miss Cotton, some as inquirers and some as young converts.'

After this time in Belfast, Elizabeth returned with Mrs Mackinnon to Dublin, where Moody had arranged for her to take meetings at the Exhibition Palace immediately on her arrival. Moody himself had taken a break with his wife into the country. On his return to the city, he immediately turned up at Elizabeth's hotel, dressed in his sealskin cap with a Murray plaid over his shoulder, to check on progress.

By the end of November the mission to Ireland was over and they all returned to the mainland by ferry to Holyhead, when Moody was once again incapacitated by sea-sickness. Elizabeth returned to London, Mrs Mackinnon to Scotland and Moody and his family to Manchester, where he was to continue the crusade.

It would be the following summer that the group would meet up again during the mission to London. In the July Elizabeth was to hold meetings for women at Camberwell Hall and help out with the inquiry room. It was sometime during this period that Elizabeth, together with the Mackinnons, encountered the frivolous side of the evangelist. They had taken Moody with his family to Crystal Palace. In her journal Mrs Mackinnon describes how they all enjoyed the train journey back when Moody was, 'tossing about coloured balloons' for his little son to play with. It is an endearing picture of a group of friends relaxing together. It is interesting to note that another member of the group was John Wanamaker (1838-1922). Wanamaker was later to open the world's largest retail store in Philadelphia, but at this time he was secretary of the YMCA and had come over from America to study in person the British mission, as he was planning to sponsor a similar campaign the following year in Philadelphia.

Elizabeth had become an important member of Moody's inner circle. It had been an inspirational period in her life. She had gained much in confidence and had witnessed, at first hand, the remarkable power of religious revival and how the simple gospel message could turn lives around. She was now more determined than ever to carry out similar work in her home town.

CHAPTER 9

Marriage and Carriden

IN THE NOVEMBER of 1877 Elizabeth received a proposal of marriage from Admiral Sir James Hope, whom she had known for some time as he was a close friend of her father. During that summer Hope had been the Chairman of the Royal Commission of Inquiry into the stability of the Invincible Class of battleship. As Chairman of the inquiry he had been supervising experiments on scale models carried out in the testing pool at the Torquay home of the naval architect, Mr J. H. Froude. Then en route back from Torquay Hope would meet up with his old friend General Cotton at Bristol, where the General had been carrying out similar experiments with his newly designed steam turbine engine, at the engineering works at Grove House, Stoke Bishop. The two men would then return to Dorking, when Admiral Hope would be a guest in the Cotton home.

At first Elizabeth was flattered by the Admiral's proposal. However, there was a large age difference. He was 69 and she was just 34. On the plus side, Admiral Hope was at the height of his fame. Indeed, he was probably the most notable naval hero since Admiral Nelson. Only recently had the Stevens Company of Coventry issued a silk embroidered bookmark with his portrait on it with his motto 'Deeds not Words' to celebrate his achievements. Such a product was a distinction reserved for only those who had done something outstanding. Besides,he was still an active man, attractive with a tall and imposing figure, and having a very pleasant personality. Also important for Elizabeth was the fact that he was a devout Christian and temperance campaigner.

Maybe she thought that by marrying an older man it would be more likely she would be able to carry on with her evangelistic and temperance work. It is difficult to speculate, but it is clear that at this stage in her life she wanted to do what she felt called by God to do. Furthermore, finding a younger man who would allow her this freedom might have been difficult. This being so, she accepted Admiral Hope's proposal and the forthcoming marriage was announced on Monday, 12 November.

Admiral Hope had been married before. His first wife had been the Honourable Frederica Kinnaird, the daughter of Lord Kinnaird, but she had died in 1856, and there had been no children, so it is possible that Admiral Hope viewed Elizabeth as his last chance to have an heir to his Scottish estate.

Admiral Hope was from a very distinguished Scottish naval family. His father was Admiral Sir George Hope, who had been at the Battle of Trafalgar with Lord Nelson, and had commanded the 74-gun battleship, HMS *Defence*. His mother was Lady Jemima Johnstone Hope, a daughter of the Earl of Hopetoun. James had been born in 1808 and followed his father into the Royal Navy. In 1820 he had entered the Royal Naval College, Portsmouth and then served in the Mediterranean and later in the West Indies. In June 1838 he was promoted to the rank of Captain and was given the command of the sloop HMS *Racer* in the West Indies. In 1844, while he was in command of the paddle steamer, HMS *Firebrand*, he was involved in joint English-French action at the naval battle of Parana during the Uruguay civil war. On account of his bravery he was mentioned in despatches and was later awarded the French Legion of Honour. With the outbreak of the Crimean War in 1854 he was put in command of HMS *Majestic*, then in 1857 he was promoted to Rear-Admiral and two years later he became Commander-in-Chief in China on the frigate HMS *Chesapeake*. In 1861 he was involved in the Tsushima Incident when he helped the Japanese repel the Russian Fleet at Tsushima Island. His period in China covered the Second

Opium War and during this time he led the attack on the Taku Forts on the Peiho River that eventually led to the capture of Peking (Beijing). During the attack on the Taku Forts he was directing operations from the bridge of HMS *Plover* when a shell fragment struck him and became deeply embedded in his thigh muscle. For a time he lay on the deck badly wounded and the battle seemed to have been lost but the situation was saved by the intervention of an American commander, who gave assistance despite his country's neutral position. As a result of his injury he was disabled for some months and partially lame afterwards, however the ship's surgeon managed to extract the shell fragment. He was wounded again in 1862 while fighting the Taiping rebels. On this occasion he was directing operations from a sedan chair (on account of his previous wound) alongside a French admiral, when an enemy shell exploded nearby and decapitated the Frenchman. He was himself thrown violently across the deck and this re-opened his thigh wound. Later that year he was appointed Commander-in-Chief of the North America Fleet and made vice-admiral. On account of the American Civil War this was a particularly difficult command. In 1870 he was promoted to Admiral and in 1878 he was made Admiral-of-the-Fleet, the highest rank in the Royal Navy. At this time he was also made the principal naval aide-de-camp to Queen Victoria. To the Queen and to most of the country he was the most notable naval officer of his generation and admired as an outstanding naval hero alongside Admiral Nelson. Even today he is held in great respect and there is a full-length portrait of him by Sydney Hodges on display at the Ministry of Defence building in Whitehall.

Reviewing this distinguished career one can appreciate how Elizabeth might have been attracted to him, despite their differing ages. The marriage took place on Thursday, 6 December 1877, by special licence, at her local parish church of St Paul's in Dorking. The witnesses recorded on the marriage certificate were her mother and father which suggests that they had supported her decision to marry Admiral Hope despite the age difference. The day was a memorable one for the local people who turned out to line the streets, for it wasn't everyday that there was a naval hero getting married in the town. One little boy who stood on the side of the road that day was William Dinnage. He was seven years old at the time, and many years later when he published his *Recollections of Old Dorking*, he recalled watching the wedding carriages make their way down the lane to the church.

On the following day, Friday 7 December, the newly married couple travelled by train to Edinburgh. Here they changed for the thirteen-mile rail journey to the small town of Linlithgow. It was 5 o'clock, and dark, by the time they arrived at Linlithgow station and they left by the south entrance to the station. Unbeknown to them the Countess of Hopetoun and her party were waiting to greet them at the north entrance. Presumably they had thought that the couple were travelling by way of Glasgow. Thus they missed the welcoming party however, there was another one waiting for them at Carriden some three miles away.

Arriving at the Carriden estate they found a grand triumphal arch had been erected and was covered in flowers with the word 'WELCOME' emblazoned above and lit up by a dazzling array of Chinese lanterns. Then as they entered the estate they could see the sides of the drive lined with people who had come from the surrounding districts of Carriden, Bo'ness and Muirhouses. As they passed by, the cheers rang out in the surrounding darkness. Further along the driveway their carriage stopped for a few minutes when they were met by a torchlight procession headed by the Carriden Brass Band, which then led the way right up to the great house. Then when Elizabeth and the admiral stepped down from their carriage the crowds cheered them. Many in the crowd were holding lighted torches and lanterns and others were waving their caps and cheering. The admiral led Elizabeth up the steep steps to the entrance to the house and then turned to address the crowd. In his address he acknowledged the honour done to him of Elizabeth consenting to be his wife, and he thanked them for their good wishes. He then invited them to partake in the generous supply of food and other good things that his staff had provided. He also announced that the following day all the children attending the schools in the district would be given treats to celebrate the special occasion. The crowd cheered them again and after partaking in the refreshments gradually dispersed. Elizabeth then for the first time entered her new home.

It was not until daylight the following morning that she was able to see the full extent of her new home. She could see immediately that it was quite unlike any place she had lived in before. It was probably early in the morning that she ventured down the steep steps at the main entrance and made her way on to the front courtyard. She could then look up at the imposing structure.

Carriden House is today very much as it was when Elizabeth lived there, however, the long drive from the main road along which she had travelled on that first night no longer exists. However, since Elizabeth's time the property has passed through various members of the Hope family and then to the Lloyd Verney family. The house itself is in a very isolated situation and on account of this, it is believed that during the Great War it had been a German spy hideaway, before being used as a convalescent home for wounded soldiers. In the 1960s the condition of the house had badly deteriorated and it was purchased by the Scottish Electricity Board which considered its demolition and a power station built on the site. Fortunately this was decided against and it went again into private ownership. (It is now a private residence, and at the time of writing is the home of the Blackbourn family.)

The main entrance is up a steep flight of stairs just as it was in Elizabeth's time. Besides the door today is a huge bell-pull, which is the same one as Elizabeth describes in her book, '*A Maiden's Work*'. The building itself is built around a sixteenth century towerhouse in rose sandstone, with a datestone of 1602. It has distinctive pointed turrets and fluted gun-loops, very much in the Scottish baronial style. High up on the front of the building is the crest of the first Admiral Hope. The house itself stands on an elevated position overlooking the Firth of Forth, which may be viewed from the balcony. Then immediately in front of the building there is an ancient burial ground, which is fenced-off with rusty iron railings, with many of the tombstones covered with thick moss, as nearby was the site of the medieval church that had been removed in 1765.

One can be sure that her husband would have told her much of the history of the place during their journey north. It had once been the site of a Roman fort, being part of the ancient Roman Antonine Wall. And he would have told her about the Roman artefacts that had been dug up from the grounds. Elizabeth would have thought about this as she explored the grounds on that first morning. She would have wandered around the extensive gardens and seen the white sails of ships on the Forth peeping through the trees.

However it would have taken Elizabeth several days to take in the full extent of the Carriden estate. At that time it covered some 735 acres, including two arable farms and a home farm. There were extensive gardens and lawns together with thick woodland that led down to the shore. The gardens were well-laid out and planted with fine parkland trees and there were picturesque glens and numerous pathways. Then beyond the extensive stables and staff cottages there was an enormous walled garden which contained numerous hothouses, fruit trees and an apiary.

On that first Sunday morning the newly married couple would have attended the small Carriden parish church just a short distance away. Then later on the admiral would have taken Elizabeth to visit Muirhouses, the model village he had built to house many of his estate workers. He would have taken her inside the substantial schoolhouse and shown her the library building nearby. They would then have inspected several of the neat cottages close by each having its own small garden.[12]

Following their first Christmas together at Carriden, on Friday 4 January, the admiral invited the Sunday school teachers and choir from the Carriden Church for tea in the drawing room. It was a good opportunity for Elizabeth to make some new friends. The choir sang some hymns and there was a musical box that provided some entertainment. Then the admiral gave a short address and introduced his new wife to the visitors. Tea and cakes followed, but unfortunately Elizabeth was taken ill and was forced to retire.

However, before she retired to lie down she was introduced to Alexander Bell, a 60-year-old ex-miner who had been a Sunday school teacher for many years. He explained to her that he was now sick and unable to work in the mine, but that he still maintained a Sunday school in a nearby cottage. He then told her that for many years he had been praying for someone to come to the area so as to revive the faith of the local people. Now with her arrival in the area he believed his prayers had been answered and he invited her to one of his classes in the town.

Three weeks later, on Thursday 24 January, there was a special event in the nearby town of Bo'ness. The town of Bo'ness (or Borrowstounness) had been a major port in the eighteenth century exporting coal and importing timber from the Baltic. It had also been a major whaling port. Elizabeth in her book about her time at Carriden, *A Maiden's Work*, mentions the main square in the town as 'Boiling Square' being the place in times gone by where whale blubber was boiled to extract the oil and fat. Now Elizabeth and her husband had been invited to attend an evening meeting in the Town Hall. When they arrived they found the building decorated with flags and coloured bunting. On entering they found a Brass band playing and they were led up on to the platform to sit alongside Mr Cadell, a local dignitary, who was the presiding chairman. After a preliminary speech the chairman presented the admiral with a silver casket containing a beautifully illuminated scroll documenting his illustrious naval career. The chairman then addressed Elizabeth and presented her with a solid silver inkstand together with a gold pen.

The chairman then addressed the audience and spoke of how grateful he was that Elizabeth had come to the area as there was a great need for someone to discourage the excessive drinking in the town. He then congratulated the admiral on winning such a fine lady for his wife and wished them a long life together. Sir James then returned the address following which Elizabeth made a short speech. In it she thanked them all for the warm welcome she had received and for the handsome present. She then spoke of her work in Dorking and of the success of the Coffee Room. She then appealed to the ladies present for them to pray, at least once a week, for those addicted to alcohol. When she had finished there was loud applause. On returning to her seat, she felt satisfied that she had now broken the ice.

The local minister the Reverend E. Smith then moved a vote of thanks and concluded by saying that he believed that the best deed Sir James had ever done was to bring Elizabeth to the neighbourhood.

On the following Friday, Elizabeth was due to give an address to the children of the Chalmers Memorial School in Linlithgow during an evening soirée held in the Free Church. But just as the children were settling down in their places it was announced that on account of her indisposition she could not attend. On hearing this news there was great disappointment in the hall as the children had heard so much about her. Then just at the last moment and to everyone's surprise she arrived accompanied by the admiral. She then gave a very interesting address that was listened to very attentively by all the children. The meeting then concluded by prayers and hymns, a pleasant time having been had by all.

These two occasions when Elizabeth had been unwell might suggest that she was having some problems adjusting to her new circumstances. If this were the case it is hardly surprising. She was now living in an entirely different environment. This part of Scotland is rather bleak and raw, particularly in the middle of winter, far different from the softer surroundings at Dorking. Also the local people were completely different, both in speech and manner. And she was just getting to know her husband, which couldn't have been easy considering their age difference, as well as the fact that they probably didn't know each other very well before. Also, she didn't have any family or friends in the area to whom she might have spoken to. Her only companion was her new sister-in-law Helen Hope, who also lived at Carriden House, but again there was a large age difference between them.

It seems likely that the admiral recognised the difficulties Elizabeth was having for he suggested that they travel back down to visit her parents in Dorking. Another indication that she was suffering from homesickness is the fact that shortly after this first Christmas she began writing a monthly circular letter for her friends in Dorking. She would sit at her writing desk in the drawing room beneath the window overlooking the ancient churchyard and give a detailed commentary of her new life. In her letter written in February 1878 one can detect her feeling of homesickness, for she wrote:

'In the absence of our friends, we rejoice to have a record of their thoughts towards us, either by message, or by letter.' And then further on... 'But so stubborn and proud are our hearts, that we have too often to be brought into the position by trouble, by the crossing of our wills as many of you have experienced. Every Christian must have periods of this bringing down, before the Lord can give the raising up.'

Shortly before they left for Dorking she followed up her invitation to visit Alexander Bell as she had been told he had not been well. On entering his modest cottage she was greeted by his unmarried daughter, Jane, who was a pleasant, intelligent young woman of similar age to Elizabeth herself. However, she was deaf and dumb, but this had no problems for Elizabeth as she had learnt to communicate using sign language with James Ansell, whom she had known at Dorking.

On meeting Alexander Bell she found him to be very poorly, however he was pleased to see her again.[13] They talked for a while and then he prayed with her, and asked for the Lord's blessing on her ministry. 'Speak to them,' he urged. 'And have all the meetings you can. God is sure to answer prayer.'

In the March of 1878 Elizabeth returned to Dorking to visit her parents. She was delighted to find that her Coffee Room was thriving. On meeting some of her friends they enquired as to how her work was progressing in Scotland. To which she replied that she had only made a start, but she needed larger premises. Later she received an unexpected invitation to attend the Public Hall in the town. On her arrival she found a large audience waiting for her. Many of them she recognised as railway workers on the Dorking-Brighton Line. She was then greeted by representatives of the railway company and presented with a pair of solid silver candlesticks, together with an illuminated script, handsomely framed and signed by some 160 employees of the company, expressing their appreciation for the encouragement she had given them towards temperance and for conducting their religious services. In reply she expressed her sincere appreciation and thanked them for their gratitude, following which she was warmly applauded.

CHAPTER 10

Lady Hope

O N HER RETURN to Carriden she received word that Mr Bell, the sick miner, had taken a turn for the worse. The following day she made her way to his modest cottage in Bo'ness to see how he was. She found the cottage again and made her way up a flight of outside stairs to the front door and knocked. It was opened by his deaf-and-dumb daughter, Jane Bell, who after greeting Elizabeth led her to see her father. Alexander Bell was lying in bed surrounded by a few of his friends and Elizabeth could see right away that his condition had deteriorated and that he had not long to live. On seeing her again he seized her hand and kissed it. 'You have come back,' he exclaimed. 'Just in time. I was wanting to see you once more. I have been very ill – yes – but it is all right. Jesus is with me. I cannot think much – no – but He thinks for me. Jesus is very kind. Oh! He is kind.' Elizabeth smiled and then knelt down besides the bed and prayed aloud; thanking God for the comforting assurances of His suffering servant. Afterwards the man's daughter led her out to the front door. Before leaving she gently embraced Jane Bell and handed her a journal article which she had copied out for her on her typewriter. It was entitled; 'A short paper for the deaf-and-dumb.'

Alexander Bell was only to live a short time longer and died on 13 May 1878. It is interesting that in his response on seeing Elizabeth again, which is given above in Elizabeth's own words, it seems to suggest that some of the local people might have felt she was not going to return to Carriden. Had there been some whispering amongst the servants of Carriden House that the new mistress was not happy? We don't know. There were clearly some problems as she adjusted to her new life, however, Elizabeth was not one to give up easily. One can be sure that on her return to Carriden she was determined to make her new life a success. She now got together with the admiral and got him to agree to build a Coffee Room in Bo'ness similar to the one in Dorking. There was certainly a need for one as the town was notorious for drunkenness. During her recent stay in Dorking she had been shown Mr Denny's plans for a Coffee Palace in the town to replace her Coffee Room. This was to be a substantial purpose built establishment with a large lecture theatre and games room. On hearing the full extent of her plans the admiral estimated that the cost of such a place in Bo'ness would be around £3,000. Although this was a considerable sum of money, (in today's terms just under £2 million) nevertheless he agreed to go along with her plans.

In the meanwhile she began to look for larger premises for her young men's Bible Class. Up to this time she had been holding this in the small vestry of the parish church. Today the church is in ruins but the lay-out of the rooms can still be made out, and one can see that the vestry was indeed very small. So Elizabeth searched around for a larger room and eventually obtained permission to use the schoolroom that was on the road that runs besides the shore. This had the capacity to hold about three hundred people.

She was therefore making some progress in continuing her work in the new place. It wasn't easy but she was determined. Just how determined she was may be seen from how she got the people of Bo'ness to listen to her message. It happened in this way. When she had visited Alexander Bell she had been introduced to another ex-miner who invited her to hold a religious meeting in Bo'ness. It was a Friday evening towards the end of June, when she drove up to the meeting hall in her waggonette. Here she found her friend, the ex-miner, trying in vain to get the local people to enter the building. But none of them would have it and they stood around smoking pipes and the women sat on their doorsteps knitting. Nobody was interested in going in to listen to her. On seeing her arrive the man was most apologetic and told her how sorry he was to have caused her a wasted journey. He then told her to go into the meeting hall while he made one last effort to persuade the locals to go in. When inside the building she could hear the man outside, desperately pleading for the people to go in and listen to her. 'The lady has come all this way. Just try it....' he implored. Finally she realised that the time had come for her to take the matter into her own hands. So standing on the platform she began to sing one of her favourite hymns accompanied by her celestina. As it was a hot evening with all the doors and windows wide open, the people in the street could hear her sweet delicate voice. One-by-one they made their way into the hall where they sat down to listen. Eventually the hall was almost full. She then did a Bible reading followed by some more hymns. She then addressed them:

'There are many of your friends outside, who have not heard either the hymns nor the Bible - shall we go and tell them outside?'

There was unanimous agreement, so she ventured out on to a sort of balcony, which served as an elevated platform from which she could speak. Soon many of those who had refused to enter the hall gathered around to listen to her and she repeated the short service again in the form of an open-air meeting. Afterwards she asked them whether they would like her to return. One man stood forward and said: 'I am sure we shall all be delighted.' Then a woman spoke up: 'We want you to come again.' Then everyone in the crowd put their hands up and it was settled. The next day was a Saturday and she visited the town again. On this occasion she was armed with tracts and religious pamphlets which she gave away. All in all, it had been an auspicious start to her ministry in Bo'ness.

By the summer of that year Elizabeth had become established

in her religious activities in Carriden and the surrounding towns. There was the Coffee Room in Bo'ness, a Bible Class for the young men, and a mothers' meeting, and as each week passed the attendances increased. The mothers' meeting was particularly successful. This was on account of her personal visits to the town carrying a large basket of flowers made up into little bouquets, which she gave away to the poor women in the crowded closes and alleyways. 'You should have seen the delight with which they welcomed the little flowers, so gay and sweet!' she later recalled. 'I think that for a moment they made many a poor mother forget her troubles....And they gave me the opportunity of inviting fresh hearers to my little cottage-meeting.'

In the July of 1878 she invited the mothers to tea on the lawn at Carriden House. Four large carts were sent to Bo'ness to convey the ladies and their children and on their arrival she was there to welcome them. It was a beautiful warm summer's day and a generous tea was provided for them on the lawn in front of the house. Afterwards she took groups of them on a tour of the gardens and then to the picturesque glen and across the stream by the stepping stones. Unfortunately one of the party, a Mrs Mary Glen slipped and fractured her leg. Fortunately Dr Hunter of Linlithgow was nearby and he attended to the lady who was then taken home in Elizabeth's own carriage. Then before the others left Elizabeth sang some hymns, accompanied by her hand harmonium, following which she gave a brief address. By 7 o'clock the ladies had all left having enjoyed a delightful day out.

It is clear that the admiral realized that his wife was happiest getting involved in this kind of activity and so he did as much as possible to encourage it. On Saturday 20 July he arranged for the children of the Falkirk Boys and Girls Religious Society to visit Carriden for a day's outing. The children met in the town centre at 7 a.m. They were then led by the Grangemouth Flute Band, all dressed in their bright uniforms and carrying banners and flags, to the quayside where they boarded the steamer, *Despatch*. The vessel had been provided gratis by its owner to take the children to Bridgeness pier where they landed at about 8 a.m. They then walked up to Carriden House where they were greeted by Elizabeth and her husband. It was a beautiful warm sunny day and the children were free to roam about the gardens. On the lawn there were races and games of football. Then there was a cricket match in which, to the surprise of everyone, the admiral took part. Elizabeth then distributed the prizes to all the winners. Afterwards when she got the children to gather around her, sitting on the grass, she began to sing hymns to them in her sweet voice, accompanied again by her hand harmonium. Then refreshments were brought out by the maids. Afterwards the head gardener, Mr Tweedie took groups of the children on a tour of the estate showing them some of the Roman remains he had unearthed. At 4 o'clock tea was served on the lawn and afterwards Elizabeth sang some more hymns and then gave a brief address. Mr R.M. Geddes, the president of the children's society, then gave a vote of thanks which was followed by the children giving three cheers. The children then made their way down to the pier and at 6 p.m. they boarded the boat to take them back to Grangemouth, where they arrived safely an hour later.

In August, that same year, her parents came to visit her and she enjoyed showing them what she was achieving in the area. It so happened that at the same time Midhat Pasha, the ex-Grand Vizier of Turkey, was staying at Binns castle nearby, as a guest of Sir Robert Dalyell. They were all invited to dine at Binns, when they were introduced to the honoured guest. Then on the following day they all dined at Hopetoun House at the invitation of the Countess and Earl of Hopetoun.

Over the following months Elizabeth took her message to the surrounding towns. On the evening of Sunday 14 September she held an evangelical rally for women at the Aytoun Hall in Auchterarder. The subject of her talk was the Queen of Sheba's visit to Solomon, on which she spoke for about an hour to a large congregation. Then on Tuesday 24 September she lectured at the Strathearn Hydropathic Establishment in Crieff at the invitation of its founder Dr Meikle. The meeting was held in the drawing room with an audience of some 300 people including many local dignitaries. Elizabeth spoke about her experience with the reformation of drunkards. The *Dundee Courier* in its report on the occasion stated: 'The address which was delivered in a pleasing and graceful manner was most interesting and was listened to by all with earnest attention. At the close a cordial vote of thanks was given to her for her admirable address.' On the following day she addressed a meeting in the reading room of the Crieff Coffee House when she urged those present to support the temperance movement.

Over the following days she travelled with her husband to visit her parents again in Dorking and en route she stopped at various places to lecture to local societies. On Friday 11 October she lectured to the Liverpool Ladies Temperance Association at the Liverpool YMCA in Mount Pleasant.

She then visited Florence Nightingale's home in Steeple Claydon where she held a meeting that created considerable local interest. This was followed by a meeting at Winslow, in North Bucks. Then at the invitation of Sir Harry Verney, (Florence Nightingale's brother-in-law) she lectured to a crowded audience in the Town Hall at Buckingham. Sir Harry Verney, (whose first wife, by coincidence was Elizabeth's namesake) was the chairman of the meeting. In his introduction he praised Elizabeth, expressing his admiration for her work in advocating temperance and for her founding the Coffee Room movement, just as his sister-in-law, Miss Nightingale had done on many previous occasions.

Then on their return journey to Carriden they stopped off at Lancaster, where they stayed for the weekend of 15 November. Her first lecture was on the Friday evening at the Mechanics Institute where she had a crowded audience. The Lord Mayor, having been delayed by a late-running train, arrived while they were singing the first hymn. He apologised for his late appearance and explained that it was his first public meeting since taking office. Elizabeth then addressed the meeting describing how she had started the Coffee Room movement in Dorking and how it had reclaimed the lives of hundreds of drunkards. On the following evening she addressed a meeting at the British Workman Public House in King Street again to an equally appreciative audience.

Soon it was Christmas again at Carriden and during the winter months of 1878/9 she occupied much of her spare time in writing. She would sit in the drawing room at her writing desk beneath the window overlooking the ancient graveyard. There were two books, the first, *Lines of Light on a Dark Background*, included her letters to her friends at Dorking. The second was, *A Maiden's Work*. This latter book is a semi-autobiographical account of her time at Carriden, that is written through the eyes of Geraldine, a young woman (presumably meant to be herself) who is living with her widowed father, Squire Grayson, who presumably represented her husband. It has to be admitted that it is a curious work for a young wife to write, and more puzzling is her admission, made in the Preface, that she would read what she had written to entertain her husband. This being said, it provides an excellent description of Carriden House, which in the book is 'Suniscourt House'.

In the August of 1879 she joined with the Earl and Countess of Hopetoun in welcoming the Crown Prince of Sweden at a reception held at Holyrood Palace. Later that year she continued with her evangelism and on Monday 29 September she visited Broughty Ferry, in Dundee. In the afternoon she held a Bible Class for Ladies at the East Free Church, and in the evening she addressed a meeting at the Templar Hall. The following day she spoke to a large gathering of ladies at the YMCA hall in Dundee. She spoke for a good hour on the Coffee Room movement and how it was started. The *Dundee Courier* reported that she 'enforced her talk with great earnestness and power of speech, the necessity for trusting in and seeking guidance from the Bible.' In the evening she spoke at a meeting in the Dunhope Church when there was a large audience. Afterwards she was surprised to meet several ex-soldiers of the militia who had been part of the military exercises held in Dorking some years before. Then in the November she spoke at the Edinburgh branch of the British Women's Temperance Society.

In June the following year she was invited by the Marchioness of Ailsa to stay at Culzean Castle, near Ayr. Evelyn Stuart, Lady Ailsa (1848-1888) was an important temperance campaigner in Scotland. She had been converted while young and had soon afterwards embraced the temperance cause. This had brought her into conflict with the brewers and gin barons and as a consequence she had received numerous death threats. These she ignored, making her more determined to continue with her anti-drink work. She built a Coffee Room in Maybole and formed the Maybole Blue Ribbon which reached a membership of some 300 people. She also built a convalescent home for women in Glasgow, as well as three mission halls, at which she was a regular preacher.

On the evening of Sunday 6 June, Elizabeth preached to a large congregation in the mission hall at Maybole. Then on the following Tuesday evening she accompanied the Marchioness to the Coffee Room in Maybole to a meeting of the Blue Ribbon Band of Abstainers. During the evening Elizabeth gave an address following which the Marchioness was presented with a gold medal which had inscribed on it: 'Presented to the most noble Marchioness of Ailsa – President of the Maybole Blue Ribbon Band of Abstainers by members and friends as a small token of their high appreciation – 9 June 1880'.

Towards the end of October that year Elizabeth and the admiral accompanied the Princess Mary Adelaide (the Duchess of Teck) on a formal visit to the area. The Duchess was with her daughter, Princess Victoria Mary of Teck. ('May,' as the princess was known, later married in 1893, Prince George and would become Queen Mary.) On Friday 22 October the Royal party crossed the Forth by the Queensferry steamer to visit Dunfermline, the ancient capital. On arrival they drove to the Town Hall for lunch and then visited the St Leonard's Power loom linen factory. Afterwards they visited the Abbey church with the tomb of Bruce and the shrine of St Margaret, and the Palace ruins. Then in the evening there was a formal dinner at the St Margaret's Hotel. The next day Elizabeth accompanied the Royal group on a formal visit to Edinburgh. On arrival in the city they were greeted by the Lord Provost and taken on a tour of the Royal Infirmary when they visited several surgical wards and one of the operating theatres. Later they visited the medical wards when Princess Mary handed out bouquets of flowers to many of the patients. After tea in the manager's office the party visited Heriot's Hospital and afterwards the National Gallery.

Having been partly responsible for the success of the Royal visit, Admiral Hope was exhausted and soon afterwards fell ill with heart failure. He was now very frail and his illness was distressing to Elizabeth, who could do very little for him. At the time she was still writing, *A Maiden's Work*. In its Preface she wrote that 'it had been written in a time of anxiety', and 'for the delight of one who in the last few months has been taken from me.' When the admiral realised that he was dying he did not wish his young wife to also suffer, so he got her to visit her parents in Dorking and they returned to Carriden with her so as to give support. At 2.30 p.m. on 9 June 1881 he passed away aged 73 years, with his family at his bedside. The cause of death on the death certificate was put down as 'heart failure 9 months and subsequent kidney failure 2 months'. His last thoughts had been with her and in his Will he addressed her affectionately as 'Dearest Elsie...' and made generous provisions for her future without him. Elizabeth was now a widow.

## CHAPTER 11

Darwin's Evangelist

O<small>N THE DEATH</small> of her husband, Elizabeth was still under forty years of age. Although the convention at this time dictated a long period of formal mourning, she clearly had different views. Although she grieved the loss of her partner, who despite their large age difference had been a good husband to her and had encouraged her in her Christian work, she nonetheless felt that his death should not prevent her from continuing the work she felt God had called her to do. So in early August, just a few weeks after the death of her husband, she visited her friend the Marchioness of Ailsa, of Culzean Castle, and together they set up a temperance tent on the racecourse at Ayr where the militia were training. The idea of a temperance tent that provided non-alcoholic drinks and food, which essentially could be mobile, proved most successful, so much so, that she was determined to take the idea down south. The place she chose to take this novel evangelising method was to the county of Kent, in particular to the hop-gardens, where in the early weeks of September she knew there would be many thousands of the poorest people of London engaged in hop-picking.

Some years later she was to write a guidebook to the Kent countryside entitled: *English Homes and Villages, Kent and Sussex*. If one reads this today one becomes quickly aware of her love for this part of the British Isles with its mellow country lanes and picturesque cottages. However, it was not the pretty scenery she was concerned with at this stage, rather it was to win souls for Christ and wage war on the drink. At the time she calculated that there were some 42,000 acres in the hop-growing business and that some 25,000 hop-pickers would descend on the district, largely from London, to pick the harvest during the first few weeks of September. In one hop-garden alone she recalls that there were more than one thousand hop-pickers. The pickers included not only men and women, but also their children. The accommodation provided by the growers was very basic. Usually the pickers slept in sheds, but when these were crowded people had to make do with sleeping under canvas. They were usually paid on a daily basis, but this led to many spending their hard-earned money in the public houses as soon as they had received it.

Elizabeth's mode of operation was very simple. Firstly, she didn't work alone. She had volunteer helpers as well as paid male assistants. The men were to help re-pitch the tent when they moved on to a new hop-garden, which they might do several times a day. They also helped to transfer furniture, food and equipment to the new location. Secondly, she would ensure that she had the co-operation of the farmers. Most of the farmers would not object to her work as she was doing them a favour by reducing the amount of drunkenness on their land. Besides financial help, the farmers also provided practical help in providing night storage for the tent and other equipment, as well as the use of a horse and cart for transporting the equipment.

In the event, Elizabeth's venture proved to be a very profitable enterprise. With the income she received most of it went on books and tracts to be given away and what was left over was used to pay the male assistants. In her published account she recalls that in the September of 1881 she made a profit of about £80 (which in today's money would be an amazing £20,000) which went towards other running expenses.

One interesting innovation she employed was the use of the magic lantern, which would have been a novelty at this time. An assistant would operate the projector and presumably the wall of the canvas tent would serve as a screen. 'Pictures from the Parables' she recalled were 'shown by limelight'. This proved very popular with the hop-pickers and certainly it would have kept them from the local public house. Following the picture-show she would then address the people with the Gospel message. There is considerable evidence that she was successful in turning around the lives of many of those who attended. She later recalled that the following year when she carried out a similar mission one man came up to her and thanked her for her tent preaching. 'The poor man wept' she recalled, as he told her how her message had converted his wife who had subsequently passed away. 'She told me,' he said, 'to tell you, if ever I saw you again, that the preaching in the tent were blessed to her soul...'

Another evangelist who was carrying out a similar tent mission in the area at this time was James Fegan. James William Condell Fegan was ten years Elizabeth's junior. He had been born in Southampton on 27 April 1852, the son of James and Anne Fegan. The family were members of the Plymouth Brethren and followed the sect's strict religious teaching. Sometime in the early 1860s the family moved to London and their son entered the City of London School. Young James Fegan left this school in 1869 and entered a firm of Colonial Brokers in the City. About a year later he had a religious experience that made him want to follow Christ by working for others less fortunate than himself. At first, this involved teaching at evening classes in a Ragged School, but his contact with so many needy street urchins made him decide to open a home for homeless boys in Deptford, which became known as, 'The Boys' Home'. Later another one was opened in Greenwich, which was called, 'The Little Wanderers' Home'. Following this he decided to abandon his business career, and started open-air preaching, subsequently opening a Gospel Hall, also in Deptford.

In 1879 Fegan's parents moved out of London to live in the Kent countryside, where they took a house called, 'The Laurels' on the Cudham Road in Downe, just a short walk away from the home of Charles Darwin. Shortly afterwards, in early 1880, his father died and James decided to spend more of his time living in Downe so as to comfort his widowed mother. It was at this time that he conceived of the idea of camping holidays for his street urchins. So later that summer he brought a group of some seventy boys from the Deptford slums to Downe when they pitched tents in one of the fields. These deprived lads would have had a marvellous time in the Kent countryside, far away from the dirt and pollution of the city. This being said, they were not allowed to go wild, and as Fegan was a firm leader he ensured that they were well disciplined. An important part of this was the religious discipline he maintained, this included Bible teaching, prayers and hymns. In order to demonstrate to the local residents how well-behaved the boys were he would visit the local landowners and this included Charles Darwin. So on one notable afternoon, Fegan marched his troop of boys up to Darwin's house and after lining them up outside, he knocked on the front door. Then when Darwin appeared the boys sang a number of hymns for him. Darwin was most impressed and gave them each a sixpence piece, after which they gave him three cheers, and then they marched back to their camp.

Later that year Fegan held a tent mission throughout the area, pitching his tent in different villages around Downe and inviting locals to his services. His revivalist mission was very successful. He had many converts, possibly on account of his preaching and the use of the new Sankey hymnbook. However, as autumn approached and the weather turned colder tent meetings became impracticable. On account of this he approached Darwin and asked for his permission to make use of the village temperance reading room, which Darwin had recently set up in a small building on the edge of his estate. In the past it had been a small schoolroom which Darwin had rented off his neighbour, Sir John Lubbock. In the event Darwin was only too happy to let him have the building and sent him the following letter:

'Dear Mr Fegan,

You ought not to have to write to me for permission to use the Reading Room. You have far more right to it than we have, for your services have done more for the village in a few months than all our efforts for many years. We have never been able to reclaim a drunkard, but through your services I do not know that there is a drunkard left in the village. Now may I have the pleasure of handing the Reading Room over to you? Perhaps, if we should want it some night for a special purpose, you will be good enough to let us use it.

Yours sincerely,

Charles Darwin'

Following the transfer of the Reading Room to Fegan it became known as the Gospel Room, and later the Gospel Hall. Fegan later recalled:

'The services I held were attended sometimes by members of the Darwin family, and regularly by members of their household. Indeed, when I had a mission in Downe, the Darwin family were considerate enough to alter their dinner hour so that their household might attend – but this was characteristic of all who served them.

At the services, Parslow, the old family butler was converted to God and brought into Church membership, also Mrs Sales, the housekeeper, "was brought into the light and others"'.

We know that services were being held in the February of 1881, for at that time, Emma Darwin wrote to her daughter Henrietta:

'Hurrah for Mr Fegan! Mrs Evans [the cook] attended a prayer meeting in which old M. made "as nice a prayer as ever you heard in your life"....' [M. is described in a footnote as 'a notable old drunkard of the village'.]

It would appear from Fegan's account that in the early 1880s Darwin's village of Downe had become a hotbed of religious revivalism, with evangelical tent services and conversions taking place, very much at the bottom of Darwin's garden. However, it was all too much for Fegan's health and he suffered a breakdown in the July of 1881 and had to go away to convalesce. As to when he returned we cannot be sure, however, we do know that he had returned to his preaching ministry by October that year, as he gave a public lecture in Manchester on 26th of that month, alongside Dr Barnardo, and the Bishop of Manchester. This being so, it is possible that Elizabeth had taken over some of his ministry while he was away, but if she did, it would not have been until later in the year. We know that she was definitely there in the September, when she took her tent mission to the hop-pickers and it is possible she may have stayed longer to fill in for Fegan. One wonders as to what might have induced her to remain?

It is possible, and this is pure speculation, that Fegan's mother, Anna Fegan, with whom Elizabeth was staying at this time, was engaged in a little match-making. Maybe she hoped that Elizabeth, now a widow, but not yet forty, might be an ideal match for her son. To her they may have appeared perfectly matched as they were both sincere evangelical Christians determined to do all they could to promote their faith and to help others. How much more could they do by being joined in matrimony? Being deeply religious herself, she might have wondered whether it was in God's plan that these two should be united together. Possibly, she might have been thinking of them becoming another William and Catherine Booth? We don't know and this remains just speculation. In the event it didn't happen and Fegan eventually married some years later, in August 1889, when his bride was Mary Pope. With regards to any relationship between Elizabeth and Fegan we simply have no information. However, what is strange is that in

119

the years that followed although Elizabeth did much work for Dr Barnardo's homes, one can find little evidence that she gave any support to Fegan's homes. This is a little curious and might suggest there had been some history between James Fegan and herself.

But this is in the realm of speculation and we must return to what we do know for certain. We can be sure that following the hop-picking season that year, Elizabeth remained in Kent to continue with her ministry of Bible reading in the villages. We can be reasonably sure that she was staying with Fegan's widowed mother, Anna Fegan, who happened to be a friend of Darwin's wife, Emma.

It is possible that Charles Darwin and his wife, Emma, had come across Elizabeth on account of her temperance crusade in Dorking, as the Darwins were frequent visitors to Dorking, as well as being firm supporters of the temperance movement. Indeed, Darwin for most of his life, had held a 'horror' of drunkenness. This was probably on account of the fact that both his grandmother, and great-grandmother had died of alcoholism. Francis Darwin, his son, recalled that his father: 'had a horror of drinking and constantly warned his boys that any one might be led into drinking too much...' It is therefore not surprising that when Emma Darwin told her husband that Elizabeth Cotton, the noted temperance campaigner and daughter of General Sir Arthur Cotton was staying nearby, that Darwin sent her an invitation to visit him.

The invitation came early one afternoon while Elizabeth was having lunch. Mrs Fegan announced to her that: 'Dr Darwin has heard that you are staying here; and would like very much to see you. He wonders whether it would be possible for you to visit him this afternoon.'

Elizabeth already knew that Charles Darwin, the great natural-ist, lived in the locality as only a few days before she had been walking through the village and had been shown the large gates and carriage drive that led to his residence. She was also well aware of the controversy concerning his theory of evolution and of the challenge that it had given to Bible-believing Christians. We cannot be sure whether, or not, she had ever read *On the Origin of Species*, however, we can be certain she had discussed it with other Christians, particularly with Henry Drummond, who at that time was formulating his own response to Darwin. This was later published in his book, *Natural Law in the Spiritual World*. Darwin's theory had certainly not weakened her faith in any way so she would not have had any concerns about possibly discussing it with Darwin himself, if the subject arose. Neither would she have felt nervous about meeting such an eminent scientist, for only a few weeks before she had had afternoon tea with Professor William Spottiswoode (1825-1883) the President of the Royal Society, on the verandah of his country house, Combe Bank, at Sundridge only a few miles away from Downe. Furthermore she was used to mixing with the intelligentsia as her uncle, the Reverend Richard Lynch Cotton, had been the vice-chancellor of Oxford University.

So later that afternoon, she left 'The Laurels' to walk the few hundred yards along the Cudham Road to Down House. Then at precisely three o'clock, with Bible in hand, she knocked on the front door. It was answered almost immediately by the butler who escorted her up the stairs to a large landing on the first floor and then led her into one of the rear facing rooms. It was a large room with a high ceiling and a fine bay window that gave an extensive view of the beautiful garden and beyond to woods and cornfields. It had been warm and fine all day and now the sun was setting giving a brilliant orange glow in the distant sky.

Entering the room she saw Darwin propped up with pillows and lying on a chaise longue. He was wearing a soft embroidered dressing gown of a rich purple shade, and on seeing her he smiled warmly and held out his hand to greet her. When writing about the meeting some years later she recalled that his 'fine features lit up as she entered the room'. This is not surprising as Darwin, although he was now elderly and frail, nonetheless still had an eye for the ladies, and she was an attractive aristocratic, feisty young woman, tall and slim with sensitive eyes and a pretty face. Furthermore, in appearance she had none of the puritan prejudices one might have expected in an evangelist, for she was elegantly dressed with fine yet modest jewellery and as she sat down beside him he could sense her pleasant perfume.

Throughout all the time Darwin had lived at Down he had carefully guarded his privacy and had lived very much as a recluse. Now in his infirmity he did welcome occasional company, but his needs in this were not indiscriminate. He certainly did not want any one visiting him that might upset himself, or Emma. Only recently he had been obliged to entertain the atheist, Dr Edward Aveling and the German freethinker Ludwig Buchner. It had been a most unpleasant encounter that had left Emma distraught and left him feeling wretched.

Elizabeth was something completely different. She was a breath of fresh air, and despite being recently widowed she had a sparkle in her eye. Although he had not met her before he had heard much about her. He knew all about her late husband, Sir James, for he was, like Nelson, a national hero, as demonstrated by him being the subject of a widely issued Stevengraph silk bookmark by Thomas Stevens and Company of Coventry. Furthermore, he knew of her success at reclaiming drunkards at her Coffee Room in Dorking. He was also aware of the remarkable achievements of her father in India, as well as his recent agricultural experiments in Dorking. He also knew of her Bible reading in the villages and of her tent missionary work to the Kent hop-pickers, and of her practice of using the hand harmonium when leading the hymn singing.

For a time they talked about mutual interests and he quickly recognised her exceptional intelligence. She then expressed some admiration for the flowers she could see in the garden below. She loved flowers, orchids in particular, and this was also one of Darwin's best-loved flowers, and as he spoke about them she could see an intense look in his eyes and a pleasing expression. She then spoke of her experiences in far off places, Tasmania where she had been born, Australia and India and the strange creatures she had seen, including the giant tortoises she had encountered while she was staying in Mauritius. These reminiscences brought back memories to Darwin of these places, as he also had visited them while on HMS *Beagle*. Then she told him of her visit to Napoleon's tomb on St Helena and how she had felt so depressed afterwards. He smiled engagingly at her and confessed to having had similar feelings on his visit to the same place many years before. He then asked her about her recent home at Carriden and she told him about some of the work she had done there in reclaiming drunkards. To Darwin it brought back happy memories of the time he had spent in the area, as a medical student at Edinburgh, with his friend Robert Grant when they had explored all along the rocky shores of the Firth of Forth collecting fascinating creatures in the tidal rock pools. Then he remembered the glimpse he once had of the turrets of Carriden House through the thickly wooded embankment, just like David Balfour had in Robert Louis Stevenson's *Kidnapped*.

At that moment they were then disturbed as the maid brought in the afternoon tea which was placed on a small table situated between them. For a time they were silent. Darwin closed his eyes for a moment and thought. He was glad he had invited her for she was so interesting, indeed he had not met a woman before who had such a knowledge of the world beyond the English Channel.

He then picked up the Bible which he had been reading before she had arrived and opened it at the page he had reached. She asked him as to what he had been reading and he replied that it was the Epistle to the Hebrews. She then opened her Bible and read some verses from the Gospels. Darwin felt comfortable with a woman reading to him as this is what Emma would do in the evening, but then it was usually a novel, Trollope or sometimes Dickens. Now Elizabeth's voice was fresh to his ears as it had a delightful ring to it that seemed to make the words she read from the page light up in his heart, so much so, that he could have listened to her for much longer. However, she closed the Bible and then, without any embarrassment, she knelt down besides the small table and on bowing her head and putting her hands together she said a short prayer.

She then got up and turned to leave, but before she did he asked her if she would come again the following day. She smiled at him and promised to return at the same time.

On returning the following day she found him again lying in the same place again propped up with pillows. This time she noticed that his white hair had been brushed back to reveal his open forehead and fine features. He reached out his hand to greet her and in the other he held an open Bible.

'What are you reading now?' she asked as she sat down beside him.

'Hebrews' he answered. 'Still Hebrews – The Royal Book, I call it. Isn't it grand?'

He then placed his finger on certain passages and began to comment on the great gospel truths they revealed. She then commented on how some people had dismissed the early chapters of the Book of Genesis and had used his name to raise doubts about the history of Creation.

At this he became greatly distressed and his fingers twitched nervously and a look of agony came across his face. Then he spoke. 'I was a young man with unformed ideas,' he said. 'I was ignorant. I threw out queries and suggestions. I was searching for the truth.' He seemed to be overcome and he paused for a moment. 'To my astonishment the ideas took off like wildfire. People have come to make a religion of them.'

She smiled across at him and nodded in agreement.

He then tenderly lifted up his Bible and spoke to her of its 'grandeur'. Suddenly he put it down and he looked across at her. 'I have a small summerhouse across the garden,' he said pointing towards the window. 'I think it must hold some thirty people.' He smiled warmly at her. 'I want you to speak there. I know you read the Bible in the village. Tomorrow – will you speak there to my servants, some tenants and my neighbours? Will you speak to them?'

She smiled at him. 'But what shall I speak on?' she asked.

'Christ Jesus,' Darwin replied without hesitation in a clear emphatic voice, 'and His salvation – is that not the best theme?'

'Of course I will,' Elizabeth replied.

At this Darwin sat up. 'And will you sing some hymns. Not the old droney hymns but the Sankey hymns.' He paused. 'You lead on your small harmonium, do you not?'

She nodded. 'Yes, of course I will,' she replied. 'And we'll have the new hymns.'

Darwin leaned back against the pillows and appeared pleased with himself. 'If you take the meeting at three o'clock,' he said pointing towards the window. 'I will have the window open and you will know that I am joining in.'

Before she left that afternoon she read a portion of Scripture to him and again knelt down and prayed with him. That was the last meeting she had with him as when later she discussed with Emma Darwin, the proposed meeting with the servants, she could tell that she was not in sympathy with holding such an evangelical service, so rather than causing any friction in the household, she felt it preferable not to go ahead with it. However, Charles Darwin was not forgotten as he remained for some time afterwards in her prayers, her only regret being that she wished she had taken a photograph of him and his surroundings to remind her of that memorable day.

It had indeed been a memorable day. She had been given a private insight into the character of probably the most famous scientist of his generation. But it had been a personal encounter and one which she was determined to keep to herself, very much like a priest would with regard to the confessional box. Accordingly she carried on with her evangelism and temperance work. It would soon be Christmas and she was looking forward to spending it with her parents in Dorking. Then in the New Year her diary was full of invitations to speak at various meetings around the country.

Her busy schedule began in the January of 1882 with a two-week mission at Wentworth Woodhouse, in Yorkshire, at the invitation of the Countess of Fitzwilliam. At that time Wentworth country house boasted the longest façade in Europe having some 240 rooms. During the mission she had the opportunity of speaking to the employees in the schoolroom connected to the stables. Then later in the mission she held a men-only meeting at the vicarage, but so many men turned up it had to be transferred to the Mechanics Institute. She spoke for more than an hour on the verse: 'Thou shalt make them drink of the fountain of thy pleasures.' Then at the conclusion she gave an invitation to those who wanted to commit themselves to Christ to stand up and come forward.

Then a few weeks later she was guest speaker at the opening of the Rushden Coffee Tavern. It was a grand occasion with the Temperance Band leading a procession through the town to the new Coffee Tavern. Then a meeting was held in the large hall in the town when she gave a talk on, 'The Origin and the moral and religious aspects of Coffee Taverns.' The local newspaper reported that her talk lasted over an hour and a half, and she had held her audience throughout. It concluded that afterwards, 'the applause was vociferous and prolonged....and that she had proceeded in a very graphic and pleasing style to explain the manner in which she was brought to commence the undertaking and the marvellous and unexpected success.'

She had now moved on from her brief encounter with Charles Darwin, but he was not forgotten.

## CHAPTER 12

A Glance at the Great Work

T HE FOLLOWING YEAR 1882 was significant for Elizabeth as it marked her fortieth birthday as well as the beginning of a new chapter in her life as a young widow. She had put her affairs in order in Scotland and had helped several of her Carriden staff obtain new positions. She now found herself with an assured annual income of more than one thousand pounds (the equivalent today would be at least one hundred thousand pounds). To give some indication as to the relative value of this income, we know that around this time, Mrs Jane Sinnett, the author of, *The By-ways of History*, had been widowed with five children, and brought them up on an annual income of about £100, this being earned by her writing. Elizabeth was therefore now a wealthy widow, however she was determined to use whatever she had in promoting the Gospel.

Her first step was to extend her Coffee Room movement which had been taken up by other social reformers such as Emma Cons (1838-1912). By this time she was involved with at least three such establishments, the first in Dorking and two others, one at Bo'ness and a third at Beckenham. A manager ran each one along similar lines, with each being financially self-sufficient. To extend this she decided to move down to the south coast where she established another one at Sandown on the Isle of Wight. This was known as the 'Dorking Coffee Tavern' and was run along similar lines to the others.

She then moved to Bournemouth where she worked with the Gospel Temperance Union in organising an important conference in the town that took place from, 12 – 18 March 1882. The most eminent speaker was Earl Cairns (1819-1885) who was the Lord Chancellor in Disraeli's government. He was well-known in political circles as an evangelical, so much so, that Disraeli had given him the nickname of 'Moody and Sankey'. Although he was not teetotal, he did advocate temperance. He had a villa in Bournemouth that was known as 'Lindisfarne', which he allowed evangelists to use for either convalescence, or for holidays.

Also speaking at the conference was Sir Bartholomew James Sulivan, a retired admiral, whose residence was in Bournemouth. He had been a lieutenant on HMS *Beagle* and had sailed with Charles Darwin and they had become close friends. In particular, Sulivan had supported Darwin when the young naturalist had fallen out with Captain FitzRoy. In subsequent years Sulivan progressed to the admiralty and later replaced FitzRoy at the Board of Trade. Now meeting Admiral Sulivan at this conference Lady Hope would have had much to talk about with him. Not only would they have talked about Darwin, but also her late husband, Admiral Hope, as Sulivan's son had served under him when he was in command of the North America fleet.

Admiral Sulivan had kept in touch with his old comrade and had sent Darwin news of the success of the missionary work of the South American Missionary Society in Tierra del Fuego. Sulivan was a member of the Missionary Committee and would regularly send Darwin copies of the Missionary Journal. Darwin later took out an annual subscription and gave financial support to the missionary society. In time Darwin was elected an honorary member, and on hearing the news of his election to the missionary society, Darwin wrote to Sulivan informing him of his pride at being elected.

Other speakers at the Bournemouth conference included the Reverend Canon Ernest Wilberforce (1840-1907), the third son of Bishop Samuel Wilberforce, otherwise known as 'Soapy Sam', (remembered now for the debate he had on Darwin's theory with

Thomas Huxley at Oxford some twenty years before). Later that year Ernest Wilberforce was appointed to the bishopric of Newcastle, and in 1896 he became Chairman of the Church of England Temperance Society. Lady Hope's role in the conference was crucial, and it was her work that made the conference such a success. On one occasion she spoke to more than a thousand women gathered in the Town Hall, when she described her work amongst the colliers of Bo'ness in Scotland, and how she had succeeded in turning many of them away from alcohol.

Later that same month she addressed a 'Blue Ribbon' temperance meeting held in the Victoria Hall in Boscombe when more than forty new pledges were taken. She then continued with this work until the middle of May when she gave her farewell address in the Town Hall. She told the audience that she was now leaving to assist in the preparations for the forthcoming second mission of Moody and Sankey to Britain.

There was also the question of her finding a permanent home. She had come to feel that this should preferably be in the heart of the capital, where she could be of use in promoting her faith and helping many of the poor and needy people. On Saturday 1st July she attended a garden party in support of the London Young Women's Institute of Brownswood Park. This was held at Grove House, Regent's Park, the residence of the Quaker Member of Parliament, Thomas Greer (1837-1905). About three hundred people attended the garden party and Elizabeth was invited to give the address. During her talk she spoke about the peace that was to be found in true religion and illustrated her talk by giving many anecdotes from her own experience. Her talk was well received and afterwards all those present enjoyed a feast of strawberries and ice cream, which was a delightful way to end a hot summer's day.

Moody and Sankey's second mission to Britain had in fact started in the autumn of 1881. As in the first campaign Moody started in the north of England and then moved on to Scotland.

For five months he worked in Glasgow, where he was assisted by Henry Drummond. In June 1882 he finished in Glasgow and then moved on to other towns in Scotland. Moody's plan was to spend two years in England, including almost a year in the capital. A large committee was set up to organise the mission and prepare the venues, which in London included the erection of large temporary conference halls. Elizabeth was an important member of this organising committee.

During the summer of 1882 Moody and his family spent some weeks relaxing in Switzerland before continuing the campaign in England and Wales. Then on Sunday 10 September the mission began in Cardiff. Services were held at the two largest meeting halls in the city. The first was the Wood Street Chapel and the other was the Circus in Westgate Street, with services being held at least twice daily. Moody had been particularly encouraged by the support he had received from local clergy. This included the influential Dean of Llandaff who not only gave financial support, but had made his presence known on the opening night despite the fact that on his arrival at the Circus he was nearly overcome by the crowds that thronged the entrance. Eventually, and with much difficulty, the dean obtained a seat in the audience, and was able to enjoy Sankey's solo and then listen to Moody preaching on the text; 'God is not mocked: whatsoever a man soweth that shall he also reap.'

On the following Monday the *Western Mail's* report on the services observed that, 'Mr Moody is not a polished orator and his power does not lie in fine flights of rhetoric or elaborate figures of speech. He is a plain practical preacher, simple in language who carries his audience into perfect sympathy with himself. His address on this occasion was a powerful one...'

The newspaper report informed its readers that there would be prayer meetings held each day in the Town Hall and that they were to be conducted by Lady Hope. Elizabeth was now an important co-worker with Moody, and was largely responsible for conducting the women's meetings. Besides the women's prayer meetings in the Town Hall, Elizabeth also took charge of services, again exclusively for women, that were held in the Wood Street Chapel at 3p.m. each day.

The *Bristol Mercury and Daily Post* of Saturday 16 September reported on the Cardiff mission and noted that all the services had been packed to capacity, with many having waited several hours before the doors were opened. It also reported that the police had been in constant attendance to ensure there were no accidents from the crush that usually occurred when the crowds were first admitted to the auditorium.

Accompanying Elizabeth on the Moody mission was Henry Drummond (1851-97). Drummond, like Elizabeth, had helped Moody on his first mission to Britain. In the years that followed that mission Drummond had been engaged in studying geology and had been involved in a geological expedition to the Rocky Mountains. His interest in geology was directed towards resolving the conflict between religious belief and the Darwinian theory of evolution. He believed that he had found a compromise between Christianity and Darwinism. This was about to be published in a book entitled, *Natural Law in the Spiritual World*, which he had just presented to his publisher. This book would establish his reputation as it went on to sell many thousands of copies. It had been based on a series of lectures he had given at Glasgow some years before. By publishing his ideas Drummond was to become the first British evangelical to promote what later became known as 'theistic evolution'. Moody, however, was never to accept this interpretation of the Bible, yet despite this, the friendship between the two men never faltered, even in years to come when Drummond became a very controversial figure and was the cause of considerable trouble to Moody. (It is interesting that in the stage play and subsequent film, *Inherit the Wind*, a fictional account of the notorious Scopes Trial, in America, when a young teacher is prosecuted for teaching Darwin's theory of evolution, the defence lawyer is called, Henry Drummond.)

At this time Elizabeth and Henry Drummond were the two most important British figures in Moody's second mission. One wonders how they got on together, particularly as he smoked cigars and enjoyed drinking wine. Indeed, their relationship is extremely difficult to unravel. Drummond, by all accounts, was tall and handsome, always well-dressed, with attractive eyes. One student described him as being 'almost a king among men'. Women usually fell for him but he remained unmarried. Furthermore, he was certainly no puritan for he once wrote: 'I have not bowed down and worshipped Mrs G [Grundy].'

Some years later Drummond became emotionally involved with Lady Aberdeen. She doted on him and he seemed to flourish in the shadow of aristocracy. Doris French in her biography of Lady Aberdeen, *Ishbel and the Empire*, published in 1988, claimed that they were lovers. But this is difficult to accept in the light of his evangelical background, and his close association with Moody, but suffice it to say Drummond and Lady Aberdeen were very close. Whether they were lovers in today's meaning of the term is open to question. Much of their correspondence - which might have helped settle the question - appears to have been destroyed, but there is a famous painting in the National Gallery of Drummond at a dinner party with Lady Aberdeen together with Prime Minister William Gladstone. There is also a notable photograph which seems to have been taken at around the same time, which shows Lady Aberdeen looking at Drummond in a way that suggests that they did have a relationship. As regards Drummond's relationship with Elizabeth we have little information. Possibly she was attracted to him - most women were - and he was clearly flattered by the attention of ladies of title. On the other hand, it is unlikely that Moody would have entrusted an important part of his mission to them, if he thought there was any romantic involvement between them.

Following the Cardiff mission the campaign moved on to Newport. On Sunday, 24 September 1882, huge crowds attended the four services that were held on that day. The *Bristol Mercury and Daily Post* reported that the 'crowding was excessive', and that 'no sooner was the hall cleared of one set of hearers than it began to fill with another'. The newspaper reported that the mission had created 'deepest excitement' and that many people had been 'carried away'. In all some two hundred individuals had responded to Moody's call for them to accept salvation through Christ Jesus. For some days afterwards Elizabeth and Henry Drummond remained in Newport to follow up those who had registered their commitment. Then on the following Monday, Elizabeth held a Bible reading at the Albert Hall in the town when there was again a very large audience.

In the first week of October Moody held meetings in Plymouth and Devonport, following this he paid a flying visit to Paris. On Sunday 8 October he held services at the American chapel in Rue de Berri, when the congregation consisted of mainly American ladies. Many had anticipated that the revivalist meetings might go over the top, so were surprised to find that Moody's preaching was very much subdued and lacking in the excitement witnessed in Britain.

On his return to England Moody held meetings in Bristol and then moved on to Oxford and Cambridge, and then to Torquay, Exeter, Southampton, Portsmouth and Brighton. In all of these meetings there would have been preparatory meetings in which Elizabeth would have played a major role.

The Cambridge meeting on Sunday 5 November proved to be very successful with about 2000 university men in attendance, with some four hundred being converted. The following week the mission was at Oxford. Meetings were held in the Corn Exchange with an overflow meeting in the Town Hall, and a meeting for undergraduates in the Clarendon Hotel. During the latter meeting there was a slight disturbance when a small group of undergrad-uates tried to disrupt the meeting. Moody responded by putting them to shame by saying that it had been the first occasion that this had happened at which he received warm approbation from the audience.

At this date we cannot be sure that Moody was fully aware of Henry Drummond's response to the Darwinian Theory. Moody himself had completely rejected Darwin's theory and held rigidly to the Genesis account of creation. He would have been only too aware that Oxford was the scene some twenty years before for the first major public confrontation between Darwin's theory and the Bible, when Thomas Huxley had savagely demolished Bishop Wilberforce. This being so he felt compelled to tackle the issue, so on the Thursday night of that week, he took on the subject. He believed in the Old Testament as much as the New, he told the audience. He felt that if one was going to give up any portion of Scripture, then one had to give it all up... 'let it all go' he contended, which was precisely the stance taken by the naturalist, P.H.Gosse a few years previously. So like Gosse, he wasn't prepared to let any of it go. Let the intellectuals scoff, he said, they had scoffed at Noah when he was building the ark, but how did they feel when the deluge came?

Following the success at the university towns Moody moved on to Southampton. The first meeting was held on Wednesday 29 November at the Victoria Skating Rink, when at least some 5000 people crowded into the building. Again it was necessary to hold an overflow meeting in the Circus, when every seat was occupied. The following week meetings were held at the King Street Chapel in Portsea. The first meeting was on Thursday 7 December. It was a bitter cold night and snow was falling, but this did nothing to deter the crowds. The *Hampshire Telegraph* reported that 'it was a remarkable sight. A sea of faces filled the body of the chapel and the galleries. So closely was the congregation crowded together that one commentator remarked that the eyelashes of those in the front seats almost brushed the carpet that covered the temporary platform'.

On the platform that evening Elizabeth gave her support to the

American evangelist, together with several others of the organising committee. However, this was a busy period for Elizabeth,
for besides being one of the principal lay helpers of the campaign,
she had other responsibilities. A few days afterwards she was
back in central London addressing a meeting of the Railway
Mission. The Railway Mission was of particular interest to her.
It had started in 1872 under the name, 'Railway Boys Mission'.
Its purpose was to give spiritual guidance to those railway staff
who had to work on Sundays, and so were unable to attend church.
It was essentially a temperance organisation with premises in
North London. There was also an institute established for the
purpose of education and recreation. The meeting that December
evening was held at the home of Samuel Sheppard at 31 Oxford
Square. In the chair was Mr. T. A. Denny, another supporter of
the Moody campaign, who some ten years later would become
her second husband. That night she addressed the meeting giving
a summary of the progress the organisation had made. In her
address she made a point of condemning the railway companies
for offering drinks to railway employees and then went on to
appeal in favour of the abolition of all Sunday travelling.

Meanwhile in the New Year Moody took his campaign to
Ireland and then over the following months he visited Nottingham
and Birmingham and then went on to the northern cities of Leeds,
Manchester and Liverpool. In the April, Moody concluded his
campaign in Liverpool before returning to America. He was not
to return to England until the November when he was to carry out
his eight-month campaign in the capital.

This break in the Moody mission allowed Elizabeth the space
and opportunity for her to develop her own work. She was no
longer content to sit in the background. She was now to take up
the challenge and take the Gospel to the people herself. How she
proposed to do this and what she achieved will be dealt with in
the following chapter.

When Moody returned to England in the November of 1883 he

began his mission to London. There had been much preparation by the organising committee of which Elizabeth was an important member. This preparation included the construction of two huge halls. There was the Priory Hall in Upper Street, Islington which had a seating capacity of some five thousand, and a second one that had been erected near the Temple Gardens on the Thames Embankment.

Elizabeth was very much aware that many of her social circle were opposed to Moody's type of evangelism. In their view this type of preaching was all right in the industrial cities of the north, but it had no place in the sophisticated city of London. To counter this view she wrote a short tract with the title, 'A Glance at the Great Work: An incident of Messrs Moody and Sankey's meeting in London.' This involved a conversation between two friends, as illustrated by the following extract:

> 'Have you been to Mr Moody's meetings?' one asked.
>
> 'I went just to see' her friend replies, 'and I liked it so I went two or three times. One night Mr Moody asked all those who wished to be prayed for to stand up and I felt a great longing so I stood up...'
>
> 'Stood up – I never heard the like,' replied her friend.
>
> ''Yes, I did indeed and others did the same. And then Mr Moody prayed for us.' She paused. 'Yes, but it was no common day to me! It was the most wonderful day of my life. To all eternity I shall bless God that ever I went to those meetings.'

Elizabeth then concluded... 'and thus ends one of the many conversations now going on in London – lip testimonies of heart change.'

On one evening a young second-year medical student was

returning from attending a maternity case when he noticed this huge tent, something like a circus, and curious as to find what was going on, he ventured inside. To his dismay he discovered that it was a religious meeting where an old reverend gentleman was on the platform uttering a prayer. As he turned to leave, a younger man stood up on the platform and started to preach. It was Dwight Moody and immediately the young man's attention was galvanised. Soon he was stirred to the heart by the Gospel message, so much so, that when Moody invited those who wished to give their lives to Christ to stand up, he felt compelled to do so. The young doctor was Wilfred Grenfell who went on to found the Labrador Medical Mission.

Over the following months it is estimated that Moody spoke to more than two million people. The halls in the capital were crowded at least twice a day, and sometimes four or five times. The impact this American evangelist had on Victorian society is difficult to calculate, but there is no doubt that it left a permanent impression on the lives of many ordinary individuals, just as his successor, Dr Billy Graham has done in more recent times.

At the close of the mission, on 19 June 1884, Moody and his family rested at the country house of Mr T. A. Denny, near Dorking. With him was an inner circle of his helpers that included Elizabeth and Henry Drummond. She was now on home territory and was not far away from where her own endeavours started just over a decade before.

## CHAPTER 13

Outcast London

SHORTLY BEFORE MOODY returned to England in the autumn of 1883, a small 32-page, anonymous penny pamphlet appeared in the London bookstores. It was entitled: *The Bitter Cry of Outcast London*: *An Inquiry into the Condition of the Abject Poor*. Its publication had an immediate and cataclysmic impact, so much so, that today it is considered one of the most important social documents published during the Victorian era. This small and rather insignificant pamphlet was to cause an enormous uproar in the months and years that followed. Indeed, many consider it to be the most influential piece of social writing that has ever been published in Britain. Suddenly, the educated middle classes became aware that there existed an underclass of the population living in ghettoes in the towns and cities of industrialised Britain, particularly in London. The anonymous author described in vivid detail the conditions of the poor, many of whom lived in what he called 'rookeries'. In order to gain entrance to them, he wrote: 'one has to penetrate courts reeking with poisonous and malodorous gases arising from accumulations of sewage and refuse scattered in all directions.' The author then revealed that there were many families living in rooms no more than eight feet square, with 'walls and ceilings black with the accretions of filth which have gathered upon them through long years of neglect.' And where there were beds, 'they were simply heaps of dirty rags'. In one room was found a man ill with smallpox, with children running about half naked and in another, where seven people were living there was a dead child. Then in one underground cellar there was a family living with four pigs.

Suddenly people in Britain awoke to the grim facts of the city slums. The author of this notorious pamphlet when it was revealed was the Congregational minister the Reverend Andrew Mearns (1837-1925). Mearns had been appointed secretary of the London Congregational Union and it was from this position that he had investigated the living conditions of the poor in London. Subsequently there arose a dispute as to its authorship when another Congregational minister, the Reverend W. C. Preston, also claimed authorship. It was eventually conceded that it had been to some extent a joint work, however, today Mearns is usually credited with it.

The Times of Friday, 1 February 1884, reported that Sir A. Otway addressing his constituents at Rochester had raised the question of 'The Cry of Outcast London' and said that it was a disgrace to a civilised nation that this state of affairs should be allowed to exist. But much earlier Mr T. A. Denny, the Christian philanthropist, (who later was to marry Elizabeth) had raised the matter of 'Outcast London' at a meeting of the Church of England Temperance Society.[14] Mr Denny expressed the conviction that nothing would be improved until the opening hours of public houses were materially restricted.

Even the newly formed Salvation Army had been slow to tackle the problem of the homeless and the city slums. Indeed, there is a report that it was some six years after the publication of 'Outcast London' before its founder, William Booth, had become aware of the problem. Apparently, one night on his way home to his genteel residence at Hadley Wood, he caught a glimpse of some vagrant paupers living in one of London's alleyways. On getting home he raised it with his son, Bramwell, and on discovering that his son had known about such homeless people in London, Booth then demanded to know why it hadn't been brought to his attention.

However, long before either the Reverend Mearns, or General William Booth, had done anything about the problem, Ellen

Henrietta Ranyard (1810-1879) had founded the London Bible and Domestic Female Mission. This organisation employed Bible women and nurses to visit the poor. By about 1880 they were employing more than a hundred female missionaries and publishing its own magazine entitled, *The Missing Link*.

It was around this time that Elizabeth became involved. The problem of the city poor had been brought to her attention while she was working with Moody in Aberdeen, almost a decade before. A little girl had spoken to her late at night. The child had been without shoes and soaking wet in the rain. At the time it had made a deep impression on her and after she returned to London she was determined to do something about it. Exactly when she started to investigate the problem is unclear, but we do know what sparked it off.

Up to this juncture her evangelism had been directed at the people living in small country towns, such as Dorking. There were of course problems, mainly as a consequence of drink, and she had addressed these with considerable success. However, in these country districts there did exist a limited form of poor relief, albeit it was not perfect, but it was much better than that in the cities. Furthermore, in the country, at least, the air was clean. In the industrial cities the situation was completely different, and as a consequence an underclass had been created from the overcrowding of an enormous number of people. It was a completely different world.

In the January of 1882 Elizabeth had met Henry Varley, the Notting Hill revivalist,[15] when he shared a platform with her at the Lecture Hall in Dorking. It is possible that he described to her the dire conditions people were suffering in the slums of that area and the great need they had for the Gospel message. This was further brought to her attention by one of her social circle when she was challenged along the lines, that it was all very well to take the gospel to 'decent' ordinary people, but what about all those living in the slums of London? Her critic might even have chastised her by saying: 'Well, you don't seem eager to take the Gospel to them ...' When Elizabeth reflected on this she began to agree with her critic. This person was right, she realised, the church is full of self-righteous, complacent so-called 'Christians', and she didn't want to be one of them. Yes, she would do something about it herself. But how was she to go about it? There were dangers - very real dangers. She had heard about those areas of the city where even policemen feared to go. Places where robbery, violence, rape and murder were commonplace. How could she, a mere woman, go to such a place? How she resolved this dilemma is an extraordinary story and until now it has not been told.

Yet, it was all published the following year in her book, *Our Golden Key – A Narrative of Facts from 'Outcast London'*.[16] This was probably published in the April, or early May, of 1884. However, when it was published it was not well received. By this time newspaper editors and the general public had been overwhelmed by the many reports on the conditions in the slums, following publication of '*The Bitter Cry of Outcast London.*' Thus the review published in the *Glasgow Herald* of 11 June 1884, complained that Elizabeth's book was rather a 'dubious contribution to the abounding literature of religious sensationalism.' Sensationalism, or not, Elizabeth maintained that the book was a true account, 'this is a truthful account of facts' she wrote, 'it was plain unvarnished facts'. However, she had to admit that the account did seem like 'fiction' but she assured her readers that it was not fiction. It was literally true, indeed it was 'only too terribly real'. The only deviation from the truth was that the names of the individuals in her account had been changed, as had the names of the places.

Of all her writings, *Our Golden Key* is probably the most difficult to assess. It is written in the form of a narrative, the central character being one Felix, a young city missionary. Immediately, despite her claim that her book was a truthful account, one questions as to whether Felix was a real individual.

It is somewhat easier to account for her choice of name. There are two possibilities. The first is that it is based, on the novel *Felix Holt* by George Eliot, which had been published in 1866. In this book Felix Holt is an idealistic young man who gives up his wealth and comfortable life for the simple life of a humble tradesman, working among ordinary working people in an attempt to improve their lot. This seems to reflect on what Elizabeth was doing herself. The second possibility is that the choice of name had come to her, possibly subconsciously, after having read the book, *The Notting Hill Mystery* by Charles Felix, which had been published, a few years before, in 1865.

The question that follows this conclusion is: Who was Felix? To understand this we must fast forward almost fifty years to when an almost identical book appeared on the bookstalls. The book was entitled, *God in the Shadows*, and its author was the Christian newspaper editor, Hugh Redwood. This was first published in 1932, and was a bestseller during the inter-war years. It followed an earlier book, *God in the Slums*, which was equally successful. The book tells the true story of Peter Rawlings who brings to public attention the plight of those people living in the slums of London. Later we discover that Peter is in fact Hugh Redwood himself, and the form of writing employed being simply a literary device.

The conclusion is that Elizabeth had adopted a similar literary device to write her exposé and that she was herself Felix. There are many clues in the book that would confirm this conclusion, but before we consider them it is interesting to note that there is a marked similarity between Hugh Redwood's book and Elizabeth's earlier work. The subject matter is identical, namely the degradation of people living in the slums of London. It is interesting that Hugh Redwood notes the strange contrast that existed between the names of the places and what they were like in reality. This is exactly a point Elizabeth made. Thus he talks about one place called, 'Honey Court', whereas she mentions

'Angel Court', places that were so different from what the names suggested. And then he changes scene to follow the slum-dwellers to the hop-fields of Kent, exactly like Elizabeth. Whether Hugh Redwood was aware of Elizabeth's earlier book is very unlikely, so the similarity is probably coincidental and arises from their mutual concern over the people living in the slums. The most notable feature of all this is the period between the publication of these two books, almost fifty years, yet very little seems to have been done to improve the slum conditions in all that time. This is a significant sociological observation that gives importance to Elizabeth's book which so far has not been recognised.

Elizabeth's account begins with Felix being shown around the area by a more experienced city missionary. The man describes how other missionaries had tried to work in the area, but time after time they had 'deserted their post'. He continued, 'the vicar cannot keep a curate. They have left him one after another...' Felix then asks why has this happened, to which the man replied, 'The hardships were too great, the atmosphere terrible, the labours were too arduous...'

Felix then ventures into the district alone and finds a little boy crying on a doorstep. 'He was miserably clothed; his few rags hanging on his limbs, scanty and bare.' Felix asks him the reason why he is crying. 'Father's dead!' the boy replied.

A little later Felix ascends up a steep flight of stairs and is met by a man carrying a wooden box on his shoulder. On inquiring as to what was in the box, Felix is told it was a dead child from upstairs, 'Been dead in that there room eleven days...we sent for the parish and now it is gone.'

Perfectly horrified Felix then goes in search for the child's mother. Eventually she is found, 'drunk on the floor...in a dead sleep...' It would appear that the father was dead and the mother lived with another man. Neither of them cared for the child. Even its little corpse, cold in death was left to lie unheeded upon a wretched bundle of rags....until consigned to a pauper's grave.

Felix then visits one of the courts, the inappropriately named 'Queen's Court', where she finds children sleeping in cupboards and on shelves, one above another, most of them naked, or ill-clothed. In another court, 'Angel Court –angelic in name but alas! Not in nature', she found its entrance, 'all black and foul with reeking odours, and footways deep in slime and mud'. Here its inhabitants were like people from the nether-world rather than 'men and women from Christian England'.

Elizabeth describes the sights and smells, in such realistic detail, that convinces one that they are first-hand descriptions, rather than if she had obtained them from another person. Take for instance when she describes the death of the Irishman 'Johnnie'. She writes: 'For nine whole days the corpse lay there unburied, the atmosphere of the room being quite unbearable.' Despite this unpleasantness she continued to visit the widow.

On one occasion Felix takes a friend from the country so as to show her the poor areas of the city. The couple make their way into one of the courts when a woman shouts down to them that there was a lady dying and would they visit her. Felix immediately goes to where the woman was and the friend follows. They enter the room. 'The grate was full of ashes, white and cold. Some bad fish lay on the table. On some heaped up rags in a corner lay an object – could you call it a woman? Her hair had not been combed for weeks. The filth of her whole body was indescribable. Her face black, her person scarcely clothed and emaciated to the last degree...' Felix kneels beside the bed and prays for the woman. On getting up and turning around finds that the friend has run off. Felix goes in search of her. 'I am very ill' complains the friend, 'take me away.' Later the friend asks Felix, 'What was that – that thing in the corner, I mean? What was it?'

'That thing?' replied Felix. 'It was a woman.'

'Oh,' the friend replied. '...what a smell! I should have died if I had stayed there much longer.'

The friend then pleads with Felix to stop working in the place.

'Don't go to such a place! DON'T I beg of you, or you will lose your life.'

In the event, Elizabeth ignored her friend's pleadings. She knew the dangers and was prepared to accept them so that she could continue to take the Gospel message to the people of the slums. Some years later when General William Booth was deciding on a title for his book that promised a solution to the problem of the slums he hit on the title: '*In Darkest England and the Way Out*'. This was a simile on David Livingstone's bestselling book, '*In Darkest Africa*', so making the point that the missionary faced as much danger in the London slums as in the heart of heathen Africa. Elizabeth would have had similar feelings and would have accepted the risks involved just as any missionary overseas would have done.

With regard to when Elizabeth embarked on her mission, one must rely, to some extent, on speculation. However, we do know when her book was published, so we can extrapolate from that fact. It was published in April 1884, for we have an early review in, *The Graphic* of Saturday, 3 May. As there are no dates given in the book it is reasonable to believe that the incidents described must have taken place during the previous summer, so this significantly takes it to be <u>before</u> publication of Mearns's '*A Bitter Cry of Outcast London*'. During the early part of 1883, Elizabeth was helping with the Moody crusade, so it would suggest that her mission took place during the six month period when Moody had returned to America, that was from about April to November, and this would concur with the weather conditions indicated in the incidents described in the book. Thus this gap in Moody's itinerary gave Elizabeth the opportunity of carrying out her own mission to the London slums.

There is the possibility that she might have amalgamated her own limited experiences with those of a more experienced city missionary. However, I have discounted this possibility. Firstly, I believe her descriptions are far too personal to have been obtained second-hand. Secondly, it was not in her character to have carried out mission work by proxy. Elizabeth, like her father, had a direct, hands-on form of Christianity, so it would be completely against her nature for her to have sat down in her comfortable home and simply taken notes from the poor missionary as he emerged from the abyss of the slums. Nevertheless, there remains the problem as to how an aristocratic and titled lady could have ventured into the dark alleyways and dangerous courts of the slums. One only has to look at some of her descriptions right at the outset of her book to realise that this would have been near impossible. For instance, when she enters one court, there were two 'wretched half-clothed women fighting desperately, striving to tear one another to pieces in their rage and fury. It was a sickening sight. Their hair was wild and unkempt; their clothes ragged; their voices shrieks from some evil depths...' And then (p75) she describes what happened when a stranger entered one of the courts: 'He was immediately seized and stripped of his coat.' On another occasion she witnessed 'a girl being dragged by two women across the court. A few hours afterwards she was beaten to death in the yard.' And on another day, 'a woman was found on the ground with the blade of a knife sticking out of her chest-bone.' So it is inconceivable that she could have entered these courts dressed as a titled lady.

So how did she go about her missionary work? The answer is to be found in the chapter entitled 'Doors Yield'. In this chapter she refers to it as 'an enigma' (p.35). How was she to gain entry to the darkest pits of sin and vice? Particularly as 'Some of the inhabitants mistook their new visitor for a quack doctor, some for a School Board officer, and some for a detective in plain clothes.' She then goes on to detail exactly how hazardous her mission was, where the populace were 'as lawless as savages'. On this particular occasion she described how she was approached by a woman who begged her to sign some papers for her 'man' who was a soldier. She followed the woman to where he was, 'through the intricacies of courts and doorways. At length to a long dark passage underground. On and on they went, till finally a door opened, and she was in a long, low room where a fire was burning in the grate. By its flickering light she could see a man sitting at a table.' Then just as she was about to ask the man a few questions *'the wall itself appeared to open'* and from it appeared 'a horribly ferocious-looking man with a heavy bludgeon uplifted' who rushed upon her with the intention of killing her. Fortunately, the woman who had brought her, rushed up to the man and seized the weapon. 'Don't touch...' she screamed. 'It's the missionary!'

It was a lucky escape. Afterwards she did some investigating and discovered that the place was a *'Thieves' Den'* and that the man who had sprung from the wall had 'mistaken his guest for a detective in plain clothes'.

The only conclusion that can be drawn from this is that Elizabeth, or Felix as she called herself, was dressed as a man. Only a man could have been mistaken as a detective in plain clothes at that time. Thus this was her solution to the problem of gaining access to the alleyways and courts. It was in the disguise of a male missionary. This is not an unreasonable conclusion as it was not unknown, at this time, for a woman to adopt a male appearance. One is reminded of one notable example, that of Dr James Barry who for some fifty years enjoyed a successful medical career in the British Army Medical Corps, rising to the ranks of Inspector General of Army Hospitals. All this time James Barry had a secret, namely that James Barry was a woman, whose disguise was so successful it had even misled Florence Nightingale. It had all been done so that James Barry, or Margaret Bulkley as she was born, had pretended to be a man in order to qualify in medicine, a profession which at this time was prohibited to women. Of course in Elizabeth's case her transition was only for a short period of time, and may even have been intermittent. This fact, she could not reveal to anyone, nor publish it in her memoir. To have done so would have created a public scandal. Yet it would not have been scandalous within the evangelical community at this time, as evangelicals would have believed that such a deception was justified for the greater good. One must remember at this time evangelical Christians sometimes acted in a way that seems contradictory to us today.

There are numerous instances when such deception was used if it was thought it would draw attention to an evil or an injustice. One example is when a young Salvation Army girl pretended to be a prostitute and actually took up residence in a brothel so that she could report on the activities that were going on inside, in particular the exploitation of young girls. In order for her to avoid suspicion she had been provided with sufficient money to pay the brothel-keeper and was so able to maintain her virtue. In the event, it was a scheme that eventually led to evidence that was presented to Parliament. And then there was the case of the campaigning journalist, William Thomas Stead, who together with Bramwell Booth, and the converted brothel-keeper Rebecca Jarrett, devised a scheme to highlight the evil trade in young girls. Stead went on to publish the resulting story in his *Pall Mall Gazette* under the headline, 'The maiden tribute of modern Babylon' and it caused one of the most sensational scandals of the Victorian age. However it also put him in jail for three months. Again this involved the use of deception to highlight a social evil. In the end it did lead to a change in the law as well as bringing to public notice the evil that was going on right in the heart of London. So when Elizabeth went undercover as a male missionary it was not such an outrageous thing for an evangelical to do. However, it was a thing that she couldn't reveal to anyone, apart from possibly, one, or two trusted friends.

It is now clear that she was not doing this dangerous work as an exercise in self-aggrandisement as she wasn't interested in gaining the praise of anyone. Thus, she did not publicise it, and certainly did not want to reveal it in her book. Indeed, just the opposite, as there are several instances in the book when she attempts to distract the reader from drawing this conclusion. For instance on one occasion she describes Felix entering 'Shades Court' where in a dark cellar there is a family sorting paper. One of the children is a little blind girl who sat at her work, 'swearing horribly, like an old woman' states Felix, to which Elizabeth (as narrator) comments: 'this is hardly our idea of a parallel. But it is evidently a very strong one to him.' This is clearly an attempt to distract the reader from drawing the conclusion that Elizabeth was herself Felix.

Then we find that following the death of 'Johnnie' the Irishman (mentioned earlier) Elizabeth continued to visit the widow. 'For nine whole days the corpse lay there unburied, the atmosphere of the room being quite unbearable...' Shortly afterwards, the widow propositions Felix with the suggestion: 'if your wife dies, I won't mind marrying you!' Elizabeth then describes the horror at the thought: 'no one who has not seen her can imagine the horrible appearance, the ghastly filth and coarse language of this poor thing...' She could not have written this if it had not happened to herself, nor would the woman have suggested marriage if Felix was not, at least in appearance, male.

Furthermore, there are numerous other clues indicating that Elizabeth was Felix. We know that Felix would stand in the courtyard and sing hymns to the occupants and we know that Elizabeth had a very attractive voice. Felix would take with him his portable harmonium, just as Elizabeth would do. Also, Felix would kneel and pray with sick residents, just as Elizabeth did. However, the strongest evidence is the fact that Felix had identifiable feminine traits that were recognised by some of the residents of the slums. There was one Sunday afternoon, when Felix was singing hymns in one of the courts accompanied by the harmonium (p.71) when a huge Irishman 'a veritable ruffian' came storming out and in a loud threatening voice demanded that the hymn singing should stop. 'None of your noise,' the Irishman demanded. 'I'll smash the thing all to bits.'

But before Felix had a chance to remonstrate another man came rushing to his rescue. 'Smash the music...NEVER!' the man said. 'I'll smash him first.' And with this he pulled off his coat in readiness for a fight.

For the next half-hour the man stood guard next to Felix, with his shirt sleeves rolled-up and his fists clenched ready to protect him from any attempt by the Irishman to stop the hymn singing and preaching. Afterwards, Felix's protector told him, 'nobody shall ever touch you when you come here. No never! You are always welcome.'

This does give the impression of a rough-and-ready man coming to the protection of a woman, just as the working men in the Coffee Room in Dorking would come to Elizabeth's aid when anyone threatened her. It seems unlikely he would have been so ready to protect a man, so Felix must have appeared somewhat effeminate. This of course would be the case if Felix was Elizabeth dressed as a man.

The playing of the portable harmonium was indeed Elizabeth's *modus operandi* as was her practice of kneeling in prayer with strangers. Thus in the instance of the Dorking cobbler, 'The strong man listened and was greatly moved. They knelt together in prayer; and oh! How earnestly this poor fellow, once so bitter an enemy, now poured out his soul in prayer to God.' So when Felix goes to visit the shoemaker, Mr Roberts of Shades Court, in the prison cell, they kneel down together and ask God for help. Elizabeth then comments: 'The man himself prayed most touchingly.' How could she have described it as 'touchingly' if she was not present? Another piece of evidence follows from what Felix tells Mr Payne of Gold Court of his own conversion some 16 years before. This would make it 1867 and this coincides with Elizabeth's own religious experience in Ireland.

Then there are numerous subtle comments that indicate that it is Elizabeth's own experience when Felix is quoted. Hence there is the instance of the woman in Queen's Court standing at a door dressed only in an old waterproof and having nothing on underneath. Felix talks to her about the Gospel and quotes from Isaiah i v.6: 'From the sole of the foot even unto the head there is no soundness in it; but wounds and bruises and putrifying sores...' The woman listened for a few moments and then opened up the front of her garment revealing her nakedness. 'Do you see any wounds or bruises here?' she asked. It is unlikely Felix would have described this to Elizabeth. The only way Elizabeth would have known about this incident was if she and Felix were one and the same. Similarly there is the incident (p.28) when a man sprang up from his seat and rushed at Felix to knock him down, uttering 'words that can hardly be repeated'. As Felix would not have mentioned them how could Elizabeth have known they could not be repeated? Then there is the occasion when Felix visits a woman dying of cholera in a small room where there are chickens running about the place. Felix was 'horrified' and tells the man 'a desperate character' living there: 'Pray don't let your wife die in a room with a hen and chickens in it.' The woman 'worn and haggard before her time' tells Felix that she had been 'a bright young woman' before she came to London from a good home in Canterbury some 17 years before and that she had been 'led astray'. Felix reads to her from the Bible, the parable of the Prodigal Son, and then kneels beside the bed in prayer. The following day Felix returns to find the woman had died. When the sheet covering the body is lifted Felix remembers the woman's parting words: 'I was a bright young woman but was led astray', emotions are overwhelmed and Felix bursts into tears. Would Felix have told Elizabeth that? It seems much more likely that it was Elizabeth that had shed the tears and that she was Felix.

Whatever one's conclusion, the remarkable thing about this episode in Elizabeth's life is that it demonstrates most dramatically that she was a very courageous woman. She remains calm in the face of violence and possible death, a fact that is reinforced when one recalls the story of the burglar and her claim that: 'I am not the sort of woman who screams.' Indeed, her entire temperance campaign had been carried out with complete disregard for her own safety, so that when her friend the Marchioness of Ailsa had received death threats following her campaign against drink, Elizabeth continued on regardless. The one incident in the slums that highlights her remarkable courage is an incident in Shades Court when a Mr and Mrs Roberts had a dispute with a neighbour. A violent struggle ensued when a large carving knife was produced that resulted in a serious stabbing. A policeman had been called to the scene but he quickly fled, but Elizabeth remained. It is clear from this that Elizabeth, just like her father, was a person of great personal courage.

CHAPTER 14

Rescue the Perishing

FOLLOWING THE PUBLICATION of her book, *Our Golden Key,* in early 1884, Elizabeth was fully engaged assisting Moody and Sankey with their revivalist campaign in Central London. Then when Moody concluded his British mission and returned to America, Elizabeth remained in London to continue her work with the poor and needy. At this time she took up residence at 12 Great Cumberland Place, which is now the site of the Cumberland Hotel. At the time it was a large Georgian house that had previously been occupied by the Scottish physician, Dr George Wyld and his family, together with several domestic servants. It was a comfortable house, in a prosperous neighbourhood, yet was not far from the location of the mission hall with which she was now associated. This was the Bible Mission at number one, Walmer Road, in Notting Hill. The area has since been subject to much re-development and the mission hall has long disappeared, however, there are illustrations of it in her book. These show that it was a small building in a terrace of ordinary houses. Inside it was a modest hall with a raised platform at the far end, with simple benches arranged in front of it. There are the usual biblical texts on the walls but what is surprising are the flags displayed around the hall, making it appear very much like a Salvation Army citadel. Although appearing similar it was not affiliated with this organisation and in the Religious Census of London that was carried out in 1886, it appears to have been a completely independent mission hall.

A search of contemporary newspapers show what Walmer

Road was like at the time. This indicated that it was quite an unpleasant area. The *Reynold's Newspaper* of Sunday, 21 November 1886, reports that an inquest had been held at the Black Bull Tavern, Notting Hill on a ten-month-old child that had been found at 18 Walmer Road. When asked about the house a juryman replied, 'It is a dirty hole, I don't think I can "keep my stomach" there.' Some way along the road was the BeeHive Public House, that was experiencing a decline in business. This may have been the result of increased competition as there is no evidence that this was due to the appearance of Elizabeth's temperance mission. Further along there was a cab business, with extensive stables, and a factory manufacturing iron bedsteads on three floors. There was also some discussion over plans to build an iron-hospital for smallpox victims, which might suggest that this disease was still a problem in the area, despite the policy of compulsory vaccination.

It was now more than a year since publication of Mearns's *Bitter Cry of Outcast London* and most churches in the area had still not woken up to the desperate conditions that existed in the slums. Yet these slums were just a stone's throw from some of the most fashionable residences in the capital. A recent Methodist leader, the late Lord Soper, commented that the slow response of the Christian churches to the revelations contained in, *Bitter Cry of Outcast London*, had been shameful. Yet, even his own church was slow to take action and it was not until four years after the Mearns pamphlet that the Methodist West London Mission was set up by the Reverend Hugh Price Hughes. This would indicate that Elizabeth was clearly way ahead of other Christians in realising that London, not Africa, or China, was the greatest and most important mission field in the world.

However, she had wider ambitions than just working in the local mission. What she wanted to achieve was far more. Not only did she want to bring people to a personal relationship with Jesus Christ but she also wanted to get these people to give up drink. She realised, as William Booth had, that alcohol was the cause of much of the misery in society. People could not pull themselves up from the ghetto if they were held back by the chains of alcohol. They had to be set free and this only came about by conversion and deciding for Christ. It was very difficult for people to do it on their own. This was why there were so many failed attempts to give up alcohol. There had to be a decision for Christ as well. One of the conclusions she had reached is that if it were possible to transfer the poor of the slums to the fashionable areas of the West End, the lives of the people would not necessarily change. Indeed, those areas to which the people had been moved to would quickly disintegrate into further slums. It was only by taking away the alcohol that it was possible to make social improvements. This was her philosophy, and it is a way of thinking that still has many advocates today.

One of her other interests at this time was the work of the Railway Mission. On the evening of Thursday, 21 February 1884, she spoke at a meeting of the Railway Mission held at the home of the prosperous accountant Arthur J. Hill at 36 Lansdowne Road in Notting Hill. She highlighted the importance of the organisation and appealed for more effort in promoting Christian views and temperance amongst the railway workers, 'in whose hands we daily place our lives in travelling.'[17]

The Railway Mission, or the Railway Men's Christian Association was an evangelical organisation founded several years before with the purpose of taking the Gospel to those working for the railway companies. Since the introduction of passenger railways in the 1820s there had been massive expansion, so that by the 1880s there were some 400,000 men working in the industry. This was a major workforce and exceeded the combined numbers working for the army, navy and police. With the railways operating every day of the week, many employees were forced to work on the Sabbath which prevented them from attending a place of worship. The answer to this was that the Railway Mission, had rooms at railway stations so that the workers could have short services on a Sunday. At the annual meeting in 1886 held at the Exeter Hall, Elizabeth was one of the main speakers. It was then announced that several new halls had been opened including one at West Brompton with a capacity to accommodate six hundred. The mission also published its own penny magazine entitled, *Railway Signal*, which had a circulation of some 22,000 copies a month. Elizabeth recognised the importance of temperance in the Railway industry with regard to the safety of the travelling public. What did concern her was the fact that some railway companies were giving away alcohol to their employees. She realised that temperance was a vital counterforce, to the free-and-easy attitude of the industry with regards to the drinking habits of its staff. She was very effective in getting this message across as soon afterwards the London-Brighton Railway Total Abstinence League was formed with the Brighton branch being named after her and called the '*Lady Hope (Brighton) Branch.*'

Over the following months Elizabeth made plans for the establishment of a coffee house in central London, similar to the one she had formed at Dorking but on a much grander scale. This was not altogether a novel innovation as Dr Barnardo had already established what he called a 'Coffee Palace' at the Edinburgh Castle, Rhodeswell Road, in Limehouse, the poor district in the East End of the capital. In an audacious transaction, sometime in 1872, Dr Barnardo had snatched this notorious public house, 'a school of vice and drunkenness' from the hands of the beer-kings and gin-princes, so that he could transform it into a temperance mission. Only recently Emma Cons (1838-1912) had formed the Coffee Tavern Company, and had opened the *Old Vic Theatre* under its new name, *the Royal Victoria Coffee and Music Hall*. Now Elizabeth had similar ambitions. She elaborated on these plans at a Drawing Room meeting held at the home of Lord and Lady Brabazon at 83 Lancaster Gate on 6 May 1884. The meeting was crowded and Elizabeth outlined her plans for a Coffee Palace in the West End. The place she had decided on was Oxford Street, where there were thousands of people passing by all day long. It was also in the heart of the city and in such a prominent position, that it would have challenged the established gin palaces and public houses. All she needed were funds to secure the purchase, however, unlike Dr Barnardo she was unable to raise sufficient, even after appealing in the press. The upshot was that the proposed Oxford Street Coffee Palace never opened its doors.

Undeterred by this failure she continued with her crusade against drink across the country. By this time she had built up a network of influential like-minded friends that led to invitations to talk at venues throughout Britain. In the September of 1884, she held a mission at the Masonic Hall, Llandudno, in North Wales. This was in response to an invitation she had received from Lady Augusta Mostyn of Gloddaeth Hall. Lady Mostyn was a young widow, like herself, and was dedicated to philanthropic causes. She was the daughter of the Earl of Abergavenny and up to 1875 had resided in Kent, so may have been acquainted with Elizabeth from this period. She was a generous benefactor and had recently funded the development of the Marine Drive around the Great Orme. Sometime later she donated the magnificent Oriel Mostyn art gallery to the people of Llandudno. In this part of North Wales she was greatly appreciated and on her death in 1912, she was referred to as 'Lady Bountiful of Gloddaeth'.

In the event Elizabeth's mission to Llandudno was a complete success and in its report, published shortly afterwards, the United Total Abstinence Society of the town noted that all her meetings were well attended, with many people having to be turned away. The *North Wales Chronicle* reporting on the mission gave glowing testimony to the success of her previous visits to the town, and mentioned, a certain John Roberts, who had gone to her meeting out of curiosity, with a bottle of gin in his pocket, but after listening to her talk he became so convinced that he handed over the bottle and signed the pledge.

On her return to London, Elizabeth continued with her fund-raising, still with hopes of opening a Coffee Palace in the West End. In the December of that year she organised an afternoon concert of sacred and secular music in the Steinway Hall, Lower Seymour Street, when Professor Andre's Alpine Choir performed Tyrolese, French and Italian songs, as well as English melodies. It was a novel way of raising money, albeit it may have led to the disapproval of some puritanical evangelicals on account of its taint of worldliness. Drawing room musical events were another of Elizabeth's means for fund-raising. Again these did not meet the approval of some evangelicals. Catherine Booth, for instance, although much in demand as a speaker at such polite society events, was very dismissive of their value. "Give up," she wrote, "the sentimental hypocrisy of singing 'Rescue the Perishing' in a drawing room to the accompaniment of a piano without dreaming of going outside to do it".

One of Elizabeth's most important supporters was Lady Henry Somerset (1851-1921) the eldest daughter of Viscount Eastnor. In 1872 she had married Lord Henry Somerset, but the marriage proved disastrous on account of his homosexuality. A notorious custody case ensued in the courts over their only child and on account of the adverse publicity she withdrew from society and devoted herself to charity work. Then following the suicide of a close friend, whilst under the influence of drink, she turned towards the temperance cause. In 1890 she was elected the President of the British Women's Temperance Association, and on account of her leadership its membership rapidly expanded. Part of this success was due to her inviting Frances Willard (1839-98), the American temperance campaigner, to Britain and they became firm friends. On the death of her father in 1883 she inherited large estates, including Eastnor Castle in Herefordshire (18,000 acres), and numerous other estates in central London and Surrey. With her aristocratic background and her large reserves of cash she became a significant figure in the temperance movement. One of her most important schemes was the farm colony for women inebriates that she built at Duxhurst, near Reigate in Surrey. This was formally opened by Princess Mary in July 1896. It was built along similar lines to that proposed by William Booth in his book, '*In Darkest England and the Way out*'. Essentially the recovering alcoholics worked in the open air growing fruit and vegetables and lived in small groups in nearby cottages. Many of these cottages had been donated by supporters and were named after them. Elizabeth was one such sponsor and her cottage was called 'Hope Cottage'. This was close to Lady Somerset's own cottage on the farm colony where she spent much of her time.

However, on occasions Lady Somerset would retreat to Eastnor Castle where she would entertain in the splendour of the mock Norman castle. About a decade earlier Elizabeth had stayed with her, over the Christmas of 1885. On Christmas day Elizabeth gave 'one of her brightest addresses' in the Great Hall to a crowded audience, and despite it being a time for festivities several pledges were taken, albeit Lady Somerset was not one of them.

In October the following year Elizabeth was again invited by Lady Somerset to present a series of lectures at the Reigate branch of the YWCA, of which she was president. The meetings, at the Public Hall, took place over several days and were packed to capacity. The *Surrey Mirror* reported on 23 October that Elizabeth's talk had been 'impressive' and that the hall was so crowded that Elizabeth and Lady Somerset had been forced to enter the hall by a side entrance. On the following evening the meeting was moved to the largest hall in the town, when again it was crowded, with some 500 women all of whom 'listened with earnest attention' to Elizabeth's 'inspiring address'.

Around this time Lady Somerset began to feel guilty in asking others to sign the pledge when she had not done so herself. Some years before Agnes Weston, another temperance campaigner, had felt exactly the same. Both these women later admitted to enjoying a glass of wine, and in both instances it led to a personal crisis of conscience. Then at a temperance meeting in Ledbury, Lady Somerset came to the 'disagreeable truth' that she must herself sign the pledge. However, she found another excuse to delay it, at least until the next meeting at Eastnor which was to be held in December. As the day approached she went to London, and on returning home, just the day before the meeting, she realised she must have one last drink, so on changing trains at Worcester she hurried to the refreshment room and ordered a double measure of the best port, which was to be her last.

Whether this had been Elizabeth's influence we do not know, but it is possible as she was now an established and very popular speaker at temperance conferences across the country. Although travelling to speaking engagements was time-consuming it nevertheless gave her the opportunity for further fund raising. In the November of 1886 Elizabeth addressed a Gospel Temperance Meeting at St Andrew's Presbyterian Church in Reading. She urged the importance of temperance and related numerous 'touching anecdotes' of her experiences of temperance work in the London slums. Then in the January of the following year she addressed the newly formed Temperance Club at the Workman's Institute at Cold Harbour, and gave her encouragement to this fledgling organisation.

In the April of 1887 she addressed the annual meeting of the East London Women's Christian Union held at Exeter Hall. On this occasion other speakers included Viscountess Lymington and Dr Alfred Carpenter. In Elizabeth's talk she outlined her conclusion that the only way to reduce the consumption of alcohol was to encourage 'temperance meals'. This was expanded on by Dr Carpenter who urged that wine should not be available at wedding receptions as it encouraged young family members to drink.[18]

On Tuesday, 20 March 1888, Elizabeth gave an address to the Birmingham Ladies Central Temperance Association, that outlined the biblical grounds for advocating temperance and she urged those who sympathised with her to spread this message. The *Birmingham Daily Post* reported that there had been a large audience and that her speech had been well received. The following day she addressed another large meeting of the Birmingham Gospel Temperance Mission held in the large lecture theatre of the Birmingham and Midland Institute. The chairman, Alderman Barrow, in his introduction, praised her for promoting temperance by the innovation of coffee houses and pointed out that a decade before there were no respectable coffee houses in Birmingham that could offer the working man an alternative to the gin palace. Now there were several, he noted, and they were 'of incalculable benefit as they had increased the sobriety of the city.' Elizabeth then spoke and summarised the recent advances of the temperance movement. 'Indulgence in strong drink only produced misery,' she said. 'We must decrease that misery,' she continued, 'by encouraging habits of temperance.' At the conclusion of her talk there was a hearty vote of thanks and a collection was made towards her project in the West End.

Just a few weeks afterwards she was speaking at a temperance meeting at St Mary's Hall, Marylebone. On the platform she was accompanied by the Duchess of Rutland who had travelled there directly from Brussels that very same morning so as to give her support.

In the autumn of that year she visited North Wales again. On 10 October, she held a meeting in the village of Rhosnessney, near Wrexham, at the invitation of Lady Cunliffe. The local newspaper reported: 'from the very commencement to the end of her address she kept her listeners in rapt silence, interrupted only by bursts of applause. Two hymns were sung at the close and several pledges taken. Such an address as Lady Hope's will remain in the minds of many and greatly assist to lessen the terrible sin of intemperance.' The following day she was speaking at the Church of England Temperance Society meeting held in the Public Hall at Wrexham. As was usual she had attracted large crowds and the hall was packed. The proceedings commenced with hymns followed by prayers and then the chairman spoke of his distress at the amount of drunkenness in the town with all its resulting misery. There was then the singing of 'Rescue the Perishing', which according to the report the following day in the *Wrexham Advertiser and North Wales News* was 'very heartily done'.

The following month Elizabeth was in Northampton. On Sunday 18th she was lecturing at the town's Temperance Hall when the hall was crowded with every seat occupied including the gallery. Following an introduction by the chairman, Colonel Ball-Acton, Elizabeth was given a warm welcome. The *Northampton Mercury* in its report published a few days later wrote, 'Her ladyship possesses a clear, strong voice and spoke with great fluency and ease and while her address was to a large extent anecdotal she at times became very eloquent and deeply pathetic. Her speech was about half-an-hour and was listened to attentively. The audience was much delighted with her remarks about the "tuff-'un" whom she induced to sign the pledge at Plymouth. He was pointed out to her by that name at a meeting and seizing her opportunity and believing the effect of his quality of toughness might have on his associates prevailed upon him and he became one of the best workers that had come forward.'

Elizabeth then outlined her work in the slums of Notting Hill and told her audience about the dying girl who was the means for getting her drunken father to give up drinking. The newspaper report continued: 'The manner in which she told this story necessitated the application of pocket handkerchiefs to the eyes in many parts of the hall.'

The following day she addressed a Drawing Room meeting of the British Women's Temperance Association, held at the home of Mr and Mrs Gibbs when some seventy ladies attended. The president of the Northampton branch was a Mrs Jackson who introduced Elizabeth and led the hymns and prayers. Elizabeth gave an interesting talk about her work at Notting Hill and outlined the chief features of her proposed Coffee Palace. Her audience listened with interest to her address and after a vote of thanks there was a collection on behalf of the proposed Coffee Palace.

CHAPTER 15

Notting Hill

WHEN ELIZABETH MARRIED Admiral Sir James Hope in 1877 she had left Dorking to live on his estate at Carriden. The Coffee Room that she had successfully established in Dorking was left to run under its own management, however, without her driving force one wonders as to how long it would have survived. In the event, a local businessman stepped in to take over where she had left off. The man was Mr E.M. Denny, the brother of Thomas Anthony Denny, who owned the Boxhurst estate, near Box Hill. He was acquainted with Elizabeth, as he had been a supporter of Messrs Moody and Sankey, and had known her following their own involvement with this campaign. When Mr Denny realised Elizabeth had moved to Scotland he decided to get involved with the Coffee Room. His first consideration was the premises, which was now inadequate for the large numbers attending, so his first decision was to obtain a new location. As he was a wealthy businessman, money was no problem, so after finding a suitable site he had plans drawn up to build a completely new building. The site chosen was in West Street and the building was completed in 1880. It was much more substantial than Elizabeth's earlier room. There were now two coffee rooms, one just for young men, where tea and coffee were available together with meals at modest prices. In addition, there was a reading room, where daily newspapers were available, a smoking room, and a games room for those who wanted to play chess or draughts. There was also an American bowling alley, and a gymnasium, together with bathing facilities. There was also accommodation, with first and second-class facilities. At the rear of the building was a large lecture theatre that could accommodate eight hundred. The aim of the institute was to promote temperance, as well as the spiritual welfare of the inhabitants of Dorking. Every evening of the week there were prayer meetings and Bible classes. The Penny Bank was restarted so as to encourage thrift, and Mrs Denny conducted regular mothers' meetings. Thus Elizabeth's ground work was continued, albeit on a much grander scale.

Although Elizabeth continued to take an interest in the changes that had taken place in Dorking since her marriage, and had kept in touch with the many friends she had made there, she nevertheless felt at this time that her major work was to be done in the slums of the capital. Her parents still lived in Dorking and whenever possible she continued to take an active role in the life of the town. Thus in the July of 1885, she visited the town and gave an address entitled, 'Gospel Temperance work in Switzerland' in the lecture hall of the new Coffee Room to a crowded audience. In it she described her recent experiences travelling in Switzerland, anecdotes from which were later published in her book, *Pictures of Silver (Thoughts gathered from the mountains and valleys of Switzerland)*.

In August that same year, she helped her parents entertain the St Paul's Band of Hope, for their annual flower show, in the grounds of their home. It was a glorious summer's day and Elizabeth gave a fascinating talk about her recent visit to Switzerland and showed some curious souvenirs she had brought back. The audience listened in rapt attention. Afterwards she distributed the prizes, a special one going to a little lad named 'Botting' who had exhibited some neatly cut wood carvings. And for those children who hadn't won a prize she gave to each of them an illuminated certificate. Afterwards, her mother, Lady Cotton, gave all the children some cakes to take home.

Then in the September, Elizabeth invited workers at the Dorking Sewerage Works to tea at the Coffee Room, when some eighty workers attended. On arriving each man was given a buttonhole carnation to wear and after a pleasant tea of meat pies and cakes they assembled in the spacious lecture hall to make a presentation to her. Afterwards the workers gave her hearty applause and rounded the evening off with three cheers.

At the Dorking Flower Show the following year Elizabeth once again gave out the prizes alongside Mrs E.M. Denny, who was later to become her sister-in-law. It was held in the new Coffee Room with her father in the Chair. Elizabeth afterwards gave an address entitled: 'Fragrant blossoms and lasting fruits' in which she outlined the benefits and pleasures to be derived from the study of flowers.

Following her visits to Dorking she would return to Great Cumberland Street to continue her work in the slums. Although her plans to open a Coffee Palace in Oxford Street had failed, she decided to look for an alternative site. Then sometime in 1884 she obtained the lease on a suitable property in Notting Hill Gate. It appeared entirely appropriate as it had a main entrance on the High Street (being No 87) and a back entrance leading on to Uxbridge Street. It had traded as a public eating-house under the name of the North End & Harvey Dining Room. She believed it was suitable for her purposes despite the fact that it suffered from a dubious reputation. (Maybe she took that as a challenge. It was certainly in Elizabeth's character to do that.) However, it was a substantial structure having been built in 1861. On the ground floor there were several large public rooms, with a large basement and several upper floors, where there were numerous rooms for lodgers. It is possible that at one time these rooms may have been used by prostitutes. Whether Elizabeth knew of these rumours is unclear. The building still exists today and is now known as the Gate Cinema. It is one of London's favourite independent cinemas, however it is much changed. It was first converted into a cinema in 1911, when it was called, 'The Electric Palace Cinema', then in 1931 it became one of the first cinemas in Britain to have been converted to showing sound movies, when it changed its name to 'The Embassy'. During the Second World War it was badly damaged by enemy bombing and the domed roof and upper floors destroyed. After the War the front was rebuilt and it was given a flat roof, so today it no longer has its original appearance, however, the rear entrance in Uxbridge Street, appears to be unchanged. (To get some idea as to how it looked at the time Elizabeth took it over one must look at the nearby Coronet Cinema on the next block, which has the original frontal features including the domed roof.)

The first thing Elizabeth did on taking over the establishment was to change its name and it became, 'The Golden Bells Coffee Palace'. Then she appointed a manager. The man given the position was William Magee and his wife Rebecca. Magee had been born in 1852 and had been in the Prince of Wales Dragoon Guards. In 1871 he had been stationed at Aldershot, so it is possible he may have encountered Elizabeth there, as she had taken her mission tent to the troops stationed there.

Shortly after opening the Coffee Palace, Elizabeth engaged Professor André and his Alpine Choir to hold a special concert, to raise funds for her work. This was at the Steinway Hall, in Lower Seymour Street on Friday morning, 19 December 1884. This was a morning concert of sacred and secular music which included Tyrolese, French, German and English melodies. Over the next few years she would use these musical events to raise funds. Thus on 2 June 1886 there was another concert at Grosvenor House, courtesy of the Duke of Westminster. She does not appear to have lacked imagination in her fund-raising. For instance, in June 1888 she organised a Swiss Fête at the Duke of Wellington's Riding School in Knightsbridge, under the patronage of Princess Mary Adelaide, the Duchess of Teck. It was a bazaar that took the form of a Swiss village, with the stalls all decorated to look like Swiss cottages. The event attracted numerous titled persons including the Countess of Dudley who had a flower stall.

The Drawing Room meeting was also a reliable means of fund-raising and one on which Elizabeth depended. Not many of them have left records but we do have one report in the *Morning Post* of Monday, 25 February 1889. This was held a few days before at the residence of Lady Gordon Cathcart, at 6 Hereford Gardens. Lady Cathcart was a widow, like Elizabeth, having extensive estates in the Highlands, with a corresponding huge annual income. As would be expected in these circumstances there was a good attendance and following singing by Miss Gertrude Nunn, Elizabeth was given the opportunity to outline what she was doing at the Golden Bells. She explained that the establishment was providing good homely accommodation for working men at modest prices, in a temperance environment. There were home comforts, a games room, a coffee bar and a reading room where daily newspapers were available. Everything was done so as to keep the men from going to public houses where they would be enticed away from the straight-and-narrow. So far, she explained they were making progress, but she urgently needed more funding. In the event, her appeal did not fall on deaf ears and there was a generous collection towards her work. There was also a decision to hold further drawing room meetings on a fortnightly basis. Yet even with this success things were getting financially stretched, so over the next few months, she was forced to make public appeals in the newspapers. One appeared in *The Morning Post* on Christmas day, it read:

"The Poor of the West End

We are working amongst many hundreds of these poor people. Will you help us to help them? Much good might be done in many ways but we need your aid. Money and clothing may be sent to Lady Hope, 12 Great Cumberland Place."

However, her plans were about to change, as Christmas 1889 turned out to be a very sad time for her. She had been looking forward to spending the Christmas period with her parents in Dorking. In particular, she was looking forward to seeing her brother, Alfred, and his wife, who were expected home from India. But, they didn't turn up and a few days after Christmas they received the news that Alfred had died at sea, and Marion, his wife, had arrived in England alone. This was devastating news for Elizabeth and her parents. Alfred was her only sibling, and the only surviving son of her parents. Alfred, like his father, had joined the Indian Army and had seen active service in the Afghan War of 1878-79. Like his father, he had served with distinction and had been mentioned in dispatches. His last leave had been in 1881 at which time he married, after a long courtship, Marion Emma Heath of Anstie Grange, which was near Dorking. The marriage had taken place on 22 June at the Holmwood Church. Elizabeth's parents had been very pleased with this match as Marion was from a distinguished naval family. Her father was Admiral Sir Leopold George Heath (1817-1907) who had commanded the steam warship HMS *Niger* during the Crimean War.[19]

The honeymoon was at the ancestral family seat at Combermere Abbey, following which Alfred and Marion returned to India. On their arrival he had been promoted to Major in the 4th Gurkhas and was attached to the Bengal Staff Corps. After another eight years in India they planned to return home to spend Christmas with their families. But then tragedy struck. They had left India on board the steamship *Raffaele Rubattino* but during the voyage he had been taken ill, probably cholera, and had died after a couple of days. He was then interred at sea, so when Marion arrived in England, she was a widow, and alone, as there were no children of the marriage.

This tragedy struck Elizabeth hard and made her think about her future. She was now the only surviving child of her parents and felt responsible for them. Her father was approaching his ninetieth year and her mother was almost eighty. Although these ages are not so unusual today, they were remarkable at the time, and must have made Elizabeth feel that she should be living nearer to them. However, there may have been other reasons why she considered moving her missionary work back to Dorking. It was the year 1889. This was the year that will always be etched in the history of the capital as it was the year of the so-called 'Whitechapel Murders'. These dreadful murders had taken place in the slums of the city and had created a frenzy in the capital. Yet Elizabeth had been working, much of the time alone, in these slum areas. These horrific murders had been carried out over the preceding months in the slums of the East End, not very far from the slums in which she was spending much of her time. We now refer to these murders as the work of the notorious 'Jack the Ripper'. Whether there was just the one murderer, or several, has never been resolved. What is certain is that they had terrorised Victorian London. The victims were all women, many of them prostitutes, and following each murder there had been sensational press coverage. Despite their strong Christian faith, Elizabeth's parents must have been concerned as to their daughter's personal safety in carrying out her missionary work in the London slums. As the 'Whitechapel Murders' were never solved, there remained much fear in central London, and beyond. One can be sure that Elizabeth would never have been fearful for her own safety, but it is reasonable to suppose that she must have considered the feelings of her parents, and as a consequence she decided to move her work back to Dorking where it had all started.

## CHAPTER 16

The Mickleham Mission

THERE MAY HAVE been another reason behind Elizabeth's decision to leave her Notting Hill Mission. The sensational reporting of the Ripper murders had led most people in central London to be fearful of going out alone at night. No one felt safe, particularly women. And then there was the mystery as to the identity of the murderer. There had been much speculation on this - indeed it continues to engage people even to this day. It is possible Elizabeth began to think about some of the men attending her Coffee Palace. In her time, she had come across many dubious characters. They seemed to drift into the Coffee Palace out of the mists and gloom of the streets, seeking a bed for the night, and then drift away, never to be seen again. Some of these men were indeed criminals. This conclusion has been reached following a search of contemporary newspapers that have revealed reports of several criminals giving the Golden Bells Coffee Palace as their place of residence. Probably the most notorious was a gang of criminals that ended up on trial at the Old Bailey. It was during this trial that the Golden Bells Mission, together with her name, were mentioned. This may have been the final straw and made her decide to leave Notting Hill.

The trial at the Old Bailey had taken place in the early weeks of 1890 and involved a gang of fraudsters. They had been involved in obtaining properties in the Notting Hill area by fear and intimidation. In some instances, they had used false references to obtain properties which they then sub-let to unsuitable tenants, and then forced landlords to pay exorbitant fees for them to evict the tenants. It was a substantial operation involving a large number of fraudsters. Some of the references that had been used had been obtained from William Magee, who was Elizabeth's manager at the Golden Bells. He was not charged in connection with the conspiracies to defraud and he may have been entirely innocent, nevertheless his behaviour, whether it was naive, or not, we don't know, yet it had been responsible for bringing Elizabeth's name up in court. In addition, one of the chief defendants was Richard Gurling. In the trial, it was reported that he had belonged to a Christian Mission in Notting Hill. The fact that William Magee was involved it is likely that this mission was Elizabeth's Golden Bells. If so, it must appear that Elizabeth had been duped by this character, for the Court was told that Gurling, 'was a most dangerous man, because under the guise of religion he was able to commit these frauds with impunity.'

The upshot was that Elizabeth decided to leave her missionary work in Notting Hill and to return the Dorking. It would appear that sometime in 1890 the lease on the Golden Bells was transferred to William Magee and he eventually purchased the property. The *London Daily News* of Saturday, 1 November 1890, under its 'Preachers for Tomorrow' column announced that a Mr J. Short was to preach at the Golden Bells, Notting Hill Gate at 7pm. It was therefore still operating as a mission at that date. But it is clear that under Magee's tenancy things were to change. The 1891 census indicates that it was no longer a temperance establishment as Magee now employed some five barmaids and three barmen.

On returning to Dorking, Elizabeth made her home in the small village of Mickleham, just a little to the north of the town. She obtained a large residence on land just east of the Old London Road. The house was originally known as 'Belledawe House' but she changed its name to 'Carriden House' to remind her of her home in Scotland. The house no longer exists as it was demolished in about 1920; however several of its outbuildings remain. These are known as 'Lodge Cottages' and are now part of the Box Hill School. There are three small cottages and the one nearest the school buildings appears to have been at one time the coach house to Carriden House. Today the principal building of this private school is the elegant Dalewood House, a Grade II listed building that was built for the silk merchant David Evans in 1883.

On establishing herself at Mickleham, Elizabeth began to enter into missionary activities in the area together with her father just as she had done some twenty years before. On Wednesday, 6 August 1890, she joined her parents at the Dorking Band of Hope annual flower show. Her father was in the chair and had donated a van-load of beautiful plants from his garden. Elizabeth gave the address and her mother distributed the prizes. A few weeks afterwards she gave a Gospel address at the Lecture Hall in Dorking on Sunday evening when the hall was crowded. She also continued her work with the YWCA and acquired new premises in Dorking for the organisation at Clarendon House. In the May of 1892 she held the annual conference of the YWCA, South-East District, at her home in Mickleham. After the Conference the delegates were entertained to afternoon tea and in the evening they celebrated the opening of the new premises when Elizabeth addressed the gathering.

It was around this time she decided to build a mission hall in Mickleham. She got plans drawn up and employed Job Pledge, of Dorking, to build it. It was this Mr Pledge (or his father) who had built her first Coffee Room many years before and she knew he was a reliable builder. The room was built to accommodate two hundred, so it must have been a substantial building. There is no trace of the building in the village today, however records indicate that it had been built near the village school.

On Wednesday, 16 September 1891, Elizabeth invited all the children of Dorking for a day's outing to her home in Mickleham. It was a beautiful sunny day and they were conveyed to Carriden House by a series of open wagons. The children had a marvellous time playing in the extensive grounds and afterwards she treated them to a bountiful supply of tea and cakes. The occasion reminded her of a similar happy time she had with her late husband in Scotland. There is evidence that this became something like an annual event as the Mickleham Parish magazine for November 1889 records a similar event having taken place some weeks previously. On that occasion all the children attending the Mickleham schools had been invited, some 120 children and several of their teachers. On this occasion the children were welcomed to Elizabeth's home by the Dorking Volunteer Band. In an adjoining field she had erected a large tent, having the word 'WELCOME' in large letters above its entrance. It was here that the children sat down for tea, but before this was served there were games and other activities. Later in the afternoon there was a display of photography and entertainment by a conjuror. Then towards the end of the day all the children were presented with a prize. The report concluded: 'Lady Hope was fully determined to follow up the kind and beautiful words which she has so often addressed to our children by equally kind and beautiful deeds. Before the last gift had been distributed, dusk rapidly came on, and it was time for the happy gathering to disperse: but ere this was done, very hearty cheers were given by the scholars for Lady Hope, and all those who had assisted her in her day's labour of love.'

Earlier that same year the Mickleham Parish Magazine gave a report of Elizabeth giving a talk to a group of mothers from Stepney in the East End who had been invited to a garden party at the Juniper Hill estate by its owner, Mr Theodore Henry Bryant (1843-1913). T.H.Bryant was the son of William Bryant who had founded the match company Bryant & May with a factory in the East End. Only the year before this company had come to public attention when it was involved with the famous women match-workers' strike led by the notorious Annie Besant. To what extent Elizabeth had other dealings with the Bryant family is unknown, but she would certainly have supported the women workers in their demand for better working conditions. But it is unlikely she would have had much sympathy with Mrs Besant, who some years previously, Darwin also had refused to help.

Although Elizabeth's health had always been good, the stress of the past few years was beginning to show. There was the loss of her husband, and the unexpected and tragic loss of her brother. Then the years she had worked in the London slums had put a strain on her constitution. Although she now had some companionship at Carriden House, with the arrival at Mickleham of her friend Gertrude Hart-Dyke (1846-1927) of Lullingstone Castle, who helped her with work with the YWCA, her health was not as strong as it had once been. Then in the January of 1892 she was struck down by a malignant strain of influenza. The epidemic had started in Australia some two years before and now it was sweeping through Europe. She was particularly badly affected and was laid low for several weeks, however she recovered. In this she was fortunate as many people had died. The disease had struck indiscriminatingly across all sectors of society, young and old, poor and rich, and many of those affected it had proved fatal. Oxford University was particularly badly affected and the start of the academic term had to be postponed, as the facilities for looking after large numbers of sick students in their colleges was inadequate. Some towns were more badly affected than others. Clitheroe in Lancashire was badly hit, as was Carlisle where the death rate was reported to be 44 per thousand. And in villages such as Charing in Kent almost every house in the village had cases to report. Many army barracks were severely affected and some police forces reported a third of all men off sick. It was so serious an epidemic that special prayers were said in some churches. But it was not just Britain that was affected. Other European countries were similarly affected with the German health department reporting that many victims over the age of sixty had died.

Elizabeth having recovered from this illness spent much of that year building up her strength again. She had her companion, Gertrude, and had become close friends with her sister-in-law, Marion, who was not too far away living with her parents at Anstie Grange, on the other side of Dorking. She had much in common with Marion, or 'May' as she was called. They were both widows and of similar age, and had close connections with the Royal Navy. So when Marion remarried in the January of 1893 it may have acted as a catalyst for Elizabeth to also consider remarriage. Marion's choice of husband had been her cousin, Major Richard Martin Crofton of the Royal Artillery. They had married at St Saviour Church in Pimlico on 5 January 1893. (Unfortunately, this second marriage was to bring her as much pain and suffering as had her first marriage, for by some strange coincidence Major Crofton, like her first husband, died aboard ship, while returning from India.[20])

So in September 1893, after being a widow for some twelve years, Elizabeth married again. Her choice of spouse was her fellow temperance campaigner, Thomas Anthony Denny, whom she had known for many years. It is difficult to know why she decided to marry at this particular time. She may have been influenced by Marion's decision to remarry, or it may have been a surprise proposal by Mr Denny. Whatever the reason, it does not seem to have been planned in advance, as the Mission Hall in Mickleham that she had been building was yet to open its doors. One therefore suspects that it was a surprise to all concerned. She had now passed her half century, so children would be an unlikely factor. Yet, what is surprising is the fact that she clearly enjoyed her independence. We know this as she was probably speaking for herself when her character Olive, in her novel, *Golden Lines*, responds to a marriage proposal:

"A hundred times I asked myself, 'Do I love him?' Could I spend a lifetime in his presence, to become his, and not my own? And again and again my heart revolted. 'I love my freedom,' I said; 'I do not want to be enchained,'....And when she did agree to marry, her thoughts were: 'My fate was sealed. I had never known before what it would be to belong to another.'[21]

However, from all reports Mr Denny comes across as a very kindly and pleasant individual, who would have had much sympathy with Elizabeth's missionary work among the poor. There is the occasion when hearing of William Booth's work amongst the poor he is reported to have reacted with 'tears in his eyes'. Yet he was a shrewd businessman, with a considerable fortune, indeed he has been described as being 'one of the richest men in England'.[22] In the 1881 Census he is recorded as living with his second wife at 7, Connaught Place, overlooking Hyde Park, with a staff of some eleven resident servants. This must raise the suggestion that Elizabeth had married him for his money, not for herself as she had sufficient money from her first husband, but so as to enable her to carry on her philanthropic enterprises. I feel that this conclusion would be unfair. Her probable feelings are best expressed by her character Elline in *Golden Lines*, when she responds to her friend Arbele's statement:

"I am afraid I am more selfish than you are," Arbele replied. "I like to have plenty of comforts round me. I should like to marry a very rich man."

"A very rich man!" Elline answered. "Save me from marrying a man whom I do not love; that is all I ask."

One can be sure that she could have done, if she had wanted to, as she was not unaware of feminine guile, which she expressed again in, *Golden Lines*:

"She amused him, she kept him up, she cheered him when he was down. The constant daily propinquity of a woman who is determined to please is dangerous to the man whom she seeks as her victim. All unsuspecting, he is in the very folds of her net, and before he knows it he is not his own."

However, even if she had wanted to trap Denny, he would have been an unlikely victim, as he had already been married twice before, and on each occasion he had chosen extremely suitable women. He had been born in Waterford, Ireland on 2 April 1818, and on 22 December 1841 married Jane Latrobe Wright at St Marylebone. Jane Wright was from a religious family of Moravians. They had one child, Jane Kathleen Henrietta born in 1848. Following the death of Jane Latrobe, Denny married again in 1868 to Mary Jane Noel (1829-87). Mary Jane was the daughter of the Hon. Reverend Baptist Wriothesley Noel (1799-1873) who was an aristocratic Church of England clergyman who later became an eminent Baptist minister. The Reverend Noel is remembered today as being one of the great evangelical preachers of the Victorian era. He was a strong advocate of Christian unity, and with his evangelical beliefs, he would have had much in common with Denny. Denny had three children with his second wife, Anthony Noel (b. 1870), Gerald (b. 1871) and Ernest Wriothesley (b. 1872). Following his second wife's death in 1887, Denny did not rush into a third marriage, as it was another six years before he proposed to Elizabeth. It is therefore clear that Denny, the shrewd and down-to-earth businessman would not have proposed marriage to Elizabeth if he was not confident that they could support each other in furthering the work of God by promoting their philanthropic causes. In the next chapter we will consider how they achieved these aims.

CHAPTER 17

Married Bliss

S O ON THE afternoon of Wednesday, 27 September 1893, Elizabeth walked down the aisle of St John the Evangelist Church, Southwark Crescent, Paddington, on the arm of her uncle, General Frederick Cotton to be married to Thomas Anthony Denny. The *Surrey Mirror*, reported that the Reverend H.P. Clarke had officiated and that it was a 'quiet wedding', with the bride wearing her travelling dress. In the register the bride was described as being a widow, 50 years of age, and the bridegroom, a widower, 75 years of age. Many in the church that afternoon would have thought that this was a perfect union as the couple were so suitably matched.

There was however the age difference, which might have raised some concern, and the fact that Mr Denny had four grown up children, the eldest being almost the same age as Elizabeth. However, they had very similar backgrounds and Christian beliefs, and as they had been friends for many years, indeed the children would, in all probability, have been quite familiar with their new step-mother.

Both Elizabeth and her new husband had supported the Moody and Sankey campaigns, and Denny had entertained Moody at his residence near Dorking when Elizabeth had also been a guest. Like Elizabeth, Denny had been involved in numerous philanthropic projects. He was a supporter of the London City Mission and had helped secure the lease on Exeter Hall for the YMCA. He had also been a major supporter of William Booth and the Salvation Army. Indeed, whenever William Booth's Salvation

Army had faced a financial crisis, Mr Denny had always been there to rescue them. Not that he was a member of this organisation. He was like his new wife, a devout Anglican. He once made the caustic comment that William Booth always took his money, but never his advice. Indeed, on several occasions he had saved the Salvation Army from bankruptcy. It is almost certain that if it hadn't been for his financial backing the so-called 'Salvation Army' would have fizzled out. There was the occasion in 1880 when William Booth's antiquated printing press proved inadequate for the demands of printing the Salvation Army's weekly journal, *The War Cry*. Mr Denny had come up with the money for a new modern printing press that was capable of printing the 200,000 copies, regularly circulated in the public houses by the 'Hallelujah lasses'. Then in 1881 Denny had been a major subscriber to the fund to send an 'expeditionary force' of Salvationists to France under the leadership of Miss Catherine Booth. The same year he had paid the rent on their headquarters and given money for the rebuilding of the Clapham Congress Hall. He had also secured for the Salvation Army, the former ice rink site in Oxford Street, which was not far from where Elizabeth had first planned her Coffee Palace.

Like Elizabeth, Denny also had concerns regarding the homeless in London. Indeed, at the same time as Elizabeth was working in the London slums, Denny, together with Lord Radstock, had acquired a large four-story warehouse in Commercial Street and had converted it into a model lodging house for working men. It was most successful and soon afterwards they were taking in some 500 men every night, charging them the very reasonable rate of 4 pence a night. Decent food was also available, and warm baths at one penny. It was a project along the lines that Elizabeth was proposing herself, so the coming together of this Christian couple promised well.

Following the wedding ceremony the couple left Paddington station for the first part of their honeymoon, which was to be in

Ireland. The second part was to be in the spring of the following year and this was to be a cruise to South Africa and then on to Egypt and the pyramids.

On their return from Ireland, Elizabeth held a social event in Mickleham, on 24 October, to commemorate the opening of her Mission Hall. About fifty villagers turned up for the occasion when there was a programme of songs and recitations, followed by a talk by Elizabeth describing some of her impressions of Ireland. However, the highlight of the evening was her demonstration of her newly acquired phonograph. This proved a fascination to the audience, particularly when she was able to demonstrate how the machine was able to record her own voice. One has to remember that the phonograph had only recently been invented (in 1877) by Thomas Edison. Indeed, when one was demonstrated at the World Fair in Paris in 1889 it had caused a sensation. It would appear that Elizabeth must have possessed one of the very first to be introduced into this country. It must have seemed something absolutely remarkable to the Mickleham locals, and would have contributed to a memorable evening.

Then in the second week of February, the following year, the newly married couple left England aboard the Royal Mail steamship S.S. *Grantully Castle* for Cape Town. The *Grantully Castle* was a large luxury cruise ship on which William Gladstone and his wife had enjoyed a cruising holiday in August 1880, at the invitation of its owner Sir Donald Currie. Now Denny and his new bride were to follow the great man. They were expected to be away for some two months as they were to travel throughout the Cape and on to Egypt. In a talk Elizabeth gave the following year at the opening of a new schoolroom attached to St John's Church, Westcott she gave some details of her experiences in Africa and Egypt. She described how in a remote part of the Cape she had come across a most successful missionary venture in the form of a van in which the missionary travelled from village to village. And on the banks of the Nile in Egypt she had met some of the brightest missionary stations. They were 'the bright lights shining for Christ in the most unlikely places'.

On their return to England they settled in Denny's town residence at 7 Connaught Place. This still exists and is an elegant Georgian mansion situated near Hyde Park. Today, as then, the area has some of the most expensive residences that can be found anywhere in the world. The former Prime Minister, Tony Blair has a residence nearby in Connaught Square, which resembles very much the mansion Elizabeth moved into following her marriage to Mr Denny.

After settling in the couple then entered into a whirlwind of evangelistic and philanthropic work. There were garden parties and drawing room meetings to which similar-minded Christians were invited. And there were charity meetings at various places across the city to attend. One interesting gathering was on Friday, 14 November 1894, when Elizabeth joined with her friend the Baroness Angela Burnett-Coutts at a meeting of the Aborigines Protection Society held at the Westminster Palace Hotel. They met Prince Nonganga, and other representatives of the Swaziland Chiefs who had come to England to present a petition to Queen Victoria seeking restitution of their rights. Apparently, following the first Boer War, a treaty had been signed between Britain and the Zulu nation giving them protection from the Boers. The envoys now expressed their anxiety as to whether Britain was going to repudiate the treaty. Attending the meeting was the ex-bishop of Natal, Dr John Colenso, who had been deposed in one of the most notorious affairs in the history of the Anglican Church, after he raised doubts as to the authority of scripture. Unfortunately we do not know whether Elizabeth had an opportunity of giving him her views on this subject.

Some weeks afterwards she had planned to perform the opening ceremony of the Children's Mission Hall at Tower Hamlets. This was a new development to provide the poor children of the East End with opportunities of welfare and schooling in a large hall that could accommodate some fifteen hundred. The opening ceremony was to take place on Saturday afternoon, 8 December, and when the time came the hall was packed to capacity, but unfortunately Elizabeth was ill and couldn't attend, so in her absence her husband performed the opening.

This would suggest that right from the beginning of their marriage they were both working to the same agenda and this is confirmed if one looks at what they did over the following years. In the March of 1899 they both attended the annual meeting of the YWCA giving it their support. In the April of that same year, they attended a meeting of the City Police Institute, which had been formed from the City of London Christian Police Association. The meeting was held in Sussex Place when Mr Denny was in the chair and Elizabeth gave the address. Then in March the following year they both attended the Metropolitan Theatre in Edgeware Road to celebrate 25 years of the Theatrical Mission which had been formed by the evangelist Mr Charles Cook. Both Elizabeth and her husband had spoken many times before at this venue, but this was a special occasion, and after Mr Denny had given a short address, Elizabeth gave the evangelistic appeal. Then in April that year they both attended the YWCA meeting at Exeter Hall, when Denny was in the chair and Elizabeth gave the address. And so it was throughout their marriage, they worked together, even as Denny neared the end of his life. Thus in the bitter cold winter of 1907, they attended the New Year Breakfast, at the Gray's Yard Ragged Church and School Mission, in Duke Street, Manchester Square, where they gave a breakfast of hot coffee, meat pies and cakes, to some six hundred destitute men and women, most of whom had spent the previous night sleeping on the Embankment, or walking the streets. A short religious service was held following which Elizabeth gave an address, and her husband, despite his advanced age, supported her.

A major mutual concern was the welfare of children and over the years they did much work for Dr Barnardo's Homes. Each year they usually celebrated Founder's Day on 4 July. In 1896 it was celebrated at the Royal Albert Hall, and again in 1898, when on that occasion, Elizabeth gave a short address. In 1903 it was celebrated at the Girls' Village at Barkingside in Essex, when Elizabeth was joined by Sir Robert Anderson. The Girls' Village had been opened in 1874 on some 30 acres of land, but by this time it had expanded to about double that size, with about sixty cottages, each accommodating between twelve and twenty girls. Many of the cottages had been paid for by supporters and were then named after the sponsor, (similar to Lady Somerset's arrangement at her Inebriate Colony at Duxhurst). On this occasion Elizabeth opened 'Hope Cottage' and Sir Robert opened a similar one.

Elizabeth had known Sir Robert and Lady Anderson for many years. Sir Robert Anderson (1841-1918) was an evangelical Christian and had been head of the C.I.D. at Scotland Yard during the 'Jack the Ripper' investigations. It is possible that this was the occasion when she discussed with him the challenge Darwinism was having to biblical interpretation. If not then, it may have been at one of their drawing room meetings at Connaught Place, when they discussed Darwin and his theory. Whenever it was, she told him how shortly before Darwin's death she had visited him on several occasions and found that he was always reading the Bible. She then told Anderson how surprised she was: more so when he asked her to lead an evangelistic service for his servants. Anderson remembered what she had told him and incorporated it in his book, *In Defence : A Plea For The Faith*, published in 1907.[23]

Besides those mentioned above, other children's societies were also supported, such as: the Homes for Working Boys in London; the Church of England Homes for Waifs and Strays, and the Care of Friendless Girls Society. In May 1900, Elizabeth and her husband gave a dinner for 340 boys in the Queen's Hall, Langham Place. In its report on the event a local newspaper wrote that, 'it was something to be remembered'.

In all the work they did together Mr Denny is reported to have been accompanied, not by Mrs Denny, but by 'Lady Hope'. It would appear that following their marriage Elizabeth had made clear to her husband that she wished to retain the title of 'Lady Hope'. We do not know how Denny felt about this, however even a generous man must have been a little hurt. His children certainly were upset and saw it as a slight on both their father and the family. In a legal sense after the death of her first husband she was still, Lady Hope, so there could not be any objection to her calling herself by that title. But on remarriage, the proper position would have been to adopt her new husband's surname and be known as Mrs Denny. Today anything goes and many women do not take their husband's name, but this was not the case in the late nineteenth century. However, it is understandable as to why Elizabeth wished to retain the title. She had been known by that title for many years. She had written numerous books with this name, and she was recognised as an evangelist as 'Lady Hope'. If the missionary speaker had been announced to be 'Lady Hope' people knew who to expect. If it had been advertised as 'Mrs Denny' no one would have known who it was. This was particularly important when it came to fund-raising. It should be pointed out that she was not unique in this. For many years Dr Barnardo was known as 'Dr' long before he had any formal medical qualifications, and legally he should not have used the title, but that was how he was known. It's unlikely his fund-raising would have been as successful if he had been 'Mr' Barnardo. Then there was 'General' William Booth of the Salvation Army. He was neither a general nor his church an army, but people understood the situation and accepted it. Thus Elizabeth on remarriage retained her previous title of 'Lady Hope' not because of any pretensions, or snobbishness, but purely on account of it being convenient to do so. However, it has to be admitted that British people now, as then, remain obsessed with titles. Of all the Christian denominations only the Society of Friends has rejected them altogether. But unfortunately, most ordinary people are impressed by titles, so it seems unfair to condemn Elizabeth if she took advantage of this, particularly when it was for the benefit of others.

Of great concern to her during these years were the changes taking place within the Church of England. In 1899 she was a foundation member of the Ladies League for Defence of the Reformed Faith of the Church of England. Lady Wimborne was appointed president of the society and their first meeting was held in the July of that year at 17 Lancaster Gate, when Elizabeth was the principal speaker. In her address she spoke of the need to combat the growth of ritualism within the church and made the point that the Church was not there for the clergy but for the laity. In the July of the following year another meeting was held at the Concert Hall, Blackheath. Again Elizabeth was the principal speaker when she warned of the danger of allowing 'foreign practices' into the Church of England. She continued: 'We must not allow the introduction of foreign practices into the Church. It was an ancient and true church and we should be determined not to let it be undermined by those men who are bringing in an entirely foreign religion, foreign to their commonsense...' at which she received much applause.

For some time Denny had been looking to purchase a new country house. He had previously owned Beedingwood, a country mansion in St Leonard's Forest in West Sussex, but had never been happy with it. Then in 1902 Buccleuch House in Richmond came on the market and he snapped it up. Buccleuch House had been owned by the fifth Duke of Buccleuch, and in 1842 he had entertained Queen Victoria and Prince Albert there. It was an elegant Georgian residence situated on the banks of the Thames. It had beautiful gardens and conservatories, including the terrace gardens that gave extensive views over the river. The extensive grounds sloping to the banks of the River Thames gave commanding views of the Petersham Meadows. Indeed, the view from this location is etched in London's literary heritage. It is mentioned in Scott's *Heart of Midlothian*, and is found in the writings of William Wordsworth. It has also inspired artists including Turner and Sir Joshua Reynolds. Besides its impressive history, it was a fine country residence. It was one of the few houses at that time completely fitted with electric lighting. It had some fourteen bedrooms, two stone staircases, two drawing rooms and several bathrooms and library. Outside there was stabling for seven horses together with a coachman's residence, and on the river there was a boathouse and landing stage.[24] It was a delightful country residence and in the years that followed Elizabeth was able to hold garden parties in the extensive gardens, as she did soon after they moved in when she held a garden party to welcome the Chinese Ambassador and Sir Harry Maclean.

## CHAPTER 18

Connaught House

IN EARLY 1899 Elizabeth heard from her mother that her father's health was of some concern. Up to that time he had been remarkably healthy, except for some loss of hearing. His mind was still sharp and active, as may be seen from the letters he wrote in his last years to his son-in-law, concerning the problems of irrigation in India. He also continued with his inventions. His most significant work during these last years had been in developing a new method of agricultural cultivation. He called this the 'Deep Culture Method'. He believed that the secret of cultivation was in deep digging to a depth of some three feet. During these years he carried out experiments on this principle on a small plot of land adjacent to his house at Dorking during which he produced remarkable results. His first experiments had been started in 1886, when he was almost 84 years of age. In letters to the press he advocated this system of cultivation and recorded yields of 50 tons of potatoes, and 25 tons of cabbages per acre. And on land put to grass he obtained more than 4 tons of hay per acre, compared to that on neighbouring land of just half a ton. These were incredible yields and attracted so much attention that he was visited by numerous agriculturists interested in his discovery. He believed that deep digging produced aeration of the soil, and that air was the key to this radical view of agriculture. His ultimate desire was to develop a method of cultivation that could make Britain self-sufficient in food. He believed his deep digging method could do this. He calculated that the country could produce enough food to support a population of some 100 million people. To aid this revolutionary system of cultivation he invented a new type of fork. This was a very strong cast-steel implement which he got manufactured and was sold in the 'One and all' shop.

In a way he was being prophetic in his concern for making Britain self-sufficient, for what concerned him was the thought that Britain might one day be at war and being dependent on foreign supplies of food might face disaster if these supplies were cut-off. (How true this turned out to be some forty years later during World War II.) He also pointed out that the deep digging system was advantageous in flood plains such as the Thames Valley, when flooding of low lying areas could be avoided. (This again was very prophetic considering the flooding that occurred in the Thames valley during the winter of 2013.)

Even in his last year he was continuing with his experiments and on his death-bed he was asking about how tall his wheat crop was in his garden. It was only in the June of 1899 that he began to show signs that his health was failing, when he complained that he felt unwell and lacked strength. On Sunday 9 July he attended church for communion and afterwards rested on the sofa in the drawing room and read his Bible. It was a beautiful evening and he managed to walk around his garden and then sat with his wife on a seat under some trees. Lady Cotton later recalled:

'His heart was full of praise for God's great goodness, especially dwelling at that time on the comfort we had had in this house and garden. "Exactly suited to us" he said and then he spoke of the beauty of the flowers...'

Elizabeth and her husband were called and arrived the next day when he gave them a warm welcome. But he was very tired and kept falling asleep. Elizabeth later recalled: 'He was dozing continually and gradually the power of speech was lost. Even in those hours of intense weakness he would rouse himself to ask about the probabilities of war in the Transvaal, the height of his wheat and we would convey it to him in large writing in his note book.'

Then on the night of the 14th he became feverish. Lady Cotton wrote: 'He poured out a remarkable prayer committing himself and those he loved to our gracious Lord in a way never to be forgotten, and the remembrance is full of comfort to those who remain.' He lingered on and passed away some ten days later. The *Morning Post* the following day, noted that at the time of his death he had been the oldest retired officer in Her Majesty's Service.

The funeral was held on Saturday 29 July at the Dorking cemetery in a very rural situation with Box Hill in the distance. The occasion took place with military honours with the Union Jack draped over the coffin, together with a beautiful wreath of white hot-house flowers from the Royal Engineers. A company of the 2nd Voluntary Brigade, the Queen's headed the funeral cortège with the general's sword now placed on top of the coffin. Then following the church service the Volunteers fired a volley over the open grave. Major-General Frederick Cotton, his brother, led the mourners, followed by Elizabeth and her husband. Other mourners included Admiral Sir Leopold Heath, his late son's father-in-law, together with Misses Cotton (his nieces) and Miss Bourdillon. Many local people attended as well as the ministers of all the various church denominations in the town.

Immediately following her father's death Elizabeth set about writing a biography of him. While he was alive her father had asked her to do this for him and he had indicated to her where she might find the relevant documents. It was a huge undertaking as much of his life had been involved with the irrigation of India. To accomplish the task she would need to have a good knowledge of the geography and economics of India, as well as technical and civil engineering aspects. In the event, she secured the assistance of William Digby (1849-1904). Digby was a well-respected journalist and politician and was well qualified to assist her. He had been born in Wisbech in Cambridgeshire and had trained as a journalist on the *Sussex Advertiser*. Following this he went to work in India, and was there during the Great Famine of 1876-78. He became much involved in the famine relief effort and wrote extensively on the subject, in particular, making the British people aware of what was happening. He was later recognised for this work on famine relief and awarded the C.I.E. (Companion of the Order of the Indian Empire). On his return to England in 1879 he was made editor of the *Liverpool and Southport Daily News*, and he subsequently entered politics becoming the first secretary of the National Liberal Club. He then used his connections with the political establishment to lobby for Indian concerns. Then in 1885 he stood as the Liberal candidate in the General Election but lost to the Conservative Party. He proved to be the ideal person to help Elizabeth piece together the legacy of her father's work in India and when the biography was published in 1900 it was well received.

One of her father's death-bed concerns was the possibility of war in South Africa. In the event war between Britain and the Boers broke out shortly after his death. The Boers had been concerned about the presence of British troops protecting mining interests in the Transvaal. When their demands were ignored they declared war on Britain. This became a second conflict against the Boers and would last for the next three years. It would become the largest military conflict Britain had been engaged in since the Napoleonic Wars a century earlier, with almost half a million men involved. It was fought over very hostile territory, and although greatly outnumbered, the Boers were able to use the terrain to their advantage. Ultimately the War was brought to an end by Britain adopting a 'Scorched Earth' policy involving complete destruction of farms and settlements and placing Boer civilians, women and children in concentration camps where many thousands died. There were many casualties on both sides, and following the war many soldiers returned to London, both traumatized and homeless. Elizabeth became acutely aware of this and made it her business to do something about it. Providing accommodation was a first priority and fortunately her new husband was the right person to advise her as he had much experience in providing decent accommodation to homeless men.

As mentioned previously Denny had opened a hostel for homeless men some years before. It had been called the 'Victoria Working Men's Home' and was situated in Commercial Street. It had originally been a warehouse that he and Lord Radstock had converted into a lodging house. When first opened it offered lodging for some 300 men, then as it proved successful an adjoining premises was acquired making it possible to take in some 500 men. The principal feature was its moderate charges. The charge for a single bed, with two blankets, two sheets and a quilt, was 4d a night or 2s a week. The floor space was partitioned off into small rooms containing about a dozen beds. In the common kitchen, food was provided, with a dinner costing 4d, and a bowl of soup one penny. Many regulars lived at Victoria Home, but it also attracted many 'drifters'. On account of this it had attracted the attention of the police, some years earlier, when they were investigating the 'Jack the Ripper' murders as several suspects had been found to be living there.

Elizabeth had always taken an interest in her husband's work with the homeless and now that he was in his eighties she began to take over much of his involvement. On account of the war in South Africa she became acutely aware of the needs of destitute soldiers arriving back in London. On 31 July 1900 she published a letter in the *Times* proposing the setting up of a soldiers' hostel in central London. 'I want immediately to take a house and set it up,' she wrote. 'In it I would have an excellent temperance bar,' she continued. 'No words of mine can describe this urgent necessity. My long experience in work of this kind enables me to say that I will willingly undertake the opening at once of such a soldiers' hotel.'

In recent times it has been recognised that many soldiers returning from action on the battlefield are suffering from Post

Traumatic Stress Disorder (PTSD). Although this had not been recognised in Elizabeth's time, she had seen many men return in a depressed mental state that led them to alcoholism and ultimately ending up destitute. 'The greatest danger these men can have,' she wrote, 'is the continual offer of drink.' As the weeks passed by she could see that the problem was getting worse. In August she appealed again in the pages of the *Times*. 'Many of our invalided men are absolutely homeless in London,' she wrote, stating that some 20,000 men had so far returned to London and had no where to stay. On 10th October she appealed again, this time quoting a letter she had received from Lord Wolseley that supported her proposals. Then a fortnight later she published another letter, in it she described how her homes in Whitechapel were taking in some 1,100 destitute men every night, but that on several nights the previous week she had been forced to turn away some 259 homeless soldiers, just back from the war. 'This will give you some idea as to the pressing need,' she wrote, 'I am prepared to open such a soldiers' hostel without delay...'

Although she was engaged in looking after her husband's hostels in the East End, the following year she was able to set up another hostel for men servants in the West End. This was called the 'Hope Club' and it was in a large house at 37 Upper Berkeley Street. It proved very successful, so much so, that she expanded it by taking over three other adjoining properties so that by 1903 it was occupying four adjacent properties. Again this was a temperance hostel. Elizabeth had realised that men servants had nowhere to stay in central London that offered an alternative to the public house. Servants could join, whether in or out of work, on paying the membership fee of ten shillings a year. There was accommodation for some sixty men, with the cost being 3s 6d a week, or 6d a night. Breakfast was 3d and a three course evening meal was only 9d. These prices were very reasonable. Furthermore, she provided the men with a homely and welcoming place to stay as there were recreation and quiet reading rooms. There was also a large hall where lectures were held so as to encourage their education. In a report published in *The Times* on 8 December 1903, its special correspondent declared that 'the whole scheme is so obviously wholesome, and completely so throughout.' He continued, 'Having inspected the whole of the buildings from basement to garrets, with scrupulous care I am able to say that the accommodation provided is very good, and that the cleanliness of every part is remarkable.' This was praise indeed, however the reporter, who was clearly knowledgeable about life below stairs, was curious as to how the various grades of man servant got on together. When he made enquiries of a butler resident at the club he was surprise to find that there was indeed equality between all the different members. 'Pantry boys and butlers are all equal here,' he was assured. 'Surely democratic equality could go no further,' he concluded. He then extended his investigations by asking other residents their impressions of Elizabeth's establishment. 'Man after man,' he wrote, 'and they were all respectable fellows, all testified as to the blessing which the club had been to them.'

One curious innovation of the Hope Club was its Coffee Vans. Elizabeth got this idea after listening to some of her residents talk about the difficulties they had when working at night, in all weathers, waiting for their masters to return from late night parties. The temptation was for them to slip into a public house, to get warm and to have a drink of alcohol. To counter this she invented the Coffee Van. Whenever a hostess organised a party she could book one of Elizabeth's coffee vans to arrive at the house and supply hot coffee and tea, together with bread and butter and cakes to the waiting footmen, grooms and coachmen. Packets of tickets could be purchased at 30s per hundred by anyone organising a party in the West End. This proved to be a brilliant idea, so much so, that *The Times*, published a letter from the Duke of Grafton praising her for it, he wrote:

'I know how much it is appreciated by servants. I must add what a real benefaction is provided by your arrangements for sending vans (when ordered by persons giving parties) for tea and coffee.'

Elizabeth's next venture was a hostel for female servants along similar lines as to the Hope Club. And then in the July of 1905 she brought out the *Home Club Magazine*. This was a monthly magazine that she edited and produced aimed at servants, as she had recognised that there was nothing comparable on the market. The first issue included a fictional serial written by herself, an article on Sunday Reading, some Nature Notes, and articles by Frank Bullen (1857-1915) a well-known writer of sea stories, entitled 'Travelling Servants' and another by the leading cookery writer of the day, Mrs Agnes Marshall (1855-1905). In announcing this new publication, *The Star* of 31 August 1905, commented that it was 'a triumph of individual energy'. Indeed it was, for she had put most of it together, including the illustrations. Nonetheless it did continue for several years, albeit its circulation could not have been very large as very few copies are around today.[25]

The following year Elizabeth embarked on her most ambitious project. This was Connaught House. This was a massive undertaking that was to put her Hope Club under the same roof as her new venture the Connaught Club. The Connaught Club was for business and professional men. Again it was a temperance club, run along strict religious principles of no gambling, no swearing, and no alcohol. It was to offer good accommodation at very competitive rates, so as to attract young men and so keep them away from other places that might offer temptations such as drink.

Elizabeth had located a large site at 75 Seymour Street on the corner of Edgware Road, near to Marble Arch. She got plans drawn up and it was built in attractive red brick and opened in 1906. During the First World War the building was taken over by the War Office, and during the Second World War it suffered bomb damage. Much of the Edgware Road section was destroyed, including some seven shops and the concert hall, however after the war all this was rebuilt. It was later taken over by the American

Red Cross in 1948 and later leased to the Victory (Ex-services) Club. This club was renamed the Victory Services Club in 1970. Anyone today visiting this establishment can appreciate the magnitude of Elizabeth's achievement. The Seymour Street frontage is as it was originally built with its distinctive red brick and elegant entrance. Today the shops on the Edgware Road are a poor replacement of those installed by Elizabeth, as is the plain grey bricks used in the rebuilding. However, inside the building it is very much as designed by Elizabeth. The concert hall, although having been rebuilt, is still impressive and a distinctive part of the establishment. The restaurant remains very much as it was in Elizabeth's day with its distinctive square pillars and elegant arched windows. The reading room is still there. The snooker room, however with its original eight-legged snooker tables, is no longer available for the residents, however on a recent visit I spoke to a long-serving member of staff who could still recall them.

In essence Elizabeth's dream was to build a great hotel for both professional men and men servants, all under one roof, that was run on the temperance principle, and at a standard that undercut anything else on offer. In this way she could achieve her aim that of getting men away from the temptations of drink. But in reality she couldn't achieve this as the economics just wouldn't add up. However, she had an answer to this dilemma. She would make it self-supporting. She would have on the ground floor businesses, in all seven shops together with a large 300-seated restaurant, with the profits going to subsidise the running costs of the hotel. In addition to this the club would have its own laundry, which she established at Windsor, which would do all the laundry for both the restaurant and hotel, with any spare capacity being offered to the public.

For a sixty-five year old woman, the Connaught House project was an incredibly ambitious scheme. Let us examine the details. Firstly, under the one roof there were two clubs for men. The

Hope Club for men servants was on the top floors, where there were 80 single bedrooms, with charges of 6s to 8s a week. The Connaught Club for business and professional men was on the lower floors, where there were some 120 single bedrooms, with charges of 8s to 12s a week. And on each floor there were numerous bathrooms. On the ground floor there was a restaurant for 300 diners, which was open to the public. Also on the ground floor were seven separate shops, including two run by Elizabeth herself. One was her Photographic studio, and the other the 'Hope Bonnet Shop' which she ran under the name 'Estelle' (after one of her novels). The window of this shop displayed a selection of fancy bonnets and across the top of the glass were the words, 'The Hope Bandeau', this being her patented invention. Another shop ran the 'Connaught General Entertainment Agency' which had direct communication, by 'electrophone', to all the London theatres, and other entertainment venues, and where bookings could be made.

Seemingly, as the Connaught Club had some magnificent facilities, no expense had been spared in setting it up. There was a magnificent concert hall, fitted with a large organ, together with an electric phonograph and cinematograph. There were sitting rooms and a large library where men could relax in red leather armchairs. There was a modern gymnasium and a large billiard room. Elizabeth herself was in overall charge, but she had appointed managers to each of the separate departments.

The newspaper correspondent, Louis Hyde, who visited Elizabeth's project and reported on it in March 1908, wrote:

'Personally Lady Hope is a motherly sort of woman without any of the frills of the ordinary type of titled lady. As she conducted me over the great building and pointed out its features and advantages I had the opportunity of judging of the intense love and respect in which she is held by those she has befriended. As we entered the reading room of the Hope Club all the occupants of the comfortable chairs jumped to their feet with a cheery "Good morning, my lady". In several cases she asked kindly after members of the families of club members who were known to be sick. As we passed into the quarters of the Connaught Club practically the same thing took place.'

Mr Hyde concluded his report by mentioning that Elizabeth's husband, although he had been lost sight of in the work of his 'brilliant wife', that 'he does not mind a bit occupying a back seat in public estimation and is one of the warmest supporters of her philanthropic schemes.' One wonders how true this was for shortly after this report was published Mr Denny changed the terms of his Will so that she was no longer one of his executors, and just a month before his death, he added a codicil to his Will, which as will be seen in the next chapter was much to her disadvantage.

## CHAPTER 19

The Hope Bandeau

IN THE YEARS that followed Elizabeth's marriage to Mr Denny we find that her priorities were changing. Before her marriage to Denny she had a clear purpose in life namely that of converting people to a true belief in Jesus Christ, and getting them to avoid drinking alcohol. However over the years of her second marriage there seems to have been a drift away from these clear objectives, towards something less defined.

This change is not completely surprising yet it would be incorrect to conclude that it was as a result of some loss of religious conviction. One can see in the lives of many notable Christian personalities that there are changes as they get older and more mature. Sir Wilfred Grenfell (1865-1940) in his autobiography, *A Labrador Doctor* looks back at his religious life and separates it into three stages. Firstly, there is youth with early religious thoughts, or lack of them. The second stage is spiritual awakening, or religious conversion and this is followed by a period of religious enthusiasm when much good work is achieved. The final stage he observed was a more temperate period, when more work may be done. Yet throughout these separate periods one's faith and certainty remained constant.

In Elizabeth's life we can recognise a similar pattern for in 1909, she published, what is essentially a guide book, entitled: *English Homes and Villages (Kent and Sussex)*. This is a delightful book, having full colour illustrations by amongst others, the noted landscape artist Charles Essenhigh Corke (1852-1922). It is largely about the attraction of the British countryside, as well as the pleasures of the new craze of motoring, but it appears to lack the religious zeal found in her earlier books. My own belief is that she wrote this book as some sort of therapy. However, how she found the time to complete it remains a mystery, considering all her other projects. Maybe she was feeling the stress of all her other work, that she needed to get some relief by taking on this project which required considerable travel, as well as research in the London Library and the British Museum.

Yet there is no evidence that she had lost any of her earlier religious zeal, indeed she was still recognised as being a leading evangelical campaigner as she was invited to preside over the annual meeting of the 'Sisterhood' of the West London Mission at St James's Hall. Yet she was different in that she had now become a Christian entrepreneur on a grand scale. At this juncture she was running what was certainly the largest temperance hotel in the world. Not only that, but she also ran several other hostels for the homeless. She was the proprietor of not only a bonnet shop, but also a photographic studio. She ran a commercial laundry in Windsor, and several all-night mobile coffee stalls. And then she became an inventor, obtained patents and set up a company to manufacture her invention. What is remarkable about this is that women in Britain were still considered to be disadvantaged, with the suffragette movement still campaigning for votes for women, yet Elizabeth seems to have ventured into all these fields completely unhindered.

Nonetheless, Elizabeth was concerned about the rights of women in society, in particular, she wanted to encourage women to engage in society to the full, and it was this principle that was behind her invention. Her invention was the 'Hope Bandeau' which was a device to replace hat pins in securing ladies hats to their head. Although only a very simple invention it would make life easier for women to enter into business and commerce without having to worry about wearing potentially dangerous hat pins.

Ladies fashions had changed over the previous couple of

decades, so that by the turn of the century, the close-fitting bonnet, which was secured by ribbons had been replaced by the wearing of hats. Only the Salvation Army women, until quite recently, would continue wearing the classic bonnet. Then during the early years of the new century hats became larger and more elaborate so that they acquired status symbols. The problem was securing them to the head. The usual method was to push long hat pins through the hair and out the crown. But following several accidents with women wearing long hat pins on trams and omnibuses their use was prohibited in some cities unless the point was shielded by a protective device. As a consequence there had been several attempts, during this period, to find an alternative to the hat pin, but none had been successful. Then Elizabeth came along with her invention, 'The Hope Bandeau'. This was a circular clip-like steel spring that was covered in velvet and fitted inside of the hat. The device could be fitted very easily to the hat, which could then be worn without any need for the use of hat pins. Elizabeth employed an engineer to construct several prototypes for her to try out and after using it for some months she decided to patent the invention. Patents were drawn up and on 12 May 1906 she submitted them to the Patent Office. Then on 21 March 1907 she was granted the Patent (No. 11,186). However, it is difficult to know exactly what she hoped to gain from patenting her invention, as at this particular time, she was fully engaged with her other projects. But she was clearly on to something useful (and possibly profitable) as some years afterwards the society magazine, *The Lady* carried an advertisement for, 'The Perfit Bandeau' which was a device very similar to what Elizabeth had patented and which had possibly been copied.

Then just a few days before Elizabeth's sixty-fifth birthday her mother, Lady Cotton, died at Dorking. She had been ill for some days, and cared for by her niece Clara Cotton. Elizabeth was distraught with grief as she had always been very close to her mother. She had dedicated the biography of her father to, 'My

Beloved Mother'. They had been through so much together, particularly as a child in India, when she had been alongside her mother through all those dark periods when she had lost one child after another. Lady Cotton's death certificate recorded, 'bronchitis and asthenia' so it was probably pneumonia, and at ninety-three there was very little that could have been done.

While recovering from the loss of her mother Elizabeth had come across the smooth-talking Gerald Fry. We do not know exactly when they first met. However, as he claimed to have been converted to Christianity at a mission while he was in prison, this may have been Elizabeth's mission, or he may have been referred to one of her hostels following his discharge from prison. Whatever the background, he struck up a relationship with her and succeeded in convincing her that he was now converted and had given up drink. He then proceeded to manipulate her with a 'tissue of lies' to exploit her vulnerability. But he was no ordinary ex-drunkard, for he appeared to display everything she most admired in a man. And like all great conmen he was completely convincing with an insatiable desire to dupe. This inevitably had left behind it a path of devastation.

On Saturday 10 February 1906 when Fry stood before the magistrate at the Maryleborne Police Court, he was described as: 'a young man neatly dressed in a light grey tweed suit'. He had been charged with cheating two cabmen out of their fare for twenty and sixteen shillings respectively. To the magistrate, Mr Plowden J.P. who listened to the evidence, the accused was clearly not the run of the mill petty thief. The more he heard that morning the more he was mystified as to the extraordinary character who now appeared before him. He was right to be puzzled by the defendant, for Guy Mortimer Fry, alias Gerald Fry, was a strangely complex, albeit pathetic young man.

What was immediately striking was that Fry was an exceptionally attractive young man, a sort of James Bond character, with an Anglo-Indian background. He had been born in May 1870, in

India, while his father, Major Walter Fry, was a surgeon in the Indian Army. In fact it is possible he might have claimed that his father had been a friend of General Cotton, as they had both served in India over the same period. But there was more, much more. He was arrogant, and charming towards women. He artfully dropped names and told her he had been to Sandhurst with Prince Francis of Teck, the son of the Duchess of Teck, whom Elizabeth greatly admired. He told her he had been an officer in the 7th Dragoon Guards, and for a time had been in the Canadian Mounted Police, then with the outbreak of the Second Boer War he had been an officer in Lord Strathcona's Horse, later transferring to Kitchener's Horse when he had been promoted to Captain. He had been awarded medals for gallantry and had excellent references from Prince Francis and Lord Strathcona, and boasted of being an associate of Cecil Rhodes, and to have taken part in the Jameson Raid. He was a cunning predator and artfully mixed fact with fiction so that they became indistinguishable. He let her see an inscribed gold-topped walking stick that had been awarded to him by the Metropolitan Police following an act of bravery. But he omitted to tell her how he had been arrested for the attempted murder of his wife and children in Harrogate some years before. To Elizabeth he was charismatic and charming and she was taken in by his story and became mesmerised by him. In truth she probably thought of him as the son she had never had. And to top it all, he was a recovered alcoholic. This was living proof that there was redemption for any man ruined by drink.

The facts, however, were very different. Guy Mortimer Fry, alias Gerald Fry, had come into her life just when she was most vulnerable. She had taken on all these different projects and was badly in need of assistance and encouragement. Her husband was now elderly and frail and unable to be of any help. This being said, it has to be admitted that she was a very trusting person and had been incredibly naive on several previous occasions. She had been fooled by the fraudsters involved in the property conspiracy that led to the Old Bailey trial some years before. It is also known that she had been duped by a number of young women, whom she had helped.

One of these women was May Gelder. She had been born in 1882 and was from a respectable family. In one of her many court appearances she was described as being 'a woman of genteel appearance'. She had worked as a sewing girl and was known to have been 'a very clever needlewoman'. One might have thought that with these attributes of good looks, skills and intelligence that she would have had no problems in life. But this could not be further from the truth. Whether May Gelder's problems arose from alcohol abuse or from a personality disorder, we do not know. What we do know is that she came to Elizabeth's attention when she took up residence at the Hope Club sometime in 1905. She claimed to have been converted at one of the Torrey-Alexander missions, probably the Albert Hall mission of February that year. She had a long history of petty crime with numerous periods of imprisonment. On meeting her Elizabeth went to great lengths to help the young woman to rebuild her life. But all her efforts failed. On one occasion Miss Gelder ordered a large quantity of expensive goods in Lady Hope's name and had them delivered to Elizabeth's address together with the outstanding bill. Then she would travel around London by taxi and put the cost down to Lady Hope. Another time she stayed at the Devonshire Hotel and claimed Lady Hope would pay the bill. The final straw came when late one evening she arrived at Elizabeth's home in Connaught Place, with a large amount of luggage, and on finding that Lady Hope was not there she told the butler that she was an invited guest. This was completely untrue and when the butler told her to leave and find a hotel she went to the Great Northern Hotel and sent the bill to Lady Hope. And so it went on. One newspaper report summed it up with the headline: 'Victimising Lady Hope'. In the end Elizabeth gave up when she discovered that the woman had committed theft and she expelled her from the Hope Club. However Miss Gelder continued to claim an association with Lady Hope in her court appearances during the following year, including: January - stealing a lady's handbag; July – unpaid taxi fares; July – stolen luggage; September – travelling on the Great Eastern Railway without a ticket; October – obtaining hair extensions from August Buch, a hairdresser of Tottenham Court Road, then running away without payment. She appears to have been obsessed with her appearance for on another occasion she was in court charged with stealing combs from a Cambridge hairdresser. In the end, Miss Cooper, Elizabeth's secretary had to attend court to explain to the magistrates that this woman had caused Lady Hope much trouble and annoyance.

Another young woman who had abused Elizabeth's help was Madge Champion. In early March 1910, Miss Champion, 18 years of age and a recovering alcoholic, had gone to Elizabeth's bank and told the manager that Lady Hope was her guardian and that she was going to receive a generous allowance from her. On the strength of this she was given a cheque book which she subsequently used to obtain drink from a wine merchant. As a consequence she appeared at Marylebone Police Court when again Lady Hope's name was brought up.

Both these occasions, and there were others, illustrate the risks Elizabeth was taking when mixing with dubious characters. It was probably this concern that worried her stepsons who had become anxious as to Elizabeth's handling of their father's fortune. In particular, they had become concerned as to how much of the family money had gone into building Connaught House. As a consequence of these concerns they threatened taking legal action and in July 1909 forced Elizabeth to relinquish the lease.

Gerald Fry was now her only support. Guy Mortimer Fry had been born in the Indian state of Tamil Nadu, at Travandrum in May 1870. He was the first born child of Major Walter Fry of the Indian Medical Service, and his wife, Mary. Walter Fry had been born on 3 March 1836, the son of John Fry, a Greenwich auctioneer. After qualifying in medicine at King's College, London, he was appointed assistant surgeon in the Indian Army Medical Services, and in early 1870, he was posted to Travandrum as a resident surgeon, where he remained throughout his army career.

On 10 January 1872, a second son was born, Herbert Walter Fry, and some years later the two brothers were sent home to England to be educated. The school where they were sent was the Claremont House Preparatory School in Wateringbury in Kent. The building still exists in the village, but it is no longer a school as it has been converted into flats. Then, the school was only small, with about 20 pupils, and was run by the principal, Ellen Wood. It was never an outstanding educational establishment and the only reason they had been sent there was that their aunt was the school's matron, so they were possibly eligible for reduced fees.

In September 1888, Guy Mortimer Fry was admitted to the Royal Military College at Sandhurst as a cadet. The records show that he was not the best of candidates. His conduct was described as 'indifferent', and his examination results were 'poor'. However, he managed to scrape through. Then on 22 October 1889 the *London Gazette* announced that he had been made 2nd Lieutenant in the 7th Dragoon Guards. Probably his most significant achievement at Sandhurst was to gain the friendship of Prince Francis of Teck, who was a fellow cadet. Prince Francis was the son of the Duchess of Teck (née Princess Mary Adelaide) and brother of Princess Mary, later to become Queen Mary. In the future, Fry would use this Royal connection as an entrée into society, as well as getting himself off the hook when in court over a misdemeanour.

The following year Fry found himself in difficulties and was forced to resign his commission. He later claimed that it had been on account of financial difficulties, but it was more likely to have been over his dependency on alcohol. He subsequently enlisted in the Royal Irish Rifles, but soon afterwards we find him in West Yorkshire living in Harrogate. One presumes he had left the Irish Rifles but as to the circumstances we don't know. What we do know is that in early 1893 he was living at the Somerset Hotel in the town. At that time the Somerset Hotel, in Parliament Street, was a recognised Yeomanry Cavalry hotel and was frequented by the 2nd West Yorkshire Regiment. As to whether Fry had any connection with this regiment is unclear. Soon after his arrival at the hotel the proprietor, George Clarkson, died suddenly leaving a widow, Clara and six children. The unexpected and sudden death of Mr Clarkson, a previously healthy, thirty-seven year old, caused a sensation in the town. Clarkson's death had occurred on Monday 23 January 1893, but up to a few days before he was perfectly healthy and had been well enough to supervise a large party of businessmen on the previous Friday night, but had taken ill shortly afterwards. In all some four doctors were called to attend to him, but their united efforts were of no avail. The sudden death of Mr Clarkson was a shock to the town as he had been a very popular figure and had been president of the local Licensed Victualler's Association.

Following her husband's death, his widow Clara, took over the hotel and became the proprietor, and then a few months later she married Fry in the Methodist Free Church in Harrogate. The wedding certificate states the bride, Clara Clarkson, 'widow, 37 years of age', and the groom Guy Mortimer Fry, a 'retired military officer' was 28 years old. In fact, Fry was 23, however, it was not uncommon at this time to exaggerate, if there was a large age difference between the couple. Then shortly after the marriage Fry began to drink heavily and to show his real colours. He became extremely violent and after a particularly shocking episode when he threatened to murder his wife and children he was arrested. Although he escaped prison it was the end of the marriage and he drifted off to live in Canada and then South Africa.

Unfortunately, Elizabeth was in the dark about all of Fry's

criminal background, so in the October of 1909, when he proposed setting up a company to market her invention she made him a co-director. The Hope Bandeau Company Ltd was set up shortly afterwards, with Fry and herself joint Directors, and she put in £2000 as capital (about £1 million in today's money).

However, when her husband was introduced to Fry he was immediately suspicious of the fellow. Although Denny was now quite frail, he still had enough wits about him to smell a rat. But when he raised these concerns with Elizabeth she would have none of it. Gerald Fry was everything she admired in a man, so she dismissed her husband's concerns. When Denny realised that he probably didn't have long to live, he immediately arranged for a codicil to be added to his Will that withdrew his previous provision for his wife to be one of his executors. Just over a month later he was dead. His death, at Buccleuch House, Richmond, was registered just after Christmas 1909, when the cause was put down as 'cardiac syncope'. When his Will was published early the following year almost all of the estate of £226,150 was left to his sons (probably equivalent to around £100 million today).

Gerald Fry immediately encouraged Elizabeth to challenge the Will in the High Court. Litigation, at great cost, was commenced, but it was a non-starter. All the stress was too much for her to take, but she made matters worse by handing over Power of Attorney to Fry and then allowed him to handle all her finances. This was disastrous as he began to empty all her bank accounts, so that over the following months he had taken some £40,000 before she realised it (about £5 million in today's money). In addition to this he had taken all the capital from the Hope Bandeau Company account and on 20 June 1911 the company was handed over to the Receiver. Time was running out for Elizabeth and she had no option but to declare herself bankrupt. It was only then that she became aware of what Fry had been doing, but it was too late.

The public examination of Elizabeth Reid Denny, widow, late

of Buccleuch House, Richmond was conducted at the High Court in London and reported in full in *The Times* of Thursday 20 July 1911. It stated:

'In July 1910, on the advice of one Fry, she took legal proceedings against her stepsons to recover possession of Connaught House, and to set aside a codicil in her late husband's Will. The proceedings were compromised by order of Court, but she did not carry out the terms of the compromise. On two separate occasions she gave a power of attorney to Fry, who had received considerable sums on her behalf and had borrowed money for her from money-lenders and others. She now contended that Fry was a debtor to her estate...'

It later transpired that her liabilities had amounted to £14,678, with only £672 7s 7d having been raised from her estate (in today's money about £5 million and £200,000, respectively). Although she had been in receipt of £1000 a year from her first husband, and £1,500 a year from Denny's Will, however, both these incomes (in today's money a total of about £500,000 per annum) had been lost on her bankruptcy.

On 9 May 1912 her case was again before the High Court, when her counsel informed the Court that her stepsons had come forward and 'in a very generous spirit' put up the sum of £4000 for the benefit of the creditors. This was accepted and she was discharged. In conclusion the Registrar said: 'he could not believe that a lady with an income of £2,500 a year would incur £14,000 of liabilities unless she was misled, and he had not the least doubt she had been misled.'

Elizabeth was now discharged. It had been a devastating period for her. She had lost everything, however she was not to give up. She still had her faith and she would rise up and start again.

## CHAPTER 20

A New Start

I N THE SUMMER of 1913 Elizabeth decided on a new start and made arrangements to travel to New York. She had been invited to attend the ninth convention of the World Women's Christian Temperance Union in Brooklyn. The WWCTU had been formed by the American prohibitionist and feminist, Miss Frances Willard in 1884. Elizabeth was acquainted with Miss Willard as she had been introduced to her at Eastnor Castle, while she had been a guest of Lady Henry Somerset, the president of the organisation.

At this time there were a bewildering number of women's organisations that went under the temperance banner but were essentially women's campaigning groups for various feminist causes that included women's rights, universal suffrage, prison reform and so on. Although many of these organisations had started out by campaigning for temperance, over time they had been taken over by other causes. One such group was the British Women's Temperance Association (BWTA) to which Elizabeth had been associated. At the time she was involved, it was one of the newly formed groups having been founded in 1876. It was only in 1890 when Lady Henry Somerset was appointed the society's president that its membership greatly increased. However, Lady Somerset was criticised by many members for being too 'progressive' and less of a prohibitionist. Furthermore, she was not content to be simply a figurehead. She wanted to take an active role in the organisation, and this upset many of the members, particularly when she advocated women's suffrage and promoted 'social purity' issues. The result was that she was accused of being too much under the influence of Frances Willard and this led to an open rebellion within the organisation. In 1893, this led to a split in the organisation, giving rise to two separate bodies, the National BWTA (NBWTA) which adopted a whole range of causes alongside that of temperance, including women's suffrage, and the Women's Total Abstinence Union (WTAU) which focussed solely on temperance.

In 1895 Elizabeth had attended the third convention of the WWCTU at the Royal Albert Hall. On the eve of the convention she had attended a reception held by Lady Somerset for many of the delegates at Reigate Priory. The convention was a huge gathering of women from some 25 different countries. There was an impressive choir of some 800 temperance ladies all dressed in blue and wearing white slashes. On exhibition at the convention was the Polyglot Petition, which consisted of 13 huge rolls containing more than seven million signatures. This was addressed to world leaders and demanded them to take a stand against alcohol abuse. It had been a massive undertaking that had been sparked off following an original suggestion by Frances Willard.

When Elizabeth attended the WWCTU convention in New York in the October of 1913, the white ribbons were again fluttering in the Brooklyn streets. It was again a huge gathering of women from many nations. Among them was Ellen Maria Stone, the famous American missionary, who had been kidnapped by terrorists in Macedonia in September 1901. This had led to what is now seen as America's first hostage crisis. It had ended with her release and she was now the representative from Bulgaria. Elizabeth was one of the British delegates, alongside Lady Aurea Howard, the daughter of Rosalind Howard, the Countess of Carlisle, who was the President of the association, but on account of illness had not been able to attend. To many this was a relief, as Rosalind, the Countess of Carlisle was a formidable woman who had upset numerous individuals in her campaign against alcohol, particularly some members of her own family when she poured all the priceless contents of the family cellar into the fountain at Castle Howard.

Towards the end of October, Elizabeth, together with Lady Aurea Howard, then attended the National Women's Christian Temperance Union's 40th convention held at Asbury Park, New Jersey. At this time Asbury Park was the centre of temperance activity in America and was a completely alcohol-free town. It had been founded in 1871 by the brush manufacturer, James A. Bradley, a strict Methodist and prohibitionist, and named after the first Methodist Episcopal bishop to be ordained in America. One past president of the local WCTU had been Mary Helen Crane, the mother of the author Stephen Crane. Over the years she had entertained many leading figures in the temperance movement at her home, Arbutus Cottage, including Frances Willard. Now all the conference delegates met at the Asbury Pavilion which was known as 'the Casino'.

These conventions proved an excellent opportunity for Elizabeth to network amongst some of the influential women of North America and it led to numerous new acquaintances and invitations to talk at churches in the area. A few weeks later she was preaching at the Methodist Episcopal Church in John Street, New York when she delivered a sermon on the role of Christians in promoting the cause of temperance. In it she outlined her plans for establishing a club in the Bowery district for inebriates, just like the ones she had established in England. However, this would have to wait. With her first winter in North America fast approaching, she decided to escape the worst of the weather by spending it in the warmer climate of the West Indies, visiting Trinidad and Haiti.

The following summer she was invited to attend the 1914 Marble House Conference in Newport, New Jersey. At this time Newport was the destination of New York society during the months of July and August, when millionaires such as the Astors and Vanderbilts displayed their wealth. Elizabeth had registered at the luxurious Imperial Hotel at Narragansett Pier, a 'grand' hotel with some 250 rooms that had been built in 1898. The purpose of the conference was to celebrate women's achievements in the world. It had been organised by Alva Vanderbilt Belmont who, on the eve of the conference, held a special reception for her daughter, the Duchess of Marlborough in the Chinese Tea-house she had built specially for the event in the gardens of the opulent Marble House. The conference had been sponsored by the women's rights group, the Political Equality League. They had set up an enormous tent on the lawn of the Marble House and erected two 75ft flagpoles with 'Votes for Women' flags fluttering from them. Consuelo, the Duchess of Marlborough (née Vanderbilt) was the main speaker of the conference. She gave a detailed account of her work in providing 'decent and respectable' hostels for working women and girls in England. This was just what Elizabeth had been doing in London before she had the misfortune to meet Gerald Fry, so there was much for her to say to Consuelo, about this type of enterprise.

It was during this conference that Elizabeth made the acquaintance of Margaret Brown. They immediately hit it off and Mrs Brown invited her to be a guest at her Newport mansion. Whether Elizabeth, at the time, knew the extent of Mrs Brown's celebrity status is unclear, but she could never have imagined as to how it would take-off in the days that followed. For Mrs Brown would become an American icon, and a legend, now known to everyone as the 'Unsinkable Molly Brown'.

Mrs J.J. Brown had been born, Margaret Tobin, on 18 July 1867 in Hannibal, Missouri, the daughter of poor Irish Catholic immigrants. Young Margaret would fulfil the American dream. She fell in love and married James Joseph Brown in 1886. He was a mining engineer and went on to make his fortune in gold mining, and became extremely wealthy. This enabled his wife to travel the world and have a millionaire lifestyle. Then her life changed. It was spring 1912 and she was doing the Grand Tour with the Astors, and while in Egypt she received word from home that a family member was ill. She altered her plans and made arrangements to return to America by the first available crossing. When she heard that she would cross the Atlantic on the maiden voyage of the most luxurious ocean liner ever built she felt quite pleased. The vessel was the White Star Liner, SS *Titanic*. In the event she was fortunate as on the morning of 14 April 1912 she found herself in Life Boat number 6. I suppose one could say, 'the rest is history', but this cliché couldn't be further from the truth, for the story of Mrs Brown in both the Broadway musical and the Hollywood film, '*The Unsinkable Molly Brown*' has been more myth than history. The truth, however, is that Mrs Brown will always be the heroine of the *Titanic*, who went on to use her celebrity status to promote social causes. And very much like Elizabeth, while other affluent women were sipping tea on their sumptuous balconies, she strove to improve social injustices. It is no wonder that on meeting these two women soon became firm friends.

Over the following days, Mrs Brown took Elizabeth around the sights of Newport. They visited the exclusive Bailey's private beach club. Here only the elite could bathe, as it had become the ultimate test of one's acceptance into Newport society. It was also a fashion parade, with the girls on the beach wearing only the latest fashion in full-skirted costumes with long black stockings. Then across the town Elizabeth and her friend encountered elegant ladies parading around in their open carriages displaying the latest fashionable feather hats. And then later they watched tennis being played at the Casino Club where the ladies wore elegant dresses of satin lace.

Later Elizabeth was guest of honour for afternoon tea with Louise Ward McAllister, a leading Newport socialite. Then in the evening they dined with Bishop James Henry Darlington, the Episcopal Bishop of Harrisburg. However, this gay social whirl was not to last for on 4 August that year, Britain declared war on Germany and Elizabeth's life was to change again.

As America remained neutral there was nothing Elizabeth could do in America, to support the war so she moved to Toronto in Canada. Here she got engaged in war work. She decided that the most important thing she could do was to help raise funds. Accordingly, she took an active role in the Imperial Order of the Daughters of the British Empire. This was a Canadian organisation that had been founded during the Second Boer War to help strengthen ties with the mother country. It was structured into district chapters and Elizabeth was associated with the Niagara chapter. On 25 November she took part in the event at the Hotel Martinique that raised money to send a number of graduate nurses to England to help treat the wounded, as well as providing surgical supplies. Among those present was Sir Courtenay Bennett, the British Consul General of New York. (He was responsible the following year for giving the go-ahead for the Cunard liner, *Lusitania* to sail from New York on 1 May 1915, despite warnings from the Germans that it was to be torpedoed.[26]) Also present was the civil engineer, Dr T. Kennard Thompson. Thompson had been born in Canada and educated at Toronto University. He was an Anglophile and as such was the President of the Canadian Club. At this time he was the Consulting Engineer for New York and had been responsible for building many of the New York skyscrapers. He was most thrilled to meet Elizabeth at this event as it gave him the opportunity of discussing her father's work on dam construction in India, and General Cotton's proposed Cape Juby project in Africa.[27] As a civil engineer he had been involved in dam building near the Niagara Falls and also had proposed a plan to expand the area of Manhattan by building coffer dams and draining away much of the surrounding water.[28]

Early the following year Elizabeth was back in New York and travelled to Philadelphia to take part in the Billy Sunday campaign. William Ashley 'Billy' Sunday (1862-1935) was the most famous American evangelist at this time. Before his conversion in 1886 he had been a celebrated baseball player with the Chicago White Stockings and the Pittsburgh Pirates. He then gave it all up to become an evangelist and a strong supporter of prohibition. He held numerous revivalist meetings across North America and made thousands of converts. He had a unique brand of preaching that involved physical gyrations and exaggerated gestures from the platform, and his language was always that of the ordinary person. On account of this he became the most popular preacher of his generation. Elizabeth certainly was impressed by his preaching. In a newspaper report on his Philadelphia mission Elizabeth was mentioned:

'Lady Hope of London, widow of Admiral Sir James Hope who made a trip from New York to Philadelphia to hear the evangelist thinks of him only in superlatives. She said: "He's a wonderful man, you know. He has such extraordinary power. I found his meetings quite delightful and charming. We have had other American evangelists in England –Torrey, Alexander and Chapman – but they do not compare with Billy Sunday."'

Elizabeth was so impressed that she continued to support Sunday's mission in other towns and cities. She was with his team in the April of 1915 at Paterson, New Jersey when the *New York Times* declared that: 'Sunday Drives out Crime'. It then reported the rare event that the Paterson Grand Jury had no serious crime to consider. Justice James F. Minturn was quoted as saying that the county was now stainless of crime and put it all down to Billy Sunday's preaching.

In the summer of 1915 Elizabeth was settled in Asbury Park, New Jersey, with friends from the temperance movement and towards the end of July she travelled to attend the Northfield Conference, the annual event held at East Northfield, Massachusetts. She was accompanied by Isabel Bierson and en route they stayed at the Bond Hotel in Hartford. The Bond Hotel, had opened its doors just two years before, and at this time was considered to have been the grandest hotel in the area. It was here she met with reporters from the local newspaper and gave them an interview. The following day they travelled to the Northfield Seminary, a girls' college that had been founded by Dwight L. Moody.

The Conference started on the morning of Tuesday 3 August. The opening events were poorly attended as apart from Elizabeth there were no other British delegates present due to the War. On account of this Professor Archibald Thomas Robertson (1863-1934) of the Southern Baptist Theological Seminary of Louisville, Kentucky was obliged to fill in for those absent. Professor Robertson was a leading New Testament scholar and was scheduled to give a series of lectures on the Epistle to the Hebrews. In his lecture Robertson touched on the subject of evolution and Darwinism and how it led to a degraded view of man. On hearing this Elizabeth felt that Robertson had been completely misled in his understanding of Darwin and wanted to put him right. On the following day after she had conducted a temperance prayer meeting she approached him and informed him that she had personal knowledge of Darwin. She then told him of her visits to Darwin towards the end of his life when she had found him studying the *Epistle to the Hebrews* and how he had declared faith in the Gospel. Robertson was so impressed that he reported what she had told him during one of his lectures the following day. It so happened that in the audience was a reporter from the leading Baptist journal, the *Watchman-Examiner*. He was immediately intrigued by this account, and shortly afterwards he interviewed Elizabeth and got her to write an account of her encounter with Darwin. A fortnight later Elizabeth's account was published in the magazine and on Saturday, 21 August 1915 it also appeared in the *Boston Evening Transcript* under the heading: 'Darwin and Christianity'. This is the published account:

"It was on one of those glorious autumn afternoons that we sometimes enjoy in England when I was asked to go in and sit with the well-known professor, Charles Darwin. He was almost bedridden for some months before he died. I used to feel when I saw him that his fine presence would make a grand picture for our Royal Academy: but never did I think so more strongly that on this particular occasion.

He was sitting up in bed, wearing a soft embroidered dressing gown of rather a rich purple shade. Propped up by pillows he was gazing out on a far-stretching scene of woods and cornfields, which glowed in the light of one of those marvellous sunsets which are the beauty of Kent and Surrey. His noble forehead and fine features seemed to be lit up with pleasure as I entered the room.

He waved his hand toward the window as he pointed out the scene beyond while in the other hand he held an open Bible which he was always studying.

"What are you reading now," I asked as I seated myself by his bedside.

"Hebrews!" he answered – "still Hebrews, 'The Royal Book' I call it. Isn't it grand?"

Then placing his finger on certain passages he commented on them.

I made some allusion to the strong opinions expressed by many persons on the history of the Creation, its grandeur and then their treatment of the earlier chapters of the Book of Genesis.

He seemed greatly distressed, his fingers twitched nervously, and a look of agony came over his face as he said:

"I was a young man with unformed ideas. I threw out queries, suggestions wondering all the time over everything; and to my astonishment the ideas took like wildfire. People made a religion of them."

Then he paused and after a few more sentences on "the holiness of God" and "the grandeur of this Book" looking at the Bible which he was holding tenderly all the time, he suddenly said:

"I have a summer-house in the garden, which holds about thirty people. It is over there," pointing through the open window. "I want you very much to speak there. I know you read the Bible in the villages. Tomorrow afternoon I should like the servants of the place, some tenants, and a few of the neighbours to gather there. Will you speak to them?"

"What shall I speak about?" I asked.

"Christ Jesus" he replied in a clear emphatic voice, adding in a lower tone, "and his salvation. Is not that the best theme? And then I want you to sing some hymns with them. You lead on your small instrument do you not?"

The wonderful look of brightness and animation on his face as he said this I shall never forget, for he added:

"If you take the meeting at three o'clock this window will be open and you will know that I am joining in with the singing."

How I wished that I could have made a picture of the fine old man and his beautiful surroundings on that memorable day!"

Elizabeth had recorded her visit as accurately as she could. Although she was now 73 years of age, her memory was still good and her mind as sharp as ever. Her meeting with Darwin had taken place some thirty years before but the memory of it was still vivid in her mind. Not that she had wanted to dwell on it. It was to her one of those experiences she had had in a very interesting life, no more than that. Darwin's theory of evolution was no challenge to her faith. It was just a theory. She had much more important concerns. This being so when the conference finished she returned to New York to continue her temperance work and later to Canada for more fund raising towards the War effort. But her account of Darwin's apparent return to faith was to have a life of its own.

Following publication in the *Watchman-Examiner* the account was taken up by other newspapers and journals across the world and the story spread. News of it was soon to reach the Darwin family in England, when it caused considerable unease. They were actively promoting a sanitised view of Darwin as the good and noble unbeliever. Now Elizabeth's story was a direct challenge to their version. And besides the family there were Darwin's disciples and followers, who for their own reasons, wanted to uphold the authorised version. It needs to be pointed out that at this time atheism was still frowned upon in respectable society. It was therefore crucial for them to maintain the impression that one could be a decent honourable individual, like Darwin, and yet still be an agnostic, or atheist.

In the event, Darwin's third son, Francis Darwin took up the challenge and made a firm response. He had published the authorised view of his father in, *Life and Letters of Charles Darwin*, shortly after Darwin's death in 1882. This was the version he wanted to maintain so on hearing Elizabeth's story he immediately put pen to paper and wrote to Professor Robertson. The letter was dated, 8 November 1915, just a few weeks after Elizabeth's story had been published. He wrote:

'Neither I nor other members of my family have any knowledge of Lady Hope and there are almost ludicrous points in her statement which make it impossible to believe that she ever visited my father at Down...I regret that you should have been misled into believing Lady Hope, but under the circumstances it was quite natural that you should have done so.'

At the same time an acquaintance living in Toronto also wrote to Robertson informing him that they had personal knowledge of Lady Hope and had trusted neither 'her judgment nor her imagination.' He then confided to Robertson that he could 'tell a tale' if necessary, and hinted that he knew of some indiscretion he could reveal about her. At the same time this unknown correspondent claimed to have the testimony of Darwin's sons as to the 'absolute inaccuracy' of the account. This letter was dated 2 November 1915, again very soon after Elizabeth's story appeared in print. In it the anonymous writer claimed the backing of Professor Poulton of Oxford. (It is somewhat ironic that Professor Edward Bagnall Poulton held the Hope chair in zoology at Oxford.) This being so, it was strong credible testimony, as Poulton was a close friend of Francis Darwin. Indeed, he was the

Richard Dawkins of the day and was in awe of Charles Darwin and maintained that *On the Origin of Species* was the greatest book ever written.

Whether Elizabeth got to know about these attempts to blacken her name is unknown. However she soon realised that there were forces lined up against her. Shortly afterwards she received a very unpleasant threatening letter from one of the Darwin sons that caused her considerable distress and made her decide not to return to England. Fortunately there were in America at this time a couple of friends who had also suffered much by similar malicious rumours. They were Lord and Lady Aberdeen.

At this time Lord and Lady Aberdeen were on a fund-raising campaign in America on behalf of the Women's National Health Association of Ireland (WNHA). In February 1915 the couple had just finished their Viceroy term of office in Ireland and following this they had planned a fund-raising tour of America. Initially they had planned it to last just six months but on account of the War and on finding much indifference amongst many people of Irish descent they had to extend this to two years. One of the chief projects of the WNHA was the fight against tuberculosis. This was Lady Aberdeen's personal crusade and she had worked tirelessly on it. She had used special horse-drawn caravans to promote information about the deadly disease to small towns and villages across Ireland. The *Times* had praised her for this work and reported that about one-sixth of the population of Ireland had been reached by the pamphlets and leaflets that had been distributed by her caravans. Her work had also been recognised by the British Medical Association when she became the first woman to be conferred an honorary membership.

Elizabeth was to join the Aberdeens at White Sulphur Springs in West Virginia in the July of 1916. They were staying at the Greenbrier Hotel, which was probably the most luxurious and exclusive hotels in the country (and still is) whilst Elizabeth had to make do at the Old White Hotel in the resort. During their stay at the resort they spent the evening of 10 July as guests of John Henry Patterson (1844-1922) the founder of the National Cash Register Company. He had recently risen to prominence on account of the significant role he had played in rescuing people during the Great Dayton Flood some months before. Now, as he had invited them to the Elmhurst Inn on the banks of the Greenbrier River at Caldwell, the Aberdeens hoped that he would make a generous contribution to their Ireland fund. The dinner had gone well, and they were pleased with the outcome. That night on motoring back to White Sulphur Springs by moonlight, Lady Aberdeen talked to Elizabeth about how much she missed their mutual friend, Henry Drummond. She spoke intimately of how much a loss his early death had been to her. Little did any of the party know that at that very moment, under the same moon, Britain was suffering its bloodiest battle of the War as the Somme offensive had begun.

The following day Elizabeth had some time alone. She had recently taken up painting in oils again, and had set up her easel at a place known locally as 'Lover's Leap'. It was part of a series of paintings she was doing about local beauty spots. While she was there she began to think again about what Ishbel (Lady Aberdeen) had told her about Drummond, then when she thought about what was happening on the Western Front she began to feel slightly uncomfortable.

However, she had agreed to participate in the Aberdeens' fund raising event on the Saturday evening of 22 July, at the Green-brier. The function was to be held in the ballroom and numerous local dignitaries had been invited. It was to be a grand affair. Judge Henry S. Priest (1853-1930) a United States federal judge for Missouri, was to preside, and Blackford Kavanaugh was to sing some Irish ballads. Lady Aberdeen's talk was entitled: 'Different Phases of Social Welfare Work in Ireland' and it was to be illustrated by 'stereopticon views and moving pictures'. Then following this Elizabeth had agreed to give a brief address.

The evening proved a complete success and the Aberdeens were pleased with the amount of money they had raised.

On 15 August the parties departed White Sulphur Springs and went their separate ways. The Aberdeens left for Manchester, Massachusetts, to continue with their fund raising, while Elizabeth left for Washington, where she intended to stay for a few days, before going on to Asbury Park in New Jersey, where she was going to stay for the remainder of the summer.

Over the following months she continued with her temperance and evangelical work. Then following America's entry into the War, she acted as secretary to a war relief organisation. At this time her health was not good and with the onset of winter she decided to travel to Florida and spend Christmas in St Petersburg in Pinellas County. On Christmas day she worked with the Salvation Army to provide a pleasant time for the local children and the poor of the town. In the morning she distributed gifts to the Sunday school children and after giving a short address she helped, Betty Foley a local community worker, serve a banquet to some 175 poor people. On the menu was roast turkey with dressing followed by cakes, tea and coffee. Elizabeth was now seventy-five years of age and had recently been diagnosed with breast cancer, yet despite this she had lost none of her determination to help others.

However, it was soon 1918, and with America now in the War there was renewed hope that the fighting in Europe might soon come to an end. Meanwhile, the Aberdeens had been reprimanded by Lloyd George for not returning to England, when they gave the response that they were taking up the challenge of 'the future reconstruction period'. Elizabeth herself felt she had to move on and with her health concerns she decided to move to the West Coast where the climate was milder.

By the autumn of that year she was settled in the Alvarado Hotel in Los Angeles. The Alvarodo was situated on the north east corner of Westlake Park. Today it no longer exists as it was demolished in 1970, but in its heyday it was probably one of the most luxurious hotels in the area. Having arrived in the city Elizabeth was soon making herself known about town. In the February of the following year she was featured in an article in the *Los Angeles Sunday Times*, which included what is probably one of the last photographs of her. It shows a resilient woman who was determined to carry on despite her problems. Also printed was one of her recent oil paintings that of Westlake Park. (Unfortunately, the journalism was less than competent as her name was given as Lady 'Clara' Hope.[29])

It was now 1919 and the War had ended, so over the following months Elizabeth visited various groups in the city giving talks about her life describing the various places she had visited. To accompany her talks she had a 'fine collection of coloured lantern slides'. Then in August she was invited to have tea with Admiral Hugh Rodman on board USS *New Mexico*, the flagship of the Pacific Fleet. Admiral Rodman had served under Admiral Lord Beatty during the War, and had been with him when he had received the surrender of the German Fleet at Scapa Flow. They had now become personal friends. At a reception of the Pilgrim Society, some months later, at the Waldorf in New York, Admiral Rodman would draw attention to the historical bond that existed between their two nations. He illustrated this by reference to the 1859 attack on the Peiho Forts by the British Squadron under Admiral Sir James Hope. In the action Admiral Hope had been seriously wounded and was only saved on account of the intervention of Admiral Tatnall of the American Squadron, despite America's neutrality in this war.

Possibly with this incident in mind, Admiral Rodman embraced the opportunity of meeting the widow of Sir James Hope, the British naval hero, of whom he had heard so much about. Then after this first meeting they met again at the Victory Ball on board the *New Mexico* later in the year.

Then on 13 November that same year there was a reception

held for her at the home of Dr and Mrs A.G.R. Castles at their castle in Hollywood. Dr Castles was a flamboyant physician and wealthy businessman who had built a huge castle in Hollywood which was called 'Castle Sans Souci' (without care). It was an enormous construction built in the Tudor-Gothic style with a huge Baronial Hall and Louis XV drawing room. It was filled with historical artefacts that he had collected from his travels around the world and there was an art gallery containing many valuable works. Dr Castles was from the aristocratic German family, Schloesser, but had changed his name on account of anti-German sentiment during the War. His wife, however, had Scottish blood and he had built 'Castle Sans Souci' to remind her of her ancestral home near Inverness. Now, it would remind Elizabeth of her previous home at Carriden.

During these months Elizabeth spoke at numerous religious meetings and she built up quite a group of like-minded friends who would meet for prayer and Bible study. They would often meet on a Sunday afternoon. It was at one of these meetings that the discussion turned to the challenge of Darwinism to the Christian faith. Elizabeth then told the group of her visits to Charles Darwin shortly before he died and how she had found him studying the Bible. In the group was Annette Parkinson who was so impressed with Elizabeth's account that she invited some of her religious friends to come on another occasion to hear the account directly from Elizabeth's own lips. Among those who came to listen were Professor Melville Dozier, the botanist, who was at this time vice-president of the college which was to become the University College of Los Angeles (UCLA); Professor and Mrs Warner and the Reverend Dr Elwood Lyon and his wife the Reverend Susie Lyon.

Mrs Parkinson realised the significance of Elizabeth's testimony and being aware that time was running out for Elizabeth, she tried to persuade her to document her account. At this suggestion Elizabeth told her about the threatening letter she had received from the Darwin family and how it had greatly upset her. Unfortunately there is no record as to the precise content of this letter, so we are left only with supposition. However, as Elizabeth was planning to leave California to return to England, she never got to further document her story.

It was only some months later on hearing of Elizabeth's death in Australia, that Mrs Parkinson arranged for those persons who had heard her account to sign an affidavit testifying to the details and to Elizabeth's 'sincerity and reliability' as a witness. This was sent to the most eminent anti-evolutionist of the day, William Jennings Bryan (1860-1925) the three times defeated Democratic candidate for the Presidency of the United States and prosecution lawyer during the famous 'Monkey Trial' of John T. Scopes in Dayton, Tennessee.

However, before Elizabeth had departed from Los Angeles she had met up with another acquaintance from the past. It was Commissioner Frederick Booth-Tucker of the Salvation Army. Booth-Tucker and his wife Mary ('Minnie') had arrived in America on 2 October 1921 on board the *Adriatic*. After a brief stay in New York at the Hotel Algonquin they travelled to Los Angeles where they were to open a new divisional headquarters. Elizabeth had much in common with Frederick Booth-Tucker as they were both from Anglo-Indian families, as indeed was his third wife, Minnie. She had been born in India, the daughter of Lestock Reid of the Bombay Civil Service. In fact, Reid was Elizabeth's middle name, so they were distantly related. Curiously they were also distantly related through the marriage of Minnie's sister to one of her mother's relatives. So on meeting again they must have had quite a lot to talk about.

Commissioner Booth-Tucker's concern on meeting Elizabeth was to obtain from her directly the details of her meeting with Charles Darwin. Since her story had appeared in the *Watchman-Examiner* there had been considerable exaggeration and speculation in the religious press. Although he had no sympathy with

Darwinism, indeed he had written that as far as he was concerned the theory of evolution was 'a foolish theory impossible of proof'. This being so, what amazed him was the observation that the men who advocated evolution were being increasingly appointed to professorships in notable colleges and their books were being heralded by publishers as 'marvels of scientific wisdom'.

It was therefore important for Booth-Tucker to hear Elizabeth's story at first hand. Elizabeth related the account once again describing in great detail all she could remember of those visits to Down House almost forty years before. After hearing it from her own lips he then told her of the unpleasant rumours that were circulating in England that raised questions as to her integrity. He then told her that Francis Darwin had publicly accused her of dishonesty.

Elizabeth then asked him for his advice as she knew he had a sharp legal mind, having been a District Judge in India, before he had joined the Salvation Army. It is clear that his advice as a lawyer would have been for her to defend her reputation in court and to sue Francis Darwin for defamation. As far as he was concerned she had no option but to defend her reputation in the High Court in London.

After much careful thought Elizabeth decided that she had no alternative but to return to England and begin legal proceedings. It is, however, unclear why she decided to return to England by way of Australia rather than the much quicker route across country and then a much shorter Atlantic crossing. It could be that she still had wealthy relatives in Australia and it was to get their financial backing for the litigation. Whatever it was, on her arrival in Sydney, she realised she could not travel much further. She was now seriously ill and shortly after arriving she was admitted to a sanatorium and later to the Burilda Private Hospital, in the Summer Hill district of Sydney. This is where she died on 8 March 1922. Then following a simple church service she was buried in the Anglican section of the Rookwood cemetery where her tombstone may be seen to this day.

CHAPTER 21

Epilogue

WHILE CHARLES DARWIN lay on his deathbed in the April of 1882, the Salvation Army held a major rally in the northern city of Sheffield. On the Easter Monday there was a mass procession through the city centre to their meeting at the Albert Hall. The march was led by mounted officers and a brass band with General William Booth and Catherine his wife following in an open carriage. However, the most conspicuous figure in the parade was Lieutenant Emmerson Davidson. He had been a champion wrestler before his conversion and was known as 'the Weardale Wrestler'. On this occasion Davidson, six-feet-four was wearing a scarlet uniform and was mounted on a white horse and was at the head of the procession. The streets were lined with curious onlookers, but amongst them there were groups of violent yobs who had been paid by the brewers to break up the parade. Davidson was a perfect target for them and they began to throw bricks and stones at him. One brick hit him on the back of the head and knocked him unconscious, however he was held on to his horse by comrades who ran beside it. Then other Salvationists ran to protect the Booths travelling in the carriage behind. Fortunately the Booths escaped unharmed but many of their followers were badly injured. Following this riot the meeting was carried on as planned and in its report the following day, the *Sheffield Daily Telegraph*, noted that William Booth had offered his forgiveness to those who had assaulted them.

Lieutenant Davidson was not so fortunate and was in a critical condition. For many months he lay in a coma and the doctors gave up all hope of him ever recovering. But during this time Elizabeth heard of his plight and sought him out. After visiting him she treated him with the 'greatest of kindness' and got him on to the road to recovery. Davidson would remember her kindness for the rest of his life. This simple act sums up the essence of Elizabeth's character, so much so, that there is little more that needs to be added.

This being so, there are however many questions that this biography has failed to answer. Why, for instance, did Elizabeth, then a seventy-year-old widow, and a recently discharged bankrupt (through no fault of her own) not go and live happily ever after, in one of those charming English villages that she loved so much? She could still have engaged in religious work with the local parish church, running the Sunday school and being active on the parish council. She could then have spent her last years tending her garden and painting local landscapes. So what made her leave the country she loved to live in a foreign place far away from family and friends? What is so ironic about this is the fact that she had spent most of her life helping the homeless, and in the end she herself ended up homeless. So why did she do this? And then there is the further question: Why did she remain in America after the outbreak of War in 1914? There could not have been anyone more patriotic than Elizabeth. The fact is she had the Empire and the Military in her blood. Indeed, she was a daughter of the British Empire with her father a General, as well as being the widow of an Admiral of the Fleet. So why, at the outbreak of War, didn't she return to Britain and play a part there. Her sister-in-law, Marion ('May') of similar age to herself, and a close friend, had contributed to the War effort by working for the Red Cross and helping tend to the wounded. So it seems difficult to understand why Elizabeth decided to remain in America.

One could point to the possible persecution from the Darwin family that she had encountered and complained of more than once. Was this the reason she settled in America? Maybe, but it might not be the whole reason. I think there might be another more substantial reason and it might also explain why Lord and Lady Aberdeen also spent much of the War years in America. The latter couple were travelling the country meeting eminent and influential individuals and supposedly raising money for their Peamount Sanatorium in Ireland. But were they not part of an 'unofficial' mission to promote Anglo-American goodwill that might go some way to getting America to abandon its neutrality in the War? Lady Pentland, the daughter of the Lady Aberdeen, suggests this in her biography of her mother.[30] Was Elizabeth also part of this covert mission?

In *The Victory at Sea,* by Rear-Admiral William Sims, of the US Navy he describes how in March 1917, while America was still technically neutral, he was dispatched in complete secrecy to England to formulate how the U.S. navy was to work with the British Fleet. He then describes his meeting with Admiral Jellicoe, the First Sea Lord, who admitted to him that Britain was losing the War, largely on account of the losses incurred by the success of the German submarines. On receiving this information Sims admitted to have been 'astounded'. The conclusion must be that if America had not entered the War on the side of the Allies at that time, then the German war machine would have ultimately been successful. Yet for America to enter the War it was essential that popular feeling was turned towards Britain and away from Germany.

As Elizabeth had such strong credentials, being the daughter of a General and widow of a famous Admiral, was she using her position to promote Anglo-American goodwill? Certainly the individuals we know she had meetings with during these years were all very influential. During the period of America's neutrality it would have been impossible for her to have been open about her real purpose. Did she act covertly? Could she have masqueraded her real purpose under the mantle of her support for prohibition? This is of course pure speculation, however it is speculation that has some basis of fact, particularly in the light of Lady Pentland's statement.

On the other hand, we also know she had received threatening letters from the Darwin family in connection with her claims as to Charles Darwin's religious views. This had made her very cautious about putting more of her account in print. However, in confidence she related her account to a number of individuals. We know she had described it to Sir Robert Anderson, the head of the CID at Scotland Yard where he had been in charge of the 'Jack the Ripper' murder investigation. Anderson later made a note of it in one of his religious books. In addition to this we know she described it on at least four other occasions. The first was to her Los Angeles friends including Professors Melville Dozier, and H.R. Warner and their wives. The second, was to the Reverend Dr Elwood Lyon and his wife the Reverend Susie Lyon of Pasadena. The third occasion was to Commissioner Frederick Booth-Tucker of the Salvation Army during their meeting in Los Angeles. The fourth occasion was in a letter to Professor James Bole (1875-1956) of Wheaton College, near Chicago. He had written to her while she was in California enquiring as to her reported visit to Charles Darwin. In reply, she told him that she had left England to avoid the persecution of the Darwin family and their evolutionary friends. He wrote to her again requesting details of her visit to Darwin and she replied giving much more detail than had been originally published in the *Watchman-Examiner* account. In particular, she claimed that she had visited him more than once. And that he had asked her to hold a meeting for his servants and for them to sing some hymns, 'not the sad, old drony ones, but the Sankey hymns'.

Unfortunately biographers of Darwin have completely ignored Elizabeth's claims, some have gone so far as to accuse her of dishonesty. Sadly, her diaries have not come to light which might have offered proof of her claims. That being said, only recently

231

have Emma Darwin's diaries been released and they show that she did visit Fegan's widowed mother around the time Elizabeth was staying with her, thus providing some support for Elizabeth's account. So in time more information may come to light to substantiate Elizabeth's account, and when it does those who have persistently denigrated her character will face the prospect of having to eat humble pie.

Meanwhile we are left to form our own opinion as to her character. My personal belief is that her account happened exactly as she has given it. I do not believe there is any evidence that she was ever dishonest. Of course, she did have her faults. She was a little naive and too trusting. She was not good at big business and had very little financial sense. But all this does not make her dishonest. Some have suggested she suffered from vanity and had created the story simply to attract attention. I feel sure that this idea will be wiped out by the evidence I have given in this biography. She had absolutely no need to create a story about Charles Darwin just to promote herself in America. This suggestion is ridiculous as she had sufficient standing without needing to do that! In conclusion, we have only her own character to speak for herself and I hope this biography has provided sufficient illumination of this to remove any doubts as to the quality of that character.

CHRONOLOGY

(Abbreviation: LH, Elizabeth Reid Cotton, later Lady Hope)

1842	9 December. LH is born in Hobart Town, Tasmania.
1855	LH and family leave India and arrive in England.
1859	24 November. Darwin's *Origin of Species* is published.
1861	4 February. LH's father is knighted by Queen Victoria.
1864	12 March. LH and father investigate Sheffield disaster.
1870	LH and family move to Tower Hill, Dorking
1872	LH opens Temperance Coffee Room in Dorking.
1874	August. LH in Scotland with Moody and Sankey.
1876	LH publishes *Our Coffee Room*, an immediate success.
1877	6 December. LH marries Admiral Sir James Hope.
1880	LH is entertained by William Spottiswoode at Combe.
1880	23 October.LH with the Princess Mary in Edinburgh.
1880	November. Admiral Hope taken ill at Carriden.
1881	9 June. Death of Admiral Sir James Hope.
1881	6 August.LH assists the Marchioness of Ailsa in Ayr.
1881	7 November.Emma Darwin visits Mrs. Fegan in Down.
1881	8 November.First visit of LH to Charles Darwin.
1882	19 April. Death of Charles Darwin.
1882	20 May. LH gives farewell address in Bournemouth.
1882	September-December. LH helps with Moody and Sankey.
1883	LH does Gospel work in 'Outcast London'.
1883	LH helps with Moody's second London Mission.
1884	LH publishes her work on 'Outcast London'.
1889	January. LH seriously ill with influenza.
1889	December. Death of LH's brother *en route* from India.
1893	27 September. LH marries T.A. Denny in Paddington.
1899	July. Death of LH's father.
1907	5 December. Death of LH's mother.
1909	25 December. Death of T.A. Denny at Buccleuch House.
1911	LH declared bankrupt.
1913	LH leaves England for New York.
1915	August. LH attends conference at Northfield College.
1915	21 August. Publication of LH's account in Boston.
1919	4 April. LH makes her Will in San Diego, California
1922	8 March. Death of LH in Sydney, Australia.

Amos, C.W. Hale, 'Darwin's Last Hours', *The Monthly Record of the Free Church of Scotland*, February, 1957, p.33.

Anderson, R., *A Doubter's Doubts about Science and Religion, or In Defence : A Plea for the Faith*, (3rd edition) Pickering and Inglis, London (1924).

Anon., 'Temperance Workers: Lady Hope', *Methodist Temperance Magazine*, (1884) vol. 17, pp. 126-128.

Atkins, Sir Hedley, *Down – The Home of the Darwins. The Story of a House and the People who lived there*. Royal College of Surgeons, London (1974).

Bagwell, Philip S., *Outcast London : A Christian response. The West London Mission of the Methodist Church 1887-1987*. Epworth Press, London (1987).

Battiscombe, Georgina, *Mrs Gladstone : The Portrait of a Marriage*. Constable, London (1956).

Black, Ros, *A Talent for Humanity. The Life and Work of Lady Henry Somerset*, Antony Rowe, Publishing, Chippenham (2019).

Cook, Sir Edward, *The Life of Florence Nightingale*. Macmillan, New York (1942).

Cotton, E. R. (Lady Hope) *Our Coffee-Room*. James Nisbet & Co., London (1876).

Cotton, E. R. (Lady Hope) *More About Our Coffee Room*. James Nisbet & Co., London (1878).

Croft, L. R., *The Life and Death of Charles Darwin*. Elmwood Books, Chorley, Lancashire (1989).

Croft, L.R., *Darwin and Lady Hope. The Untold Story*, Elmwood Books, Preston, Lancashire (2012).

Croft, L.R., 'The Lady Hope Story', *The English Churchman*, 8 January (2016) p.9.

Croft, L.R., *The Lady Hope Story as told in Thirty Paintings*, Blurb, eBooks (2016).

Darton, J. M., *The Heroism of Christian Women of our own Time. What they have done and are doing*. W. Swan Sonnenschein (1880).

Darwin, Sir Francis, *The Life and Letters of Charles Darwin*. Volumes I-III, John Murray, London (1887).

Dorsett, Lyle W., *A Passion for Souls : The Life of D.L. Moody*. Moody Publishers, Chicago (1997).

Drewry, Mick, *Inudation. The History, the Times and the People of The Great Sheffield Flood of 1864*. YouBooks, Sheffield (2014).

Drummond, Henry, *Natural Law in the Spiritual World*. Hodder & Stoughton, London (1898).

Evelyn, Helen, *The History of the Evelyn Family with a special memoir of William John Evelyn M.P.* Eveleigh Nash, London (1915).

Evensen, B. J., *God's Man for the Gilded Age. D.L.Moody and the Rise of Modern Mass Evangelism*. Oxford University Press, Oxford (2003).

Felix, Charles, *The Notting Hill Mystery*. Saunders, Otley and Co., London (1865).

Fitzpatrick, Kathleen, *Lady Henry Somerset*, Jonathan Cape, London (1923).

French, Doris, *Ishbel and the Empire. A Biography of Lady Aberdeen*, Dundurn Press, Toronto and London (1988).

Fullerton, W. Y., *J.W.C. Fegan – A Tribute*. Marshall, Morgan and Scott, London (1930).

Hammond, J. L. & B., *Lord Shaftesbury*. Penguin Books Ltd., London (1936).

Hattersley, Roy, *Blood and Fire – William and Catherine Booth and their Salvation Army*. Little Brown & Co., London (1999).

Healey, Edna, *Emma Darwin. The Inspirational Wife of a Genius*. Hodder Headline, London (2001).

Heathcote, T.A., *The British Admirals of the Fleet 1734-1995. A Biographical Dictionary*. Leo Cooper, Barnsley (2002).

Hope, Lady, 'Darwin and Christianity. A Remarkable Story told of the Great Scientist and author when he was approaching the end of Earthly life.' *Boston Evening Transcript*, Saturday 21 August, 1915.

Hope, Lady, *Invitations*. Drummond's Tract Depot. Stirling (n.d.) [1877].

Hope, Lady, *Lines of Light on a Dark Background*. James Nisbet, London (1879).

Hope, Lady, *Sunny Footsteps or when I was a child*. James Nisbet & Co., London (1879).

Hope, Lady, *Touches of Real Life*. James Nisbet & Co., London (1880).

Hope, Lady, *A Maiden's Work*. James Nisbet & Co., London (1882).

Hope, Lady, *His Handiwork*. S.M. Partridge & Co., London (1883).

Hope, Lady, *Gathered Clusters from Scripture Pages*. Macniven & Wallace, Edinburgh (1883).

Hope, Lady, *Our Golden Key. A Narrative of facts from 'Outcast London'*. Seeley, Jackson & Halliday, London (1884).

Hope, Lady, *Loving Work in the Highways and Byways*. T. Nelson & Sons, London (1888).

Hope, Lady, *General Sir Arthur Cotton R.E., K.C.S.I. His Life and Work. With some Famine Prevention Studies by William Digby C.I.E.* Hodder & Stoughton, London (1900).

Hope, Lady, *Heavenly Blossoms on Earth's Pathway*. The Christian Colportage Association, London (n.d.) [1900].

Hope, Lady, *English Homes and Villages (Kent and Sussex)*. J. Salmon, Sevenoaks, Kent (1909).

Iversen, Kristen, *Molly Brown. Unravelling the Myth*. Johnson Books, Boulder (2010).

Jackson, A. A. (ed.), *Dorking : A Surrey Market Town through Twenty Centuries*. Dorking Local History Group, Dorking, Surrey (1991).

Litchfield, H.E. (ed.), *Emma Darwin – A Century of Family Letters* (2 vols) John Murray, London (1915).

Litchfield, R. B., 'Charles Darwin's Death-Bed. Story of Conversion denied.' *The Christian*, 23 February (1922) p. 12.

MacKenzie, F.A., *Booth-Tucker. Sadhu and Saint*. Hodder and Stoughton, London (1930).

Mackinnon, Jane, *Recollections of D.L. Moody*, Privately Printed, Oliphant, Anderson, & Ferrier, Edinburgh (1905).

Moody, W. R., *The Life of Dwight L. Moody*. Morgan & Scott, London (1900).

Moore, James, *The Darwin Legend*. Hodder & Stoughton, London (1995).

Moore-Anderson, A.P., *Sir Robert Anderson and Lady Agnes Anderson*. Marshall, Morgan and Scott, London (1947).

Munro, J. Forbes, *Maritime Enterprise and Empire : Sir William Mackinnon and his business Network 1823-93*. The Boydell Press, Woodbridge, Suffolk (2003).

Pentland, Marjorie, *A Bonnie Fechter the Life of Ishbel Marjoribanks Marchioness of Aberdeen*, Batsford, London (1952).

Prochaska, F. K., *Women and Philanthropy in Nineteenth Century England*. Clarendon Press, Oxford (1980).

Rose, Charles, *Recollections of Old Dorking*. (Reprinted from the West Surrey Times) Guildford (n.d.).

Thorne, G., *The Great Acceptance: The Life Story of F.N.Charrington*, Hodder and Stoughton, London (1913).

Tucker, F. B., 'Charles Darwin's Last Days'. *The Christian*, 9 March (1922) p. 26.

Ward, Henshaw, *Charles Darwin. The Man and His Warfare*. John Murray, London (1927).

Woodham-Smith, Cecil, *Florence Nightingale 1820-1910*. Constable, London (1950).

Williams, H., *Booth-Tucker, William Booth's First Gentleman*. Hodder & Stoughton, London (1980).

ACKNOWLEDGEMENTS

I am indebted to many people who have helped me put together the life of Elizabeth Lady Hope. This has been a difficult project on account of the scarcity of primary sources such as letters and diaries. Nonetheless by careful study it has been possible to piece together the life of this exceptional woman. Fortunately, I have accumulated most of her published material in original form and have been able to visit many of the places associated with her. I am particularly fortunate to have been welcomed by Mrs Barbara Blackbourn, who, at the time of writing, was the owner of Carriden House, who gave me access to the parts of the house associated with Lady Hope. I am most grateful that she went to some trouble showing me the stone bench overlooking the Firth of Forth, now overgrown with brambles, where Lady Hope would sit and meditate. I am also grateful for Mr Martin Tracey, of the Victory Services Club, Marble Arch, for allowing me free access to what had been Lady Hope's Connaught Club. Also to Mr John Pratlen TD bursar of the Box Hill School, Mickleham, for giving me information on Lady Hope's Carriden House at Mickleham and allowing me to explore the grounds of the school. I am also grateful to Judith Kinloch of Mickleham for information regarding Lady Hope's Mission Hall in the village. Also, I would like to thank Mr Russell Grigg for providing me with a photograph of Lady Hope's grave in Sydney, Australia. In addition, I would like to give special thanks to those individuals who have helped me clarify many matters, particularly, my former colleague from Stonyhurst College, Dr Pat Gavin; also Dr Paul Marston of the University of Central Lancashire, and Professor Andy McIntosh of the University of Leeds. Finally, I would like to thank my family, in particular my wife, Mary, for her understanding and patience over many years while this project occupied much of my time. My daughter, Jane, who gave assistance in editing the manuscript, and her husband, Adam, who was always prepared to give technical help in using my computer. Many thanks to all.

[1] In the cholera epidemic of 1849, there were some thousands deaths a week in London alone. At the time the cause of the disease was unknown. It was another six years before Dr John Snow linked the disease to the impure water supply.

[2] The five evangelical Catherines of the Victorian Age were: Catherine Marsh, Catherine Gladstone (wife of the Prime Minister), Catherine Booth (wife of William Booth, founder of the Salvation Army), Catherine Tait (the wife of the Archbishop of Canterbury), and Catherine Pennefather.

[3] This property still exists having recently defeated a demolition proposal. It had been an educational study centre. It is now a listed building.

[4] Lady Hope, *Heavenly Blossoms on Earth's Pathway*, p.72-76

[5] The appearance of the Garth Nursing Home, in Tower Hill, Dorking, has changed very little from when it was the home of the Cotton family. However, much of the garden has been converted into a car park and there has been an extension built. The entrance is very much as it was with a magnificent stairway, leading to wide landing area, which opens up completely with the skylights above.

[6] Lady Hope, 'Trained Nursing in Workhouse Infirmaries', *Good Words*, (1881) Donald Macleod (editor) Isbister and Co., London. (pp. 351-354).

[7] *Our Coffee Room*, p.71.

[8] William Henry Dinnage (1870-1063) in *Dinnage's Recollections of Old Dorking*.

[9] Cf. 'Florence Nightingale on women, medicine, midwifery and prostitution.'

[10] Wellcome Library MS 9007/48

[11] C.H. Spurgeon, *Messrs. Moody and Sankey in Great Britain,* Sword and Trowel, (February 1876).

[12] Muirhouses today is very much the same as it was when Elizabeth arrived in the area, although the schoolhouse and library are today private houses. The village is now a conservation area.

[13] Alexander Bell almost certainly was suffering from coalminer's pneumoconiosis, as he had been working all his life in the coal mine. His death certificate stated cause of death: 'asthma, dropsy 12 months'.

[14] On 20 November 1883, at a meeting of the society held at St James's Hall to mark the 21st anniversary of the C of E Temperance Society.

[15] Henry Varley shared a platform with Elizabeth on Thursday 19th January 1882 at the Lecture Hall, Junction Road, Dorking.

[16] *Our Golden Key* by Lady Hope was published in April/May of 1884.

[17] *Daily News*, Friday 22 February 1884.

[18] Dr Alfred Carpenter (1825-1892) was a well known temperance advocate. He had a large medical practice in Croydon and was president of the Temperance Society. He was a personal friend of Prime Minister Gladstone.

[19] HMS *Niger* played a crucial role in the bombardment of Sevastopol on 17 October 1854.

[20] Major Crofton died aboard ship returning from India in 1899. In the 1911 census Marion is recorded as living with her widowed sister Ada Randolph Broadwood in Belgrave. During the First World War she worked for the Red Cross and helped run a canteen for munition workers at King's Cross. She died on 14 May 1949 in her 93rd year (cf. *The Times,* 17 May 1949).

21 *Golden Lines*, page 136.

22 *The Great Acceptance : The Life Story of F.N.Charrington*, by Guy Thorne (p. 61)

23 Sir Robert Anderson wrote: 'I may add that a friend of mine who was much with Darwin during his last illness assures me that he expressed the greatest reverence for the Scriptures and bore testimony to their value.'

24 Buccleuch House no longer exists. It was demolished in 1938. There are now gardens where it once stood, however the views from the location are delightful.

25 Although it is recorded in the British Library catalogue, the author on requesting a copy was informed that it could not be found.

26 The *Lusitania* was torpedoed by a German submarine on 7 May 1915, some eleven miles off the coast of Ireland with much loss of life.

27 The Cape Juby Project was to construct an inland lake in the Sahara desert by building a canal from the Atlantic Ocean at Cape Juby on the coast of Morocco. General Cotton was an enthusiastic supporter of the project which had been originally proposed by Donald Mackenzie in 1877.

28 Dr T. Kennard Thompson's plan for expanding the land area of New York is contained in an article in *Popular Science* of January 1916 (p.57) entitled: 'A Really Greater New York'.

29 American journalists at this time were keen to print stories about English aristocrats. During her visit to America, at around this time, Lady Henry Somerset complained that she was interviewed by reporters 'day and night'. She commented: 'The newspapers are too funny – I have been interviewed from morning till night....they are a perfect nuisance.' And as regards their accuracy she complained: 'the report of what I

said is unrecognizable ! but emanated entirely from the reporter's brain.' (cf. p.153 in *Lady Henry Somerset* by Kathleen Fitzpatrick)

30 (cf. pp. 181-182) Marjorie Pentland, *A Bonnie Fechter : the Life of Ishbel Marjoribanks Marchioness of Aberdeen*, Batsford, London (1952).

This is not a comprehensive review of Lady Hope's writing which was extensive and included more than thirty books together with many tracts and contributions to numerous religious journals and serials. Also for some years she edited several magazines. The following are notes relating only to those books that are mentioned in the main text of this biography.

1. **OUR COFFEE ROOM**
With a Preface by Lieut-Gen Sir Arthur Cotton R.E.; K.C.S.I.

(i) Published (1876) by James Nisbet & Co, 21 Berners Street, London.

Pp. x + 248, small crown 8vo, with engraved frontispiece of Dorking Coffee Room. Issued in blue cloth boards with gilt lettering.

(Author's copy is a presentation copy inscribed by Lady Hope to: "*Mr and Mrs Peter Mackinnon, with best regards and kind love from, E.R. Cotton, May 6, 1876*".)

(ii) Another copy. Fourth edition dated 1876. As above but with 'Preface to Second Edition' (vii-x).

(iii) Another copy. Dated 1878. As (ii) but with 'Fourteenth thousand' on title page.

(iv) Another copy. First American edition, dated 1877. Published by the National Temperance Society, 58 Reade Street, New York. Pp. 278. Small crown 8vo. Issued with blue cloth boards with title in black.

(v) **Florence Nightingale Associated Copies**

(a) Second edition (1876) now in private ownership. It is inscribed by Florence Nightingale : "*For Robert Robinson, with Florence Nightingale's kindest regards : London, July 18, 1876*"

(Robert Robinson was a drummer boy of the 68th Light Infantry during the Crimean War when Miss Nightingale nursed him back to health.)

(b) Another copy in the Parkes family archives, New South Wales Library, Sydney, Australia. It is inscribed by Florence Nightingale : "*To Henry Parkes, the successful founder of New South Wales Education, Florence Nightingale ventures to offer this account of a small but successful attempt at Education for mature years by the daughter of her friend Sir Arthur Cotton, London : Sept 1876.*"

(Sir Henry Parkes (1815-1896) had emigrated to Australia in 1839. He became a noted journalist and politician, becoming a member of the first Australian government in 1856.)

(c) Another copy. Located in the Florence Nightingale museum, Lambeth Palace Road, London SE1. It is inscribed by Florence Nightingale and dated 3 March, 1876. (Object No. 0413)

(d) Another copy together with *More about Our Coffee Room* that had been donated and inscribed by Florence Nightingale to the library of the Whatstandwell Coffee Room in Derbyshire. The present location is unknown.

(e) Another copy Florence Nightingale gave to Margaret Verney. In her letter she wrote: "*I venture to send you, if you have not seen it, 'Our Coffee-Room' by my dear old friend Sir Arthur Cotton, the Indian irrigation engineer, or rather by his daughter. Its real reality of religion surpasses anything, I think, I ever met with. One may not agree with much in it, but I have read nothing which (from that reality) has given me so much pleasure since Agnes Jones went 'home'*". (Present location is unknown.)

2. MORE ABOUT OUR COFFEE ROOM

With a Preface by the Earl of Shaftesbury in which he writes:

'The pious, amiable and accomplished young lady whose efforts are therein recorded, has given an example of what may be done by the exertions, though but of one person, founded on an intense love of the gospel, and burning desire to convey it to the souls of others. Every one who reads her achievements cannot but rejoice in the harvest she has reaped'

Published (1878) by James Nisbet & Co, 21 Berners Street, London. Third thousand (with Addenda).

Pp. xii + 248, small crown 8vo. Issued with brown cloth boards.

3. SUNNY FOOTSTEPS or WHEN I WAS A CHILD

Published (1879) by James Nisbet & Co, of 21 Berners Street, London.

Pp xii + 122, small 4to with engraved frontispiece together with five more pages of illustrations . Issued in maroon cloth boards with gilt decoration on front.

In the Preface, Lady Hope writes:

'As I have many little friends who from time to time, have asked me to 'tell them a story', often adding the request, 'let it be about yourself – when you were a little girl'. I have ventured to offer to them this true account of some of my early experiences, and hope that in reading my little book they may have half as much pleasure as I have had in writing it.'

4. LINES OF LIGHT ON A DARK BACKGROUND

Published (1879) by James Nisbet & Co, London.

Pp vi + 190, small 8vo.

In this book Lady Hope details how the Coffee Room movement has been successful in promoting temperance. 'We rejoice in the spread of temperance....I offer these pages to those who are interested in the good of their fellow-countrymen.'

Included in the book are copies of her letters written to her friends in Dorking and cover the period January to December 1878. In one letter she writes:

'My present drawing room is garnished with the many handsome gifts of those loving and grateful people. A highly ornamental clock in perfect taste stands on the mantelpiece, keeping excellent time. This was a gift of 150 working men their names all having signed to the address that accompanied it. A silver and walnut writing set, and envelope case reminds me every day while I sit at my writing table of the kind wishes of the men's Bible class. Also beautiful silver candlesticks from 160 guards and other employees of the London – Brighton line. A workbox from the mother's meeting and other mementoes' of my most happy years of labour (if it can be called such) in the delicious vales of Surrey.'

5. A MAIDEN'S WORK

Published (1882) by James Nisbet & Co, 21 Berners Street, London.

Pp. 296, 8vo. Issued with grey cloth covers.

The Preface is in black borders (she was widowed during the writing of this book). In it she writes : 'Written as it has been in a time of anxiety and chiefly for the delight of one who in the last few months has been taken from me...' It is dated December 1881, six months after her husband had died, and is written at Dorking, having returned home to live with her parents.

It is largely a semi-autobiographical account of her time married to Admiral Sir James Hope. She writes as 'Geraldine' who is living in a large mansion with her widowed father 'Mr Grayson'. The house is situated overlooking the sea in the North and it is clearly Carriden House. The book therefore provides an excellent insight as to what life was like at this time, in this rather bleak part of the country, and how she achieved success in her situation.

6. OUR GOLDEN KEY – A NARRATIVE OF FACTS FROM 'OUTCAST LONDON'

Published (1884) by Seeley, Jackson and Halliday, Fleet Street, London.

Pp, x + 166, 8vo, with 8 pages of engravings. Issued with navy cloth boards with gilt decorated front cover.

This book describes Lady Hope's work in the Notting Hill slums. The preface is signed E.R. Hope of 12 Great Cumberland Place.

7. A GLANCE AT THE GREAT WORK.

An incident of Messrs Moody and Sankey's meetings in London.
    This is a religious tract.
    Published (1884) by Morgan & Scott, London. Pp, 31, 16vo.

8. WILD HYACINTHS

Published (1883) by John F. Shaw & Co, of 48 Paternoster Row.
    Pp. 336, crown 8vo, with frontispiece engraving. Issued with pale blue cloth boards with elaborate gilt decoration.

    This is a religious novel for young women, something between a religious tract and a romance novelette. It is a story of Elline, a young woman, in search of faith and her relationships. It is possibly based on Lady Hope's experiences in Ireland before she moved to Dorking.

9. GOLDEN LINES of ELLINE'S EXPERIENCES

(i) New edition of *Wild Hyacinths* with new title. Published (1898) by John Shaw & Co, 48 Paternoster Row, London.

    Pp, 336, crown 8vo, with frontispiece engraving as Wild Hyacinths and plain title page. Issued with light brown cloth boards with gilt decoration.

    (ii) Another issue with same frontispiece as (i). Issued with light red cloth boards with some gilt decoration together with an illustration of what appears to be a Roman maiden sitting on the steps of a temple.

    (iii) Another issue with brown cloth boards with illustration of young woman in long dress and scarf holding a bunch of keys to unlock a gate.

    (iv) Another issue as (iii) but in green cloth.

    This book proved to be very popular and was re-issued many times.

10. PICTURES OF SILVER (Thoughts gathered from the mountains and valleys of Switzerland.)

Published (1886) by James F. Hawkins & Co. Pp, 96, 16vo.

This short book gives details of Lady Hope's visit to Switzerland. She describes visiting the little church at Staubach in the Lanterbrunnen Valley and to the spectacular Falls of Trummelbach. 'Nature speaks aloud to us' she wrote and then described how she 'stood amazed at the sight and sound of the great waterfall...and in the cloud of spray that surrounded the torrent, two shining rainbows...could anything have been more beautiful?'

11. HEAVENLY BLOSSOMS ON EARTH'S PATHWAY

In the Preface Lady Hope outlines the purpose of her writing:

'In answer to the request of a few of my friends I have published some of the incidents which have happened to myself in that daily experience..' Then in the chapter entitled 'Our Comforter' she relates the incident of meeting the young doctor on Dorking railway station who subsequently committed suicide. In recalling it she was greatly upset and concluded the chapter: 'We can hardly do better perhaps in closing this chapter than to contrast the terrible darkness of this short history with a very different scene.' She then went on to describe her meeting with the old man on a beach in County Down that led to a spiritual renewal.

(i) Published (1899) by The Christian Colportage Association, 7 Farringdon Street, London. Pp, x + 142, 8vo; issued in cream cloth boards with elaborate gilt decoration to the front cover and gilding to all page edges.

(ii) Another issue in plain red cloth boards (a popular edition) with title in black. Pp, x + 142.

12. GENERAL SIR ARTHUR COTTON R.E., K.C.S.I. – His Life and Work by his daughter Lady Hope.

(With some famine prevention studies by William Digby C.I.E.)

At the beginning of the book Lady Hope dedicates the work:

'To my Beloved Mother whose interest and sympathy through a long life cheered and supported my father in his arduous tasks for the benefit of humanity.'

Then in the Preface she expands on this writing: 'My father used to sometimes say – "I am a man of one idea" but though it was true that the question of Indian irrigation was the leading feature of his public life, he had a vast number of other interests, every one of them tending towards the benefit of mankind...'

Published (1900) by Hodder & Stoughton, 27 Paternoster Row, London.

Pp, xiv + 600 with 20 plates and folding maps. Issued in maroon cloth boards with gilt lettering on spine.

(Author's copy has inscription in Lady Cotton's hand to :

'*Charlotte Bourdillon in Remembrance, Christmas 1900*')

Note: Miss Bourdillon was a family friend and is listed as having attended General Cotton's funeral.

13. ENGLISH HOMES AND VILLAGES (KENT and SUSSEX)

Published (1909) by J. Salmon, High Street, Sevenoaks.

Pp, xvi + 296, with 63 colour plates (including one painting by Lady Hope of the view from Frant Court) and 17 B/W plates. Issued in fine green cloth boards with gilt decoration on front cover.

The book is dedicated (by permission) to the Princess of Wales, later to become Queen Mary. (She had known the Princess from the time she helped her distribute flowers to patients in the Edinburgh Royal Infirmary in October 1880.)

(The author's copy is inscribed by Lady Hope : '*To Mr Mosdaccah Smith from the Authoress, E.R. Hope.*')

admiration of FN, 74; charisma of, 76, 84, 197-198; helps DM's mission, 78-94, 129-137; strength of faith, 83, 199, 209; friendship with Jane Mackinnon, 82-83, 92-94; first meeting with DM, 83; knowledge of scripture, 83; ability to preach,, 84-85, 93, 106-107, 157; attractive voice, 84, 149, 109, 162; meeting with CD, 114-126, 217-219; temperance work, 114, 126-129, 195-196; relationship with Fegan, 116-120; relationship with Drummond, 121, 131-133, 137, 222; opens Golden Bells coffee palace, 166-168; faults of character, 171-172, 203-209, 232; second marriage, 176-181, 198-199; Connaught Club, 195-196; deceived by Fry, 202, 208-209; financial matters and bankruptcy, 205, 208-209; death of 227

255

256

Watchman-Examiner (Baptist journal), 217, 219, 226, 231

Wentworth Woodhouse (LH's mission to), 126

Wesley, John (attitude to drink), 62

Western Mail, 130

Weston, Agnes (temperance worker), 159

Whatstandwell (FN's Coffee Room), 75

Whitechapel murders, 170

White Sulphur Springs (LH's visit to), 221-223

Wick (DM takes mission to), 88

Willard, Frances (American temperance campaigner), 158, 210

Wimpole Street (Marylebone), 22

Woodcot, Dorking (residence of Cotton family), 43

Woodcote Oxfordshire (birthplace of GC), 6

Wrexham (LH's mission to), 161

Wrexham Advertiser and North Wales News, 162

WWCTU (World Women's Christian Temperance Union), 210

York, (DM starts mission at), 80

YMCA, 79-80, 94, 110-111

YWCA, 159, 173, 175, 183,

The Zeminder, the Sun and the Watering Pot as Affecting Life or Death in India (FN), 43

Python for Unix and Linux System Administration

Other resources from O'Reilly

Related titles

Essential System
Administration

Learning Python

Linux Networking
Cookbook™

Linux Security Cookbook™

Mac OS X for Unix Geeks

Programming Python

Python Cookbook™

Python in a Nutshell

Unix in a Nutshell

oreilly.com

oreilly.com is more than a complete catalog of O'Reilly books. You'll also find links to news, events, articles, weblogs, sample chapters, and code examples.

oreillynet.com is the essential portal for developers interested in open and emerging technologies, including new platforms, programming languages, and operating systems.

Conferences

O'Reilly brings diverse innovators together to nurture the ideas that spark revolutionary industries. We specialize in documenting the latest tools and systems, translating the innovator's knowledge into useful skills for those in the trenches. Visit *conferences.oreilly.com* for our upcoming events.

Safari Bookshelf (*safari.oreilly.com*) is the premier online reference library for programmers and IT professionals. Conduct searches across more than 1,000 books. Subscribers can zero in on answers to time-critical questions in a matter of seconds. Read the books on your Bookshelf from cover to cover or simply flip to the page you need. Try it today for free.

Python for Unix and Linux System Administration

Noah Gift and Jeremy M. Jones

O'REILLY®

Beijing · Cambridge · Farnham · Köln · Sebastopol · Taipei · Tokyo

Python for Unix and Linux System Administration

by Noah Gift and Jeremy M. Jones

Published by O'Reilly Media, Inc., 1005 Gravenstein Highway North, Sebastopol, CA 95472.

O'Reilly books may be purchased for educational, business, or sales promotional use. Online editions are also available for most titles (*http://safari.oreilly.com*). For more information, contact our corporate/institutional sales department: (800) 998-9938 or *corporate@oreilly.com*.

Editor: Julie Steele	**Cover Designer:** Karen Montgomery	
Production Editor: Loranah Dimant	**Interior Designer:** David Futato	
Production Services: nSight, Inc.	**Illustrator:** Robert Romano	

Printing History:

August 2008:   First Edition.

ISBN: 978-0-596-51582-9

[M]

1218651032

I dedicate this book to Dr. Joseph E. Bogen, my mom, and my wife, Leah—three people who have loved me and believed in me when it counted the most.

—Noah

I dedicate this book to my wife, Debra, and my children, Zane and Justus. You encouraged me, bore with me with great patience, and gave me many smiles along the journey of writing this book. This book is as much yours as it is mine.

—Jeremy

Table of Contents

Foreword

I was excited to preview this book on using Python for system administration. I remembered how I felt when I discovered Python after many years of programming in other languages: it was like a breath of spring air and the warmth of the sun after a long winter indoors. Code was suddenly easy and fun to write again, and I finished programs much more quickly than before.

As a system administrator, most of my own Python use is for system and network management tasks. I already knew how useful a good book focusing on system administration with Python would be. I am happy to say that this is that book. Overall, Noah and Jeremy have created an interesting, intelligent work on Python that is planted firmly in the system administration sphere. I found the book both very useful and enjoyable to read.

The two opening chapters are a great introduction to Python for system administrators (and others) who are new to Python. I consider myself an intermediate Python programmer, and I learned a lot from the book. I suspect even Python wizards will come across a few new tricks in here. I can especially recommend the chapters on networking and managing network services, SNMP, and management of heterogeneous systems as particularly useful and well focused on nontrivial, real-world tasks that system administrators face every day.

—Æleen Frisch, July 2008

Preface

Conventions Used in This Book

The following typographical conventions are used in this book:

Italic
    Indicates new terms, URLs, email addresses, filenames, and file extensions.

`Constant width`
    Used for program listings, in text to refer to program elements, such as variable or function names, databases, data types, environment variables, statements, utilities, keywords, utilities, and modules.

`Constant width bold`
    Shows commands or other text that should be typed literally by the user.

`Constant width italic`
    Shows text that should be replaced with user-supplied values or by values determined by context.

 This icon signifies a tip, suggestion, or general note.

 This icon indicates a warning or caution.

Using Code Examples

This book is here to help you get your job done. In general, you may use the code that is included in this book in your programs and documentation. You do not need to contact us for permission unless you're reproducing a significant portion of the code. For example, writing a program that uses several chunks of code from this book does not require permission; selling or distributing a CD-ROM of examples from O'Reilly books does require permission. Answering a question by citing this book and quoting example code does not require permission; incorporating a significant amount of example code from this book into your product's documentation does require permission.

We appreciate, but do not require, attribution. An attribution usually includes the title, author, publisher, and ISBN, for example: "*Python for Unix and Linux System Administration* by Noah Gift and Jeremy M. Jones. Copyright 2008 Noah Gift and Jeremy M. Jones, 978-0-596-51582-9."

If you feel your use of code examples falls outside fair use or the permission given above, feel free to contact us at *permissions@oreilly.com*.

Safari® Books Online

Safari When you see a Safari® Books Online icon on the cover of your favorite technology book, that means the book is available online through the O'Reilly Network Safari Bookshelf.

Safari offers a solution that's better than e-books. It's a virtual library that lets you easily search thousands of top tech books, cut and paste code samples, download chapters, and find quick answers when you need the most accurate, current information. Try it for free at *http://safari.oreilly.com*.

How to Contact Us

Please address comments and questions concerning this book to the publisher:

> O'Reilly Media, Inc.
> 1005 Gravenstein Highway North
> Sebastopol, CA 95472
> 800-998-9938 (in the United States or Canada)
> 707-829-0515 (international or local)
> 707-829-0104 (fax)

We have a web page for this book, where we list errata, examples, and any additional information. You can access this page at:

> *http://www.oreilly.com/9780596515829*

To comment or ask technical questions about this book, send email to:

> *bookquestions@oreilly.com*

For more information about our books, conferences, Resource Centers, and the O'Reilly Network, see our website at:

> *http://www.oreilly.com*

Acknowledgments

Noah's Acknowledgments

As I sit writing an acknowledgment for this book, I have to first mention Dr. Joseph E. Bogen, because he made the single largest impact on me, at a time that it mattered the most. I met Dr. Bogen while I was working at Caltech, and he opened my eyes to another world giving me advice on life, psychology, neuroscience, math, the scientific study of consciousness, and much more. He was the smartest person I ever met, and was someone I loved. I am going to write a book about this experience someday, and I am saddened that he won't be there to read it, his death was a big loss.

I want to thank my wife, Leah, who has been one of the best things to happen to me, ever. Without your love and support, I never could have written this book. You have the patience of a saint. I am looking forward to going where this journey takes us, and I love you. I also want to thank my son, Liam, who is one and a half, for being patient with me while I wrote this book. I had to cut many of our guitar, piano, and pushup lessons short, so I owe you payback times two, little goat.

To my mom, I love you, and thank you for encouraging me throughout life.

Of course, I want to thank Jeremy M. Jones, my coauthor, for agreeing to write this book with me. I think we were a great team with different, but complementary styles, and we wrote a great book. You have taught me a lot about Python, and have been a good partner and friend. Thanks!

Titus Brown, whom I suppose I have to call Dr. Brown now, was the person that got me interested in Python to begin with, when I met him at Caltech. He is another example of how one person can make a difference, and I am glad to consider him an "old" friend, the kind money can't buy. He kept asking me, "Why don't you use Python?" And then one day I did. If it wasn't for Titus, I would certainly have continued down the Java and Perl path. You can read his blog here: *http://ivory.idyll.org/blog*.

Shannon Behrens has a heart of solid gold, a mind as sharp as a razor, and a knowledge of Python that is truly scary. I first met Shannon through Titus, ironic again, but he and I became quick friends. Shannon is the real deal in every sense of the word, and has taught me a tremendous amount about Python, in fact, staggering would be a better word. His help with Python, and editing this book has been incredible, and I owe him tremendously. I shudder to think of what it would have looked like without him. I can't ever imagine a company being foolish enough to let him get away, and I look forward to helping him with his first book. Finally, he is just an incredible technical reviewer. You can read his blog here: *http://jjinux.blogspot.com/*.

Doug Hellmann was our other star technical reviewer and was exceptionally productive and helpful. Jeremy and I are extremely fortunate to get someone of his caliber to review the book. He went above and beyond his call of duty, and is truly a force of efficiency to reckon with. He was also a great source of motivation while we worked together at Racemi. You can read his blog here: *http://blog.doughellmann.com/*.

Thanks to Scott Leerseen for reviewing our book and giving us good advice along the way. I also especially enjoyed our code review battles. Just remember, I am always right.

Thanks to Alfredo Deza for the work on making an Ubuntu virtual machine for the book, your expertise was greatly appreciated.

A very large thanks to Liza Daly, for providing good feedback on some really early, and rough, parts of our book. This was tremendously helpful.

Special thanks to Jeff Rush for his advice and reference material on Buildout, Eggs, and Virtualenv.

Thanks to Aaron Hillegass who has given me some great advice and help along the way, and who has a great training company, Big Nerd Ranch. He is a special person, who I am lucky to have met. Thanks to Mark Lutz, who I had the pleasure of taking a Python training course from, and who has written some great books on Python.

Thanks to the people in the Python community in Atlanta, and the members of PyAtl: *http://pyatl.org*; you have all taught me a great deal. Rick Copeland, Rick Thomas, Brandon Rhodes, Derek Richardson, Jonathan La Cour, a.k.a Mr. Metaclass, Drew Smathers, Cary Hull, Bernard Matthews, Michael Langford, and many more I have forgotten to mention. Brandon and Rick Copeland in particular have been very helpful and are awesome Python programmers. You can read Brandon's blog at *http://rhodes mill.org/brandon/*.

Thanks to Grig Gheorghiu for giving us expert sysadmin and testing advice and for giving us a kick in the butt when we needed one.

Thanks to my former employer Racemi, and the CTO/Founder, Charles Watt. I learned a lot from you and was glad you knew which competitive buttons to push. Just remember I will kick your butt at writing code, a 26-mile run, or a 200-mile bike ride any day, just tell me where and when.

Thanks to Dr. Nanda Ganesan, who was a great mentor in graduate school at CSULA. You taught me a lot about information technology and life and encouraged me to think big.

Thanks to Dr. Cindy Heiss, who was my professor for my undergraduate degree in nutritional science. You got me started on web development, encouraged me to believe in myself, and ultimately made an impact on my life, thanks!

Thanks to Sheldon Blockburger, who let me try out for Division I decathlon as a walk-on at Cal Poly SLO. Even though I didn't make the team, you showed me how to be a fierce competitor and warrior, and taught me the self-discipline to run 200-meter intervals by myself. I believe weekly 200-meter interval workouts make me a better software engineer.

There were many other people who helped tremendously along the way, including Jennifer Davis, yet another friend from Caltech, who gave us some great feedback; some of my friends and coworkers at Turner; Doug Wake, Wayne Blanchard, Sam Allgood, Don Voravong; some of my friends and coworkers from Disney Feature animation, including Sean Someroff, Greg Neagle, and Bobby Lea. Greg Neagle in particular taught me a lot about OS X. Also, thanks to J.F. Panisset, who I met at Sony Imageworks, for teaching me quite a bit about engineering in general. Although he is now a CTO, he is another rare catch for any company.

I would like to thank a few others who made some important contributions: Mike Wagner, Chris McDowell, and Shaun Smoot.

Thanks to Bruce J. Bell, who I worked with at Caltech. He taught me quite a bit about Unix and programming over the years, and I owe him greatly for it. You can read his material here: *http://www.ugcs.caltech.edu/~bruce/*.

Also thanks to Alberto Valez, my boss at Sony Imageworks, for being possibly the best boss I ever had and giving me the chance to completely automate my job. Thanks to film editor Ed Fuller, who helped with advice on the book, and was a good friend during this process.

Thanks to many people in the Python community. First, thanks to Guido van Rossum for writing a great language, for being a great leader, and for being patient with me when I asked for advice on the book. There are so many rock stars in the Python community who crank out useful tools that I use everyday. They include Ian Bicking, Fernando Perez and Villi Vainio, Mike Bayer, Gustavo Niemeyer, etc. Thanks! Thanks to the great book by David Beazely, and his fantastic tutorial at PyCon 2008 on Generators. Thanks to other writers about Python and systems administration as well. You can find links to their work here: *http://wiki.python.org/moin/systems_administration*. Thanks also to the Repoze crew: Tres Seaver and Chris McDonough (*http://repoze.org/index.html*).

Special thanks to the great tools, advice, and tolerance from Phillip J. Eby on the setuptools section. Also, thanks to Jim Fulton who tolerated my questions about ZODB and buildout, with a crazy schedule. Additional thanks to Martijn Fassen, who taught me about ZODB and Grok. If you want to see the future of Python web development, check out Grok: *http://grok.zope.org/*.

Thanks to *Red Hat Magazine* staff, Julie Bryce, Jessica Gerber, Bascha Harris, and Ruth Suehle, for letting me try out ideas we used in this book in the form of articles. Also, thanks to Mike McCrary at IBM Developerworks, for letting me write articles to try out ideas we used in this book.

I want to thank the multitudes of people who told me at one point in my life that I couldn't do something. At almost every step, I have met discouraging people who told me everything from I would never get into the college I wanted to to I would never learn to program. Thank you for giving me the extra motivation to succeed at my dreams.

Humans can create their own reality if they truly believe in themselves, and I would encourage everyone to give themselves a chance to do what they truly want to do.

Finally, thanks to O'Reilly and Tatiana Apandi, for believing in my original pitch for a book on Python and Systems Administration. You took a chance and believed in me and Jeremy, and I thank you for that. Although Tatiana left O'Reilly near the end of our book to pursue her dreams, her impact was still felt. I also want to thank our new editor Julie Steele, who has been supportive and helpful every step of the way. You have really provided a sea of calm that I personally appreciated greatly. I look forward to hearing great things in the future from Julie, and I'm excited to work with her again.

Jeremy's Acknowledgments

After reading Noah's list of thanks, it makes me feel both ungrateful, because I know my list won't be that long, and at a loss, because I think he covered nearly everyone that I wanted to thank.

First, I must thank my God, through Whom I can do all things and without Whom, I can do nothing.

First in an earthly sense, I thank my wife, Debra. You kept the children engaged with other activities while I worked on the book. You enforced the so-often reapeated rule "Don't bother Daddy while he's working on his book." You encouraged me when I needed it, and you also gave me a lot of space, which is what I needed most. Thank you. I love you. I could not have written this book without you.

I also must thank my sweet children, Zane and Justus, for their patience through the process of my writing this book. I missed out on a lot of trips to Stone Mountain with you both. I still put one of you to bed most nights, but I missed out on staying in there long enough to fall asleep with you, like I used to. I missed out on the last several weeks of Kid's Rock on Wednesday nights. I missed out on so much, but you bore it patiently. So, thank you for your patience. And thank you for your excitement as you hear that I'm almost done with the book. I love you both.

I want to thank my parents, Charles and Lynda Jones, for their support through the course of my writing this book. But more than that, I want to thank them for being a living example of a strong work ethic, of earning everything you have, of working hard to better yourself, and of spending money wisely. Those are lessons I hope to pass on to Zane and Justus.

Thank you to Noah Gift, my coauthor, for getting me into this mess. It has been hard, harder than I thought and definitely one of the hardest things I've ever done in my life. I think it says a lot about a person when you work on something like this with him and at the end, you can still think of him as your friend. Thanks, Noah. This book would not have begun if not for you.

I want to thank our team of reviewers. I think that Noah has already thanked all of you, but I want to thank everyone that I can: Doug Hellman, Jennifer Davis, Shannon JJ Behrens, Chris McDowell, Titus Brown, and Scott Leerseen. You guys were awesome. There were times when I thought that I had something spot-on and you readjusted my thinking. Or you just brought a completely different perspective to the book and helped me see my work through a different set of eyes. (That was mostly you, Jennifer. If the text processing chapter is useful for sysadmins, it's mostly because of you.) Thank you all.

I also want to thank our editors, Tatiana Apandi and Julie Steele. You guys handled the hard stuff, freeing us up to work on the book. You both eased our burden along the way. Thank you.

I'd also like to thank Fernando Perez and Ville Vainio for your amazing feedback. I hope I've done IPython justice. And thank you for IPython. I feel like I couldn't live without it.

Thank you Duncan McGreggor, for helping me get the Twisted code in better shape. Your comments were extemely helpful. And thank you for working on Twisted. It is an amazing framework. I hope to use it more, real soon now.

I thank Bram Moolenaar and everyone who has ever worked on the Vim editor. Almost every word and XML tag that I wrote flowed through capabilities Vim. I picked up a few tricks along the way that I'll incorporate into my daily editing habits. Vim made me more productive. Thank you.

I also want to thank Linus Torvalds, the Debian folks, the Ubuntu folks, and anyone else who has ever worked on Linux. Almost every word that I typed was done on Linux. You made it incredibly simple to set up new environments and test different things. Thank you.

Finally, but by no means least, I want to thank Guido van Rossum and everyone who has ever done any work on Python. I have been benefitting from your work for a number of years now. I was hired for my last two jobs because of Python. Python, the language, and Python, the community, have been both a great joy for me since I started working with it sometime around 2001–2002. Thank you. Python has been very good to me.

## CHAPTER 1

Introduction

Why Python?

If you are a system administrator, it is likely that you have encountered Perl, Bash, ksh, or some other scripting language. You may have even used one or more yourself. Scripting languages are often used to do repetitive, tedious work at a rate and with an accuracy that far surpass what you could accomplish without them. All languages are tools. They are simply a means to get work done. They have value only insofar as they help you get your job done better. We believe that Python is a valuable tool, specifically because it enables you to get your work done efficiently.

So is Python better than Perl, Bash, Ruby, or any other language? It's really difficult to put that sort of qualitative label on a programming language, since the tool is so closely tied to the thought process of the programmer who is using it. Programming is a subjective, deeply personal activity. For the language to be excellent, it must fit the person using it. So we're not going to argue that Python is better, but we will explain the reasons that we believe Python can be an excellent choice. We'll also explain why it is a great fit for performing sysadmin tasks.

The first reason that we think that Python is excellent is that it is easy to learn. If a language can't help you become productive pretty quickly, the lure of that language is severely diminished. Why would you want to spend weeks or months studying a language before you are able to write a program that does something useful? This is especially the case for sysadmins. If you are a sysadmin, your work can pile up faster than you can unpile it. With Python, you can start writing useful scripts literally in hours rather than in days or weeks. If you can't learn a language quickly enough to start writing scripts with it almost immediately, you should strongly question whether you should be learning it.

However, a language that is easy to learn but doesn't allow you to do fairly complex tasks isn't worth much either. So the second reason that we consider Python to be an excellent programming language is that, while it lets you start simply, it also allows you to perform tasks that are as complex as you can imagine. Do you need to read through a logfile line by line and pull out some pretty basic information? Python can handle that. Or do you need to parse through a logfile, extract every piece of information that it provides, compare usage from each IP address in this logfile to usage in each logfile (which are stored in a relational database, by the way) from the past three months, and then store the results to a relational database? Sure, Python can do that as well. Python is being used on some pretty complex problems, such as analysis of genomic sequences, multithreaded web servers, and heavy duty statistical analysis. You may never have to work on anything like that, but it's nice to know that when you need to do complex things, the language is able to work with you.

Additionally, if you are able to perform complex operations, but the maintainability of your code suffers along the way, that isn't a good thing. Python doesn't prevent code maintenance problems, but it does allow you to express complex ideas with simple language constructs. Simplicity is a huge factor in writing code that is easy to maintain later. Python has made it pretty simple for us to go back over our own code and work on it after we haven't touched it in months. It has also been pretty simple for us to work on code that we haven't seen before. So the language, that is the language's syntax and common idioms, are clear and concise and easy to work with over long periods of time.

The next reason we consider Python to be an excellent language is its readability. Python relies on whitespace to determine where code blocks begin and end. The indentation helps your eyes quickly follow the flow of a program. Python also tends to be "word-based." By that we mean that while Python uses its share of special characters, features are often implemented as keywords or with libraries. The emphasis on words rather than special characters helps the reading and comprehension of code.

Now that we've outlined a few of Python's benefits, we'll show some comparisons of code examples in Python, Perl, and Bash. Along the way, we'll also look at a few more of Python's benefits. Here is a simple example, in Bash, of showing all the combinations of 1, 2 and a, b:

```
#!/bin/bash

for a in 1 2; do
    for b in a b; do
        echo "$a $b"
    done
done
```

And here is a comparable piece of Perl:

```
#!/usr/bin/perl

foreach $a ('1', '2') {
    foreach $b ('a', 'b') {
        print "$a $b\n";
    }
}
```

This is a pretty simple nested loop. Let's compare these looping mechanisms with a for loop in Python:

```
#!/usr/bin/env python

for a in [1, 2]:
    for b in ['a', 'b']:
        print a, b
```

Next, we'll demonstrate using conditionals in Bash, Perl, and Python. We have a simple if/else condition check here. We're just checking to see whether a certain file path is a directory:

```
#!/bin/bash

if [ -d "/tmp" ] ; then
    echo "/tmp is a directory"
else
    echo "/tmp is not a directory"
fi
```

Here is the Perl equivalent of the same script:

```
#!/usr/bin/perl

if (-d "/tmp") {
    print "/tmp is a directory\n";
}
else {
    print "/tmp is not a directory\n";
}
```

And here is the Python equivalent of the script:

```
#!/usr/bin/env python

import os

if os.path.isdir("/tmp"):
    print "/tmp is a directory"
else:
    print "/tmp is not a directory"
```

Another point in favor of Python's excellence is its simple support for object-oriented programming (OOP). And, actually, the converse of that is that you don't have to do OOP if you don't want to. But if you do, it's dead simple in Python. OOP allows you to easily and cleanly break problems apart and bundle pieces of functionality together into single "things" or "objects." Bash doesn't support OOP, but both Perl and Python do. Here is a module in Perl that defines a class:

```
package Server;
use strict;

sub new {
    my $class = shift;
    my $self  = {};
    $self->{IP} = shift;
    $self->{HOSTNAME} = shift;
    bless($self);
```

```perl
        return $self;
    }

    sub set_ip {
        my $self = shift;
        $self->{IP} = shift;
        return $self->{IP};
    }

    sub set_hostname {
        my $self = shift;
        $self->{HOSTNAME} = shift;
        return $self->{HOSTNAME};
    }

    sub ping {
        my $self = shift;
        my $external_ip = shift;
        my $self_ip = $self->{IP};
        my $self_host = $self->{HOSTNAME};
        print "Pinging $external_ip from $self_ip ($self_host)\n";
        return 0;
    }

    1;
```

And here is a piece of code that uses it:

```perl
#!/usr/bin/perl

use Server;

$server = Server->new('192.168.1.15', 'grumbly');
$server->ping('192.168.1.20');
```

The code that makes use of the OO module is straightforward and simple. The OO module may take a bit more mental parsing if you're not familiar with OOP or with the way that Perl tackles OOP.

A comparable Python class and use of the class looks something like this:

```python
#!/usr/bin/env python

class Server(object):
    def __init__(self, ip, hostname):
        self.ip = ip
        self.hostname = hostname
    def set_ip(self, ip):
        self.ip = ip
    def set_hostname(self, hostname):
        self.hostname = hostname
    def ping(self, ip_addr):
        print "Pinging %s from %s (%s)" % (ip_addr, self.ip, self.hostname)

if __name__ == '__main__':
```

```
server = Server('192.168.1.20', 'bumbly')
server.ping('192.168.1.15')
```

Both the Perl and Python examples demonstrate some of the fundamental pieces of OOP. The two examples together display the different flavors that each respective language provides while reaching toward its respective goals. They both do the same thing, but are different from one another. So, if you want to use OOP, Python supports it. And it's quite simple and clear to incorporate it into your programming.

Another element of Python's excellence comes not from the language itself, but from the community. In the Python community, there is much consensus about the way to accomplish certain tasks and the idioms that you should (and should not) use. While the language itself may support certain phrasings for accomplishing something, the consensus of the community may steer you away from that phrasing. For example, `from module import *` at the top of a module is valid Python. However, the community frowns upon this and recommends that you use either: `import module` or: `from module import resource`. Importing all the contents of a module into another module's namespace can cause serious annoyance when you try to figure out how a module works, what functions it is calling, and where those functions come from. This particular convention will help you write code that is clearer and will allow people who work on your code after you to have a more pleasant maintenance experience. Following common conventions for writing your code will put you on the path of best practices. We consider this a good thing.

The Python Standard Library is another excellent attribute of Python. If you ever hear the phrase "batteries included" in reference to Python, it simply means that the standard library allows you to perform all sorts of tasks without having to go elsewhere for modules to help you get it done. For example, though it isn't built-in to the language directly, Python includes regular expression functionality; sockets; threads; date/time functionality; XML parsers; config file parser; file and directory functionality; data persistence; unit test capabilities; and http, ftp, imap, smpt, and nntp client libraries; and much more. So once Python is installed, modules to support all of these functions will be imported by your scripts as they are needed. You have all the functionality we just listed here. It is impressive that all of this comes with Python without requiring anything else. All of this functionality will help you out immensely as you write Python programs to do work for you.

Easy access to numerous third-party packages is another real advantage of Python. In addition to the many libraries in the Python Standard Library, there are a number of libraries and utilities that are easily accessible on the internet that you can install with a single shell command. The Python Package Index, PyPI (*http://pypi.python.org*), is a place where anyone who has written a Python package can upload it for others to use. At the time we are writing this book, there are over 3,800 packages available for download and use. Packages include IPython, which we cover in the following chapter; Storm (an object-relational mapper, which we cover in Chapter 12); and Twisted, a network framework, which we cover in Chapter 5—just to name 3 of the over 3,800 packages.

Once you start using PyPI, you'll find it nearly indispensible for finding and installing useful packages.

Many of the benefits that we see in Python stem from the central philosophy of Python. When you type import this at a Python prompt, you will see *The Zen of Python* by Tim Peters. Here it is:

```
In [1]: import this
The Zen of Python, by Tim Peters

Beautiful is better than ugly.
Explicit is better than implicit.
Simple is better than complex.
Complex is better than complicated.
Flat is better than nested.
Sparse is better than dense.
Readability counts.
Special cases aren't special enough to break the rules.
Although practicality beats purity.
Errors should never pass silently.
Unless explicitly silenced.
In the face of ambiguity, refuse the temptation to guess.
There should be one-- and preferably only one --obvious way to do it.
Although that way may not be obvious at first unless you're Dutch.
Now is better than never.
Although never is often better than *right* now.
If the implementation is hard to explain, it's a bad idea.
If the implementation is easy to explain, it may be a good idea.
Namespaces are one honking great idea -- let's do more of those!
```

This statement isn't a dogmatic imperative that is strictly enforced at all levels of development of the language, but the spirit of it seems to permeate much of what happens in and with the language. And we have found this spirit to be a beautiful thing. This is perhaps the essence of why we choose to use Python day after day. This philosophy resonates within us as what we want and expect from a language. And if this resonates with you, then Python is probably a good choice for you as well.

Motivation

If you justpicked up this book in a bookstore or are reading an introduction online somewhere, you may be asking yourself, how hard it is going to be to learn Python and if it is even worth it. Although Python is catching on like wildfire, there are many sysadmins who have been exposed to Bash and Perl only. If you find yourself in this category, you should take comfort in knowing that Python is very easy to learn. In fact, although it is a matter of opinion, Python is considered by many to be the easiest language to learn and teach, period!

If you already know Python, or are a programming guru in another language, you will probably be able to jump right into any of the following chapters without reading this intro and immediately start being productive using our examples. We made a concerted effort to create examples that will actually help you get your job done. There are examples of ways to discover and monitor subnets automatically with SNMP, to convert to an interactive Python shell called IPython, to build data processing pipelines, to write custom metadata management tools with object-relational mappers, to perform network programming, to write command-line tools, and much more.

If you are coming from a shell programming/scripting background, though, don't worry at all. You, too, can learn Python quite easily. You need only motivation, curiosity, and determination, the same factors that led you to pick up this book and look at the introduction in the first place.

We sense there are still a few skeptics out there. Maybe some of the things you have heard about programming have scared you. One common, and horribly false, misconception is that only some people can learn to program, and they are a mysterious and elite few. The frank truth is that anyone can learn how to program. A second, equally false, misconception is that earning a computer science degree is the only way a person can truly become a software engineer. But some of the most prolific software developers do not have engineering degrees. There are people with philosophy, journalism, nutritional science, and English degrees who are competent Python programmers. Having a degree in computer science is not a requirement to learn Python, although it certainly doesn't hurt.

Another funny, and false, misconception is that you must have started to program in your teenage years, or you will never learn to program. While this makes people who were lucky enough to have someone in their life that encouraged them to program at a young age feel good, it is another myth. It is very helpful to have started learning programming at a young age, but age is not a requirement to learn Python. Learning Python is most certainly not a "young person's game," as we have heard some people say. There are countless cases of developers who learned to program in their late 20s, 30s, 40s, and onward.

If you have gotten this far, we should point out that you, the reader, have an advantage many people do not. If you decided to pick up a book on Python for Unix and Linux system administration, then you most likely know something about how to execute commands from a shell. This is a tremendous advantage to learning to become a Python programmer. Having an understanding of the way to execute commands from a terminal is all that is required for this introduction to Python. If you truly believe you will learn how to program with Python, then read the next section immediately. If you don't believe it yet, then reread this section again, and convince yourself it really is just a matter of getting your mind to understand you do have the power to learn how to program in Python. It is really that simple; if you make this decision, it will change your life.

The Basics

This introduction to Python is going to be very different from any other one we've seen, as it will use an interactive shell called IPython and a regular Bash shell. You will need to open two terminal windows, one with IPython and one with Bash. In every example, we will compare what we do in Python with a Bash example. The first steps are to download the correct version of IPython for your platform and install it. You can get a copy at *http://ipython.scipy.org/moin/Download.* If for some reason, you can't get IPython to install you can also just use a regular Python shell. You can also download a copy of the virtual machine that includes all of the software for the book, as we have a copy of IPython preconfigured and ready to run. You just need to type in ipython, and you will get a prompt.

Once you have installed IPython and have an IPython shell prompt, it should look something like this:

```
[ngift@Macintosh-7][H:10679][J:0]# ipython
Python 2.5.1 (r251:54863, Jan 17 2008, 19:35:17)
Type "copyright", "credits" or "license" for more information.

IPython 0.8.2 -- An enhanced Interactive Python.
?         -> Introduction and overview of IPython's features.
%quickref -> Quick reference.
help      -> Python's own help system.
object?   -> Details about 'object'. ?object also works, ?? prints more.

In [1]:
```

An IPython shell is quite a bit like a regular Bash shell and can execute commands such as ls, cd, and pwd, but you can read the next chapter for more of a scoop on IPython. This chapter is about learning Python, so on to the tutorial.

In your Python terminal, type in the following:

```
In [1]: print "I can program in Python"
I can program in Python
```

In your Bash terminal, type in the following:

```
[ngift@Macintosh-7][H:10688][J:0]# echo "I can program in Bash"
I can program in Bash
```

In these two examples, there isn't much of a difference in Python and Bash; we hope it takes some of the mystery out of Python.

Executing Statements in Python

If you spend a lot of your day typing commands into a terminal, then you are used to executing statements and, perhaps, redirecting the output to a file or to another Unix command. Let's look at the way we would execute a command in Bash and then compare that to the way it works in Python. In the Bash terminal, type the following:

```
[ngift@Macintosh-7][H:10701][J:0]# ls -l /tmp/
total 0
-rw-r--r--  1 ngift  wheel  0 Apr  7 00:26 file.txt
```

In the Python terminal, type the following:

```
In [2]: import subprocess

In [3]: subprocess.call(["ls","-l ","/tmp/"])
total 0
-rw-r--r--  1 ngift  wheel  0 Apr  7 00:26 file.txt
Out[3]: 0
```

The Bash example shouldn't need any explanation as it is a simple ls command, but if you have never seen Python code before, the Python example probably looks a bit strange. You might be thinking, "What the heck is this import subprocess thing?" One of the powerful features of Python is its ability to import modules or other files that contain code and reuse them in a new program. If you are familiar with "sourcing" a file in Bash, then you will recognize some similarities. In this particular situation, all that is important to know is that you import the subprocess and use it in the syntax that is shown. We will get into the particulars of how subprocess and import work later, but for now, ignore why it works and copy the code:

```
subprocess.call(["some_command", "some_argument", "another_argument_or_path"])
```

You can run any shell command in Python just as it would be run with Bash. Given this bit of information, you can now create a Python version of ls. Just open up your favorite text editor in another terminal tab or window and place this in a file named *pyls.py*, and make it executable by using chmod +x pyls.py. See Example 1-1.

Example 1-1. Python wrapper for ls command

```
#!/usr/bin/env python
#Python wrapper for the ls command

import subprocess

subprocess.call(["ls","-l"])
```

Now if you run this script, you will get the exact same output that you would get if you ran ls -ls from the command line:

```
[ngift@Macintosh-7][H:10746][J:0]# ./pyls.py
total 8
-rwxr-xr-x  1 ngift  staff  115 Apr  7 12:57 pyls.py
```

While this may seem silly, (and it is silly actually), it gives you a good idea of a common use of Python in systems programming. Often, you use Python to "wrap" other scripts or Unix commands. Given this new bit of information, you could happily start writing some basic scripts if you just put one command after another in a file and ran it. Let's take a look at something pretty simple that does just that. To follow along from home, either cut and paste the code in Example 1-2, or run the scripts *pysysinfo.py* and *bash-sysinfo.sh* located in the source code that is included with this chapter. See Examples 1-2 and 1-3.

Example 1-2. System information script—Python

```python
#!/usr/bin/env python
#A System Information Gathering Script
import subprocess

#Command 1
uname = "uname"
uname_arg = "-a"
print "Gathering system information with %s command:\n" % uname
subprocess.call([uname, uname_arg])

#Command 2
diskspace = "df"
diskspace_arg = "-h"
print "Gathering diskspace information %s command:\n" % diskspace
subprocess.call([diskspace, diskspace_arg])
```

Example 1-3. System information script—Bash

```bash
#!/usr/bin/env bash
#A System Information Gathering Script

#Command 1
UNAME="uname -a"
printf "Gathering system information with the $UNAME command: \n\n"
$UNAME

#Command 2
DISKSPACE="df -h"
printf "Gathering diskspace information with the $DISKSPACE command: \n\n"
$DISKSPACE
```

If we look at both of the scripts, we see that they look a lot a like. And if we run them, we see that the output of each is identical. One quick note though: splitting the command from the argument is completely optional using `subprocess.call`. You can also use this syntax:

```python
subprocess.call("df -h", shell=True)
```

So far so good, but we still haven't explained `import` and `subprocess` completely. In the Python version of the script, we imported the `subprocess` module because it already contained the code to make system calls in Python.

As we mentioned earlier, importing a module like `subprocess` is just importing a file that contains code you can use. You can create your own module or file and reuse code you have written in the same way you import `subprocess`. Importing is not magic at all, it is just a file with some code in it. One of the nice things about the IPython shell that you have open is its ability to inspect inside modules and files, and see the attributes that are available inside them. In Unix terms, this is a lot like running the ls command inside of */usr/bin*. If you happen to be on a new system such as Ubuntu or Solaris, and you are used to Red Hat, you might do an ls of */usr/bin* to see if tools such as wget, curl, or lynx are available. If you want to use a tool you find inside */usr/bin*, you would simply type **/usr/bin/wget**, for example.

Modules such as subprocess are very similar. With IPython you can use tab complete to look at the tools that are available inside a module. Let's walk through subprocess using tab complete to look at the attributes available inside of it. Remember, a module is just a file with some code in it. Here is what a tab complete looks like with the subprocess module in IPython:

```
In [12]: subprocess.
subprocess.CalledProcessError   subprocess.__hash__        subprocess.call
subprocess.MAXFD                subprocess.__init__        subprocess.check_call
subprocess.PIPE                 subprocess.__name__        subprocess.errno
subprocess.Popen                subprocess.__new__         subprocess.fcntl
subprocess.STDOUT               subprocess.__reduce__      subprocess.list2cmdline
subprocess.__all__              subprocess.__reduce_ex__   subprocess.mswindows
subprocess.__builtins__         subprocess.__repr__        subprocess.os
subprocess.__class__            subprocess.__setattr__     subprocess.pickle
subprocess.__delattr__          subprocess.__str__         subprocess.select
subprocess.__dict__             subprocess._active         subprocess.sys
subprocess.__doc__              subprocess._cleanup        subprocess.traceback
subprocess.__file__             subprocess._demo_posix     subprocess.types
subprocess.__getattribute__     subprocess._demo_windows
```

To replicate this same behavior, you simply need to type:

```
import subprocess
```

and then type:

```
subprocess.
```

and press Tab to get a tab completion of the attributes available. In the third column of our example, notice that you see **subprocess.call**. Now, to see more information about how to use **subprocess.call**, type:

```
In [13]: subprocess.call?
```

```
Type:          function
Base Class:    <type 'function'>
String Form:   <function call at 0x561370>
Namespace:     Interactive
File:          /System/Library/Frameworks/Python.framework/Versions/2.5/lib/python2.5/
          subprocess.py
Definition:    subprocess.call(*popenargs, **kwargs)
Docstring:
    Run command with arguments. Wait for command to complete, then
    return the returncode attribute.

    The arguments are the same as for the Popen constructor. Example:
```

```
retcode = call(["ls", "-l"])
```

Think of the special question mark syntax as a manpage query. If you want to know how a tool works in Unix, simply type:

```
man name_of_tool
```

It is the same with an attribute located inside a module such as `subprocess.call`. In IPython, when you type a question mark after the attribute you want to find information about, the documentation that has been included with the attribute will print out. If you do this on most attributes in the standard library, you should find some helpful information to properly use them. Keep in mind that you can also refer to the Python Standard Library documentation as well.

When we look at this documentation, "Docstring" is the official term, we see an example of the way to use `subprocess.call` and a description of what it does.

Summary

You now have enough information to call yourself a Python programmer. You know how to write a simple Python script, how to translate simple scripts from Bash and call them with Python, and, finally, how to find documentation about new modules and attributes. In the next section, you'll see how to better organize these flat sequences of commands into functions.

Using Functions in Python

In the previous section we went through executing statements one after another, which is pretty useful, because it means we were able to automate something that we would normally have to do manually. The next step to automating our code execution is to create functions. If you are not already familiar with writing functions in Bash or another language, then one way to think about functions is as miniscripts. A function allows you to create blocks of statements that get called in groups that live inside of the function. This is quite a bit like the Bash script we wrote in which there were two commands enclosed in a script. One of the differences between a Bash script and a function is that you can include many function scripts. Ultimately, you can have multiple functions that group statements together in a script, and then that group of statements can be called to run a miniprogram at the proper time in your script.

At this point, we need to talk about the topic of whitespace. In Python, a uniform level of indentation must be maintained in nesting code. In another language, like Bash, when you define a function you put brackets around the code inside of a function. With Python, you must indent the code inside of the bracket. This can trip up newcomers to the language, at first, but after a while it will grow on you, and you will realize that this encourages readable code. If you have trouble getting any of these examples to work interactively, make sure you refer to the actual source code to see the proper indentation level. The most common practice is to set a tab to indent exactly four spaces.

Let's take a look at how this works in Python and Bash. If you still have the IPython shell open, you don't need to create a Python script file, although you can if you like. Just type the following into the interactive IPython prompt:

```
In [1]: def pyfunc():
   ...:     print "Hello function"
   ...:
   ...:

In [2]: pyfunc
Out[2]: <function pyfunc at 0x2d5070>

In [3]: pyfunc()
Hello function

In [4]: for i in range(5):
   ...:     pyfunc()
   ...:
   ...:
Hello function
Hello function
Hello function
Hello function
Hello function
```

In this example, you can see that putting a print statement in a function allows you not only to call the function later but also to call it as many times as we want. In line [4], we use a programming idiom, or technique, that executes the function five times. If you haven't seen that technique before, understand that it calls the function five times.

We can do the same thing in a live Bash shell as well. Here is one way:

```
bash-3.2$ function shfunc()
> {
>     printf "Hello function\n"
> }
bash-3.2$ for (( i=0 ; i < 5 ; i++))
> do
>     shfunc
> done
Hello function
Hello function
Hello function
Hello function
Hello function
```

In the Bash example, we created a simple function shfunc, and then called it five times, just like we did with the Python function earlier. One thing to notice is that the Bash example requires more "baggage" to do the same thing that Python does. Notice the difference between the Bash for loop and the Python for loop. If this is your first exposure to a function in Bash or Python, you should make some other functions in your IPython window before you continue.

Functions are not magic, and writing multiple functions interactively is a great way to take away the mystery if this is your first experience with them. Here are a couple of examples of simple functions:

```
In [1]: def print_many():
   ...:     print "Hello function"
   ...:     print "Hi again function"
   ...:     print "Sick of me yet"
   ...:
   ...:

In [2]: print_many()
Hello function
Hi again function
Sick of me yet

In [3]: def addition():
   ...:     sum = 1+1
   ...:     print "1 + 1 = %s" % sum
   ...:
   ...:

In [4]: addition()
1 + 1 = 2
```

Now we have a few silly examples under our belt, in addition to the silly examples that you tried out on your own as well, right? So we can go back to the script we wrote that prints system information and convert those statements into functions. See Example 1-4.

Example 1-4. Converted Python system info script: pysysinfo_func.py

```
#!/usr/bin/env python
#A System Information Gathering Script
import subprocess

#Command 1
def uname_func():

    uname = "uname"
    uname_arg = "-a"
    print "Gathering system information with %s command:\n" % uname
    subprocess.call([uname, uname_arg])

#Command 2
def disk_func():

    diskspace = "df"
    diskspace_arg = "-h"
    print "Gathering diskspace information %s command:\n" % diskspace
    subprocess.call([diskspace, diskspace_arg])
```

```
#Main function that call other functions
def main():
    uname_func()
    disk_func()

main()
```

Given our experiments with functions, this converted example of our previous script that we simply placed these statements inside functions and then used the main function to call them all at once. If you are not familiar with this style, you might not have known that it is common to create several functions inside a script and then call them all with one main function. One of many reasons for this is that if you decide to reuse this script for another program, you can either call the functions independently or together with the main method. The key is that you decide after the module is imported.

When there is no control flow, or main function, then all of the code gets executed immediately when it is imported. This may be OK for a one-off script, but if you plan to create reusable tools, and you should, then it is a good practice to create functions that encapsulate specific actions, and then have a main function that executes the whole program.

For comparison's sake, let's convert our previous Bash system information script to use functions as well. See Example 1-5.

Example 1-5. Converted Bash system info script: bashsysinfo_func.sh

```
#!/usr/bin/env bash
#A System Information Gathering Script

#Command 1
function uname_func ()
{
    UNAME="uname -a"
    printf "Gathering system information with the $UNAME command: \n\n"
    $UNAME
}
#Command 2
function disk_func ()
{
    DISKSPACE="df -h"
    printf "Gathering diskspace information with the $DISKSPACE command: \n\n"
    $DISKSPACE
}

function main ()
{
    uname_func
    disk_func
}

main
```

Looking at our Bash example, you can see it has quite a bit in common with its Python cousin. We created two functions and then called those two functions by calling the main function. If this is your first experience with functions, then we would highly recommend that you comment out the main method by placing a pound sign in front of both the Bash and the Python scripts and running them again. You should get absolutely nothing when you run both scripts, because the program should execute, but won't call the two functions inside.

At this point, you are now a programmer capable of writing simple functions in both Bash and Python. Programmers learn by doing, though, so at this point we highly recommend that you change the system calls in these two Bash and Python programs and make them your own. Give yourself some bonus points if you add several new functions to the script and call them from a main function.

Reusing Code with the Import Statement

One problem with learning something new is that, if it is abstract, like calculus, for example, it is hard to justify caring about it. When was the last time you used the math you learned in high school at the grocery store? In our previous examples, we showed you how to create functions as an alternative to executing shell commands one after another in a script. We also told you that a module is really just a script, or some lines of code in a file. It isn't anything tricky, but it does need to be arranged in a particular way so that it can be reused in another future program. Here is the point where we show you why you should care. Let's import the previous system information scripts in both Bash and Python and execute.

Open the IPython and Bash windows if you closed them so that we can demonstrate very quickly why functions are important for code reuse. One of the first scripts we created in Python was a sequence of commands in a file named *pysysinfo.py*. In Python because a file is a module and vice versa, we can import this script file into IPython. Keep in mind that you never need to specify the *.py* portion of the file you are importing. In fact if you do this, the import will not work. Here is what it looks like when we do that on Noah's Macbook Pro laptop:

```
In [1]: import pysysinfo
Gathering system information with uname command:

Darwin Macintosh-8.local 9.2.2 Darwin Kernel Version 9.2.2: /
   Tue Mar  4 21:17:34 PST 2008; root:xnu-1228.4.31~1/RELEASE_I386 i386
Gathering diskspace information df command:

Filesystem      Size   Used  Avail Capacity  Mounted on
/dev/disk0s2    93Gi   88Gi  4.2Gi    96%    /
devfs          110Ki  110Ki   0Bi    100%    /dev
fdesc          1.0Ki  1.0Ki   0Bi    100%    /dev
map -hosts      0Bi    0Bi    0Bi    100%    /net
map auto_home   0Bi    0Bi    0Bi    100%    /home
```

```
/dev/disk1s2   298Gi 105Gi 193Gi   36%   /Volumes/Backup
/dev/disk2s3   466Gi 240Gi 225Gi   52%   /Volumes/EditingDrive
```

Wow, that is pretty cool, right? If you import a file full of Python code it seems to runs great. But, actually, there are a few problems with this. If you plan to run Python code, it should always be executed from the command line as a part of a script or program you write. Using import is to help with this "reusing code" idea we keep throwing around. Here is the punch line: what if you only wanted to print the output of the diskspace portion of the script? The answer is you can't. That is why you use functions. They allow you to control when and how parts of your program run so that they don't all run at once, as they do in this example. Don't just take our word for it, though. If you import the example of a script that puts these commands into functions, you'll see what we mean.

Here is the output from the IPython terminal:

```
In [3]: import pysysinfo_func
Gathering system information with uname command:

Darwin Macintosh-8.local 9.2.2 Darwin Kernel Version 9.2.2:
    Tue Mar  4 21:17:34 PST 2008; root:xnu-1228.4.31~1/RELEASE_I386 i386
Gathering diskspace information df command:

Filesystem     Size   Used  Avail Capacity  Mounted on
/dev/disk0s2   93Gi   88Gi  4.1Gi   96%     /
devfs          110Ki  110Ki  0Bi   100%     /dev
fdesc          1.0Ki  1.0Ki  0Bi   100%     /dev
map -hosts     0Bi    0Bi    0Bi   100%     /net
map auto_home  0Bi    0Bi    0Bi   100%     /home
/dev/disk1s2   298Gi  105Gi 193Gi   36%     /Volumes/Backup
/dev/disk2s3   466Gi  240Gi 225Gi   52%     /Volumes/EditingDrive
```

Now we get the exact same output that we get from script that doesn't contain functions. If you are puzzled, this is a good sign. To see the reason we get the same exact output, we just need to look at the source code. If you are following along at home, open up another terminal tab or window and look at the script pysysinfo_func:

```
#Main function that call other functions
def main():
    uname_func()
    disk_func()

main()
```

The problem is that main function we created at the end of the last chapter is coming back to bite us. On one hand we want to be able to run our script on the command line to get the output, but on the other hand when we import it we don't want all of the output all at once. Fortunately, the need to use a module as both a script that gets executed from the command line and as a reusable module is very common in Python. The solution is to change the way the main method gets called by replacing the last part of the script to look like this:

```
      #Main function that call other functions
      def main():
          uname_func()
          disk_func()

      if __name__ == "__main__":
          main()
```

This is an "idiom," a technique that is commonly used to solve a problem. Any code that you indent underneath this statement gets run only when it is executed from the command line. To see this, either replace this in your copy of the script or import the fixed version of the script pysysinfo_func_2.py.

Now, if we go back to our IPython interpreter and import this new script, we should see this:

```
      In [1]: import pysysinfo_func_2
```

This time, the main method is not called, because of the fix we made. So, to return to our original point about reusable code, we have three functions that we can use in other programs or use to interact with the IPython shell. Remember earlier we said how it would be nice to call only the function that prints the disk usage without having to call the function that calls the other commands, too. First, though, we need to review an IPython trick that we showed you before. Remember that you can use Tab to complete a module, and it will show you all of the attributes that are available to use. Here's what that looks like:

```
      In [2]: pysysinfo_func_2.
      pysysinfo_func_2.__builtins__       pysysinfo_func_2.disk_func
      pysysinfo_func_2.__class__          pysysinfo_func_2.main
      pysysinfo_func_2.__delattr__        pysysinfo_func_2.py
      pysysinfo_func_2.__dict__           pysysinfo_func_2.pyc
      pysysinfo_func_2.__doc__            pysysinfo_func_2.subprocess
      pysysinfo_func_2.__file__           pysysinfo_func_2.uname_func
      pysysinfo_func_2.__getattribute__
      pysysinfo_func_2.__hash__
```

In this example, we can ignore anything with double underscores, because these are special methods that are beyond the scope of this introduction. Because IPython is also a regular shell, it picks up the filename and the byte-compiled Python file with the .pyc extension. Once we filter past all of those names, we can see that there is a pysysinfo_func_2.disk_func. Let's go ahead and call that function:

```
      In [2]: pysysinfo_func_2.disk_func()
      Gathering diskspace information df command:

      Filesystem       Size  Used  Avail Capacity  Mounted on
      /dev/disk0s2     93Gi  89Gi  4.1Gi    96%    /
      devfs           111Ki 111Ki   0Bi    100%    /dev
      fdesc           1.0Ki 1.0Ki   0Bi    100%    /dev
      map -hosts        0Bi   0Bi   0Bi    100%    /net
      map auto_home     0Bi   0Bi   0Bi    100%    /home
```

```
/dev/disk1s2   298Gi  105Gi  193Gi   36%   /Volumes/Backup
/dev/disk2s3   466Gi  240Gi  225Gi   52%   /Volumes/EditingDrive
```

You might have realized by now that functions are always "called" or run by attaching the "()" after the name. In this case, we ran just that one function inside of a file that contained three functions: the function we just called disk_func, the uname_func, and finally the main function. Aha! We finally have our code reuse. We were able to import something we wrote earlier and interactively run just the part of it we needed. Of course, we can also run the other two functions we wrote separately. Let's take a look at that:

```
In [3]: pysysinfo_func_2.uname_func()
Gathering system information with uname command:

Darwin Macintosh-8.local 9.2.2 Darwin Kernel Version 9.2.2:
    Tue Mar  4 21:17:34 PST 2008; root:xnu-1228.4.31~1/RELEASE_I386 i386

In [4]: pysysinfo_func_2.main()
Gathering system information with uname command:

Darwin Macintosh-8.local 9.2.2 Darwin Kernel Version 9.2.2:
    Tue Mar  4 21:17:34 PST 2008; root:xnu-1228.4.31~1/RELEASE_I386 i386
Gathering diskspace information df command:

Filesystem      Size   Used  Avail Capacity  Mounted on
/dev/disk0s2    93Gi   89Gi  4.1Gi   96%     /
devfs          111Ki  111Ki   0Bi   100%     /dev
fdesc          1.0Ki  1.0Ki   0Bi   100%     /dev
map -hosts       0Bi    0Bi   0Bi   100%     /net
map auto_home    0Bi    0Bi   0Bi   100%     /home
/dev/disk1s2   298Gi  105Gi  193Gi   36%     /Volumes/Backup
/dev/disk2s3   466Gi  240Gi  225Gi   52%     /Volumes/EditingDrive
```

If you look carefully, you'll see that we ran both of the other functions. Remember, the main function runs everything at once.

Often, the point of writing a reusable module is so that you can take some of the code and use it over and over again in a new script. So practice that by writing another script that uses one of the functions. See Example 1-6.

Example 1-6. Reusing code with import: new_pysysinfo

```
#Very short script that reuses pysysinfo_func_2 code
from pysysinfo_func_2 import disk_func
import subprocess

def tmp_space():
    tmp_usage = "du"
    tmp_arg = "-h"
    path = "/tmp"
    print "Space used in /tmp directory"
    subprocess.call([tmp_usage, tmp_arg, path])

def main():
    disk_func()
```

```
    tmp_space()

if __name__ == "__main__":
    main()
```

In this example, not only do we reuse the code we wrote earlier, but we use a special Python syntax that allows us to import the exact function we need. What's fun about reusing code is that it is possible to make a completely different program just by importing the function from our previous program. Notice that in the main method we mix the function from the other module we created, `disk_func()`, and the new one we just created in this file.

In this section, we learned the power of code reuse and how simple it really is. In a nutshell, you put a function or two in a file and then, if you also want it to run as script, place that special `if__name__ == "__main__":` syntax. Later you can either import those functions into IPython or simply reuse them in another script. With the information you have just learned, you are truly dangerous. You could write some pretty sophisticated Python modules and reuse them over and over again to create new tools.

## CHAPTER 2

IPython

One of Python's strengths is its interactive interpreter, or shell. The shell provides a way to quickly test ideas, test features and interfaces of modules you are working with, and perform some one-off tasks for which you would otherwise have written a three line script. The way that we tend to code is by simultaneously running a text editor and a Python prompt (actually, an IPython prompt, but we'll get to that in a moment), frequently interacting with them both, switching back and forth between shell and editor, and often pasting code from one to the other. This approach allows us to see immediate results from Python about the way it handles code and to quickly get the code in the text editor working the way we want it to.

At its heart, IPython is a bundle of interactive Python goodness. It is an amazing Python shell, far superior to the standard Python shell. It also provides the ability to create highly customized console-based command environments; it allows for easy inclusion of an interactive Python shell into any Python application; and it can even be used as a system shell, with some level of success. This chapter will focus on using IPython to improve your productivity on *nix-shell and Python-related tasks.

IPython also has an active, incredibly helpful community behind it. You can sign up for the mailing list at *http://lists.ipython.scipy.org/mailman/listinfo/ipython-user*. There is an excellent wiki at *http://ipython.scipy.org/moin*. And, as part of the wiki, there is a cookbook at *http://ipython.scipy.org/moin/Cookbook*. So, you can read or contribute to any of these resources as you wish. Another area that you can contribute to is the development of IPython. IPython development recently switched to a distributed source control system, so you can just branch their code and start hacking. And if you do something that could benefit others, you can submit your changes to them.

Fernando Perez

Fernando Perez received his Ph.D. in physics and then worked on numerical algorithm development at the Applied Mathematics Department of the University of Colorado. He is currently a research scientist at the Helen Wills Neuroscience Institute at the University of California, Berkeley, focusing on the development of new analysis methods for brain imaging problems and high-level scientific computing tools. Toward the end of his graduate studies, he became involved with the development of Python tools for scientific computing. He started the open source IPython project in 2001, when he was looking for a more efficient interactive workflow for everyday scientific tasks. Thanks to the participation of a growing community of collaborators, this project has grown over the years to be useful to other programmers outside of scientific fields.

Ville Vainio

Ville Vainio received his B.Sc. degree in software engineering, in 2003, from Satakunta University of Applied Sciences, Pori Faculty of Technology in Finland. As of this book's writing, he is employed as a software specialist in the Smartphone department of Digia Plc, doing C++ development for Symbian OS platforms from Nokia and UIQ. During his studies, he functioned as software engineer at Cimcorp Oy, developing communications software, in Python, for industrial robots. Ville is a long-time IPython enthusiast, and the maintainer of the stable branch (0.x series), since January 2006. His IPython work started with a series of patches to make IPython behave better as a system shell on Windows, and the system shell use case is still a strong personal focus. He lives with his fiancée in Pori, Finland, and is doing his MSc thesis project at Tampere University of Technology's Pori Unit, on ILeo, the IPython-Leo bridge that makes Leo a full-fledged IPython notebook.

Installing IPython

There are a few options for installing IPython. The first and most rudimentary is source distribution. The download page for IPython is located at *http://ipython.scipy.org/dist/*. At the time of this writing, the latest IPython release was 0.8.2 and 0.8.3 was nearing completion. To install from source, go to *http://ipython.scipy.org/dist/ipython-0.8.2.tar.gz* and download the *tar.gz* file. You can unzip the downloaded file using `tar zxvf ipython-0.8.2.tar.gz`. The unzipped directory will contain a *setup.py* file. Call Python on the *setup.py* with an `install` paramater (e.g., `python setup.py install`). This will install the libraries for IPython in your *site-packages* directory and create an **ipython** script in your *scripts* directory. On UNIXes, this is typically the same directory that the **python** binary is located in. If you are using a **python** that was installed with your system's package manager, it (and consequently **ipython**) will likely be located in */usr/bin*. We've installed the source distribution of the latest development code for IPython, so you will see 0.8.3 in some examples.

A second option for installing IPython is to use a package from your system's package management system. On Debian and Ubuntu, *.deb* packages are available to install. Installation is simply *apt-get install ipython*. Ubuntu installs the IPython libraries to the appropriate location (*/usr/share/python-support/ipython* with a tangle of *.pth* files and symbolic links to make things work right). It also installs the **ipython** binary to */usr/bin/ipython*.

The third option for installing IPython is to use a Python package. You may be unaware that such a thing as a Python package exists, but they do. Python packages are files bundled together in a ZIP format, and the resulting file has a *.egg* extension. Eggs (as they are often simply called) can be installed with the **easy_install** utility. One of the cool features of **easy_install** is that it checks a central repository of eggs and then figures out what to install. There is a bit more to it behind the scenes, but as far as the user is concerned, it is relatively easy. The repository is called the Python Package Index or PyPI for short (though some affectionately call it the Python CheeseShop). To **easy_install** IPython, simply log on as the user that has permissions to write to your Python's *site-packages* directory and *easy_install ipython*.

The fourth option is to use IPython without installing it at all. "What?" You might well ask. Well, if you download the source distribution and just run **ipython.py** from the root of that set of files, you will have a running instance of the IPython version that you downloaded. That can be a pretty useful way to go if you don't want to clutter up your *site-packages* directory, but you'll want to be aware of some limitations. If you run IPython from the directory to which you untarred it and you don't modify your **PYTHONPATH** environment variable, you won't be able to use it as a library.

Basic Concepts

After you've installed IPython, when you run **ipython** for the first time, you will see something like this:

```
jmjones@dink:~$ ipython
*************************************************************************
Welcome to IPython. I will try to create a personal configuration directory
where you can customize many aspects of IPython's functionality in:

/home/jmjones/.ipython

Successful installation!

Please read the sections 'Initial Configuration' and 'Quick Tips' in the
IPython manual (there are both HTML and PDF versions supplied with the
```

distribution) to make sure that your system environment is properly configured
to take advantage of IPython's features.

Important note: the configuration system has changed! The old system is
still in place, but its setting may be partly overridden by the settings in
"~/.ipython/ipy_user_conf.py" config file. Please take a look at the file
if some of the new settings bother you.

Please press <RETURN> to start IPython.

After you hit the Return key, your cursor will be waiting for you at a prompt, and
IPython will display the following text:

```
jmjones@dinkgutsy:stable-dev$ python ipython.py
Python 2.5.1 (r251:54863, Mar  7 2008, 03:39:23)
Type "copyright", "credits" or "license" for more information.

IPython 0.8.3.bzr.r96 -- An enhanced Interactive Python.
?         -> Introduction and overview of IPython's features.
%quickref -> Quick reference.
help      -> Python's own help system.
object?   -> Details about 'object'. ?object also works, ?? prints more.

In [1]:
```

Interacting with IPython

It's common to feel some helplessness when presented with a new shell prompt for the
very first time. It's not at all obvious exactly what to do. Remember the first time you
logged into a Unix box and were presented with a (ba|k|c|z)sh prompt? Since you are
reading this book, we assume you have attained some level of familiarity over the Unix
shell. If that is the case, then gaining some level of mastery over IPython will be easy.

One of the reasons that it is unclear what you should do when you first see the IPython
prompt, is that what you can do is virtually unlimited. So it is more appropriate to think
in terms of what you want to do. All of the features of the Python language are available
to you from within the IPython prompt. Plus, there are a number of IPython "magic"
functions available to you. And you can easily execute any Unix shell command from
within IPython and then store the output into a Python variable. The next few examples
will demonstrate what you can expect from IPython with its default configuration.

Here are the input and output of a few simple assignment operations:

```
In [1]: a = 1

In [2]: b = 2

In [3]: c = 3
```

This doesn't look much different from what you would see if you entered the same
thing at a standard Python prompt. We simply assigned 1, 2, 3 to a, b, c, respectively.

The biggest difference you'll see between the IPython and standard Python shells is that IPython gives you a numbered prompt.

Now that we have values (1, 2, and 3) stored in a few variables (a, b, and c, respectively), we can see the values that those variables contain:

```
In [4]: print a
1

In [5]: print b
2

In [6]: print c
3
```

This is a contrived example. We just typed in the values, so we can, at worst, just scroll up to see what the values were. Each variable that we displayed took six characters more than was necessary to display its value. Here's a slightly less verbose way of showing the value:

```
In [7]: a
Out[7]: 1

In [8]: b
Out[8]: 2

In [9]: c
Out[9]: 3
```

While the outlook values look pretty much the same, there is a difference. The print statements use the "unofficial" string representation, while the bare variable names use the "official" string representation. This distinction is typically more important when you are dealing with custom classes than when you are dealing with built-in classes. Here is an example of the different string representations in use:

```
In [10]: class DoubleRep(object):
   ....:     def __str__(self):
   ....:         return "Hi, I'm a __str__"
   ....:     def __repr__(self):
   ....:         return "Hi, I'm a __repr__"
   ....:
   ....:

In [11]: dr = DoubleRep()

In [12]: print dr
Hi, I'm a __str__

In [13]: dr
Out[13]: Hi, I'm a __repr__.
```

We created the class DoubleRep with two methods, __str__ and __repr__, to demonstrate the difference between printing an object and showing the "official" string representation of it. The special method __str__ on an object will be called when the "unofficial" string representation is needed. The special method __repr__ on an object will be called when the "official" representation is needed. After instantiating our DoubleRep object and assigning the variable dr as its value, we printed out the value of dr. The __str__ method was called. Next, we simply typed in the variable name and the __repr__ method was called. The point of all this is that when we simply type in the name of a variable, the result that IPython displays is the "official" string representation. When we tell IPython to print the variable, we see the "unofficial" string representation. In Python in general, __str__ is what gets called when you call str(obj) on an object or when it is used in a formatted string like this: "%s" % obj. When repr(obj) gets called, or when it is used in a formatting string like this: "%r" % obj, __repr__ is what gets called.

This behavior isn't particular to IPython, however. This is exactly how the standard Python shell works. Here is the same DoubleRep example using the standard Python shell:

```
>>> class DoubleRep(object):
...     def __str__(self):
...         return "Hi, I'm a __str__"
...     def __repr__(self):
...         return "Hi, I'm a __repr__"
...
>>>
>>> dr = DoubleRep()
>>> print dr
Hi, I'm a __str__
>>> dr
Hi, I'm a __repr__
```

You may have noticed that the standard Python prompt and the IPython prompt look different. The standard Python prompt consists of three greater-than signs (>>>), whereas the IPython prompt consists of the word "In," followed by a number in brackets, followed by a colon (In [1]:). A likely reason for this is that IPython keeps track of the commands that you input and stores them in a list named In. After you've assigned 1, 2, 3 to a, b, c, in the previous example, here is what the In list would look like:

```
In [4]: print In
['\n', u'a = 1\n', u'b = 2\n', u'c = 3\n', u'print In\n']
```

The output from the IPython prompt is different from the output from the standard Python prompt as well. The IPython prompt seems to distinguish between two types of output: written output and evaluated output. In reality, IPython really doesn't distinguish between the two types. What happens is that print calls are a side effect of computation; so IPython doesn't see them, and so it can't trap them. These print side effects just wind up on stdout, which is where the calling process sent them. However, as IPython executes user's code, it checks return values. If the return value is not None, it prints it at an Out [number]: prompt.

The standard Python prompt does not even appear to distinguish between these two types of output. If a statement that you typed into an IPython prompt evaluates to some value other than None, IPython will write it to a line that starts with Out, followed by a bracketed number, followed by a colon, and, finally, followed by the value that the statement evaluated to (i.e., Out[1]: 1). Here is an example of what happens when IPython assigns an integer to a variable, evaluates the variable, displays its value, and then prints out that value. Note the differences among the tasks of assigning to the variable, showing what the variable value evaluates to, and printing the value of the variable. First, the IPython prompt:

```
In [1]: a = 1

In [2]: a
Out[2]: 1

In [3]: print a
1

In [4]:
```

Next, the standard Python prompt:

```
>>> a = 1
>>> a
1
>>> print a
1
>>>
```

There is really no difference between the way IPython and Python assign the integer, IPython prompt, and the standard Python prompt. Both immediately returned an input prompt to the user. But in showing the "official" string representation of a variable, IPython and standard Python are different. IPython shows only an Out prompt, while Python showed the output. For printing, there was no difference; both showed the output with no prompt.

This In [some number]: and Out [some number]: business may have you wondering if there is a deeper difference between IPython and standard Python, or if the difference is purely cosmetic. The difference is definitely deeper. In fact, the difference represents an area of functionality that places IPython into what seems to be a different category of interactive shell from the standard Python shell.

There are two built-in variables that you will want to be aware of. They are In and Out. The former is an IPython input list object and the latter is a dict object. Here is what type says about the ins and outs of In and Out:

```
In [1]: type(In)
Out[1]: <class 'IPython.iplib.InputList'>

In [2]: type(Out)
Out[2]: <type 'dict'>
```

After you start using In and Out, this will make sense.

So, what do these datatypes hold?

```
In [3]: print In
['\n', u'type(In)\n', u'type(Out)\n', u'print In\n']

In [4]: print Out
{1: <class 'IPython.iplib.InputList'>, 2: <type 'dict'>}
```

As you may expect, In and Out, respectively, hold the input that you typed in and the output that non-None statements and expressions evaluated to. Since each line must necessarily have input, it would seem to make sense to keep track of input in some sort of list-like structure. But keeping track of the output in a list-like structure would result in a number of empty fields or fields containing only None. So, since not every line will have evaluatable non-None output, it makes sense to keep track of output in a dictionary-like data structure or even a pure dict object.

Tab Completion

Another of the incredibly useful data-entry features of IPython is tab completion by default. The standard Python shell has tab-completion capability if it is compiled with readline support, but you have to do something like the following:

```
>>> import rlcompleter, readline
>>> readline.parse_and_bind('tab: complete')
```

This will give us functionality as follows:

```
>>> import os
>>> os.lis<TAB>
>>> os.listdir
>>> os.li<TAB><TAB>
os.linesep  os.link     os.listdir
```

After importing rlcompleter and readline and setting the readline tab complete option, we were able to import os, type in os.lis, hit the Tab key once, and have it complete to os.listdir. We were also able to enter os.li, hit the Tab key twice, and get a list of possible completions.

We get this same behavior with IPython for without any extra configuration necessary. Well, it's free with the standard Python shell as well, but with IPython, it's the default behavior. Here is the previous example run with IPython:

```
In [1]: import os

In [2]: os.lis<TAB>
In [2]: os.listdir
In [2]: os.li<TAB>
os.linesep  os.link     os.listdir
```

Notice that we had to hit the Tab key only once on the last part of the example.

The os.TAB example really only shows off the attribute lookup and completion functionality of IPython, but another cool thing that IPython will complete on is module imports. Open a new IPython shell so that you can see IPython help us find a module to import:

```
In [1]: import o
opcode        operator      optparse      os            os2emxpath    ossaudiodev

In [1]: import xm
xml           xmllib        xmlrpclib
```

Notice that all of the items that import completed on were modules, so this wasn't accidental behavior. This is a feature.

IPython exposes two types of completion: "complete" and "menu-complete." The difference between the two is that "complete" expands the current "word" as far as it can and then provides a list of alternatives, while "menu-complete" expands the word fully to match one of the alternatives, and then each subsequent press of the Tab key morphs the word into the next alternative. IPython's default completion option is "complete." We'll get into configuring your IPython in just a bit.

Magic Edit

The last basic input and output topic we will cover is the "magic" edit function. (We will go over magic functions in the next section.) Strictly line-oriented user interaction with a shell has tremendous, but limited, usefulness. Since that statement sounds like a contradiction, we'll unpack it. Typing commands into a shell one line at a time is very useful. You type in a command; the shell goes off and does its thing; you sometimes sit and wait for it to return; you type in your next command. This is not a bad cycle. In fact, it's quite effective. But sometimes it would be nice to work with a block of lines all at the same time. And it would be nice to work with them in your text editor of choice, although readline support in IPython does improve its usefulness, in this respect. We are aware of using a text editor to create Python modules, but that isn't what we're talking about here. We're talking about more of a compromise between line-oriented input and text editor input to feed commands to the shell. If we can say that adding support for working with blocks of lines of commands would be better, then we can say that a strictly line-oriented interface is limited. So, we can say that a strictly line-oriented interface is exceptionally useful but limited at the same time.

The magic edit function acts as the compromise we just mentioned between pure command-line interaction with the Python shell and interaction using a text editor. The benefit of the compromise is that you have the full power of both environments at your fingertips. You have the benefit of the full-featured power of your text editor of choice. You can easily edit blocks of code and change lines of code around within a loop or a method or function. Plus, you have the nimbleness and agility that comes from directly interacting with the shell. When you combine these two approaches to working with code, a synergistic benefit emerges. You are able to maintain the environment you were working in directly from within your shell, and you can pause, edit, and execute code from within an editor. When you resume working within your shell, you will see the changes you just made in your editor.

Configuring IPython

The final "basic" information you need to know in order to begin is how to configure IPython. If you didn't assign a different location when you ran IPython for the first time, it created an *.ipython* directory in your home directory. Inside the *.ipython* directory is a file called *ipy_user_conf.py*. This user file is simply a configuration file that uses Python syntax. In order to help you give IPython the look and feel that you want it to have, the config file contains a wide variety of elements that you can customize. For example, you can choose the colors used in the shell, the components of the shell prompt, and the text editor that will automatically be used use when you %edit text. We won't go into any more detail than that here. Just know that the config file exists, and it is worth looking through to see if there are some elements you need to or want to configure.

Help with Magic Functions

As we've already said, IPython is incredibly powerful. One reason for this power is that there is an almost overwhelming number of built-in magic functions. Just what is a magic function? The IPython documentation says:

> IPython will treat any line whose first character is a % as a special call to a 'magic' function. These allow you to control the behavior of IPython itself, plus a lot of system-type features. They are all prefixed with a % character, but parameters are given without parentheses or quotes.
>
> Example: typing '%cd mydir' (without the quotes) changes your working directory to 'mydir', if it exists.

Two of the "magic" functions can help you wade through all of this functionality and sort out what might be useful for you. The first magic help function that we'll look at is lsmagic. lsmagic gives a listing of all the "magic" functions. Here is the output of running lsmagic:

```
In [1]: lsmagic
Available magic functions:
%Exit %Pprint %Quit %alias %autocall %autoindent %automagic %bg
%bookmark %cd %clear %color_info %colors %cpaste %debug %dhist %dirs
%doctest_mode %ed %edit %env %exit %hist %history %logoff %logon
%logstart %logstate %logstop %lsmagic %macro %magic %p %page %pdb
%pdef %pdoc %pfile %pinfo %popd %profile %prun %psearch %psource
%pushd %pwd %pycat %quickref %quit %r %rehash %rehashx %rep %reset
%run %runlog %save %sc %store %sx %system_verbose %time %timeit
%unalias %upgrade %who %who_ls %whos %xmode

Automagic is ON, % prefix NOT needed for magic functions.
```

As you can see, there is an almost unwieldy number of functions for you to work with. In fact, as of this writing, there are 69 magic functions for you to use. You may find it helpful to list the magic functions like this:

```
In [2]: %<TAB>
%Exit              %debug            %logstop          %psearch          %save
%Pprint            %dhist            %lsmagic          %psource          %sc
%Quit              %dirs             %macro            %pushd            %store
%alias             %doctest_mode     %magic            %pwd              %sx
%autocall          %ed               %p                %pycat            %system_verbose
%autoindent        %edit             %page             %quickref         %time
%automagic         %env              %pdb              %quit             %timeit
%bg                %exit             %pdef             %r                %unalias
%bookmark          %hist             %pdoc             %rehash           %upgrade
%cd                %history          %pfile            %rehashx          %who
%clear             %logoff           %pinfo            %rep              %who_ls
%color_info        %logon            %popd             %reset            %whos
%colors            %logstart         %profile          %run              %xmode
%cpaste            %logstate         %prun             %runlog
```

Typing %-TAB will give you a nicer view of all 69 magic functions. The point of using the lsmagic function and %-TAB is to see a quick rundown of all the available functions when you're looking for something specific. Or, you can use them to quickly browse through all the functions to see what is available. But unless you see a description, the list isn't going to help you understand what each function does.

That is where magic, the next help function comes in. The name of this magic function is itself "magic." Running magic brings up a pageable help document that the program uses for all of the built-in magic functions in IPython. The help format includes the function name, the use of the function (where applicable), and a description of the way the function works. Here is the help on the magic page function:

```
%page:
    Pretty print the object and display it through a pager.

    %page [options] OBJECT

    If no object is given, use _ (last output).

    Options:

      -r: page str(object), don't pretty-print it.
```

Depending on your pager, you can search and scroll after executing the magic function. This can come in handy if you know what function you need to look up and want to jump right to it rather than scrolling around hunting for it. The functions are arranged alphabetically, so that will help you find what you're looking for whether you search or scroll.

You can also use another help method that we will get to later in this chapter. When you type in the name of the magic function for which you want help, followed by a question mark (?), it will give you almost the same information that %magic will give you. Here is the output of %page ?:

```
In [1]: %page ?
Type:             Magic function
Base Class:       <type 'instancemethod'>
String Form:      <bound method InteractiveShell.magic_page of
                  <IPython.iplib.InteractiveShell object at 0x2ac5429b8a10>>
Namespace:        IPython internal
File:             /home/jmjones/local/python/psa/lib/python2.5/site-packages/IPython/Magic.py
Definition:       %page(self, parameter_s='')
Docstring:
    Pretty print the object and display it through a pager.

    %page [options] OBJECT

    If no object is given, use _ (last output).

    Options:

        -r: page str(object), don't pretty-print it.
```

And here is one final piece of IPython help that is great for generating a summary of the way things work, as well as a summary of the magic functions themselves. When you type in %quickref at an IPython prompt, you'll see a paged reference that begins this way:

```
IPython -- An enhanced Interactive Python - Quick Reference Card
===============================================================

obj?, obj??       : Get help, or more help for object (also works as
                    ?obj, ??obj).
?foo.*abc*        : List names in 'foo' containing 'abc' in them.
%magic            : Information about IPython's 'magic' % functions.

Magic functions are prefixed by %, and typically take their arguments without
parentheses, quotes or even commas for convenience.

Example magic function calls:

%alias d ls -F    : 'd' is now an alias for 'ls -F'
alias d ls -F     : Works if 'alias' not a python name
alist = %alias    : Get list of aliases to 'alist'
cd /usr/share     : Obvious. cd -<tab> to choose from visited dirs.
%cd??             : See help AND source for magic %cd

System commands:

!cp a.txt b/      : System command escape, calls os.system()
cp a.txt b/       : after %rehashx, most system commands work without !
cp ${f}.txt $bar  : Variable expansion in magics and system commands
files = !ls /usr  : Capture sytem command output
files.s, files.l, files.n: "a b c", ['a','b','c'], 'a\nb\nc'
```

and ends with this:

%time:
        Time execution of a Python statement or expression.
%timeit:
        Time execution of a Python statement or expression
%unalias:
        Remove an alias
%upgrade:
         Upgrade your IPython installation
%who:
        Print all interactive variables, with some minimal formatting.
%who_ls:
        Return a sorted list of all interactive variables.
%whos:
        Like %who, but gives some extra information about each variable.
%xmode:
        Switch modes for the exception handlers.

The starting portion of %quickref is a reference to various usage scenarios for IPython. The rest of %quickref is a minisummary of each of the %magic functions. The minisummaries in %quickref each contain the first line of the full help on each of the %magic functions found elsewhere. For example, here is the full help description of %who:

```
In [1]: %who ?
Type:            Magic function
Base Class:      <type 'instancemethod'>
String Form:     <bound method InteractiveShell.magic_who of
                 <IPython.iplib.InteractiveShell object at 0x2ac9f449da10>>
Namespace:       IPython internal
File:            /home/jmjones/local/python/psa/lib/python2.5/site-packages/IPython/
                 Magic.py
Definition:      who(self, parameter_s='')
Docstring:
    Print all interactive variables, with some minimal formatting.

    If any arguments are given, only variables whose type matches one of
    these are printed. For example:

      %who function str

    will only list functions and strings, excluding all other types of
    variables. To find the proper type names, simply use type(var) at a
    command line to see how python prints type names. For example:

      In [1]: type('hello')
      Out[1]: <type 'str'>

    indicates that the type name for strings is 'str'.

    %who always excludes executed names loaded through your configuration
    file and things which are internal to IPython.

    This is deliberate, as typically you may load many modules and the
    purpose of %who is to show you only what you've manually defined.
```

The help line for %who in the %quickref is identical to the first line of the Docstring that is returned by %who ?.

Unix Shell

Working in a Unix shell certainly has its benefits (a unified approach to working through problems, a rich set of tools, a fairly terse yet simple syntax, standard I/O streams, pipes, and redirection to name a few), but it's nice for us to be able to add a touch of Python to this old friend. IPython has some features that make bridging the two very valuable.

alias

The first feature of a Python/Unix shell bridge that we will look at is the alias magic function. With alias you can create an IPython shortcut to execute system commands. To define an alias, simply type alias followed by the system command (and any arguments for that command). For example:

```
In [1]: alias nss netstat -lptn

In [2]: nss
(Not all processes could be identified, non-owned process info
 will not be shown, you would have to be root to see it all.)
Active Internet connections (only servers)
Proto Recv-Q Send-Q Local Address       Foreign Address     State
tcp       0      0 0.0.0.0:80            0.0.0.0:*           LISTEN
tcp       0      0 127.0.0.1:631         0.0.0.0:*           LISTEN
```

There are a few ways to get different input into an alias. One option is the do-nothing approach. If all the extras you wanted to pass into your command can be lumped together, the do-nothing approach may be for you. For example, if you wanted to grep the results of the netstat command above for 80, you could do this:

```
In [3]: nss | grep 80
(Not all processes could be identified, non-owned process info
 will not be shown, you would have to be root to see it all.)
tcp       0      0 0.0.0.0:80            0.0.0.0:*           LISTEN     -
```

This isn't passing in extra options, but for the sake of how things are happening, it winds up being the same thing.

Next, there is the do-everything approach. It's pretty similar to the do-nothing approach except that, by implicitly handling all arguments, you're explicitly handling all subsequent arguments. Here is an example that shows how to treat the subsequent arguments as a single group:

```
In [1]: alias achoo echo "|%l|"

In [2]: achoo
||
```

```
In [3]: achoo these are args
|these are args|
```

This demonstrates the %1 (percent sign followed by the letter "l") syntax that is used to insert the rest of the line into an alias. In real life, you would be most likely to use this to insert everything after the alias somewhere in the middle of the implemented command that the alias is standing in for.

And here is the do-nothing example retooled to handle all arguments explicitly:

```
In [1]: alias nss netstat -lptn %1

In [2]: nss
(Not all processes could be identified, non-owned process info
 will not be shown, you would have to be root to see it all.)
Active Internet connections (only servers)
Proto Recv-Q Send-Q Local Address        Foreign Address      State
tcp        0      0 0.0.0.0:80           0.0.0.0:*            LISTEN
tcp        0      0 127.0.0.1:631        0.0.0.0:*            LISTEN

In [3]: nss | grep 80
(Not all processes could be identified, non-owned process info
 will not be shown, you would have to be root to see it all.)
tcp        0      0 0.0.0.0:80           0.0.0.0:*            LISTEN
```

In this example, we really didn't need to put the %1 in there at all. If we had just left it out, we would have gotten up with the same result.

To insert different parameters throughout a command string, we would use the %s substitution string. This example shows how to run the parameters:

```
In [1]: alias achoo echo first: "|%s|", second: "|%s|"

In [2]: achoo foo bar
first: |foo|, second: |bar|
```

This can be a bit problematic, however. If you supply only one parameter and two were expected, you can expect an error:

```
In [3]: achoo foo
ERROR: Alias <achoo> requires 2 arguments, 1 given.
---------------------------------------------------------------------------
AttributeError                            Traceback (most recent call last)
```

On the other hand, providing more parameters than expected is safe:

```
In [4]: achoo foo bar bam
first: |foo|, second: |bar| bam
```

foo and bar are properly inserted into their respective positions, while bam is appended to the end, which is where you would expect it to be placed.

You can also persist your aliases with the %store magic function, and we will cover how to do that later in this chapter. Continuing with the previous example, we can persist the achoo alias so that the next time we open IPython, we'll be able to use it:

```
In [5]: store achoo
Alias stored: achoo (2, 'echo first: "|%s|", second: "|%s|"')

In [6]:
Do you really want to exit ([y]/n)?
(psa)jmjones@dinkgutsy:code$ ipython -nobanner

In [1]: achoo one two
first: |one|, second: |two|
```

Shell Execute

Another, and possibly easier, way of executing a shell command is to place an exclamation point (!) in front of it:

```
In [1]: !netstat -lptn
(Not all processes could be identified, non-owned process info
 will not be shown, you would have to be root to see it all.)
Active Internet connections (only servers)
Proto Recv-Q Send-Q Local Address           Foreign Address         State
tcp        0      0 0.0.0.0:80              0.0.0.0:*               LISTEN
tcp        0      0 127.0.0.1:631           0.0.0.0:*               LISTEN
```

You can pass in variables to your shell commands by prefixing them with a dollar sign
($). For example:

```
In [1]: user = 'jmjones'

In [2]: process = 'bash'

In [3]: !ps aux | grep $user | grep $process
jmjones   5967 0.0  0.4  21368  4344 pts/0     Ss+  Apr11   0:01 bash
jmjones   6008 0.0  0.4  21340  4304 pts/1     Ss   Apr11   0:02 bash
jmjones   8298 0.0  0.4  21296  4280 pts/2     Ss+  Apr11   0:04 bash
jmjones  10184 0.0  0.5  22644  5608 pts/3     Ss+  Apr11   0:01 bash
jmjones  12035 0.0  0.4  21260  4168 pts/15    Ss   Apr15   0:00 bash
jmjones  12943 0.0  0.4  21288  4268 pts/5     Ss   Apr11   0:01 bash
jmjones  15720 0.0  0.4  21360  4268 pts/17    Ss   02:37   0:00 bash
jmjones  18589 0.1  0.4  21356  4260 pts/4     Ss+  07:04   0:00 bash
jmjones  18661 0.0  0.0    320    16 pts/15    R+   07:06   0:00 grep bash
jmjones  27705 0.0  0.4  21384  4312 pts/7     Ss+  Apr12   0:01 bash
jmjones  32010 0.0  0.4  21252  4172 pts/6     Ss+  Apr12   0:00 bash
```

This listed all **bash** sessions belonging to jmjones.

Here's an example of the way to store the result of a ! command:

```
In [4]: l = !ps aux | grep $user | grep $process

In [5]: l

Out[5]: SList (.p, .n, .l, .s, .grep(), .fields() available). Value:
0: jmjones   5967 0.0  0.4  21368  4344 pts/0     Ss+  Apr11   0:01 bash
1: jmjones   6008 0.0  0.4  21340  4304 pts/1     Ss   Apr11   0:02 bash
2: jmjones   8298 0.0  0.4  21296  4280 pts/2     Ss+  Apr11   0:04 bash
3: jmjones  10184 0.0  0.5  22644  5608 pts/3     Ss+  Apr11   0:01 bash
```

```
4: jmjones   12035  0.0  0.4  21260  4168 pts/15  Ss   Apr15  0:00 bash
5: jmjones   12943  0.0  0.4  21288  4268 pts/5   Ss   Apr11  0:01 bash
6: jmjones   15720  0.0  0.4  21360  4268 pts/17  Ss   02:37  0:00 bash
7: jmjones   18589  0.0  0.4  21356  4260 pts/4   Ss+  07:04  0:00 bash
8: jmjones   27705  0.0  0.4  21384  4312 pts/7   Ss+  Apr12  0:01 bash
9: jmjones   32010  0.0  0.4  21252  4172 pts/6   Ss+  Apr12  0:00 bash
```

You may notice that the output stored in the variable 1 is different from the output in the previous example. That's because the variable 1 contains a list-like object, while the previous example showed the raw output from the command. We'll discuss that list-like object later in "String Processing."

An alternative to ! is !!, except that you can't store the result in a variable as you are running it, !! does the same thing that ! does. But you can access it with the _ or _[0-9]* notation that we'll discuss later in "History results."

Programming a quick ! or !! before a shell command is definitely less work than creating an alias, but you may be better off creating aliases in some cases and using the ! or !! in others. For example, if you are typing in a command you expect to execute all the time, create an alias or macro. If this is a one time or infrequent occurrence, then just use ! or !!.

rehash

There is another option for aliasing and/or executing shell commands from IPython: rehashing. Technically, this is creating an alias for shell commands, but it doesn't really feel like that is what you're doing. The rehash "magic" function updates the "alias table" with everything that is on your PATH. You may be asking, "What is the alias table?" When you create an alias, IPython has to map the alias name to the shell command with which you wanted it to be associated. The alias table is where that mapping occurs.

 The preferred way of rehashing the alias table is to use the rehashx magic function rather than rehash. We will present both to demonstrate the ways they work, and then we will describe their differences.

IPython exposes a number of variables that you have access to when running IPython, such as In and Out, which we saw earlier. One of the variables that IPython exposes is _IP, which is actually the interactive shell object. An attribute named alias_table hangs on that object. This is where the mapping of alias names to shell commands takes place. We can look at this mapping in the same way we would look at any other variable:

```
In [1]: _IP.alias_table

Out[1]:
{'cat': (0, 'cat'),
 'clear': (0, 'clear'),
 'cp': (0, 'cp -i'),
```

```
'lc': (0, 'ls -F -o --color'),
'ldir': (0, 'ls -F -o --color %l | grep /$'),
'less': (0, 'less'),
'lf': (0, 'ls -F -o --color %l | grep ^-'),
'lk': (0, 'ls -F -o --color %l | grep ^l'),
'll': (0, 'ls -lF'),
'lrt': (0, 'ls -lart'),
'ls': (0, 'ls -F'),
'lx': (0, 'ls -F -o --color %l | grep ^-..x'),
'mkdir': (0, 'mkdir'),
'mv': (0, 'mv -i'),
'rm': (0, 'rm -i'),
'rmdir': (0, 'rmdir')}
```

It looks like a dictionary:

```
In [2]: type(__IP.alias_table)

Out[2]: <type 'dict'>
```

Looks can be deceiving, but they're not this time.

Right now, this dictionary has 16 entries:

```
In [3]: len(__IP.alias_table)

Out[3]: 16
```

After we **rehash**, this mapping gets much larger:

```
In [4]: rehash

In [5]: len(__IP.alias_table)

Out[5]: 2314
```

Let's look for something that wasn't there before, but should be there now—the transcode utility should be in the alias table now:

```
In [6]: __IP.alias_table['transcode']

Out[6]: (0, 'transcode')
```

 When you see a variable or attribute name that begins with a double underscore (__), it usually means that the author of that code doesn't want you to change. We're accessing __IP here, but it's only to show you the internals structure. If we wanted to access the official API for IPython, we would use the _ip object that is accessible at the IPython prompt.

rehashx

Excepting that **rehashx** looks for things on your PATH that it thinks are executable to add to the alias table, **rehashx** is similar to **rehash**. So, when we start a new IPython shell and rehashx, we would expect the alias table to be the same size as or smaller than the result of rehash:

```
In [1]: rehashx

In [2]: len(__IP.alias_table)

Out[2]: 2307
```

Interesting; rehashx produces an alias table with seven fewer items than rehash. Here are the seven differences:

```
In [3]: from sets import Set

In [4]: rehashx_set = Set(__IP.alias_table.keys())

In [5]: rehash

In [6]: rehash_set = Set(__IP.alias_table.keys())

In [7]: rehash_set - rehashx_set

Out[7]: Set(['fusermount', 'rmmod.modutils', 'modprobe.modutils', 'kallsyms', 'ksyms', /
        'lsmod.modutils', 'X11'])
```

And if we look to see why rmmod.modutils didn't show up when we ran rehashx but did show up when we ran for rehash, here is what we find:

```
jmjones@dinkgutsy:Music$ slocate rmmod.modutils
/sbin/rmmod.modutils
jmjones@dinkgutsy:Music$ ls -l /sbin/rmmod.modutils
lrwxrwxrwx 1 root root 15 2007-12-07 10:34 /sbin/rmmod.modutils -> insmod.modutils
jmjones@dinkgutsy:Music$ ls -l /sbin/insmod.modutils
ls: /sbin/insmod.modutils: No such file or directory
```

So, you can see that rmmod.modutils is a link to insmod.modutils, and insmod.modutils doesn't exist.

cd

If you have the standard Python shell, you may have noticed that it can be hard to determine which directory you're in. You can use os.chdir() to change the directory, but that isn't very convenient. You could also get the current directory via os.getcwd(), but that's not terribly convenient either. Since you are executing Python commands rather than shell commands with the standard Python shell, maybe it isn't that big of a problem, but when you are using IPython and have easy access to the system shell, having comparably easy access to directory navigation is critical.

Enter cd magic. It seems like we're making a bigger deal out of this than it warrants: this isn't a revolutionary concept; it's not all that difficult. But just imagine if it were missing. That would be painful.

In IPython, cd works mostly as it does in Bash. The primary usage is cd direc
tory_name. That works as you would expect it to from your Bash experience. With no
arguments, cd takes you to your home directory. With a space and hyphen as an
argument, cd - takes you to your previous directory. There are three additional options
that Bash cd doesn't give you.

The first is the -q, or quiet, option. Without this option, IPython will output the directory into which you just changed. The following example shows the ways to change
a directory both with and without the -q option:

```
In [1]: cd /tmp
/tmp

In [2]: pwd

Out[2]: '/tmp'

In [3]: cd -
/home/jmjones

In [4]: cd -q /tmp

In [5]: pwd

Out[5]: '/tmp'
```

Using the -q prevented IPython from outputting the /tmp directory we had gone into.

Another feature that IPython's cd includes is the ability to go to defined bookmarks.
(We'll explain how to create bookmarks soon.) Here is an example of how to change
a directory for which you have created a bookmark:

```
In [1]: cd -b t
(bookmark:t) -> /tmp
/tmp
```

This example assumes that we have bookmarked /tmp the name t. The formal syntax
to change to a bookmarked directory is cd -b bookmark_name, but, if a bookmark of
bookmark_name is defined and there is not a directory called bookmark_name in the
current directory, the -b flag is optional; IPython can figure out that you are intending
to go into a bookmarked directory.

The final extra feature that cd offers in IPython is the ability to change into a specific
directory given a history of directories that have been visited. The following is an example that makes use of this directory history:

```
0: /home/jmjones
1: /home/jmjones/local/Videos
2: /home/jmjones/local/Music
3: /home/jmjones/local/downloads
4: /home/jmjones/local/Pictures
5: /home/jmjones/local/Projects
6: /home/jmjones/local/tmp
```

```
7: /tmp
8: /home/jmjones
```

```
In [2]: cd -6
/home/jmjones/local/tmp
```

First, you see there is a list of all the directories in our directory history. We'll get to where it came from in a moment. Next, we pass the numerical argument -6. This tells IPython that we want to go to the item in our history marked "6", or */home/jmjones/local/tmp*. Finally, you can see that these are now in */home/jmjones/local/tmp*.

bookmark

We just showed you how to use a cd option to move into a bookmarked directory. Now we'll show you how to create and manage your bookmarks. It deserves mentioning that bookmarks persist across IPython sessions. If you exit IPython and start it back up, your bookmarks will still be there. There are two ways to create bookmarks. Here is the first way:

```
In [1]: cd /tmp
/tmp
```

```
In [2]: bookmark t
```

By typing in bookmark t while we're in */tmp*, a bookmark named t is created and pointing at */tmp*. The next way to create a bookmark requires typing one more word:

```
In [3]: bookmark muzak /home/jmjones/local/Music
```

Here, we created a bookmark named muzak that points to a local music directory. The first argument is the bookmark's name, while the second is the directory the bookmark points to.

The -l option tells IPython to get the list of bookmarks, of which we have only two. Now, let's see a list of all our bookmarks:

```
In [4]: bookmark -l
Current bookmarks:
muzak -> /home/jmjones/local/Music
t     -> /tmp
```

There are two options for removing bookmarks: remove them all, or remove one at a time. In this example, we'll create a new bookmark, remove it, and then remove all in the following example:

```
In [5]: bookmark ulb /usr/local/bin
```

```
In [6]: bookmark -l
Current bookmarks:
muzak -> /home/jmjones/local/Music
t     -> /tmp
ulb   -> /usr/local/bin
```

```
In [7]: bookmark -d ulb

In [8]: bookmark -l
Current bookmarks:
muzak -> /home/jmjones/local/Music
t     -> /tmp
```

An alternative to using bookmark -l is to use cd -b:

```
In [9]: cd -b<TAB>
muzak   t       txt
```

And after a few backspaces, we'll continue where we left off:

```
In [9]: bookmark -r

In [10]: bookmark -l
Current bookmarks:
```

We created a bookmark named ulb pointing to */usr/local/bin*. Then, we deleted it with the -d bookmark_name option for bookmark. Finally, we deleted all bookmarks with the -r option.

dhist

In the cd example above, we show a list of the directories we had visited. Now we'll show you how to view that list. The magic command is dhist, which not only saves the session list, but also saves the list of directories across IPython sessions. Here is what happens when you run dhist with no arguments:

```
In [1]: dhist
Directory history (kept in _dh)
0: /home/jmjones
1: /home/jmjones/local/Videos
2: /home/jmjones/local/Music
3: /home/jmjones/local/downloads
4: /home/jmjones/local/Pictures
5: /home/jmjones/local/Projects
6: /home/jmjones/local/tmp
7: /tmp
8: /home/jmjones
9: /home/jmjones/local/tmp
10: /tmp
```

A quick way to access directory history is to use cd -<TAB> like this:

```
In [1]: cd -
-00 [/home/jmjones]                  -06 [/home/jmjones/local/tmp]
-01 [/home/jmjones/local/Videos]     -07 [/tmp]
-02 [/home/jmjones/local/Music]      -08 [/home/jmjones]
-03 [/home/jmjones/local/downloads]  -09 [/home/jmjones/local/tmp]
-04 [/home/jmjones/local/Pictures]   -10 [/tmp]
-05 [/home/jmjones/local/Projects]
```

There are two options that make `dhist` more flexible than `cd -<TAB>`. The first is that you can provide a number to specify how many directories should be displayed. To specify that we want to see only the last five directories that were visited, we would input the following:

```
In [2]: dhist 5
Directory history (kept in _dh)
6: /home/jmjones/local/tmp
7: /tmp
8: /home/jmjones
9: /home/jmjones/local/tmp
10: /tmp
```

The second option is that you can specify a range of directories that were visited. For example, to view from the third through the sixth directories visited, we would enter the following:

```
In [3]: dhist 3 7
Directory history (kept in _dh)
3: /home/jmjones/local/downloads
4: /home/jmjones/local/Pictures
5: /home/jmjones/local/Projects
6: /home/jmjones/local/tmp
```

Notice that the ending range entry is noninclusive, so you have to indicate the directory immediately following the final directory you want to see.

pwd

A simple but nearly necessary function for directory navigation, `pwd` simply tells you what your current directory is. Here is an example:

```
In [1]: cd /tmp
/tmp

In [2]: pwd

Out[2]: '/tmp'
```

Variable Expansion

The previous eight or so IPython features are definitely helpful and necessary, but the next three features will give great joy to power users. The first of these is variable expansion. Up to this point, we've mostly kept shell stuff with shell stuff and Python stuff with Python stuff. But now, we're going to cross the line and mingle the two of them. That is, we're going to take a value that we get from Python and hand it to the shell:

```
In [1]: for i in range(10):
   ...:     !date > ${i}.txt
   ...:
   ...:
```

```
In [2]: ls
0.txt  1.txt  2.txt  3.txt  4.txt  5.txt  6.txt  7.txt  8.txt  9.txt

In [3]: !cat 0.txt
Sat Mar  8 07:40:05 EST 2008
```

This example isn't all that realistic. It is unlikely that you will want to create 10 text files that all contain the date. But the example does show how to mingle Python code and shell code. We iterated over a list created by the range() function and stored the current item in the list in variable i. For each time through the iteration, we use the shell execution ! notation to call out to the date command-line system utility. Notice that the syntax we use for calling date is identical to the way we would call it if we had defined a shell variable i. So, the date utility is called, and the output is redirected to the file *{current list item}.txt*. We list the files after creating them and even cat one out to see that it contains something that looks like a date.

You can pass any kind of value you can come up with in Python into your system shell. Whether it is in a database or in a pickle file, generated by computation, an XMLRPC service, or data you extract from a text file, you can pull it in with Python and then pass it to the system shell with the ! execution trick.

String Processing

Another incredibly powerful feature that IPython offers is the ability to string process the system shell command output. Suppose we want to see the PIDs of all the processes belonging to the user jmjones. We could do that by inputting the following:

```
ps aux | awk '{if ($1 == "jmjones") print $2}'
```

This is pretty tight, succinct, and legible. But let's tackle the same task using IPython. First, let's grab the output from an unfiltered ps aux:

```
In [1]: ps = !ps aux

In [2]:
```

The result of calling ps aux, which is stored in the variable ps, is a list-like structure whose elements are the lines that were returned from the shell system call. It is list-like, in this case, because we mean that it inherits from the built-in list type, so it supports all the methods of that type. So, if you have a function or method that expects a list, you can pass one of these result objects to it as well. In addition to supporting the standard list methods, it also supports a couple of very interesting methods and one attribute that will come in handy. Just to show what the "interesting methods" do, we'll divert from our end goal of finding all processes owned by jmjones for just a moment. The first "interesting method" we'll look at is the grep() method. This is basically a simple filter that determines which lines of the output to keep and which to leave off. To see if any of the lines in the output match lighttpd, we would input the following:

```
In [2]: ps.grep('lighttpd')
```

```
Out[2]: SList (.p, .n, .l, .s, .grep(), .fields() available). Value:
0: www-data  4905  0.0  0.1........0:00 /usr/sbin/lighttpd -f /etc/lighttpd/l
```

We called the grep() method and passed it the regular expression 'lighttpd'. Remember, regular expressions passed to grep() are case-insensitive. The result of this grep() call was a line of output that showed that there was a positive match for the 'lighttpd' regular expression. To see all records except those that match a certain regular expression, we would do something more like this:

```
In [3]: ps.grep('Mar07', prune=True)
```

```
Out[3]: SList (.p, .n, .l, .s, .grep(), .fields() available). Value:
0: USER       PID %CPU %MEM    VSZ   RSS TTY      STAT START   TIME COMMAND
1: jmjones 19301  0.0  0.4  21364  4272 pts/2    Ss+  03:58  0:00 bash
2: jmjones 21340  0.0  0.9 202484 10184 pts/3    Sl+  07:00  0:06 vim ipytho
3: jmjones 23024  0.0  1.1  81480 11600 pts/4    S+   08:58  0:00 /home/jmjo
4: jmjones 23025  0.0  0.0      0     0 pts/4    Z+   08:59  0:00 [sh] <defu
5: jmjones 23373  5.4  1.0  81160 11196 pts/0    R+   09:20  0:00 /home/jmjo
6: jmjones 23374  0.0  0.0   3908   532 pts/0    R+   09:20  0:00 /bin/sh -c
7: jmjones 23375  0.0  0.1  15024  1056 pts/0    R+   09:20  0:00 ps aux
```

We passed in the regular expression 'Mar07' to the grep() method and found that most of the processes on this system were started on March 7, so we decided that we wanted to see all processes *not* started on March 7. In order to exclude all 'Mar07' entries, we had to pass in another argument to grep(), this time a keyword argument: prune=True. This keyword argument tells IPython, "Any records you find that match the stated regular expression—throw them out." And as you can see, there are no records that match the 'Mar07' regex.

Callbacks can also be used with grep(). This just means that grep() will take a function as an argument and call that function. It will pass the function to the item in the list that it is working on. If the function returns True on that item, the item is included in the filter set. For example, we could do a directory listing and filter out only files or only directories:

```
In [1]: import os
```

```
In [2]: file_list = !ls
```

```
In [3]: file_list
```

```
Out[3]: SList (.p, .n, .l, .s, .grep(), .fields() available). Value:
0: ch01.xml
1: code
2: ipython.pdf
3: ipython.xml
```

This directory listing shows four "files." We can't tell from this list which are files and which are directories, but if we filter using the os.path.isfile() test, we can see which ones are files:

```
In [4]: file_list.grep(os.path.isfile)
```

```
Out[4]: SList (.p, .n, .l, .s, .grep(), .fields() available). Value:
0: ch01.xml
1: ipython.pdf
2: ipython.xml
```

This left out the "file" named *code*, so code must not be a file at all. Let's filter for directories:

```
In [5]: file_list.grep(os.path.isdir)
```

```
Out[5]: SList (.p, .n, .l, .s, .grep(), .fields() available). Value:
0: code
```

Now that we see that code is, in fact, a directory, another interesting method is `fields()`. After (or, we guess, even before) you filter your result set down to the desired level of specificity, you can display exactly the fields that you want to display. Let's take the non-Mar07 example that we just walked through and output the user, pid, and start columns:

```
In [4]: ps.grep('Mar07', prune=True).fields(0, 1, 8)
```

```
Out[4]: SList (.p, .n, .l, .s, .grep(), .fields() available). Value:
0: USER PID START
1: jmjones 19301 03:58
2: jmjones 21340 07:00
3: jmjones 23024 08:58
4: jmjones 23025 08:59
5: jmjones 23373 09:20
6: jmjones 23374 09:20
7: jmjones 23375 09:20
```

First, notice that whatever it is that `fields()` does, we're doing it to the result of the `grep()` method call. We are able to do this because `grep()` returns an object of the same type as the `ps` object that we started with. And `fields()` itself returns the same object type as `grep()`. Since that is the case, you can chain `grep()` and `fields()` calls together. Now, on to what is going on here. The `fields()` method takes an indefinite number of arguments, and these arguments are expected to be the "columns" from the output, if the output lines were split on whitespace. You can think of this very much like the default splitting that awk does to lines of text. In this case, we called `fields()` to view columns 0, 1, and 8. These are, respectively, USERNAME, PID, and STARTTIME.

Now, back to showing the PIDs of all processes belonging to jmjones:

```
In [5]: ps.fields(0, 1).grep('jmjones').fields(1)
```

```
Out[5]: SList (.p, .n, .l, .s, .grep(), .fields() available). Value:
0: 5385
1: 5388
2: 5423
3: 5425
4: 5429
5: 5431
```

```
6: 5437
7: 5440
8: 5444
<continues on...>
```

This example first trims the result set back to only two columns, 0 and 1, which are the username and PID, respectively. Then, we take that narrower result set and grep() for 'jmjones'. Finally, we take that filtered result set and request the second field by calling fields(1). (Remember, lists start at zero.)

The final piece of string processing that we want to showcase is the s attribute of the object trying to directly access your process list. This object is probably not going to give you the results you were looking for. In order to get the system shell to work with your output, use the s attribute on your process list object:

```
In [6]: ps.fields(0, 1).grep('jmjones').fields(1).s

Out[6]: '5385 5388 5423 5425 5429 5431 5437 5440 5444 5452 5454 5457 5458 5468
5470 5478 5480 5483 5489 5562 5568 5593 5595 5597 5598 5618 5621 5623 5628 5632
5640 5740 5742 5808 5838 12707 12913 14391 14785 19301 21340 23024 23025 23373
23374 23375'
```

The s attribute gives us a nice space-separated string of PIDs that we can work with in a system shell. We wanted to, we could store that stringified list in a variable called pids and do something like kill $pids from within IPython. But that would send a SIGTERM to every process owned by jmjones, and it would kill his text editor and his IPython sessions.

Earlier, we demonstrated that we could accomplish the stated goals for our IPython script with the following awk one-liner:

```
ps aux | awk '{if ($1 == "jmjones") print $2}'
```

We will be ready to accomplish this goal after we've introduced one more concept. The grep() method takes a final optional parameter called field. If we specify a field parameter, the search criteria has to match that field in order for that item to be included in the result set:

```
In [1]: ps = !ps aux

In [2]: ps.grep('jmjones', field=0)

Out[2]: SList (.p, .n, .l, .s, .grep(), .fields() available). Value:
0: jmjones     5361  0.0  0.1  46412  1828 ?        SL   Apr11
   0:00 /usr/bin/gnome-keyring-daemon -d
1: jmjones     5364  0.0  1.4 214948 14552 ?        Ssl  Apr11
   0:03 x-session-manager
....
53: jmjones   32425  0.0  0.0   3908   584 ?        S    Apr15
   0:00 /bin/sh /usr/lib/firefox/run-mozilla.
54: jmjones   32429  0.1  8.6 603780 88656 ?        Sl   Apr15
   2:38 /usr/lib/firefox/firefox-bin
```

This matched the exact rows that we wanted, but printed out the whole row. To get at just the PID, we'll have to do something like this:

```
In [3]: ps.grep('jmjones', field=0).fields(1)

Out[3]: SList (.p, .n, .l, .s, .grep(), .fields() available). Value:
0: 5361
1: 5364
....
53: 32425
54: 32429
```

And with that, we are able to meet the goal of performing that specific awk filter.

sh Profile

One IPython concept that we haven't described yet is a profile. A profile is simply a set of configuration data that is loaded when you start IPython. You can customize a number of profiles to make IPython perform in different ways depending on a session's needs. To invoke a specific profile, use the -p command-line option and specify the profile you'd like to use.

The sh, or shell, profile is one of the built-in profiles for IPython. The sh profile sets some configuration items so that IPython becomes a more friendly system shell. Two examples of configuration values that are different from the standard IPython profile are that sh displays the current directory and it rehashes your PATH so that you have instant access to all of the same executables that you would have in, say, Bash.

In addition to setting certain configuration values, the sh profile also enables a few shell-helpful extensions. For example, it enables the envpersist extension. The envpersist extension allows you to modify various environment variables easily and persistently for your IPython sh profile, and you don't have to update a .bash_profile or .bashrc.

Here, is what our PATH looks like:

```
jmjones@dinkgutsy:tmp$ ipython -p sh
IPython 0.8.3.bzr.r96    [on Py 2.5.1]
[~/tmp]|2> import os
[~/tmp]|3> os.environ['PATH']
        <3> '/home/jmjones/local/python/psa/bin:
        /home/jmjones/apps/lb/bin:/home/jmjones/bin:
        /usr/local/sbin:/usr/local/bin:/usr/sbin:
        /usr/bin:/sbin:/bin:/usr/games'
```

Now we add :/appended to the end of our current PATH:

```
[~/tmp]|4> env PATH+=:/appended
PATH after append = /home/jmjones/local/python/psa/bin:
/home/jmjones/apps/lb/bin:/home/jmjones/bin:
/usr/local/sbin:/usr/local/bin:/usr/sbin:/usr/bin:
/sbin:/bin:/usr/games:/appended
```

and /prepended: to the beginning of our current PATH:

```
[~/tmp]|5> env PATH-=/prepended:
PATH after prepend = /prepended:/home/jmjones/local/python/psa/bin:
/home/jmjones/apps/lb/bin:/home/jmjones/bin:/usr/local/sbin:
/usr/local/bin:/usr/sbin:/usr/bin:/sbin:/bin:/usr/games:/appended
```

This shows the PATH environment variable using os.environ:

```
[~/tmp]|6> os.environ['PATH']
        <6> '/prepended:/home/jmjones/local/python/psa/bin:
        /home/jmjones/apps/lb/bin:/home/jmjones/bin:
        /usr/local/sbin:/usr/local/bin:/usr/sbin:/usr/bin:/sbin:
        /bin:/usr/games:/appended'
```

Now we'll exit our IPython shell:

```
[~/tmp]|7>
Do you really want to exit ([y]/n)?
jmjones@dinkgutsy:tmp$
```

Finally, we'll open a new IPython shell to see what the PATH environment variable shows:

```
jmjones@dinkgutsy:tmp$ ipython -p sh
IPython 0.8.3.bzr.r96    [on Py 2.5.1]
[~/tmp]|2> import os
[~/tmp]|3> os.environ['PATH']
        <3> '/prepended:/home/jmjones/local/python/psa/bin:
        /home/jmjones/apps/lb/bin:/home/jmjones/bin:/usr/local/sbin:
        /usr/local/bin:/usr/sbin:/usr/bin:/sbin:/bin:/usr/games:/appended'
```

Interestingly, it shows our prepended and appended values, even though we didn't update any profile scripts. It persisted the change to PATH without any additional work on our part. Now let's display all persistent changes to environment variables:

```
[~/tmp]|4> env -p
        <4> {'add': [('PATH', ':/appended')], 'pre': [('PATH', '/prepended:')], 'set': {}}
```

We can delete any persistent changes to PATH:

```
[~/tmp]|5> env -d PATH
Forgot 'PATH' (for next session)
```

and we can check to see the value of PATH:

```
[~/tmp]|6> os.environ['PATH']
        <6> '/prepended:/home/jmjones/local/python/psa/bin:/home/jmjones/apps/lb/bin:
        /home/jmjones/bin:/usr/local/sbin:/usr/local/bin:/usr/sbin:/usr/bin:
        /sbin:/bin:/usr/games:/appended'
```

Even after we've told IPython to remove the persistent entries for PATH, they are still there. But that makes sense. That just means that IPython should remove the directive to persist those entries. Note that the process started with certain values in an environment variable will retain those values unless something changes them. The next time the IPython shell starts, things should be different:

```
[~/tmp]|7>
Do you really want to exit ([y]/n)?
jmjones@dinkgutsy:tmp$ ipython -p sh
IPython 0.8.3.bzr.r96    [on Py 2.5.1]
```

```
[~/tmp]|2> import os
[~/tmp]|3> os.environ['PATH']
        <3> '/home/jmjones/local/python/psa/bin:/home/jmjones/apps/lb/bin:
        /home/jmjones/bin:/usr/local/sbin:/usr/local/bin:/usr/sbin:/usr/bin:
        /sbin:/bin:/usr/games'
```

And, just as we would expect, this is back to what it was before we started making changes to our PATH.

One other useful feature in the sh profile is mglob. mglob has a simpler syntax for a lot of common uses. For example, to find all of the .py files in the Django project, we could just do this:

```
[django/trunk]|3> mglob rec:*py
               <3> SList (.p, .n, .l, .s, .grep(), .fields() available). Value:
0: ./setup.py
1: ./examples/urls.py
2: ./examples/manage.py
3: ./examples/settings.py
4: ./examples/views.py
...
1103: ./django/conf/project_template/urls.py
1104: ./django/conf/project_template/manage.py
1105: ./django/conf/project_template/settings.py
1106: ./django/conf/project_template/__init__.py
1107: ./docs/conf.py
[django/trunk]|4>
```

The rec directive simply says to look recursively for the following pattern. In this case, the pattern is *py. To show all directories in the Django root directory, we would issue a command like this:

```
[django/trunk]|3> mglob dir:*
               <3> SList (.p, .n, .l, .s, .grep(), .fields() available).
               Value:
               0: examples
               1: tests
               2: extras
               3: build
               4: django
               5: docs
               6: scripts
               </3>
```

The mglob command returns a Python list-like object, so anything we can do in Python, we can do to this list of returned files or folders.

This was just a taste of how the sh behaves. There are some sh profile features and feature options that we didn't cover.

Information Gathering

IPython is much more than just a shell in which you can actively get work done. It also works as a tool to gather up all sorts of information about the code and objects you are working with. It can be such an asset in digging up information that it can feel like a forensic or investigatory tool. This section will outline a number of the features that can help you gather information.

page

If an object you are dealing with has too much of a representation to fit on one screen, you may want to try the magic page function. You can use page to pretty print your object and run it through a pager. The default pager on many systems is less, but yours might use something different. Standard usage is as follows:

```
In [1]: p = !ps aux
==
['USER       PID %CPU %MEM    VSZ   RSS TTY      STAT START   TIME COMMAND',
 'root         1  0.0  0.1   5116  1964 ?        Ss   Mar07   0:00 /sbin/init',
< ... trimmed result ... >
In [2]: page p
['USER       PID %CPU %MEM    VSZ   RSS TTY      STAT START   TIME COMMAND',
 'root         1  0.0  0.1   5116  1964 ?        Ss   Mar07   0:00 /sbin/init',
< ... trimmed result ... >
```

Here, we stored the result of the system shell command ps aux in the variable p. Then, we called page and passed the process result object to it. The page function then opened less.

There is one option for page: -r. This option tells page not to pretty print the object, but to run its string representation (result of str()) through the pager instead. For our process output object, that would look like this:

```
In [3]: page -r p
ilus-cd-burner/mapping-d', 'jmjones    5568  0.0  1.0 232004 10608 ?          S
Mar07   0:00 /usr/lib/gnome-applets/trashapplet --', 'jmjones    5593  0.0  0.9
188996 10076 ?          S    Mar07   0:00 /usr/lib/gnome-applets/battstat-apple',
'jmjones    5595  0.0  2.8 402148 29412 ?          S    Mar07   0:01 p
< ... trimmed result ... >
```

This non-pretty-printed result is not pretty, indeed. We recommend starting out with the pretty printer and then working from there.

pdef

The magic pdef function prints the definition headers or the function signature of any callable object. In this example, we create our own function with a docstring and return statement:

```
In [1]: def myfunc(a, b, c, d):
   ...:     '''return something by using a, b, c, d to do something'''
   ...:     return a, b, c, d
   ...:

In [2]: pdef myfunc
myfunc(a, b, c, d)
```

The pdef function ignored our docstring and return statement, but printed out the function signature portion of the function. You can use this on any callable function. This function even works if the source code is not available as long as it has access to either the *.pyc* file or the egg.

pdoc

The pdoc function prints the docstring of the function you pass to it. Here, we run the same myfunc() function that we used in the pdef example through pdoc:

```
In [3]: pdoc myfunc
Class Docstring:
    return something by using a, b, c, d to do something
Calling Docstring:
    x.__call__(...) <==> x(...)
```

This one is pretty self-explanatory.

pfile

The pfile function will run the file that contains an object through the pager if it can find the containing file:

```
In [1]: import os

In [2]: pfile os

r"""OS routines for Mac, NT, or Posix depending on what system we're on.

This exports:
   - all functions from posix, nt, os2, mac, or ce, e.g. unlink, stat, etc.

< ... trimmed result ... >
```

This opened the os module and ran it through less. This can definitely be handy if you are trying to understand the reason a piece of code is behaving in a particular way. It will not work if the only access to the file is an egg or a *.pyc* file.

 You can see the same information from the ?? operator that you can from the magic functions %pdef, %pdoc, and %pfile. The preferred method is ??.

pinfo

The pinfo function and related utilities have become such a convenience for us that it's hard to imagine not having them. The pinfo function provides information such as type, base class, namespace, and docstring. If we have a module that contains:

```
#!/usr/bin/env python

class Foo:
    """my Foo class"""
    def __init__(self):
        pass

class Bar:
    """my Bar class"""
    def __init__(self):
        pass

class Bam:
    """my Bam class"""
    def __init__(self):
        pass
```

then we can request information from the module itself:

```
In [1]: import some_module

In [2]: pinfo some_module
Type:           module
Base Class:     <type 'module'>
String Form:    <module 'some_module' from 'some_module.py'>
Namespace:      Interactive
File:           /home/jmjones/code/some_module.py
Docstring:
    <no docstring>
```

We can request information from a class in the module:

```
In [3]: pinfo some_module.Foo
Type:           classobj
String Form:    some_module.Foo
Namespace:      Interactive
File:           /home/jmjones/code/some_module.py
Docstring:
    my Foo class

Constructor information:
Definition:     some_module.Foo(self)
```

We can request information from an instance of one of those classes:

```
In [4]: f = some_module.Foo()

In [5]: pinfo f
Type:           instance
Base Class:     some_module.Foo
```

```
String Form:    <some_module.Foo instance at 0x86e9e0>
Namespace:      Interactive
Docstring:
    my Foo class
```

A question mark (?) preceeding or following an object name provides the same functionality as `pinfo`:

```
In [6]: ? f
Type:           instance
Base Class:     some_module.Foo
String Form:    <some_module.Foo instance at 0x86e9e0>
Namespace:      Interactive
Docstring:
    my Foo class


In [7]: f ?
Type:           instance
Base Class:     some_module.Foo
String Form:    <some_module.Foo instance at 0x86e9e0>
Namespace:      Interactive
Docstring:
    my Foo class
```

But two question marks (??) preceeding or following an object name provides us with even more information:

```
In [8]: some_module.Foo ??
Type:           classobj
String Form:    some_module.Foo
Namespace:      Interactive
File:           /home/jmjones/code/some_module.py
Source:
class Foo:
    """my Foo class"""
    def __init__(self):
        pass
Constructor information:
Definition:     some_module.Foo(self)
```

The ?? notation provides us with all the information that `pinfo` provided us plus the source code for the requested object. Because we only asked for the class, ?? gave us the source code for this class rather than for the whole file. This is one of the features of IPython that we find ourselves using more than nearly any other.

psource

The `psource` function shows the source code for the element you define, whether that's a module or something in a module, like a class or function. It runs the source code through a pager in order to display it. Here is an example of `psource` for a module:

```
In [1]: import some_other_module

In [2]: psource some_other_module
#!/usr/bin/env python

class Foo:
    """my Foo class"""
    def __init__(self):
        pass

class Bar:
    """my Bar class"""
    def __init__(self):
        pass

class Bam:
    """my Bam class"""
    def __init__(self):
        pass

def baz():
    """my baz function"""
    return None
```

Here is an example of **psource** for a class in a module:

```
In [3]: psource some_other_module.Foo
class Foo:
    """my Foo class"""
    def __init__(self):
        pass
```

and here is an example of **psource** for a function in a module:

```
In [4]: psource some_other_module.baz
def baz():
    """my baz function"""
    return None
```

psearch

The **psearch** magic function will look for Python objects by name, with the aid of wild-cards. We'll just briefly describe the **psearch** function here and if you want to know more, you can find documentation on the magic functions by typing **magic** at an IPython prompt, and then searching within the alphabetical list for **psearch**.

Let's start by declaring the following objects:

```
In [1]: a = 1

In [2]: aa = "one"

In [3]: b = 2

In [4]: bb = "two"
```

```
In [5]: c = 3

In [6]: cc = "three"
```

We can search for all of the objects starting with a, b, or c as follows:

```
In [7]: psearch a*
a
aa
abs
all
any
apply

In [8]: psearch b*
b
basestring
bb
bool
buffer

In [9]: psearch c*
c
callable
cc
chr
classmethod
cmp
coerce
compile
complex
copyright
credits
```

Notice all the objects that were found in addition to a, aa, b, bb, c, cc; those are built-ins.

There is a quick and dirty alternative to using psearch: the ? operator. Here's an example:

```
In [2]: import os

In [3]: psearch os.li*
os.linesep
os.link
os.listdir

In [4]: os.li*?
os.linesep
os.link
os.listdir
```

Instead of psearch, we were able to use *?.

There is an option to search -s or exclude searching -e a given namespace built-in to psearch. Namespaces include builtin, user, user_global, internal, and alias. By default, psearch searches `builtin` and `user`. To explicitly search `user` only, we would pass a `-e builtin` psearch option to exclude searching the `builtin` namespace. This is a little counterintuitive, but it makes an odd sort of sense. The default search path for psearch is `builtin` and `user`, so if we specify a `-s user`, searching `builtin` and `user` would still be what we're asking it to do. In this example, the search is run again; notice that these results exclude the built-ins:

```
In [10]: psearch -e builtin a*
a
aa

In [11]: psearch -e builtin b*
b
bb

In [12]: psearch -e builtin c*
c
cc
```

The psearch function also allows searching for specific types of objects. Here, we search the `user` namespace for integers:

```
In [13]: psearch -e builtin * int
a
b
c
```

and here we search for strings:

```
In [14]: psearch -e builtin * string
__
__
__name__
aa
bb
cc
```

The __ and ___ objects that were found are IPython shorthand for previous return results. The __name__ object is a special variable that denotes the name of the module. If __name__ is '__main__', it means that the module is being run from the interpreter rather than being imported from another module.

who

IPython provides a number of facilities for listing all interactive objects. The first of these is the who function. Here is the previous example, including the a, aa, b, bb, c, cc variables, with the addition of the magic who function:

```
In [15]: who
a       aa      b       bb      c       cc
```

That's pretty straightforward; it returns a simple listing of all interactively defined objects. You can also use who to filter on types. For example:

```
In [16]: who int
a        b        c

In [17]: who str
aa       bb       cc
```

who_ls

Except that it returns a list rather than printing the names of the matching variables, who_ls is similar to who. Here is an example of the who_ls function with no arguments:

```
In [18]: who_ls

Out[18]: ['a', 'aa', 'b', 'bb', 'c', 'cc']
```

and here is an example of filtering based on the types of objects:

```
In [19]: who_ls int

Out[19]: ['a', 'b', 'c']

In [20]: who_ls str

Out[20]: ['aa', 'bb', 'cc']
```

Since who_ls returns a list of the names, you can access the list of names using the _ variable, which just means "the last output." Here is the way to iterate the last returned list of matching variable names:

```
In [21]: for n in _:
   ....:     print n
   ....:
   ....:
aa
bb
cc
```

whos

The whos function is similar to the who function except that whos prints out information that who doesn't. Here is an example of the whos function used with no command-line arguments:

```
In [22]: whos
Variable   Type    Data/Info
-----------------------------
a          int     1
aa         str     one
b          int     2
bb         str     two
c          int     3
cc         str     three
n          str     cc
```

And as we can with who, we can filter on type:

```
In [23]: whos int
Variable   Type    Data/Info
----------------------------
a          int     1
b          int     2
c          int     3

In [24]: whos str
Variable   Type    Data/Info
----------------------------
aa         str     one
bb         str     two
cc         str     three
n          str     cc
```

History

There are two ways to gain access to your history of typed-in commands in IPython. The first is readline-based; the second is the hist magic function.

Readline support

In IPython, you have access to all the cool features that you would expect to be in a readline-enabled application. If you are used to searching your Bash history using Ctrl-s, you won't have a problem transitioning to the same functionality in IPython. Here, we've defined a few variables, then searched back through the history:

```
In [1]: foo = 1

In [2]: bar = 2

In [3]: bam = 3

In [4]: d = dict(foo=foo, bar=bar, bam=bam)

In [5]: dict2 = dict(d=d, foo=foo)

In [6]: <CTRL-s>

(reverse-i-search)`fo': dict2 = dict(d=d, foo=foo)

<CTRL-r>

(reverse-i-search)`fo': d = dict(foo=foo, bar=bar, bam=bam)
```

We typed Ctrl-r to start the search, then typed in fo as the search criteria. It brought up the line we entered that is denoted by IPython as In [5]. Using readline's search functionality, we hit Ctrl-r and it matched the line we entered that is denoted by IPython as In [4].

There are many more things you can do with readline, but we'll touch only briefly on them. Ctrl-a will take you to the beginning of a line and Ctrl-e will take you to the end of a line. Ctrl-f will move forward one character and Ctrl-b will move backward one character. Ctrl-d deletes one character and Ctrl-h deletes one character backward (backspace). Ctrl-p moves one line backward in the history and Ctrl-n moves one line forward in your history. For more readline functionality, enter man readline on your *nix system of choice.

hist command

In addition to providing access to the history functionality of the readline library, IPython also provides its own history function named history or hist for short. With no parameters, hist prints a sequential list of the input commands received from the user. By default, this list will be numbered. In this example, we set a few variables, change the directory, and then run the hist command:

```
In [1]: foo = 1

In [2]: bar = 2

In [3]: bam = 3

In [4]: cd /tmp
/tmp

In [5]: hist
1: foo = 1
2: bar = 2
3: bam = 3
4: _ip.magic("cd /tmp")
5: _ip.magic("hist ")
```

Items 4 and 5 in the history above are magic functions. Note that they have been modified by IPython and you can see what is going on under the covers through the IPython magic() function call.

To suppress the line numbers, use the -n option. Here is an example using the -n option for hist:

```
kIn [6]: hist -n
foo = 1
bar = 2
bam = 3
_ip.magic("cd /tmp")
_ip.magic("hist ")
_ip.magic("hist -n")
```

It is very helpful if you've been working in IPython and want to paste a section of your IPython code into a text editor.

The -t option returns a "translated" view of the history that shows the way IPython sees the commands that have been entered. This is the default. Here is the history we've built up so far run through with the -t flag:

```
In [7]: hist -t
1: foo = 1
2: bar = 2
3: bam = 3
4: _ip.magic("cd /tmp")
5: _ip.magic("hist ")
6: _ip.magic("hist -n")
7: _ip.magic("hist -t")
```

The "raw history," or -r, flag will show you exactly what you typed. Here is the result of the earlier example, adding the "raw history" flag:

```
In [8]: hist -r
1: foo = 1
2: bar = 2
3: bam = 3
4: cd /tmp
5: hist
6: hist -n
7: hist -t
8: hist -r
```

IPython's -g flag function also provides a facility to search through your history for a specific pattern. Here is the earlier example with the -g flag used to search for hist:

```
In [9]: hist -g hist
0187: hist
0188: hist -n
0189: hist -g import
0190: hist -h
0191: hist -t
0192: hist -r
0193: hist -d
0213: hist -g foo
0219: hist -g hist
===
^shadow history ends, fetch by %rep <number> (must start with 0)
=== start of normal history ===
5 : _ip.magic("hist ")
6 : _ip.magic("hist -n")
7 : _ip.magic("hist -t")
8 : _ip.magic("hist -r")
9 : _ip.magic("hist -g hist")
```

Notice that the term "shadow history" is returned in the previous example. "Shadow history" is a history of every command you have ever entered. Those items are displayed at the beginning of the result set and begin with a zero. History results from this session are stored at the end of the result set and do not start with a zero.

History results

In both Python and IPython, you can access not only your history of the commands you entered, but also access the history of your results. The first way to do this is using the _ flag, which means "the last output." Here is an example of the way the _ function works in IPython:

```
In [1]: foo = "foo_string"

In [2]: _

Out[2]: ''

In [3]: foo

Out[3]: 'foo_string'

In [4]: _

Out[4]: 'foo_string'

In [5]: a = _

In [6]: a

Out[6]: 'foo_string'
```

When we defined foo in In [1], the _ in In [2] returned an empty string. When we output foo in In [3], we were able to use _ to get the result back in In [4]. And in In [5], we were able to save it off to a variable named a.

Here is the same example using the standard Python shell:

```
>>> foo = "foo_string"
>>> _
Traceback (most recent call last):
  File "<stdin>", line 1, in <module>
NameError: name '_' is not defined
>>> foo
'foo_string'
>>> _
'foo_string'
>>> a = _
>>> a
'foo_string'
```

We see pretty much the same thing in the standard Python shell that we see in IPython, except that trying to access _ before anything has been output results in a NameError exception.

IPython takes this "last output" concept a step further. In the description of the "Shell Execute" function, we described the ! and !! operators and explained that you can't store the results of !! in a variable but can use it later. In a nutshell, you can access any result that was output using the syntax underscore (_) followed by a number_[0-9]* syntax. The number must correspond to the Out [0-9]* result that you want to see.

To demonstrate this, we'll first list files but not do anything with the output:

```
In [1]: !!ls apa*py

Out[1]: SList (.p, .n, .l, .s, .grep(), .fields() available). Value:
0: apache_conf_docroot_replace.py
1: apache_log_parser_regex.py
2: apache_log_parser_split.py

In [2]: !!ls e*py

Out[2]: SList (.p, .n, .l, .s, .grep(), .fields() available). Value:
0: elementtree_system_profile.py
1: elementtree_tomcat_users.py

In [3]: !!ls t*py

Out[3]: SList (.p, .n, .l, .s, .grep(), .fields() available). Value:
0: test_apache_log_parser_regex.py
1: test_apache_log_parser_split.py
```

We should have access to Out [1-3] by using _1, _2, and _3. So, we'll attach a more meaningful name to them:

```
In [4]: apache_list = _1

In [5]: element_tree_list = _2

In [6]: tests = _3
```

Now, apache_list, element_tree_list, and tests contain the same elements that were output in Out [1], Out [2], and Out [3], respectively:

```
In [7]: apache_list

Out[7]: SList (.p, .n, .l, .s, .grep(), .fields() available). Value:
0: apache_conf_docroot_replace.py
1: apache_log_parser_regex.py
2: apache_log_parser_split.py

In [8]: element_tree_list

Out[8]: SList (.p, .n, .l, .s, .grep(), .fields() available). Value:
0: elementtree_system_profile.py
1: elementtree_tomcat_users.py

In [9]: tests

Out[9]: SList (.p, .n, .l, .s, .grep(), .fields() available). Value:
0: test_apache_log_parser_regex.py
1: test_apache_log_parser_split.py
```

But the whole point of all this is that, in IPython, you can access previous output results with either the naked _ special variable, or with an explicit numbered output reference by using _ followed by a number.

Automation and Shortcuts

As if IPython hasn't done enough to improve your productivity, it also provides a number of functions and features to help you automate your IPython tasks and usage.

alias

We'll first mention the `alias` "magic" command. We already covered this earlier in this chapter, so we won't rehash usage of it again. But we wanted to just point out here that `alias` cannot only help you use *nix shell commands directly from within IPython, it can help you automate tasks as well.

macro

The `macro` function lets you define a block of code that can be executed later inline with whatever code you are working on. This is different from creating functions or methods. The macro, in a sense, becomes aware of the current context of your code. If you have a common set of processing steps you frequently execute on all your files, you can create a macro to work on the files. To get a feel for the way a macro will work on a list of files, look at the following example:

```
In [1]: dirlist = []

In [2]: for f in dirlist:
   ...:     print "working on", f
   ...:     print "done with", f
   ...:     print "moving %s to %s.done" % (f, f)
   ...:     print "*" * 40
   ...:
   ...:

In [3]: macro procdir 2
Macro `procdir` created. To execute, type its name (without quotes).
Macro contents:
for f in dirlist:
    print "working on", f
    print "done with", f
    print "moving %s to %s.done" % (f, f)
    print "*" * 40
```

At the time that we created the loop in In [2], there were no items in dirlist for the loop to walk over, but because we anticipated that future iterations would include items in dirlist, we created a macro named procdir to walk over the list. The syntax for creating a macro is macro macro_name range_of_lines, where the range of lines is a list of the lines from your history that you want incorporated into the macro. The lines for your macro list should be designated by a space-separated list of either numbers or ranges of numbers (such as 1-4).

In this example, we create a list of filenames and store them in dirlist, then execute the macro procdir. The macro will walk over the list of files in dirlist:

```
In [4]: dirlist = ['a.txt', 'b.txt', 'c.txt']

In [5]: procdir
------> procdir()
working on a.txt
done with a.txt
moving a.txt to a.txt.done
***************************************
working on b.txt
done with b.txt
moving b.txt to b.txt.done
***************************************
working on c.txt
done with c.txt
moving c.txt to c.txt.done
***************************************
```

Once you have a macro defined, you can edit it. This will open in your defined text editor. This can be very helpful when you are tweaking a macro to make sure it is right before you persist it.

store

You can persist your macros and plain Python variables with the store magic function. The simple standard use of store is store variable. However, store also takes a number of parameters that you may find useful: the -d variable function deletes the specified variable from the persistence store; -z function deletes all stored variables; and the -r function reloads all variables from the persistence store.

reset

The reset function deletes all variables from the interactive namespace. In the following example, we define three variables, use whos to verify they are set, reset the namespace, and use whos again to verify that they are gone:

```
In [1]: a = 1

In [2]: b = 2

In [3]: c = 3

In [4]: whos
Variable   Type     Data/Info
----------------------------
```

```
a          int    1
b          int    2
c          int    3

In [5]: reset
Once deleted, variables cannot be recovered. Proceed (y/[n])?  y

In [6]: whos
Interactive namespace is empty.
```

run

The run function executes the specified file in IPython. Among other things, this allows you to work on a Python module in an external text editor and interactively test changes you are making in it from within IPython. After executing the specified program, you are returned back to the IPython shell. The syntax for using run is run options speci fied_file args.

The -n option causes the module's __name__ variable to be set *not* to '__main__', but to its own name. This causes the module to be run much as it would be run if it were simply imported.

The -i option runs the module in IPython's current namespace and, thereby, gives the running module access to all defined variables.

The -e option causes IPython to ignore calls to sys.exit() and SystemExit exceptions. If either of these occur, IPython will just continue.

The -t option causes IPython to print out information about the length of time it took the module to run.

The -d option causes the specified module to be run under the Python debugger (pdb).

The -p option runs the specified module under the Python profiler.

save

The save function will save the specified input lines to the specified output file. Syntax for using save is save options filename lines. The lines may be specified in the same range format as is used for macro. The only save option is -r, which designates that raw input rather than translated should be saved. Translated input, which is standard Python, is the default.

rep

The final automation-enabling function is rep. The rep function takes a number of parameters that you might find useful. Using rep without parameters takes the last result that was processed and places a string representation of it on the next input line. For example:

```
In [1]: def format_str(s):
   ...:     return "str(%s)" % s
   ...:

In [2]: format_str(1)

Out[2]: 'str(1)'

In [3]: rep

In [4]: str(1)
```

The rep call at In [3] causes the text you see to be placed on In [4]. This allows you to programatically generate input for IPython to process. This comes in handy, particularly when you are using a combination of generators and macros.

A fairly common use case for rep without arguments is lazy, mouseless editing. If you have a variable containing some value, you can edit that value directly. As an example, assume that we are using a function that returns to the bin directory for specific installed packages. We'll store the *bin* directory in a variable called a:

```
In [2]: a = some_blackbox_function('squiggly')

In [3]: a

Out[3]: '/opt/local/squiggly/bin'
```

If we type rep right here, we'll see **/opt/local/squiggly/bin** on a new input line with a blinking cursor expecting us to edit it:

```
In [4]: rep

In [5]: /opt/local/squiggly/bin<blinking cursor>
```

If we wanted to store the base directory of the package rather than the bin directory, we can just delete the bin from the end of the path, prefix the path with a new variable name, follow that with an equal sign and quotation marks, and suffix it with just a quotation mark:

```
In [5]: new_a = '/opt/local/squiggly'
```

Now we have a new variable containing a string that is the base directory for this package.

Sure, we could have just copied and pasted, but that would have been more work. Why should you leave the comfort of your cozy keyboard to reach for the mouse? You can now use new_a as a base directory for anything that you need to do regarding the squiggly package.

When one number is given as an argument to rep, IPython brings up the input from that particular line of history and places it on the next line, and then places the cursor at the end of that line. This is helpful for executing, editing, and re-executing single lines or even small blocks of code. For example:

```
In [1]: map = (('a', '1'), ('b', '2'), ('c', '3'))

In [2]: for alph, num in map:
   ...:     print alph, num
   ...:
   ...:
a 1
b 2
c 3
```

Here, we edit In [2] and print the number value times 2 rather than a noncomputed value. We could either type the for loop in again, or we can use rep:

```
In [3]: rep 2

In [4]: for alph, num in map:
    print alph, int(num) * 2
   ...:
   ...:
a 2
b 4
c 6
```

The rep function also takes ranges of numbers for arguments. The numeric range syntax is identical to the macro numeric range syntax that we discussed elsewhere in this chapter. When you specify a range for rep, the lines are executed immediately. Here is an example of rep:

```
In [1]: i = 1

In [2]: i += 1

In [3]: print i
2

In [4]: rep 2-3
lines [u'i += 1\nprint i\n']
3

In [7]: rep 2-3
lines [u'i += 1\nprint i\n']
4
```

We defined a counter incrementer and code that prints out the current count in In [1] through In [3]. In In [4] and In [7], we told rep to repeat lines 2 and 3. Notice that 2 lines (5 and 6) are missing since they were executed after In [4].

The last option for rep that we'll go over is passing in a string. This is more like "passing in a word to rep" or even "passing in a nonquoted search string to rep." Here is an example:

```
In [1]: a = 1

In [2]: b = 2
```

```
In [3]: c = 3

In [4]: rep a

In [5]: a = 1
```

We defined a few variables and told **rep** to repeat the last line that has an "a" in it. It brought `In [1]` back to us to edit and re-execute.

Summary

IPython is one of the most well-worn tools in our toolbox. Having mastery of a shell is like having mastery of a text editor: the more proficient you are, the more quickly you can cut through the tedious parts of the task you are working on. When we started working with IPython a few years ago, it was an amazingly powerful tool. Since then, it has grown into even more. The **grep** function and the ability to do string processing are just two of the things that come to mind when we think about the really useful, powerful features that keep emerging from the IPython community. We highly recommend that you dig deeper into IPython. Mastering it is a time investment that you won't regret.

## CHAPTER 3

Text

Nearly every system administrator has to deal with text whether it is in the form of logfiles, application data, XML, HTML, configuration files, or the output of some command. Often, utilities like **grep** and **awk** are all you need, but sometimes a tool that is more expressive and elegant is needed to tackle complex problems. When you need to create files with data extracted from other files, redirecting text from the output of a process (again, grep and awk come to mind) to a file is often good enough. But there are also times when a tool that is more easily extensible is better-suited for the job.

As we explained in the "Introduction," our experience has shown that that Python qualifies as more elegant, expressive, and extensible than Perl, Bash, or other languages we have used for programming. For more discussion of why we value Python more highly than Perl or Bash (and you could make application to **sed** and **awk**), see Chapter 1. Python's standard library, language features, and built-in types are powerful tools for reading text files, manipulating text, and extracting information from text files. Python and its standard library contain a wealth of flexibility and functionality for text processing using the string type, the file type, and the regular expression module. A recent addition to the standard library, ElementTree, is immensely helpful when you need to work with XML. In this chapter, we will show you how to effectively use the standard library and built-in components that help with processing text.

Python Built-ins and Modules

str

A string is simply a sequence of characters. If you ever need to deal with textual data, you'll almost certainly need to work with it as a string object or a series of string objects. The string type, **str**, is a powerful, flexible means for manipulating string data. This section shows you how to create strings and what you can do with them once they've been created.

Creating strings

The most common way to create a string is to surround the text with quotation marks:

```
In [1]: string1 = 'This is a string'

In [2]: string2 = "This is another string"

In [3]: string3 = '''This is still another string'''

In [4]: string4 = """And one more string"""

In [5]: type(string1), type(string2), type(string3), type(string4)
Out[5]: (<type 'str'>, <type 'str'>, <type 'str'>, <type 'str'>)
```

Single, double, and triple quotation marks accomplish the same thing: they all create an object of type str. Single and double quotation marks are identical in the creation of strings; you can use them interchangeably. This is different from the way quotation marks work in Unix shells, in which the marks cannot be used interchangeably. For example:

```
jmjones@dink:~$ FOO=sometext
jmjones@dink:~$ echo "Here is $FOO"
Here is sometext
jmjones@dink:~$ echo 'Here is $FOO'
Here is $FOO
```

Perl also uses between single and double quotes in string creation. Here's a comparable example in a Perl script:

```
#!/usr/bin/perl

$FOO = "some_text";
print "-- $FOO --\n";
print '-- $FOO --\n';
```

And here is the output from this simple Perl script:

```
jmjones@dinkgutsy:code$ ./quotes.pl
-- some_text --
-- $FOO --\njmjones@dinkgutsy:code$
```

This is a distinction that Python does not make. Python leaves the distinction to the programmer. For example, if you needed to embed double quotation marks within the string and did not want to have to escape them (with a backslash). Conversely, if you needed to embed single quotes within the string and did not want to have to escape them, you would use double quotes. See Example 3-1.

Example 3-1. Python single/double quote comparison

```
In [1]: s = "This is a string with 'quotes' in it"

In [2]: s
Out[2]: "This is a string with 'quotes' in it"
```

```
In [3]: s = 'This is a string with \'quotes\' in it'

In [4]: s
Out[4]: "This is a string with 'quotes' in it"

In [5]: s = 'This is a string with "quotes" in it'

In [6]: s
Out[6]: 'This is a string with "quotes" in it'

In [7]: s = "This is a string with \"quotes\" in it"

In [8]: s
Out[8]: 'This is a string with "quotes" in it'
```

Notice in lines 2 and 4 that embedding an escaped quote of the same type as the enclosing quote coerces the enclosing quotation mark to the opposite quotation mark type. (Actually, it's just coercing the representation of the string to show the "right" quotation mark types.)

There are times when you might want a string to span multiple lines. Sometimes embedding \n in the string where you want line breaks solves the problem for you, but this can get unwieldy. Another, often cleaner alternative is to use triples quotes, which allow you to create multiline strings. Example 3-2 is an example of trying to use single quotes for multiline strings and succeeding with triple quotes.

Example 3-2. Triple quotes

```
In [6]: s = 'this is
---------------------------------------------------------------
  File "<ipython console>", line 1
    s = 'this is
                ^
SyntaxError: EOL while scanning single-quoted string


In [7]: s = '''this is a
   ...: multiline string'''

In [8]: s
Out[8]: 'this is a\nmultiline string'
```

And just to complicate matters, there is another way to denote strings in Python called "raw" strings. You create a raw string by placing the letter r immediately before the quotation mark when you are creating a string. Basically, the effect of creating a raw string as opposed to a non-raw (would that be cooked?) string is that Python does not interpret escape sequences in raw strings, whereas it does interpret escape sequences in regular strings. Python follows a set of rules similar to those used by Standard C regarding escape sequences. For example, in regular strings, \t is interpreted as a tab character, \n as a newline, and \r as a line feed. Table 3-1 shows escape sequences in Python.

Table 3-1. Python escape sequences

Sequence	Interpreted as
\newline	Ignored
\\	Backslash
\'	Single quote
\"	Double quote
\a	ASCII Bell
\b	ASCII backspace
\f	ASCII form feed
\n	ASCII line feed
\N{name}	Named character in Unicode database (Unicode strings only)
\r	ASCII carriage return
\t	ASCII horizontal tab
\uxxxx	Character with 16-bit hex value xxxx (Unicode only)
\Uxxxxxxxx	Character with 32-bit hex value xxxx (Unicode only)
\v	ASCII vertical tab
\ooo	Character with octal value oo
\xhh	Character with hex value hh

Escape sequences and raw strings are useful to remember, particularly when you are dealing with regular expressions, which we will get to later in this chapter. Example 3-3 shows escape sequences used with raw strings.

Example 3-3. Escape sequences and raw strings

```
In [1]: s = '\t'

In [2]: s
Out[2]: '\t'

In [3]: print s


In [4]: s = r'\t'

In [5]: s
Out[5]: '\\t'

In [6]: print s
\t

In [7]: s = '''\t'''

In [8]: s
Out[8]: '\t'
```

```
In [9]: print s


In [10]: s = r'''\t'''

In [11]: s
Out[11]: '\\t'

In [12]: print s
\t

In [13]: s = r'\''

In [14]: s
Out[14]: "\\'"

In [15]: print s
\'
```

When escape sequences are interpreted, \t is a tab character. When escape sequences are not interpreted, \t is simply a string that contains the two characters \ and t. Strings created with any of the quote characters, whether double or single, laid out individually or three in a row, allow \t to be interpreted as a tab character. Any of those same strings prefixed with an r allow \t to be interpreted as the two characters \ and t.

Another bit of fun from this example is the distinction between __repr__ and __str__. When you type a variable name at an IPython prompt and hit enter, its __repr__ representation is displayed. When we type print followed by a variable name and then hit enter, its __str__ representation is printed out. The print function interprets the escape sequences in the string and displays them appropriately. For more discussion on __repr__ and __str__ , see "Basic Concepts" in Chapter 2.

Built-in methods for str data extraction

Because strings are objects, they provide methods that can be called to perform operations. But by "method," we don't mean only those methods that the str type provides for us; we mean all the ways that are available to extract data from an object of str type. This includes all the str methods, and it also includes the in and not in text operators you saw in our first example.

Technically, the in and not in test operators call a method on your str object, __contains__() in Example 3-1 (shown earlier). For more information on how this works, see the Appendix. You can use both in and not in to determine if a string is a part of another string. See Example 3-4.

Example 3-4. In and not in

```
In [1]: import subprocess

In [2]: res = subprocess.Popen(['uname', '-sv'], stdout=subprocess.PIPE)
```

```
In [3]: uname = res.stdout.read().strip()

In [4]: uname

Out[4]: 'Linux #1 SMP Tue Feb 12 02:46:46 UTC 2008'

In [5]: 'Linux' in uname

Out[5]: True

In [6]: 'Darwin' in uname

Out[6]: False

In [7]: 'Linux' not in uname

Out[7]: False

In [8]: 'Darwin' not in uname

Out[8]: True
```

If `string2` contains `string1`, `string1 in string2` returns `True`, otherwise, it returns `False`. So, checking to see if `"Linux"` was in our `uname` string returned `True`, but checking to see if `"Darwin"` was in our `uname` returned false. And we demonstrated `not in` just for fun.

Sometimes you only need to know if a string is a substring of another string. Other times, you need to know where in a string the substring occurs. `find()` and `index()` let you do that. See Example 3-5.

Example 3-5. find() and index()

```
In [9]: uname.index('Linux')

Out[9]: 0

In [10]: uname.find('Linux')

Out[10]: 0

In [11]: uname.index('Darwin')
---------------------------------------------------------------------------
<type 'exceptions.ValueError'>           Traceback (most recent call last)

/home/jmjones/code/<ipython console> in <module>()

<type 'exceptions.ValueError'>: substring not found

In [12]: uname.find('Darwin')

Out[12]: -1
```

If string1 is in string2 (as in our previous example), string2.find(string1) returns the index of the first character of string1, otherwise, it returns -1. (Don't worry—we'll get into indexes in a moment.) Likewise, if string1 is in string2, string2.index(string1) returns the index of the first character of string1, otherwise, it raises a ValueError exception. In the example, the find() method found "Linux" at the beginning of the string, so it returned 0 indicating that the index of the first character of "Linux" was 0. However, the find() method couldn't find "Darwin" anywhere, so it returned -1. When Python was looking for Linux, the index() method behaved in the same way the find() method does when looking for "Linux". However, when looking for "Darwin", index() threw a ValueError exception, indicating that it could not find that string.

So, what can you do with these "index" numbers? What good are they? Strings are treated as lists of characters. The "index" that find() and index() return simply shows which character of the larger string is the beginning of the match. See Example 3-6.

Example 3-6. String slice

```
In [13]: smp_index = uname.index('SMP')

In [14]: smp_index

Out[14]: 9

In [15]: uname[smp_index:]

Out[15]: 'SMP Tue Feb 12 02:46:46 UTC 2008'

In [16]: uname[:smp_index]

Out[16]: 'Linux #1 '

In [17]: uname

Out[17]: 'Linux #1 SMP Tue Feb 12 02:46:46 UTC 2008'
```

We were able to see every character from the index of finding "SMP" to the end of the string with the slice syntax string[index:]. We were also able to see every character from the beginning of the uname string to the index of finding "SMP" with the slice syntax string[:index]. The slight variation between these two is which side of the index the colon (:) finds itself on.

The point of this string slicing example, and of the in/not in tests, is to show you that strings are sequences and so they behave in a way that is similar to the way that sequences such as lists work. For a more thorough discussion of the way sequences work, see "Sequence Operations" in Chapter 4 of *Python in a Nutshell* (O'Reilly) by Alex Martelli (also available online on Safari at *http://safari.oreilly.com/0596100469/pytho nian-CHP-4-SECT-6*).

Two other strings that are occasionally methods are startswith() and endswith(). As their names imply, they can help you determine whether a string "starts with" or "ends with" a particular substring. See Example 3-7.

Example 3-7. startswith() and endswith()

```
In [1]: some_string = "Raymond Luxury-Yacht"

In [2]: some_string.startswith("Raymond")
Out[2]: True

In [3]: some_string.startswith("Throatwarbler")
Out[3]: False

In [4]: some_string.endswith("Luxury-Yacht")
Out[4]: True

In [5]: some_string.endswith("Mangrove")
Out[5]: False
```

So, you can see that Python returns the information that the string "Raymond Luxury-Yacht" begins with "Raymond" and ends with "Luxury-Yacht." It does not begin with "Throatwarbler," nor does it end with "Mangrove." It is pretty simple to achieve the same result using slicing, but slicing is messy and can be tedious as well. See Example 3-8.

Example 3-8. Startswith() endswith() replacement hack

```
In [6]: some_string[:len("Raymond")] == "Raymond"
Out[6]: True

In [7]: some_string[:len("Throatwarbler")] == "Throatwarbler"
Out[7]: False

In [8]: some_string[-len("Luxury-Yacht"):] == "Luxury-Yacht"
Out[8]: True

In [9]: some_string[-len("Mangrove"):] == "Mangrove"
Out[9]: False
```

A slice operation creates and returns a new string object rather than modifying the string in line. Depending on how frequently you slice a string in a script, there could be a noticable memory and performance impact. Even if there is no discernible performance impact, it's probably a good habit to refrain from using the slice operation in cases in which startswith() and endswith() will do what you need to do.

We were able to see that the string "Raymond" appeared in some_string from its beginning through however many characters are in the string "Raymond." In other words, we were able to see that some_string starts with the string "Raymond" without calling the startswith() method. And likewise for ending with "Luxury-Yacht."

Without any arguments, lstrip(), rstrip(), and strip() are methods that remove leading, trailing, and both leading and trailing whitespace, respectively. Examples of whitespace include tabs, space characters, carriage returns, and line feeds. Using lstrip() without arguments removes any whitespace that appears at the beginning of a string and then returns a new string. Using rstrip() without arguments removes any whitespace that appears at the end of a string and then returns a new string. Using strip() without arguments removes all whitespace at the beginning or end of a string and then returns a new string. See Example 3-9.

 All of the strip() methods create and return new string objects rather than modifying the strings in line. This might never cause problems for you, but it's something to be aware of.

Example 3-9. lstrip(), rstrip(), and strip()

```
In [1]: spacious_string = "\n\t Some Non-Spacious Text\n \t\r"

In [2]: spacious_string
Out[2]: '\n\t Some Non-Spacious Text\n \t\r'

In [3]: print spacious_string

        Some Non-Spacious Text


In [4]: spacious_string.lstrip()
Out[4]: 'Some Non-Spacious Text\n \t\r'

In [5]: print spacious_string.lstrip()
Some Non-Spacious Text


In [6]: spacious_string.rstrip()
Out[6]: '\n\t Some Non-Spacious Text'

In [7]: print spacious_string.rstrip()

        Some Non-Spacious Text

In [8]: spacious_string.strip()
Out[8]: 'Some Non-Spacious Text'

In [9]: print spacious_string.strip()
Some Non-Spacious Text
```

But strip(), rstrip(), and lstrip() all take one optional argument: a string whose characters are to be appropriately stripped off of the string. This means that the `strip()`s don't just remove whitespace; they'll remove anything you tell them to remove:

```
In [1]: xml_tag = "<some_tag>"

In [2]: xml_tag.lstrip("<")

Out[2]: 'some_tag>'

In [3]: xml_tag.lstrip(">")

Out[3]: '<some_tag>'

In [4]: xml_tag.rstrip(">")

Out[4]: '<some_tag'

In [5]: xml_tag.rstrip("<")

Out[5]: '<some_tag>'
```

Here, we stripped off the left and right angle brackets from an XML tag one at a time. But what if we wanted to strip off both of them at the same time? Then we could do this:

```
In [6]: xml_tag.strip("<").strip(">")

Out[6]: 'some_tag'
```

Since the `strip()`s return a string, we can call another string operation directly after a `strip()` call. Here, we chained `strip()` calls together. The first `strip()` call took off the starting character (the left angle bracket) and returned a string, and the second `strip()` call took off the ending character (the right angle bracket) and returned the string `"some_tag"`. But there's an easier way:

```
In [7]: xml_tag.strip("<>")

Out[7]: 'some_tag'
```

You might have assumed that the `strip()`s stripped off an exact occurrence of the string you fed it, but the `strip`s actually remove any sequential occurrence of the specified characters from the appropriate side of the string. In that last example, we told `strip()` to remove `"<>"`. That doesn't mean to exactly match `"<>"` and remove any occurrences of those two characters that are adjacent to one another in that order; it means remove any occurrences of `"<"` or `">"` that are adjacent to one another on either end of the string.

Here is perhaps a clearer example:

```
In [8]: gt_lt_str = "<><><>gt lt str<><><>"

In [9]: gt_lt_str.strip("<>")

Out[9]: 'gt lt str'
```

```
In [10]: gt_lt_str.strip("><")
```

```
Out[10]: 'gt lt str'
```

We stripped off any occurrences of "<" or ">" on either side of the string. So we wound up with something that was just letters and spaces.

This still might not work exactly as you're expecting. For example:

```
In [11]: foo_str = "<foooooooo>blah<foo>"
```

```
In [12]: foo_str.strip("<foo>")
```

```
Out[12]: 'blah'
```

You may have expected strip() to match and strip the right side but not the left. But it matched and stripped the sequential occurrence of "<", "f", "o", and ">". And no, we didn't leave out an "o". Here is one final clarifying example for the strip():

```
In [13]: foo_str.strip("><of")
```

```
Out[13]: 'blah'
```

This stripped "<", "f", "o", even though the characters were not in that order.

The methods upper() and lower() are useful, particularly when you need to compare two strings without regard to whether the characters are upper- or lowercase. The upper() method returns a string, which is the uppercase of the original. The lower() method returns a string, which is the lowercase of the original. See Example 3-10.

Example 3-10. upper() and lower()

```
In [1]: mixed_case_string = "VOrpal BUnny"
```

```
In [2]: mixed_case_string == "vorpal bunny"
Out[2]: False
```

```
In [3]: mixed_case_string.lower() == "vorpal bunny"
Out[3]: True
```

```
In [4]: mixed_case_string == "VORPAL BUNNY"
Out[4]: False
```

```
In [5]: mixed_case_string.upper() == "VORPAL BUNNY"
Out[5]: True
```

```
In [6]: mixed_case_string.upper()
Out[6]: 'VORPAL BUNNY'
```

```
In [7]: mixed_case_string.lower()
Out[7]: 'vorpal bunny'
```

If you need to extract a piece of a string based on some kind of delimiter, the split() method may provide exactly what you are looking for. See Example 3-11.

Example 3-11. split()

```
In [1]: comma_delim_string = "pos1,pos2,pos3"

In [2]: pipe_delim_string = "pipepos1|pipepos2|pipepos3"

In [3]: comma_delim_string.split(',')
Out[3]: ['pos1', 'pos2', 'pos3']

In [4]: pipe_delim_string.split('|')
Out[4]: ['pipepos1', 'pipepos2', 'pipepos3']
```

Typical use of the `split()` method is to pass in the string that you want to split. Often, this is a single character such as a comma or pipe, but it can also be a string of more than one character. We split `comma_delim_string` on a comma and `pipe_delim_string` on the pipe (|) character by passing the comma and the pipe characters to `split()`. The return value of `split()` is a list of strings, each of which is a contiguous group of characters that fell between the specified delimiters. When you need to split on a number of characters rather than just a single character, the `split()` method accommodates that, too. As we are writing this book, there is no character type in Python, so what we passed in to `split()`, although it was a single character in both cases, was actually a string. So when we pass several characters in to `split()`, it will work with them. See Example 3-12.

Example 3-12. split() multiple delimiter example

```
In [1]: multi_delim_string = "pos1XXXpos2XXXpos3"

In [2]: multi_delim_string.split("XXX")
Out[2]: ['pos1', 'pos2', 'pos3']

In [3]: multi_delim_string.split("XX")
Out[3]: ['pos1', 'Xpos2', 'Xpos3']

In [4]: multi_delim_string.split("X")
Out[4]: ['pos1', '', '', 'pos2', '', '', 'pos3']
```

Notice that we first specified "XXX" as the delimiting string for `multi_delim_string`. As we expected, this returned `['pos1', 'pos2', 'pos3']`. Next, we specified "XX" as the delimiting string and `split()` returned `['pos1', 'Xpos2', 'Xpos3']`. `Split()` looked for the characters that appeared between each instance of the "XX" delimiter. "Pos1" appeared from the beginning of the string to the first "XX" delimiter; "Xpos2" appeared from the first occurrence of "XX" to the second appearance of it; and "Xpos3" appeared from the second occurrence of "XX" to the end of the string. The last `split()` used a single "X" character as the delimiting string. Notice that, in the positions where there were adjacent "X" characters, there is an empty string ("") in the returned list. This simply means that there is nothing between the adjacent "X" characters.

But what if you only want to split the string on the first "n" occurrences of the specified delimiters? `Split()` takes a second parameter, called `max_split`. When an integer value for `max_split` is passed in, `split()` will only split the string the number of times the `max_split` argument dictates:

```
In [1]: two_field_string = "8675309,This is a freeform, plain text, string"

In [2]: two_field_string.split(',', 1)
Out[2]: ['8675309', 'This is a freeform, plain text, string']
```

We split on a comma and told `split()` to only split on the first occurrence of the delimiter. Although there are multiple commas in this example, the string is split only on the first one.

If you need to split on whitespace in order to retrieve, for example, words from a piece of prose-like text, `split()` is an easy tool for accomplishing that:

```
In [1]: prosaic_string = "Insert your clever little piece of text here."

In [2]: prosaic_string.split()
Out[2]: ['Insert', 'your', 'clever', 'little', 'piece', 'of', 'text', 'here.']
```

Because no parameters have been passed in, `split()` defaults to splitting on whitespace.

Most of the time, you will probably see the results you expected to see. However, if you have a multiline piece of text, you might see results that you were not expecting. Often, when you have a multiline piece of text, you intend to deal with one line at a time. But you might find that the program split on every word in the string:

```
In [1]: multiline_string = """This
   ...: is
   ...: a multiline
   ...: piece of
   ...: text"""

In [2]: multiline_string.split()
Out[2]: ['This', 'is', 'a', 'multiline', 'piece', 'of', 'text']
```

In this case, `splitlines()` will get you closer to what you wanted:

```
In [3]: lines = multiline_string.splitlines()

In [4]: lines

Out[4]: ['This', 'is', 'a multiline', 'piece of', 'text']
```

`Splitlines()` returned a list of each line within the string and preserved groups of "words." From here, you can iterate over each line and split the line into words:

```
In [5]: for line in lines:
   ...:     print "START LINE::"
   ...:     print line.split()
   ...:     print "::END LINE"
   ...:
START LINE::
['This']
::END LINE
START LINE::
```

```
['is']
::END LINE
START LINE::
['a', 'multiline']
::END LINE
START LINE::
['piece', 'of']
::END LINE
START LINE::
['text']
::END LINE
```

Sometimes you don't want to pull a string apart or extract information from it; some-times you need to piece a string together from data you already have. In these cases, join() can help:

```
In [1]: some_list = ['one', 'two', 'three', 'four']

In [2]: ','.join(some_list)
Out[2]: 'one,two,three,four'

In [3]: ', '.join(some_list)
Out[3]: 'one, two, three, four'

In [4]: '\t'.join(some_list)
Out[4]: 'one\ttwo\tthree\tfour'

In [5]: ''.join(some_list)
Out[5]: 'onetwothreefour'
```

Given the list some_list, we were able to assemble the strings 'one', 'two', 'three', and 'four' into a number of variations. We joined the list some_list with a comma, a comma and a space, a tab, and an empty string. Join() is a string method, so calling join() on a string literal such as ',' is perfectly valid. Join() takes a sequence of strings as an argument. It packs the sequence of strings together into a single string so that each item of the sequence appears in order, but the string on which you called join() appears between each item in the sequence.

We have a word of warning regarding join() and the argument it expects. Note that join() expects a sequence of strings. What happens if you pass in a sequence of integers? Kaboom!

```
In [1]: some_list = range(10)

In [2]: some_list
Out[2]: [0, 1, 2, 3, 4, 5, 6, 7, 8, 9]

In [3]: ",".join(some_list)
---------------------------------------------------------------------------
exceptions.TypeError                           Traceback (most recent call last)

/Users/jmjones/<ipython console>

TypeError: sequence item 0: expected string, int found
```

The traceback to the exception that `join()` raises is pretty self-explanatory, but since this is a common error, it is worth understanding. You can easily avoid this pitfall with a simple list comprehension. Here we enlist the help of a list comprehension to convert all the elements of `some_list`, all of which are integers, to strings:

```
In [4]: ",".join([str(i) for i in some_list])
Out[4]: '0,1,2,3,4,5,6,7,8,9'
```

Or, you could use a generator expression:

```
In [5]: ",".join(str(i) for i in some_list)

Out[5]: '0,1,2,3,4,5,6,7,8,9'
```

For more information on using list comprehensions, see the section "Control Flow Statements" in Chapter 4 of *Python in a Nutshell* (also available online on Safari at *http://safari.oreilly.com/0596100469/pythonian-CHP-4-SECT-10*).

The last method for creating or modifying strings of text is the `replace()` method. `Replace()` takes two arguments: the string that is to be replaced and the string to replace it with, respectively. Here is a simple `replace()` example:

```
In [1]: replacable_string = "trancendental hibernational nation"

In [2]: replacable_string.replace("nation", "natty")
Out[2]: 'trancendental hibernattyal natty'
```

Notice that `replace()` doesn't care if the string to replace is in the middle of a word or if it is a full word. So, in cases in which you need to replace only a specific sequence of characters with another specific sequence of characters, `replace()` is the tool to use.

However, there are times when you need a finer level of control, when replacing one sequence of characters with another sequence of characters isn't enough. Sometimes you need to be able to specify a pattern of characters to find and replace. Patterns can also help with searching for text from which to extract data. In cases in which using patterns is more helpful, regular expressions can help. We'll look at regular expressions next.

 As slice operations and the `strip()` methods do, `replace()` creates a new string rather than modify the string in line.

Unicode strings

So far, all of the examples of strings we've looked at have been exclusively of the built-in string types (`str`), but Python has another string type with which you will want to be familiar: Unicode. When you see any characters on a computer screen, the computer is dealing with those characters internally as numbers. Until Unicode, there were many different sets of number-to-character mappings, depending on the language and platform. Unicode is a standard that provides a single number-to-character mapping regardless of the language, platform, or even the program that is dealing with the text. In this section, we will introduce the concept of Unicode and the way that Python deals with it. For a more in-depth explanation of Unicode, see A. M. Kuchling's excellent Unicode tutorial at *http://www.amk.ca/python/howto/unicode*.

Creating a Unicode string is as simple as creating a regular string:

```
In [1]: unicode_string = u'this is a unicode string'

In [2]: unicode_string
Out[2]: u'this is a unicode string'

In [3]: print unicode_string
this is a unicode string
```

Or, you can use the built-in unicode() function:

```
In [4]: unicode('this is a unicode string')
Out[4]: u'this is a unicode string'
```

This doesn't seem like it buys us much, particularly as it is just dealing with characters from one language. But what if you have to deal with characters from multiple languages? Unicode will help you here. To create a character in a Unicode string with a specific numerical value, you can use the \uXXXX or \uXXXXXXXX notation. For example, here is a Unicode string that contains Latin, Greek, and Russian characters:

```
In [1]: unicode_string = u'abc_\u03a0\u03a3\u03a9_\u0414\u0424\u042F'

In [2]: unicode_string
Out[2]: u'abc_\u03a0\u03a3\u03a9_\u0414\u0424\u042f'
```

Python generates a string (str) dependant on the encoding you use. On the Python that comes standard with Mac, if you attempted to print the string from the previous example, an error would be returned, printing:

```
In [3]: print unicode_string
---------------------------------------------------------------------------
UnicodeEncodeError                        Traceback (most recent call last)

/Users/jmjones/<ipython console> in <module>()

UnicodeEncodeError: 'ascii' codec can't encode characters in position 4-6:
    ordinal not in range(128)
```

We have to give it an encoding that knows how to handle all the characters that we give it:

```
In [4]: print unicode_string.encode('utf-8')
abc_ΠΣΩ_ДФЯ
```

Here, we encoded the string that contained Latin, Greek, and Russian characters to UTF-8, which is a common encoding for Unicode data.

Unicode strings contain the same facilities, such as the in test, and methods that we've already talked about for regular strings:

```
In [5]: u'abc' in unicode_string
Out[5]: True

In [6]: u'foo' in unicode_string
Out[6]: False

In [7]: unicode_string.split()
Out[7]: [u'abc_\u03a0\u03a3\u03a9_\u0414\u0424\u042f']

In [8]: unicode_string.
unicode_string.__add__            unicode_string.expandtabs
unicode_string.__class__          unicode_string.find
unicode_string.__contains__       unicode_string.index
unicode_string.__delattr__        unicode_string.isalnum
unicode_string.__doc__            unicode_string.isalpha
unicode_string.__eq__             unicode_string.isdecimal
unicode_string.__ge__             unicode_string.isdigit
unicode_string.__getattribute__   unicode_string.islower
unicode_string.__getitem__        unicode_string.isnumeric
unicode_string.__getnewargs__     unicode_string.isspace
unicode_string.__getslice__       unicode_string.istitle
unicode_string.__gt__             unicode_string.isupper
unicode_string.__hash__           unicode_string.join
unicode_string.__init__           unicode_string.ljust
unicode_string.__le__             unicode_string.lower
unicode_string.__len__            unicode_string.lstrip
unicode_string.__lt__             unicode_string.partition
unicode_string.__mod__            unicode_string.replace
unicode_string.__mul__            unicode_string.rfind
unicode_string.__ne__             unicode_string.rindex
unicode_string.__new__            unicode_string.rjust
unicode_string.__reduce__         unicode_string.rpartition
unicode_string.__reduce_ex__      unicode_string.rsplit
unicode_string.__repr__           unicode_string.rstrip
unicode_string.__rmod__           unicode_string.split
unicode_string.__rmul__           unicode_string.splitlines
unicode_string.__setattr__        unicode_string.startswith
unicode_string.__str__            unicode_string.strip
unicode_string.capitalize         unicode_string.swapcase
unicode_string.center             unicode_string.title
unicode_string.count              unicode_string.translate
unicode_string.decode             unicode_string.upper
unicode_string.encode             unicode_string.zfill
unicode_string.endswith
```

You might not need Unicode right now. But it's important that you become familiar with it if you want to continue programming with Python.

re

Since Python comes with "batteries included," you might expect that it would include a regular expression library. You won't be disappointed. The emphasis in this section will be on using Python to work with regular expressions rather than on the ins and outs of regular expression syntax. So if you aren't familiar with regular expressions, we recommend that you pick up a copy of *Mastering Regular Expressions* (O'Reilly) by Jeffrey E. F. Friedl (also available on Safari at *http://safari.oreilly.com/0596528124*). This section will assume that you are comfortable with regular expressions, but if you're not, it will be helpful to have Friedl's text at hand.

If you're familiar with Perl, you're probably used to using regular expressions with =~. Python's inclusion of regular expressions comes by way of a library rather than syntactic features of the language. So, in order to work with regular expressions, you first have to import the regular expression module **re**. Here is a basic example of the way regular expressions are created and used. See Example 3-13.

Example 3-13. Basic regular expression usage

```
In [1]: import re

In [2]: re_string = "{{(.*?)}}"

In [3]: some_string = "this is a string with {{words}} embedded in\
   ...:  {{curly brackets}} to show an {{example}} of {{regular expressions}}"

In [4]: for match in re.findall(re_string, some_string):
   ...:      print "MATCH->", match
   ...:
MATCH-> words
MATCH-> curly brackets
MATCH-> example
MATCH-> regular expressions
```

The first thing we did was to import the **re** module. As you might have guessed, **re** stands for "regular expression." Next, we created a string, **re_string**, which is the pattern we look for in the example. This pattern will match two consecutive open curly brackets ({{) followed by any text (or no text) followed by two consecutive close curly brackets (}}). Next, we created a string, **some_string**, which contains a mix of groups of words enclosed in double curly brackets and words not enclosed in curly brackets. Finally, we iterated over the results of the **re** module's findall() function as it searched **some_string** for the pattern found in **re_string**. And you can see, it printed out **words**, **curly brackets**, **example**, and **regular expressions**, which are all the words enclosed in double curly brackets.

There are two ways to work with regular expressions in Python. The first is to use the functions in the **re** module directly, as in the previous example. The second is to create a compiled regular expression object and use the methods on that object.

So what is a compiled regular expression? It is simply an object that was created by passing in a pattern to re.compile(); it contains a number of regular expression methods that were created by passing in a pattern to re.compile(). There are two primary differences between using the compiled and noncompiled examples. First, instead of keeping a reference to the regular expression pattern "{{(.*?)}}", we created a compiled regular expression object and used the pattern to create it. Second, instead of calling findall() on the re module, we called findall() on the compiled regular expression object.

For more information on the re module's contents, which includes available functions, see the Module Contents section of the *Python Library Reference, http://docs.py thon.org/lib/node46.html.* For more information on compiled regular expression objects, see the Regular Expression Objects section of the *Python Library Reference, http://docs.python.org/lib/re-objects.html.*

Example 3-14 shows our double curly bracket example reworked to show how to use a compiled regular expression object.

Example 3-14. Simple regular expression, compiled pattern

```
In [1]: import re

In [2]: re_obj = re.compile("{{(.*?)}}")

In [3]: some_string = "this is a string with {{words}} embedded in\
   ...:  {{curly brackets}} to show an {{example}} of {{regular expressions}}"

In [4]: for match in re_obj.findall(some_string):
   ...:      print "MATCH->", match
   ...:
MATCH-> words
MATCH-> curly brackets
MATCH-> example
MATCH-> regular expressions
```

The method that you choose to work with regular expressions in Python is partially a matter of preference and expression. However, there can be performance implications when you use the functions in the re module rather than creating a compiled regular expression object. Those performance problems can be exacerbated if you are in some kind of a loop that will repeat a lot, such as a loop that applies the regular expression to each line of a text file with hundreds of thousands of lines. In the examples below, we run a simple regex script using both compiled and noncompiled regular expressions, against a file containing 500,000 lines of text. When we run the Unix timeit utility against the results of each script test, you'll be able to see the difference in performance. See Example 3-15.

Example 3-15. re no compile code performance test

```python
#!/usr/bin/env python

import re

def run_re():
    pattern = 'pDq'

    infile = open('large_re_file.txt', 'r')
    match_count = 0
    lines = 0
    for line in infile:
        match = re.search(pattern, line)
        if match:
            match_count += 1
        lines += 1
    return (lines, match_count)

if __name__ == "__main__":
    lines, match_count =  run_re()
    print 'LINES::', lines
    print 'MATCHES::', match_count
```

The timeit utility executes a piece of code a number of times and reports back the time of the best run. Here are the results from running the Python timeit utility within IPython on this code:

```
In [1]: import re_loop_nocompile

In [2]: timeit -n 5 re_loop_nocompile.run_re()
5 loops, best of 3: 1.93 s per loop
```

This example executed the run_re() function in three sets of five iterations each and reported back that the best run took an average of 1.93 seconds per loop. The reason timeit runs the same piece of code a number of times is to reduce the likelihood that other processes running at the same time are affected by the test results.

And here are the results from running the Unix time utility against the same code:

```
jmjones@dink:~/code$ time python re_loop_nocompile.py
LINES:: 500000 MATCHES:: 242

real    0m2.113s
user    0m1.888s
sys     0m0.163s
```

Example 3-16 is the same regular expression example, except that we are using re.compile() to create a compiled pattern object.

Example 3-16. re compile code performance test

```python
#!/usr/bin/env python

import re
```

```
def run_re():
    pattern = 'pDq'
    re_obj = re.compile(pattern)

    infile = open('large_re_file.txt', 'r')
    match_count = 0
    lines = 0
    for line in infile:
        match = re_obj.search(line)
        if match:
            match_count += 1
        lines += 1
    return (lines, match_count)

if __name__ == "__main__":
    lines, match_count =  run_re()
    print 'LINES::', lines
    print 'MATCHES::', match_count
```

Running this script through the Python `timeit` utility in IPython yields these results:

```
In [3]: import re_loop_compile

In [4]: timeit -n 5 re_loop_compile.run_re()
5 loops, best of 3: 860 ms per loop
```

And running the same script through the Unix `time` utility yields these results:

```
jmjones@dink:~/code$ time python
re_loop_compile.py LINES:: 500000 MATCHES:: 242

real    0m0.996s
user    0m0.836s
sys     0m0.154s
```

The clear winner is the compiled version. It took half the time to run as measured by both the Unix `time` and the Python `timeit` utilities. So we highly recommend that you get into the habit of creating compiled regular expression objects.

As we discussed earlier in this chapter, raw strings can be used to denote strings that do not interpret escape sequences. Example 3-17 shows raw strings used in regular expressions.

Example 3-17. Raw strings and regular expressions

```
In [1]: import re

In [2]: raw_pattern = r'\b[a-z]+\b'

In [3]: non_raw_pattern = '\b[a-z]+\b'

In [4]: some_string = 'a few little words'

In [5]: re.findall(raw_pattern, some_string)
```

```
Out[5]: ['a', 'few', 'little', 'words']

In [6]: re.findall(non_raw_pattern, some_string)

Out[6]: []
```

The regular expression pattern \b matches word boundaries. So in both the raw and regular strings, we were looking for individual lowercase words. Notice that `raw_pattern` matched the word boundaries appropriately on `some_string` and `non_raw_pattern` didn't match anything at all. `Raw_pattern` recognized \b as two characters rather than interpreting it as an escape sequence for the backspace character. `Non_raw_pattern` interpreted the \b characters as an escape sequence representing the backspace character. The regular expression function `findall()` was then able to use the raw string pattern to find words. However, when `findall()` looked for the non-raw pattern, it didn't find any backspace characters.

For `non_raw_pattern` to match a string, we would have to put backspace characters around it, as we did with "little" here:

```
In [7]: some_other_string = 'a few \blittle\b words'

In [8]: re.findall(non_raw_pattern, some_other_string)
Out[8]: ['\x08little\x08']
```

Notice that `findall()` matched the hex notation "\x08" before and after the word "little." That hex notation corresponds to the backspace character that we inserted with the escape sequence "\b".

So, as you can see, raw strings are helpful when you intend to use some of the backslashed special sequences such as "\b" for word boundaries, "\d" for digits, and "\w" for alpha numeric characters. For a full listing of these backslashed special sequences, see the Regular Expression Syntax section in the *Python Library Reference* at *http://docs.python.org/lib/re-syntax.html*.

Examples 3-14 through 3-17 really were quite simple, both in the regular expression used as well as the different methods we applied to it. Sometimes, this limited use of the power of regular expressions is all you need. Other times, you'll need to make use of more of the power that is contained in the regular expression library.

The four primary regular expression methods (or functions) which are most likely to be used often are `findall()`, `finditer()`, `match()`, and `search()`. You might also find yourself using `split()` and `sub()`, but probably not as often as you will use the others.

`Findall()` will find all occurrences of the specified pattern in the search string. If `findall()` matches the pattern, the type of data structure it will return will depend on whether the pattern specified a group.

A quick reminder about regex: grouping allows you to specify text within a regular expression that you want to extract from the result. See "Common Metacharacters and Fields" in Friedl's *Mastering Regular Expressions* for more information, or go online to *http://safari.oreil ly.com/0596528124/regex3-CHP-3-SECT-5?imagepage=137*.

If you didn't specify a group in the regular expression pattern but a match is found, `findall()` will return a list of strings. For example:

```
In [1]: import re

In [2]: re_obj = re.compile(r'\bt.*?e\b')

In [3]: re_obj.findall("time tame tune tint tire")
Out[3]: ['time', 'tame', 'tune', 'tint tire']
```

The pattern doesn't specify any groups, so `findall()` returns a list of strings. An interesting side point is that the last element of the returned list contains two words, tint and tire. The regular expression was intended to match words that start with "t" and end with "e". But the `.*?` command matches anything, including whitespace. `Findall()` matched everything it was supposed to. It found a word which started with "t" (tint). It continued looking through the string until it found a word that ended with "e" (tire). So, the match "tint tire" was appropriate. To exclude the whitespace, you would use `r'\bt\w*e\b'`:

```
In [4]: re_obj = re.compile(r'\bt\w*e\b')

In [5]: re_obj.findall("time tame tune tint tire")
Out[5]: ['time', 'tame', 'tune', 'tire']
```

The second type of data structure that could be returned is a list of tuples. If you did specify a group and there was a match, then `findall()` returns a list of tuples. Example 3-18 is a simple example of such a pattern and a string.

Example 3-18. Simple grouped group with findall()

```
In [1]: import re

In [2]: re_obj = re.compile(r"""(A\W+\b(big|small)\b\W+\b
   ...: (brown|purple)\b\W+\b(cow|dog)\b\W+\b(ran|jumped)\b\W+\b
   ...: (to|down)\b\W+\b(the)\b\W+\b(street|moon).*?\.)""",
   ...: re.VERBOSE)

In [3]: re_obj.findall('A big brown dog ran down the street. \
   ...: A small purple cow jumped to the moon.')

Out[3]:
[('A big brown dog ran down the street.',
  'big',
  'brown',
  'dog',
  'ran',
```

```
    'down',
    'the',
    'street'),
   ('A small purple cow jumped to the moon.',
    'small',
    'purple',
    'cow',
    'jumped',
    'to',
    'the',
    'moon')]
```

Though it is simple, this example shows some important points. First, notice that this simple pattern is ridiculously long and contains enough nonalphanumeric characters to make your eyes bleed if you stare at it for too long. That seems to be a common theme with many regular expressions. Next, notice that the pattern contains explicit nested groups. The outer group should match all the characters beginning with the letter "A" through to the ending period. The characters between the beginning A and the ending period make up inner groups that should match "big or small," "brown or purple," and so on. Next, the return value of `findall()` is a list of tuples. The elements of those tuples are each of the groups we specified in the regular expression. The entire sentence is the first element of the tuple as it is the largest, outermost group. Each of the subgroups is a subsequent element of the tuple. Finally, notice that the last argument to `re.compile()` was `re.VERBOSE`. This allowed us to write the regular expression string in verbose mode, which simply means that we were able to split the regular expression across lines without the split interfering with the pattern matching. Whitespace that fell outside of a class grouping was ignored. Though we chose not to do it here, verbose also allows us to insert comments at the end of each line of `regex` to document what each particular piece of a regular expression does. One of the difficulties of regular expressions in general is that the description of the pattern that you want to match often becomes huge and difficult to read. The `re.VERBOSE` function lets you write simpler regular expressions, so it is a great tool for improving the maintenance of code that includes regular expressions.

A slight variation of `findall()` is `finditer()`. Rather than returning a list of tuples as `findall()`does, `finditer()` returns an iterator, as its name implies. Each item of the iterator is a regular expression match object, which we'll discuss later in this chapter. Example 3-19 is the same simple example using `finditer()` rather than `findall()`.

Example 3-19. finditer() example

```
In [4]: re_iter = re_obj.finditer('A big brown dog ran down the street. \
   ...: A small purple cow jumped to the moon.')

In [5]: re_iter

Out[5]: <callable-iterator object at 0xa17ad0>

In [6]: for item in re_iter:
```

```
...:     print item
...:     print item.groups()
...:
<_sre.SRE_Match object at 0x9ff858>
('A big brown dog ran down the street.', 'big', 'brown', 'dog', 'ran',
    'down', 'the', 'street')
<_sre.SRE_Match object at 0x9ff940>
('A small purple cow jumped to the moon.', 'small', 'purple', 'cow',
    'jumped', 'to', 'the', 'moon')
```

If you have never encountered iterators before, you can think of them as similar to lists that are built as they are needed. One reason this definition is flawed is that you can't refer to a specific item in the iterator by its index, as you can some_list[3] for a list. One consequence of this limitation is that you don't have the ability to slice iterators, as you can some_list[2:6] for a list. Regardless of this limitation, though, iterators are lightweight and powerful, particularly when you only need to iterate over some sequence, because the entire sequence is not loaded up into memory but is retrieved on demand. This allows an iterator to have a smaller memory footprint than its corresponding list counterpart. It also means an iterator will start up with a shorter wait time for accessing the items in the sequence.

Another reason to use finditer() rather than findall() is that each item of finditer() is a match object rather than just a simple list of strings or list of tuples corresponding to the text that matched.

Match() and search() provide similar functionality to one another. Both apply a regular expression to a string; both specify where in the string to start and end looking for the pattern; and both return a match object for the first match of the specified pattern. The difference between them is that match() starts trying to match at the beginning of the string at the place within the string where you specified it should start looking and does not move to random places within the string, but search(), however, will try to match the pattern anywhere in the string or from the place within the string that you tell it to start, ending at the place within the string where you told it to finish. See Example 3-20.

Example 3-20. Comparison of match() and search()

```
In [1]: import re

In [2]: re_obj = re.compile('FOO')

In [3]: search_string = ' FOO'

In [4]: re_obj.search(search_string)

Out[4]: <_sre.SRE_Match object at 0xa22f38>

In [5]: re_obj.match(search_string)

In [6]:
```

Even though search_string contains the pattern that match() was looking for, it failed to turn up a match because the substring of search_string that would have turned up a match didn't start at the beginning of search_string. The search() call turned up a match object.

Search() and match() calls accept start and end parameters that specify the places in a string at which Python should start and end looking for a pattern. See Example 3-21.

Example 3-21. Start and end parameters for search( ) and match( )

```
In [6]: re_obj.search(search_string, pos=1)

Out[6]: <_sre.SRE_Match object at 0xabe030>

In [7]: re_obj.match(search_string, pos=1)

Out[7]: <_sre.SRE_Match object at 0xabe098>

In [8]: re_obj.search(search_string, pos=1, endpos=3)

In [9]: re_obj.match(search_string, pos=1, endpos=3)

In [10]:
```

The parameter pos is an index that specifies the place in the string where Python should look for the pattern. Specifying the start parameter pos for search() didn't change anything; but specifying pos for match() caused it to match the pattern it failed to match without the pos parameter. Setting the end parameter endpos to 3 caused both search() and match() to fail to match the pattern because the pattern begins after the third character position.

As findall() and finditer() answer the question, "What did my pattern match?," a major question that search() and match() answer is, "Did my pattern match?" Search() and match() also answer the question, "What first thing did my pattern match?," but often, the thing you really want to know is, "Did my pattern match?" For example, let's say you are writing code to read in logfiles and wrap each line in HTML so that it displays nicely. You want all "ERROR" lines to display in red, so you would probably loop through each line in the file, check it against a regular expression, and, if search() turned up a hit on its "ERROR" search, you would format the line to display in red.

Search() and match() are beneficial, not only because they indicate whether a pattern matched a piece of text; they also return a match() object. Match() objects contain various pieces of data that can come in handy when you're walking through pieces of text. Particularly interesting match() methods include start(), end(), span(), groups(), and groupdict().

Start(), end(), and span() specify the places in the searched string that the matched pattern begins and ends. Start() returns an integer that identifies the position in the string at which the pattern match begins. End() returns an integer that identifies the position at which the pattern match ends. And `span()` returns a tuple containing the beginning and end of the match.

`Groups()` returns a tuple of the match, each element of which is a group that the pattern specified. This tuple is similar to each tuple in the list that `findall()` returns. `Group dict()` returns a dictionary of named groups in which the names are found in the regular expression itself using the `(?P<group_name>pattern)` syntax.

In summary, to use regular expressions effectively, it is important to get in to the habit of using compiled regular expression objects. Use `findall()` and `finditer()` when you want to see what elements your pattern matched in a piece of text. Remember that `finditer()` is more flexible than `findall()` since it returns an iterator of `match` objects. For a more detailed overview of the regular expression library, see Chapter 9 of *Python in a Nutshell* by Alex Martelli (O'Reilly). To see regular expressions in action, see *Data Crunching* by Greg Wilson (The Pragmatic Bookshelf).

Apache Config File Hacking

Now that you've been introduced to Python regular expressions, let's work through an Apache config file:

```
NameVirtualHost 127.0.0.1:80
<VirtualHost localhost:80>
    DocumentRoot /var/www/
    <Directory />
        Options FollowSymLinks
        AllowOverride None
    </Directory>
    ErrorLog /var/log/apache2/error.log
    LogLevel warn
    CustomLog /var/log/apache2/access.log combined
    ServerSignature On
</VirtualHost>
<VirtualHost local2:80>
    DocumentRoot /var/www2/
    <Directory />
        Options FollowSymLinks
        AllowOverride None
    </Directory>
    ErrorLog /var/log/apache2/error2.log
    LogLevel warn
    CustomLog /var/log/apache2/access2.log combined
    ServerSignature On
</VirtualHost>
```

This is a slightly modified config file from a stock Apache 2 installation on Ubuntu. We created named virtual hosts so that we could have something to work with. We also modified the */etc/hosts* file so that it contains this line:

```
127.0.0.1    local2
```

This allows us to point a browser on that box at `local2` and have it resolve to 127.0.0.1, which is a localhost. So, what is the point of this? If you go to *http://local2*, your browser will pass the hostname along in an HTTP request. Here is an HTTP request to `local2`:

```
GET / HTTP/1.1
Host: local2
User-Agent: Mozilla/5.0 (X11; U; Linux x86_64; en-US; rv:1.8.1.13)
Gecko/20080325 Ubuntu/7.10 (gutsy) Firefox/2.0.0.13
Accept: text/xml,application/xml,application/xhtml+xml,text/html
Accept-Language: en-us,en;q=0.5
Accept-Encoding: gzip,deflate
Accept-Charset: ISO-8859-1,utf-8;q=0.7,*;q=0.7
Keep-Alive: 300
Connection: keep-alive
If-Modified-Since: Tue, 15 Apr 2008 17:25:24 GMT
If-None-Match: "ac5ea-53-44aecaf804900"
Cache-Control: max-age=0
```

Notice the line starting with `Host:`. When Apache gets this request, it routes it to the virtual host that matches the `local2` name.

So, what we want to do is to write a script that parses through an Apache config file, like the one we just presented, finds a specified `VirtualHost` section, and replaces the `DocumentRoot` for that `VirtualHost`. This script does just that:

```python
#!/usr/bin/env python

from cStringIO import StringIO
import re

vhost_start = re.compile(r'<VirtualHost\s+(.*?)>')
vhost_end = re.compile(r'</VirtualHost')
docroot_re = re.compile(r'(DocumentRoot\s+)(\S+)')

def replace_docroot(conf_string, vhost, new_docroot):
    '''yield new lines of an httpd.conf file where docroot lines matching
       the specified vhost are replaced with the new_docroot
    '''
    conf_file = StringIO(conf_string)
    in_vhost = False
    curr_vhost = None
    for line in conf_file:
        vhost_start_match = vhost_start.search(line)
        if vhost_start_match:
            curr_vhost = vhost_start_match.groups()[0]
            in_vhost = True
        if in_vhost and (curr_vhost == vhost):
            docroot_match = docroot_re.search(line)
            if docroot_match:
                sub_line = docroot_re.sub(r'\1%s' % new_docroot, line)
                line = sub_line
        vhost_end_match = vhost_end.search(line)
        if vhost_end_match:
            in_vhost = False
        yield line
```

```
if __name__ == '__main__':
    import sys
    conf_file = sys.argv[1]
    vhost = sys.argv[2]
    docroot = sys.argv[3]
    conf_string = open(conf_file).read()
    for line in replace_docroot(conf_string, vhost, docroot):
        print line,
```

This script initially sets up three compiled regular expression objects: one to match the start of the VirtualHost, one to match the end of the VirtualHost, and one to match the DocumentRoot line. We also created a function to do the dirty work for us. The function is named replace_docroot() and it takes as its arguments the string body of the config file, the name of the VirtualHost to match, and the DocumentRoot to which we want to point the VirtualHost. The function sets up a state machine that checks to see if we are in a VirtualHost section. It also keeps track of the VirtualHost in which it is contained. When it is in the VirtualHost that the calling code specified, this function looks for any occurrence of the DocumentRoot directive and changes that directive's directory to the one the calling code specified. As replace_docroot() iterates over each line in the config file, it yields either the unmodified input line or the modified DocumentRoot line.

We created a simple command-line interface to this function. It isn't anything fancy that uses optparse, nor does it do error checking on the number of arguments that you give it, but it's functional. Now we'll run the script on the same Apache config file we presented earlier, and change VirtualHost local2:80 to use /tmp as its VirtualHost. This command-line interface prints out the lines from the function replace_docroot() rather than writing them to a file:

```
jmjones@dinkgutsy:code$ python apache_conf_docroot_replace.py
    /etc/apache2/sites-available/psa
    local2:80 /tmp
NameVirtualHost 127.0.0.1:80
<VirtualHost localhost:80>
        DocumentRoot /var/www/
        <Directory />
                Options FollowSymLinks
                AllowOverride None
        </Directory>
        ErrorLog /var/log/apache2/error.log
        LogLevel warn
        CustomLog /var/log/apache2/access.log combined
        ServerSignature On
</VirtualHost>
<VirtualHost local2:80>
        DocumentRoot /tmp
        <Directory />
                Options FollowSymLinks
                AllowOverride None
        </Directory>
        ErrorLog /var/log/apache2/error2.log
```

```
LogLevel warn
CustomLog /var/log/apache2/access2.log combined
ServerSignature On
</VirtualHost>
```

The only line that is different is the `DocumentRoot` line from the `local2:80 VirtualHost` section. Here is a difference of the two after we redirected the output of the script to a file:

```
jmjones@dinkgutsy:code$ diff apache_conf.diff /etc/apache2/sites-available/psa
20c20
<         DocumentRoot /tmp
---
>         DocumentRoot /var/www2/
```

Modifying an Apache config file to change the `DocumentRoot` is a very simple task, but if you have to change the document root often, or if you have many virtual hosts that you need to vary, it's worth writing a script like the one we just wrote. However, this was a pretty simple script to create. It would be pretty simple to modify the script to comment out a `VirtualHost` section, change the `LogLevel` directive, or change the place to which the `VirtualHost` will log.

Working with Files

Learning to deal with files is key to processing textual data. Often, text that you have to process is contained in a text file such as a logfile, config file, or application data file. When you need to consolidate the data that you are analyzing, you often need to create a report file of some sort or put it into a text file for further analysis. Fortunately, Python contains an easy-to-use built-in type called `file` that can help you do all of those things.

Creating files

It may seem counterintuitive, but in order to read an existing file, you have to create a new `file` object. But don't confuse creating a new `file` object with creating a new file. Writing to a file requires that you create a new `file` object and might require that you create a new file on disk, so it may be less counterintuitive than creating a `file` object for reading would be. The reason that you create a `file` object is so that you can interact with that file on disk.

In order to create a `file` object, you use the built-in function `open()`. Here is an example of code that opens a file for reading:

```
In [1]: infile = open("foo.txt", "r")

In [2]: print infile.read()
Some Random
    Lines
Of
    Text.
```

Because open is built-in, you don't need to import a module. Open() takes three pa-rameters: a filename, the mode in which the file should be opened, and a buffer size. Only the first parameter, filename, is mandatory. The most common values for mode, are "r" (read mode; this is the default), "w" (write mode), and "a" (append mode). A complementary mode that can be added to the other modes is "b," or binary mode. The third parameter, buffer size, directs the operating the way to buffer the file.

In the previous example, we specified that we would like to open() the "file foo.txt" in read mode and be able to refer to that new readable file object with the variable infile. Once we have infile, we are free to call the read() method on it, which reads the entire contents of the file.

Creating a file for writing is very similar to the way we created the file for reading. Instead of using an "r" flag, you use a "w" flag:

```
In [1]: outputfile = open("foo_out.txt", "w")

In [2]: outputfile.write("This is\nSome\nRandom\nOutput Text\n")

In [3]: outputfile.close()
```

In this example, we specified that we would like to open() the file "foo_out.txt" in write mode and be able to refer to that new writable file object with the variable output file. Once we have outputfile, we can write() some text to it and close() the file.

While these are the simple ways of creating files, you probably want to get in the habit of creating files in a more error-tolerant way. It is good practice to wrap your file opens with a try/finally block, especially when you are using write() calls. Here is an example of a writeable file wrapped in a try/finally block:

```
In [1]: try:
   ...:     f = open('writeable.txt', 'w')
   ...:     f.write('quick line here\n')
   ...: finally:
   ...:     f.close()
```

This way of writing files causes the close() method to be called when an exception happens somewhere in the try block. Actually, it lets the close() method be closed even when no exception occurred in the try block. Finally blocks are executed after try blocks complete, whether an exception is found or not.

A new idiom in Python 2.5 is the with statement, which lets you use context managers. A context manager is simply an object with an __enter__() and __exit__(). When an object is created in the with expression, the context manager's __enter__() method is called. When the with block completes, even if an exception occurs, the context man-ager's __exit__() is called. File objects have __enter__() and __exit__() methods defined. On __exit__(), the file object's close() method is called. Here is an example of the with statement:

```
In [1]: from __future__ import with_statement
```

```
In [2]: with open('writeable.txt', 'w') as f:
   ...:     f.write('this is a writeable file\n')
   ...:
   ...:
```

Even though we didn't call close() on file object f, the context manager closes it after exiting the with block:

```
In [3]: f
Out[3]: <closed file 'writeable.txt', mode 'w' at 0x1382770>

In [4]: f.write("this won't work")
---------------------------------------------------------------------------
ValueError                                Traceback (most recent call last)

/Users/jmjones/<ipython console> in <module>()

ValueError: I/O operation on closed file
```

As we expected, the file object is closed. While it is a good practice to handle possible exceptions and make sure your file objects are closed when you expect them to be, for the sake of simplicity and clarity, we will not do so for all examples.

For a complete list of the methods available on file objects, see the File Objects section of *Python Library Reference* at *http://docs.python.org/lib/bltin-file-objects.html*.

Reading files

Once you have a readable file object, which you opened with the r flag, there are three common file methods that will prove useful for getting data contained in the file: read(), readline(), and readlines(). Read(), not surprisingly, reads data from an open file object, returns the bytes that it has read, and returns a string object of those bytes. Read() takes an optional bytes parameter, which specifies the number of bytes to read. If no bytes are specified, read() tries to read to the end of the file. If more bytes are specified than there are bytes in the file, read() will read until the end of the file and return the bytes which it has read.

Given the following file:

```
jmjones@dink:~/some_random_directory$ cat foo.txt Some Random
    Lines
Of
    Text.
```

Read() works on a file like this.

```
In [1]: f = open("foo.txt", "r")

In [2]: f.read()
Out[2]: 'Some Random\n    Lines\nOf \n    Text.\n'
```

Notice that the newlines are shown as a \n character sequence; that is the standard way to refer to a newline.

And if we only wanted the first 5 bytes of the file, we could do something like this:

```
In [1]: f = open("foo.txt", "r")

In [2]: f.read(5)
Out[2]: 'Some '
```

The next method for getting text from a file is the `readline()` method. The purpose of `readline()` is to read one line of text at a time from a file. `Readline()` takes one optional parameter: `size`. Size specifies the maximum number of bytes that `readline()` will read before returning a string, whether it has reached the end of the line or not. So, in the following example, the program will read the first line of text from the `foo.txt`, and then it will read the first 7 bytes of text from the second line, followed by the remainder of the second line:

```
In [1]: f = open("foo.txt", "r")

In [2]: f.readline()
Out[2]: 'Some Random\n'

In [3]: f.readline(7)
Out[3]: '    Lin'

In [4]: f.readline()
Out[4]: 'es\n'
```

The final `file` method that we will discuss for getting text out of a file is `readlines()`. `Readlines()` is not a typo, nor is it a cut-and-paste error from the previous example. `Readlines()` reads in all of the lines in a file. Well, that is almost true. `Readlines()` has a sizehint option that specifies the approximate total number of bytes to read in. In the following example, we created a file, *biglines.txt*, that contains 10,000 lines, each of which contains 80 characters. We then open the file, state that we want the first N lines in the file, which will total about 1024 bytes (the number of lines and bytes that were read) and then we read the rest of the lines in the file:

```
In [1]: f = open("biglines.txt", "r")

In [2]: lines = f.readlines(1024)

In [3]: len(lines)
Out[3]: 102

In [4]: len("".join(lines))
Out[4]: 8262

In [5]: lines = f.readlines()

In [6]: len(lines)
Out[6]: 9898

In [7]: len("".join(lines))
Out[7]: 801738
```

Command [3] shows that we read 102 lines and command [4] shows that those lines totaled 8,262 bytes. How is 1,024 the "approximate" number of bytes read if the actual number of bytes read was 8,262? It rounded up to the internal buffer size, which is about 8 KB. The point is that `sizehint` does not always do what you think it might, so it's something to keep in mind.

Writing files

Sometimes you have to do something with files other than just reading data in from them; sometimes you have to create your own file and write data out to it. There are two common `file` methods that you will need to know in order to write data to files. The first method, which was demonstrated earlier, is `write()`. `write()` takes one parameter: the string to write to the file. Here is an example of data being written to a file using the `write()` method:

```
In [1]: f = open("some_writable_file.txt", "w")

In [2]: f.write("Test\nFile\n")

In [3]: f.close()

In [4]: g = open("some_writable_file.txt", "r")

In [5]: g.read()
Out[5]: 'Test\nFile\n'
```

In command [1], we opened the file with the w mode flag, which means writable. Command [2] writes two lines to the file. In command [4], we are using the variable name g this time for the file object to cut down on confusion, although we could have used f again. And command [5] shows that the data we wrote to the file is the same as what comes out when we `read()` it again.

The next common data writing method is `writelines()`. `Writelines()` takes one mandatory parameter: a sequence that `writelines()` will write to the open file. The sequence can be any type of iterable object such as a list, tuple, list comprehension (which is a list), or a generator. Here is an example of a generator expression `writelines()` used with writelines to write data to a file:

```
In [1]: f = open("writelines_outfile.txt", "w")

In [2]: f.writelines("%s\n" % i for i in range(10))

In [3]: f.close()

In [4]: g = open("writelines_outfile.txt", "r")

In [5]: g.read()

Out[5]: '0\n1\n2\n3\n4\n5\n6\n7\n8\n9\n'
```

And here is an example of a generator function being used to write data to a file (this is functionally equivalent to the previous example, but it uses more code):

```
In [1]: def myRange(r):
   ...:     i = 0
   ...:     while i < r:
   ...:         yield "%s\n" % i
   ...:         i += 1
   ...:
   ...:

In [2]: f = open("writelines_generator_function_outfile", "w")

In [3]: f.writelines(myRange(10))

In [4]: f.close()

In [5]: g = open("writelines_generator_function_outfile", "r")

In [6]: g.read()
Out[6]: '0\n1\n2\n3\n4\n5\n6\n7\n8\n9\n'
```

It is important to note that writelines() does not write a newline (\n) for you; you have to supply the \n in the sequence you pass in to it. It's also important to know you don't have to use it only to write line-based information to your file. Perhaps a better name would have been something like writeiter(). In the previous examples, we happened to write text that had a newline, but there is no reason that we had to.

Additional resources

For more information on file objects, please see Chapter 7 of *Learning Python* by David Ascher and Mark Lutz (O'Reilly) (also online in Safari at *http://safari.oreilly.com/0596002815/lpython2-chp-7-sect-2*) or the File Objects section of the *Python Library Reference* (available online at *http://docs.python.org/lib/bltin-file-objects.html*).

For more information on generator expressions, please see the "generator expressions" section of the *Python Reference Manual* (available online at *http://docs.python.org/ref/genexpr.html*). For more information on the yield statement, see the "yield statement" section of the Python Reference Manual (available online at *http://docs.python.org/ref/yield.html*).

Standard Input and Output

Reading text on a process's standard input and writing to a process's standard output will be familiar to most system administrators. Standard input is simply data going into a program that the program can read when it runs. Standard output is the output of a program, written there by the program as it is running. A benefit of using standard input and standard output is that it allows commands to be chained together with other utilities.

The Python Standard Library contains a built-in module named sys that provides easy access to standard input and standard output. The standard library provides access to both standard input and output as file-like objects, even though they are not directly connected to a file on disk. Since they are file-like objects, you can use the same methods on them that you can use on files. You can treat them as though they were files on disk and access the appropriate methods for doing so.

Standard input is accessed by importing the sys module and referring to its stdin attribute (sys.stdin). Sys.stdin is a readable file object. Notice what happens when we create a "real" file object by opening a file on disk called foo.txt and then compare that open file object with sys.stdin:

```
In [1]: import sys

In [2]: f = open("foo.txt", "r")

In [3]: sys.stdin
Out[3]: <open file '<stdin>', mode 'r' at 0x14020>

In [4]: f
Out[4]: <open file 'foo.txt', mode 'r' at 0x12179b0>

In [5]: type(sys.stdin) == type(f)
Out[5]: True
```

The Python interpreter sees them as the same type, so they use the same methods. While they are technically the same type and use the same methods, some of the methods will behave differently on the file-like objects. For example, sys.stdin.seek() and sys.stdin.tell() are available, but they raise an exception (specifically IOError) when you call them. The main point here, though, is that they are file-like objects and you can pretty much just treat them the same as you would disk-based files.

Accessing sys.stdin is pretty much meaningless at a Python (or IPython) prompt. Importing sys and doing sys.stdin.read() just blocks indefinitely. In order to show you how sys.stdin works, we've created a script that reads from sys.stdin() and prints each line back out with a corresponding line number. See Example 3-22.

Example 3-22. Enumerating sys.stdin.readline

```python
#!/usr/bin/env python

import sys

counter = 1
while True:
    line = sys.stdin.readline()
    if not line:
        break
    print "%s: %s" % (counter, line)
    counter += 1
```

In this example, we created the variable counter to keep track of the line it is on. It then enters a while loop and begins reading lines from standard input. For each line, it prints out the line number and the line contents. As the program loops, this script deals with all lines that come in, even if they seem to be blank. And blank lines aren't totally blank, of course; they consist of a newline (\n). When the script hits "end of file," this script breaks out of the loop.

Here is the output when who is piped through the previous script:

```
jmjones@dink:~/psabook/code$ who | ./sys_stdin_readline.py
1: jmjones  console  Jul  9 11:01

2: jmjones  ttyp1    Jul  9 19:58

3: jmjones  ttyp2    Jul 10 05:10

4: jmjones  ttyp3    Jul 11 11:51

5: jmjones  ttyp4    Jul 13 06:48

6: jmjones  ttyp5    Jul 11 21:49

7: jmjones  ttyp6    Jul 15 04:38
```

As a point of interest, the previous example could have been written much more simply and shorter using the enumerate function. See Example 3-23.

Example 3-23. sys.stdin readline example

```
#!/usr/bin/env python

import sys

for i, line in enumerate(sys.stdin):
    print "%s: %s" % (i, line)
```

Just as you access standard input by importing the sys module and then using the stdin attribute, you access standard output by importing the sys module and referring to the stdout attribute. And just as sys.stdin is a readable file object, sys.stdout is a writable file object. And just as sys.stdin has the same type as a readable file object, so sys.stdout has the same type as a writable file object:

```
In [1]: import sys

In [2]: f = open('foo.txt', 'w')

In [3]: sys.stdout
Out[3]: <open file '<stdout>', mode 'w' at 0x14068>

In [4]: f
Out[4]: <open file 'foo.txt', mode 'w' at 0x1217968>

In [5]: type(sys.stdout) == type(f)
Out[5]: True
```

As a relevant aside, this last point is not unexpected since a readable file and a writable file also share the same type:

```
In [1]: readable_file = open('foo.txt', 'r')

In [2]: writable_file = open('foo_writable.txt', 'w')

In [3]: readable_file
Out[3]: <open file 'foo.txt', mode 'r' at 0x1243530>

In [4]: writable_file
Out[4]: <open file 'foo_writable.txt', mode 'w' at 0x1217968>

In [5]: type(readable_file) == type(writable_file)
Out[5]: True
```

The important thing to know about the type that `sys.stdout` has is that it can be treated in pretty much the same way as a writable `file` can be treated, just as `sys.stdin` can be treated as a readable `file`.

StringIO

So, what happens if you have written a text munging function which knows how to deal with a `file` object, but you stumble across a case in which data that you need to process is available as a text string rather than a `file`? An easy solution is that you can use `import StringIO`:

```
In [1]: from StringIO import StringIO

In [2]: file_like_string = StringIO("This is a\nmultiline string.\n
readline() should see\nmultiple lines of\ninput")

In [3]: file_like_string.readline()
Out[3]: 'This is a\n'

In [4]: file_like_string.readline()
Out[4]: 'multiline string.\n'

In [5]: file_like_string.readline()
Out[5]: 'readline() should see\n'

In [6]: file_like_string.readline()
Out[6]: 'multiple lines of\n'

In [7]: file_like_string.readline()
Out[7]: 'input'
```

In this example, we created a `StringIO` object passing the string `This is a\nmultiline string.\nreadline() should see\nmultiple lines of\ninput` into the constructor. We were then able to call the `readline()` method on the `StringIO` object. While `read line()` was the only method we called, it is by no means the only `file` method available:

```
In [8]: dir(file_like_string)
Out[8]:
['__doc__',
 '__init__',
 '__iter__',
 '__module__',
 'buf',
 'buflist',
 'close',
 'closed',
 'flush',
 'getvalue',
 'isatty',
 'len',
 'next',
 'pos',
 'read',
 'readline',
 'readlines',
 'seek',
 'softspace',
 'tell',
 'truncate',
 'write',
 'writelines']
```

To be sure there are differences, but the interface allows an easy transition between files and strings. Here is a comparison of the methods and attributes on a `file` with the methods and attributes on a `StringIO` object:

```
In [9]: f = open("foo.txt", "r")

In [10]: from sets import Set

In [11]: sio_set = Set(dir(file_like_string))

In [12]: file_set = Set(dir(f))

In [13]: sio_set.difference(file_set)
Out[13]: Set(['__module__', 'buflist', 'pos', 'len', 'getvalue', 'buf'])

In [14]: file_set.difference(sio_set)
Out[14]: Set(['fileno', '__setattr__', '__reduce_ex__', '__new__', 'encoding',
'__getattribute__', '__str__', '__reduce__', '__class__', 'name',
'__delattr__', 'mode', '__repr__', 'xreadlines', '__hash__', 'readinto',
'newlines'])
```

So, as you can see, if you need to treat a string as a `file`, `StringIO` can be a huge help.

urllib

What if the file you are interested in reading happens to be on the interweb? Or, what if you want to reuse a piece of code that you wrote which expects a `file` object? The built-in file type doesn't know about the interweb, but the `urllib` module can help.

If all you want to do is read() a file from some web server somewhere, urllib.urlopen() provides an easy solution. Here is a simple example:

```
In [1]: import urllib

In [2]: url_file = urllib.urlopen("http://docs.python.org/lib/module-urllib.html")

In [3]: urllib_docs = url_file.read()

In [4]: url_file.close()

In [5]: len(urllib_docs)
Out[5]: 28486

In [6]: urllib_docs[:80]
Out[6]: '<!DOCTYPE html PUBLIC "-//W3C//DTD HTML 4.0 Transitional//EN">\
    n<html>\n<head>\n<li'

In [7]: urllib_docs[-80:]
Out[7]: 'nt...</a></i> for information on suggesting changes.\
    n</address>\n</body>\n</html>\n'
```

First, we imported urllib. Next, we created a file-like object from urllib and named it url_file. Then, we read the contents of url_file into a string called urllib_docs. And just to show that we actually retrieved something that looks like it might have come from the Internet, we sliced the first and last 80 characters from the retrieved document. Notice that the urllib file object supported the read() and close() methods. It also supports readline(), readlines(), fileno(), info(), and geturl().

If you need more power, such as the ability to use a proxy server, you can find more information about urllib at *http://docs.python.org/lib/module-urllib.html*. Or if you need even more power like digest authentication and cookies, check out urllib2 at *http://docs.python.org/lib/module-urllib2.html*.

Log Parsing

No discussion of text processing from a sysadmin's point of view would be complete without addressing parsing a logfile, so here it is. We have laid the foundation for you to be able to open a logfile, read in each line, and read the data in the way that works best for you. Before we begin coding this example, we have to ask ourselves, "What do we want this logfile reader to do?" Our answer is pretty simple: read in an Apache access log and determine the number of bytes each unique client retrieved.

According to *http://httpd.apache.org/docs/1.3/logs.html*, the "combined" log format looks something like this:

```
127.0.0.1 - frank [10/Oct/2000:13:55:36 -0700] "GET /apache_pb.gif HTTP/1.0"
200 2326 "http://www.example.com/start.html" "Mozilla/4.08 [en] (Win98; I
;Nav)"
```

And this matched the data in our Apache logfile. The two pieces of information from each line of the logfile that we will be interested in are the IP address of the client and the number of bytes that were transferred. The IP address is the first field in the logfile; in this case, the address is 127.0.0.1. The number of bytes that were transferred is the second from the last field, right before the referrer; in this case 2326 bytes were transferred. So how do we get at the fields? See Example 3-24.

Example 3-24. Apache logfile parser—split on whitespace

```
#!/usr/bin/env python
"""
USAGE:

apache_log_parser_split.py some_log_file

This script takes one command line argument: the name of a log file
to parse. It then parses the log file and generates a report which
associates remote hosts with number of bytes transferred to them.
"""

import sys

def dictify_logline(line):
    '''return a dictionary of the pertinent pieces of an apache combined log file

    Currently, the only fields we are interested in are remote host and bytes sent,
    but we are putting status in there just for good measure.
    '''
    split_line = line.split()
    return {'remote_host': split_line[0],
            'status': split_line[8],
            'bytes_sent': split_line[9],
    }

def generate_log_report(logfile):
    '''return a dictionary of format remote_host=>[list of bytes sent]

    This function takes a file object, iterates through all the lines in the file,
    and generates a report of the number of bytes transferred to each remote host
    for each hit on the webserver.
    '''
    report_dict = {}
    for line in logfile:
        line_dict = dictify_logline(line)
        print line_dict
        try:
            bytes_sent = int(line_dict['bytes_sent'])
        except ValueError:
            ##totally disregard anything we don't understand
            continue
        report_dict.setdefault(line_dict['remote_host'], []).append(bytes_sent)
    return report_dict
```

```
if __name__ == "__main__":
    if not len(sys.argv) > 1:
        print __doc__
        sys.exit(1)
    infile_name = sys.argv[1]
    try:
        infile = open(infile_name, 'r')
    except IOError:
        print "You must specify a valid file to parse"
        print __doc__
        sys.exit(1)
    log_report = generate_log_report(infile)
    print log_report
    infile.close()
```

This example is pretty simple. The __main__ section does only a few things. First, it does minimal checking on the command-line arguments to ensure that at least one argument was passed in. If the user passed in no arguments on the command line, the script prints a usage message and terminates. For a fuller discussion of how to better handle command-line arguments and parameters, see Chapter 13. Next, __main__ attempts to open the specified logfile. If it fails to open the logfile, it prints a usage message and terminates. Next, it passes the logfile to the generate_log_report() function and prints the results.

Generate_log_report() creates a dictionary that serves as the report. It then iterates over all the lines of the logfile and passes each line to dictify_logline(), which returns a dictionary that contains the information we needed. Then, it checks to see if the bytes_sent value is an integer. If it is, it proceeds; if the bytes_sent value is not an integer, it continues to the next line. After that, it updates the report dictionary with the data that dictify_logline() returned to it. Finally, it returns the report dictionary to the __main__ section.

Dictify_logline() simply splits the log line on whitespace, pulls certain items from the resulting list, and returns a dictionary with the data from the split line.

So, does it work? Mostly. Check out the unit test in Example 3-25.

Example 3-25. Unit test for Apache logfile parser—split on whitespace

```
#!/usr/bin/env python

import unittest
import apache_log_parser_split

class TestApacheLogParser(unittest.TestCase):

    def setUp(self):
        pass

    def testCombinedExample(self):
        # test the combined example from apache.org
        combined_log_entry = '127.0.0.1 - frank [10/Oct/2000:13:55:36 -0700] '\
```

```
    '"GET /apache_pb.gif HTTP/1.0" 200 2326 "http://www.example.com/start.html" '\
    '"Mozilla/4.08 [en] (Win98; I ;Nav)"'
    self.assertEqual(apache_log_parser_split.dictify_logline(combined_log_entry),
        {'remote_host': '127.0.0.1', 'status': '200', 'bytes_sent': '2326'})

def testCommonExample(self):
    # test the common example from apache.org
    common_log_entry = '127.0.0.1 - frank [10/Oct/2000:13:55:36 -0700] '\
    '"GET /apache_pb.gif HTTP/1.0" 200 2326'
    self.assertEqual(apache_log_parser_split.dictify_logline(common_log_entry),
        {'remote_host': '127.0.0.1', 'status': '200', 'bytes_sent': '2326'})

def testExtraWhitespace(self):
    # test for extra whitespace between fields
    common_log_entry = '127.0.0.1       -       frank [10/Oct/2000:13:55:36 -0700] '\
    '"GET /apache_pb.gif HTTP/1.0" 200 2326'
    self.assertEqual(apache_log_parser_split.dictify_logline(common_log_entry),
        {'remote_host': '127.0.0.1', 'status': '200', 'bytes_sent': '2326'})

def testMalformed(self):
    # test for extra whitespace between fields
    common_log_entry = '127.0.0.1       -       frank [10/Oct/2000:13:55:36 -0700] '\
    '"GET /some/url/with white space.html HTTP/1.0" 200 2326'
    self.assertEqual(apache_log_parser_split.dictify_logline(common_log_entry),
        {'remote_host': '127.0.0.1', 'status': '200', 'bytes_sent': '2326'})

if __name__ == '__main__':
    unittest.main()
```

It works with the combined and common log formats, but a slight modification of the request field causes the unit test to fail. Here is the result of a test run:

```
jmjones@dinkgutsy:code$ python test_apache_log_parser_split.py
...F
======================================================================
FAIL: testMalformed (__main__.TestApacheLogParser)
----------------------------------------------------------------------
Traceback (most recent call last):
  File "test_apache_log_parser_split.py", line 38, in testMalformed
    {'remote_host': '127.0.0.1', 'status': '200', 'bytes_sent': '2326'})
AssertionError: {'status': 'space.html', 'bytes_sent': 'HTTP/1.0"',
'remote_host': '127.0.0.1'} != {'status': '200', 'bytes_sent': '2326',
'remote_host': '127.0.0.1'}


----------------------------------------------------------------------
Ran 4 tests in 0.001s

FAILED (failures=1)
```

Because of one colon in the date field converted to a space, all the fields of this logfile were shifted one place to the right. A healthy level of paranoia is a good thing. But based on the specification for the logfile formats, you're probably pretty safe extracting the remote host and number of bytes that were transferred based on whitespace-separated fields. However, Example 3-26 is the same example using regular expressions.

Example 3-26. Apache logfile parser—regex

```python
#!/usr/bin/env python
"""
USAGE:

apache_log_parser_regex.py some_log_file

This script takes one command line argument: the name of a log file
to parse. It then parses the log file and generates a report which
associates remote hosts with number of bytes transferred to them.
"""

import sys
import re
log_line_re = re.compile(r'''(?P<remote_host>\S+) #IP ADDRESS
                            \s+ #whitespace
                            \S+ #remote logname
                            \s+ #whitespace
                            \S+ #remote user
                            \s+ #whitespace
                            \[[^\[\]]+\] #time
                            \s+ #whitespace
                            "[^"]+" #first line of request
                            \s+ #whitespace
                            (?P<status>\d+)
                            \s+ #whitespace
                            (?P<bytes_sent>-|\d+)
                            \s* #whitespace
                            ''', re.VERBOSE)

def dictify_logline(line):
    '''return a dictionary of the pertinent pieces of an apache combined log file

    Currently, the only fields we are interested in are remote host and bytes sent,
    but we are putting status in there just for good measure.
    '''
    m = log_line_re.match(line)
    if m:
        groupdict = m.groupdict()
        if groupdict['bytes_sent'] == '-':
            groupdict['bytes_sent'] = '0'
        return groupdict
    else:
        return {'remote_host': None,
                'status': None,
                'bytes_sent': "0",
        }

def generate_log_report(logfile):
    '''return a dictionary of format remote_host=>[list of bytes sent]

    This function takes a file object, iterates through all the lines in the file,
    and generates a report of the number of bytes transferred to each remote host
    for each hit on the webserver.
    '''
```

```
    report_dict = {}
    for line in logfile:
        line_dict = dictify_logline(line)
        print line_dict
        try:
            bytes_sent = int(line_dict['bytes_sent'])
        except ValueError:
            ##totally disregard anything we don't understand
            continue
        report_dict.setdefault(line_dict['remote_host'], []).append(bytes_sent)
    return report_dict


if __name__ == "__main__":
    if not len(sys.argv) > 1:
        print __doc__
        sys.exit(1)
    infile_name = sys.argv[1]
    try:
        infile = open(infile_name, 'r')
    except IOError:
        print "You must specify a valid file to parse"
        print __doc__
        sys.exit(1)
    log_report = generate_log_report(infile)
    print log_report
    infile.close()
```

The only function we changed from the **regex** example to the "split on whitespace"
example was dictify_logline(). This implies that we left the return type for the function exactly as it was in the **regex** example. Rather than splitting the log line on whitespace, we used a compiled regular expression object, log_line_re, to match() the log
line. If it matched, we returned a potentially, slightly modified groupdict() in which
bytes_sent was set to *0* when the field contained - (because - means nothing). In the
case that nothing matched, we returned a dictionary with the same keys, but with
None and *0* for the values.

So, does the regular expression version work work better than the string splitting one?
Actually, it does. Here is a unit test for the new **regex** version of the Apache parsing
script:

```
#!/usr/bin/env python

import unittest
import apache_log_parser_regex

class TestApacheLogParser(unittest.TestCase):

    def setUp(self):
        pass

    def testCombinedExample(self):
        # test the combined example from apache.org
```

```
                combined_log_entry = '127.0.0.1 - frank [10/Oct/2000:13:55:36 -0700] '\
                '"GET /apache_pb.gif HTTP/1.0" 200 2326 '\
                '"http://www.example.com/start.html" "Mozilla/4.08 [en] (Win98; I ;Nav)"'
                self.assertEqual(apache_log_parser_regex.dictify_logline(combined_log_entry),
                    {'remote_host': '127.0.0.1', 'status': '200', 'bytes_sent': '2326'})

        def testCommonExample(self):
            # test the common example from apache.org
            common_log_entry = '127.0.0.1 - frank [10/Oct/2000:13:55:36 -0700] '\
                '"GET /apache_pb.gif HTTP/1.0" 200 2326'
            self.assertEqual(apache_log_parser_regex.dictify_logline(common_log_entry),
                    {'remote_host': '127.0.0.1', 'status': '200', 'bytes_sent': '2326'})

        def testMalformedEntry(self):
            # test a malformed modification dereived from the example at apache.org
            #malformed_log_entry = '127.0.0.1 - frank [10/Oct/2000 13:55:36 -0700] '\
            #'"GET /apache_pb.gif HTTP/1.0" 200 2326 '\
            #'"http://www.example.com/start.html" "Mozilla/4.08 [en] (Win98; I ;Nav)"'

            malformed_log_entry = '127.0.0.1 - frank [10/Oct/2000:13:55:36 -0700] '\
                '"GET /some/url/with white space.html HTTP/1.0" 200 2326'
            self.assertEqual(apache_log_parser_regex.dictify_logline(malformed_log_entry),
                    {'remote_host': '127.0.0.1', 'status': '200', 'bytes_sent': '2326'})

    if __name__ == '__main__':
        unittest.main()
```

And here is the result of the unit test:

```
jmjones@dinkgutsy:code$ python test_apache_log_parser_regex.py
...
-----------------------------------------------------------------------
Ran 3 tests in 0.001s

OK
```

ElementTree

If the text that you need to parse is XML, then you probably want to approach things a bit differently than if it were, say, a line-oriented logfile. You probably don't want to read the file in line by line and look for patterns, and you probably don't want to rely too much on regular expressions. XML uses a tree-structure, so reading in lines probably isn't what you want. And using regular expressions to build a tree data structure will be a huge headache for any files larger than trivially tiny.

So, what can you use? There are typically two approaches to handling XML. There is "simple API for XML," or SAX. The Python Standard Library contains a SAX parser. SAX is typically blazingly fast and doesn't automatically grab a lot of memory as it is parsing your XML. But it is callback-based, so in certain pieces of data, when it hits sections of your XML document, like start and end tags, it just calls certain methods and passes. This means that you have to set up handlers for your data and maintain your own state, which can be a difficult. These two things make the "simple" in "simple

API for XML" seem a bit farfetched. The other approach for handling XML is to use a Document Object Model, or DOM. The Python Standard Library also contains a DOM XML library. DOM is typically slower and consumes more memory than SAX because it reads the whole XML tree into memory and builds objects for each node in the tree. The benefit of using DOM is that you don't have to keep track of your own state, since each node is aware of who its parents and children are. But the DOM API is cumbersome at best.

A third option is ElementTree. ElementTree is an XML parsing library that has been included in the standard library since Python 2.5. ElementTree feels like a lighter weight DOM with a usable, indeed a friendly, API. In addition to the code usability, it is fast and consumes little memory. We give ElementTree a hearty recommendation. If you have XML parsing to do, try ElementTree first.

To start parsing an XML file using ElementTree, simply import the library and parse() a file:

```
In [1]: from xml.etree import ElementTree as ET

In [2]: tcusers = ET.parse('/etc/tomcat5.5/tomcat-users.xml')

In [3]: tcusers

Out[3]: <xml.etree.ElementTree.ElementTree instance at 0xabb4d0></xml>
```

So that we could save keystrokes as we use the library, we imported the ElementTree module under the name ET so that we could save on keystrokes as we use the library. Then, we told ElementTree to parse the users XML file from an installed Tomcat servlet engine. We called the ElementTree object tcusers. The type of tcusers is xml.etree.ElementTree.ElementTree.

We removed the license and a usage note, and the Tomcat users file that we just parsed has the following content:

```
<?xml version="1.0" encoding="UTF-8"?>
<tomcat-users>
  <user name="tomcat" password="tomcat" roles="tomcat" />
  <user name="role1"  password="tomcat" roles="role1"  />
  <user name="both"   password="tomcat" roles="tomcat,role1" />
</tomcat-users>
```

When ElementTree parsed the Tomcat XML file, it created a tree object, which we referred to as tcusers, that we could use to get at the various nodes in the XML file. Two of the most interesting methods on this tree object are find() and findall(). Find() finds the first node that matches the query that you pass it and returns an Element object based on that node. Findall() finds all occurrences of nodes matching the query that you pass it and returns a list of Element objects based on those matching nodes.

The type of pattern that both find() and findall() look for is a limited subset of XPath expressions. Valid search criteria for ElementTree includes the tagname * to match all child elements, . to match the current element, and // to match all nodes that are descendents of the search starting point. The slash (/) character can be used to separate the match criteria. Using the Tomcat user file, we'll use find() and a tagname to pull out the first user node:

```
In [4]: first_user = tcusers.find('/user')

In [5]: first_user

Out[5]: <Element user at abdd88>
```

We fed find() the search criteria '/user'. The leading slash character specified the absolute path starting at the root node. The text 'user' specified the tagname to look for. So, find() returned the first node with a tag of user. You can see that the object we referred to as first_user is of type Element.

Some of the more interesting Element methods and attributes include Attrib, find(), findall(), get(), tag, and text. attrib is a dictionary of the attributes of the Element that it belongs to. find() and findall() work here the same way they do on Element Tree objects. Get() is a dictionary method that retrieves the specified attribute or, if the attribute is not defined, returns None. Both attrib and get() access the same dictionary of attributes for the current XML tag. tag is an attribute that contains the tag name of the current Element. text is an attribute that contains the text contained as a text node in the current Element.

Here is the XML element ElementTree created for the first_user Element object:

```
<user name="tomcat" password="tomcat" roles="tomcat" />
```

Now we are going to call the methods of and reference the attributes of the tcusers object:

```
In [6]: first_user.attrib

Out[6]: {'name': 'tomcat', 'password': 'tomcat', 'roles': 'tomcat'}

In [7]: first_user.get('name')

Out[7]: 'tomcat'

In [8]: first_user.get('foo')

In [9]: first_user.tag

Out[9]: 'user'

In [10]: first_user.text
```

Now that you've seen some of the basics of what ElementTree will do, we'll look at a slightly more involved, more formal example. We will parse the Tomcat users file and look for any user nodes where the name attribute matches the one we specify (in this case, 'tomcat'). See Example 3-27.

Example 3-27. ElementTree parse of Tomcat users file

```
#!/usr/bin/env python

from xml.etree import ElementTree as ET

if __name__ == '__main__':
    infile = '/etc/tomcat5.5/tomcat-users.xml'
    tomcat_users = ET.parse(infile)
    for user in [e for e in tomcat_users.findall('/user') if
        e.get('name') == 'tomcat']:
        print user.attrib
```

The only trick in this example is that we've used a list comprehension to match on the name attribute. Running this example returns the following result:

```
jmjones@dinkgutsy:code$ python elementtree_tomcat_users.py
{'password': 'tomcat', 'name': 'tomcat', 'roles': 'tomcat'}
```

Finally, here is an example of ElementTree used to extract some information from a poorly written piece of XML. Mac OS X has a utility called system_profiler that will display a bulk of information about your system. XML is one of two output formats that system_profiler supports, but it appears that XML was an afterthought. The piece of information that we want to extract is the operating system version and is contained in a portion of the XML file that looks like this:

```
<dict>
    <key>_dataType</key>
    <string>SPSoftwareDataType</string>
    <key>_detailLevel</key>
    <integer>-2</integer>
    <key>_items</key>
    <array>
        <dict>
            <key>_name</key>
            <string>os_overview</string>
            <key>kernel_version</key>
            <string>Darwin 8.11.1</string>
            <key>os_version</key>
            <string>Mac OS X 10.4.11 (8S2167)</string>
        </dict>
    </array>
```

So, why do we think this XML format is poorly written? There are no attributes on any XML tags. The tag types are mainly data types. And elements such as alternating key and string tags are under the same parent. See Example 3-28.

Example 3-28. Mac OS X system_profiler output parser

```
#!/usr/bin/env python
import sys

from xml.etree import ElementTree as ET
e = ET.parse('system_profiler.xml')
```

```
if __name__ == '__main__':
    for d in e.findall('/array/dict'):
        if d.find('string').text == 'SPSoftwareDataType':
            sp_data = d.find('array').find('dict')
            break
    else:
        print "SPSoftwareDataType NOT FOUND"
        sys.exit(1)

    record = []
    for child in sp_data.getchildren():
        record.append(child.text)
        if child.tag == 'string':
            print "%-15s -> %s" % tuple(record)
            record = []
```

Basically, the script looks for any dict tag that has a string child element whose text value is 'SPSoftwareDataType'. The information that the script is looking for is under that node. The only thing that we used in this example that we didn't discuss previously was the getchildren() method. This method simply returns a list of the child nodes of a particular element. Other than that, this example should be pretty clear, even though the XML might have been written better. Here is the output the script generates when it is run on a laptop running Mac OS X Tiger:

```
dink:~/code jmjones$ python elementtree_system_profile.py
_name          -> os_overview
kernel_version -> Darwin 8.11.1
os_version     -> Mac OS X 10.4.11 (8S2167)
```

ElementTree has been a great addition to the Python Standard Library. We have been using it for quite a while now and have been happy with what it has done for us. You can try out the SAX and DOM libraries in the Python Standard Library, but we think you will come back to ElementTree.

Summary

This chapter outlined some of the fundamentals of handling text in Python. We dealt with the built-in string type, regular expressions, standard input and output, StringIO, and the urllib module from the standard library. We then pulled many of these things together into two examples that parsed Apache logfiles. Finally, we discussed some of the essentials of the ElementTree library and showed two examples of the way to use it in the real world.

It seems that when a lot of Unix folks think of wrangling text in a way that is beyond what is comfortable to do with grep or awk, the only advanced alternative that they consider is Perl. While Perl is an extremely powerful language, particularly in the area of dealing with text, we think that Python has just as much to offer as Perl does. In fact, if you look at the clean syntax and the ease with which you can go from procedural code to object-oriented code, we think that Python has a distinct advantage over Perl, even in the text handling arena. So, we hope that the next time you have a text handling task to work on, you'll reach for Python first.

## CHAPTER 4

Documentation and Reporting

As we do, you may find that one of the most tedious, least desirable aspects of your job is to document various pieces of information for the sake of your users. This can either be for the direct benefit of your users who will read the documentation, or perhaps it may be for the indirect benefit of your users because you or your replacement might refer to it when making changes in the future. In either case, creating documentation is often a critical aspect of your job. But if it is not a task that you find yourself longing to do, it might be rather neglected. Python can help here. No, Python cannot write your documentation for you, but it can help you gather, format, and distribute the information to the intended parties.

In this chapter, we are going to focus on: gathering, formatting, and distributing information about the programs you write. The information that you are interested in sharing exists somewhere; it may be in a logfile somewhere; it may be in your head; it may be accessible as a result of some shell command that you execute; it may even be in a database somewhere. The first thing you have to do is to gather that information. The next step in effectively sharing this information is to format the data in a way that makes it meaningful. The format could be a PDF, PNG, JPG, HTML, or even plain text. Finally, you need to get this information to the people who are interested in it. Is it most convenient for the interested parties to receive an email, or visit a website, or look at the files directly on a shared drive?

Automated Information Gathering

The first step of information sharing is gathering the information. There are two other chapters in this book dedicated to gathering data: *Text Processing* (Chapter 3) and *SNMP* (Chapter 7). Text processing contains examples of the ways to parse and extract various pieces of data from a larger body of text. One specific example in that chapter is parsing the client IP address, number of bytes transmitted, and HTTP status code out of each line in an Apache web server log. And SNMP contains examples of system queries for information ranging from amount of installed RAM to the speed of network interfaces.

Gathering information can be more involved than just locating and extracting certain pieces of data. Often, it can be a process that involves taking information from one format, such as an Apache logfile, and storing it in some intermediate format to be used at a later time. For example, if you wanted to create a chart that showed the number of bytes that each unique IP address downloaded from a specific Apache web server over the course of a month, the information gathering part of the process could involve parsing the Apache logfile each night, extracting the necessary information (in this case, it would be the IP address and "bytes sent" for each request), and appending the data to some data store that you can open up later. Examples of such data stores include relational databases, object databases, pickle files, CSV files, and plain-text files.

The remainder of this section will attempt to bring together some of the concepts from the chapters on text processing and data persistence. Specifically, it will show how to build on the techniques of data extraction from Chapter 3 and data storage from Chapter 12. We will use the same library from the text processing. We will also use the shelve module, introduced in Chapter 12, to store data about HTTP requests from each unique HTTP client.

Here is a simple module that uses both the Apache log parsing module created in the previous chapter and the shelve module:

```python
#!/usr/bin/env python

import shelve
import apache_log_parser_regex

logfile = open('access.log', 'r')
shelve_file = shelve.open('access.s')

for line in logfile:
    d_line = apache_log_parser_regex.dictify_logline(line)
    shelve_file[d_line['remote_host']] = \
        shelve_file.setdefault(d_line['remote_host'], 0) + \
        int(d_line['bytes_sent'])

logfile.close()
shelve_file.close()
```

This example first imports shelve and apache_log_parser_regex. Shelve is a module from the Python Standard Library. Apache_log_parser_regex is a module we wrote in Chapter 3. We then open the Apache logfile, access.log, and a shelve file, access.s. We iterate over each line in the logfile and use the Apache log parsing module to create a dictionary from each line. The dictionary consists of the HTTP status code for the request, the client's IP address, and the number of bytes transferred to the client. We then add the number of bytes for this specific request to the total number of bytes already tallied in the shelve object for this client IP address. If there is no entry in the shelve object for this client IP address, the total is automatically set to zero. After iterating through all the lines in the logfile, we close the logfile and the shelve object. We'll use this example later in this chapter when we get into formatting information.

Receiving Email

You may not think of receiving email as a means of information gathering, but it really can be. Imagine that you have a number of servers, none of which can easily connect to the other, but each of which has email capabilities. If you have a script that monitors web applications on these servers by logging in and out every few minutes, you could use email as an information passing mechanism. Whether the login/logout succeeds or fails, you can send an email with the pass/fail information in it. And you can gather these email messages for reporting or for the purpose of alerting someone if it's down.

The two most commonly available protocols for retrieving email server are IMAP and POP3. In Python's standard "batteries included" fashion, there are modules to support both of these protocols in the standard library.

POP3 is perhaps the more common of these two protocols, and accessing your email over POP3 using `poplib` is quite simple. Example 4-1 shows code that uses `poplib` to retrieve all of the email that is stored on the specified server and writes it to a set of files on disk.

Example 4-1. Retrieving email using POP3

```python
#!/usr/bin/env python

import poplib

username = 'someuser'
password = 'S3Cr37'

mail_server = 'mail.somedomain.com'

p = poplib.POP3(mail_server)
p.user(username)
p.pass_(password)
for msg_id in  p.list()[1]:
    print msg_id
    outf = open('%s.eml' % msg_id, 'w')
    outf.write('\n'.join(p.retr(msg_id)[1]))
    outf.close()
p.quit()
```

As you can see, we defined the `username`, `password`, and `mail_server` first. Then, we connected to the mail server and gave it the defined username and password. Assuming that all is well and we actually have permission to look at the email for this account, we then iterate over the list of email files, retrieve them, and write them to a disk. One thing this script doesn't do is delete each email after retrieving it. All it would take to delete the email is a call to `dele()` after `retr()`.

IMAP is nearly as easy as POP3, but it's not as well documented in the Python Standard Library documents. Example 4-2 shows IMAP code that does the same thing as the code did in the POP3 example.

Example 4-2. Retrieving email using IMAP

```
#!/usr/bin/env python

import imaplib

username = 'some_user'
password = '70P53Cr37'

mail_server = 'mail_server'

i = imaplib.IMAP4_SSL(mail_server)
print i.login(username, password)
print i.select('INBOX')
for msg_id in  i.search(None, 'ALL')[1][0].split():
    print msg_id
    outf = open('%s.eml' % msg_id, 'w')
    outf.write(i.fetch(msg_id, '(RFC822)')[1][0][1])
    outf.close()
i.logout()
```

As we did in the POP3 example, we defined the `username`, `password`, and `mail_server` at the top of the script. Then, we connected to the IMAP server over SSL. Next, we logged in and set the email directory to `INBOX`. Then we started iterating over a search of the entire directory. The `search()` method is poorly documented in the Python Standard Library documentation. The two mandatory parameters for `search()` are character set and search criterion. What is a valid character set? What format should we put in there? What are the choices for search criteria? What format is required? We suspect that a reading of the IMAP RFC could be helpful, but fortunately there is enough documentation in the example for IMAP to retrieve all messages in the folder. For each iteration of the loop, we write the contents of the email to disk. A small word of warning is in order here: this will mark all email in that folder as "read." This may not be a problem for you, and it's not a big problem as it may be if this deleted the messages, but it's something that you should be aware of.

Manual Information Gathering

Let's also look at the more complicated path of manually gathering information. By this, we mean information that you gather with your own eyes and key in with your own hands. Examples include a list of servers with corresponding IP addresses and functions, a list of contacts with email addresses, phone numbers, and IM screen names, or the dates that members of your team are planning to be on vacation. There are certainly tools available that can manage most, if not all, of these types of information. There is Excel or OpenOffice Spreadsheet for managing the server list. There is Outlook or Address Book.app for managing contacts. And either Excel/OpenOffice Spreadsheet or Outlook can manage vacations. This may be the solution for the situations that arise when technologies are freely available and use an editing data format that is plain text and which provides output that is configurable and supports HTML (or preferably XHTML).

```
#import "MyDocument.h"

@implementation MyDocument

- (id)init
{
    if (![super init]) {
        return nil;
    }

    // What you see for a new document
    textStorage = [[NSTextStorage alloc] init];
    return self;
}

- (NSString *)windowNibName
{
    return @"MyDocument";
}

- (void)prepareEditView
{
    // The layout manager monitors the text storage and
    // layout the text in the text view
    NSLayoutManager *lm = [editView layoutManager];

    // Detach the old text storage
    [[editView textStorage] removeLayoutManager:lm];

    // Attach the new text storage
    [textStorage addLayoutManager:lm];
}

- (void)windowControllerDidLoadNib:(NSWindowController *) aController
{
    [super windowControllerDidLoadNib:aController];

    // Show the text storage in the text view
    [self prepareEditView];
}
```

```
#pragma mark Saving and Loading

// Saves (the URL is always a file:)
- (BOOL)writeToURL:(NSURL *)absoluteURL
            ofType:(NSString *)typeName
             error:(NSError **)outError;
{
    return [[textStorage string] writeToURL:absoluteURL
                                 atomically:NO
                                   encoding:NSUTF8StringEncoding
                                      error:outError];
}

// Reading (the URL is always a file:)
- (BOOL)readFromURL:(NSURL *)absoluteURL
            ofType:(NSString *)typeName
             error:(NSError **)outError
{
    NSString *string = [NSString stringWithContentsOfURL:absoluteURL
                                                encoding:NSUTF8StringEncoding
                                                   error:outError];

    // Read failed?
    if (!string) {
        return NO;
    }
    [textStorage release];
    textStorage = [[NSTextStorage alloc] initWithString:string
                                             attributes:nil];

    // Is this a revert?
    if (editView) {
        [self prepareEditView];
    }

    return YES;
}

#pragma mark Generating and Saving HTML

- (NSData *)dataForHTML
{
    // Create a task to run rst2html.py
    NSTask *task = [[NSTask alloc] init];

    // Guess the location of the executable
    NSString *path = @"/usr/local/bin/rst2html.py";

    // Is that file missing? Try inside the python framework
    if (![[NSFileManager defaultManager] fileExistsAtPath:path]) {
        path = @"/Library/Frameworks/Python.framework/Versions/Current/bin/rst2html.py";
    }
    [task setLaunchPath:path];

    // Connect a pipe where the ReST will go in
    NSPipe *inPipe = [[NSPipe alloc] init];
    [task setStandardInput:inPipe];
    [inPipe release];

    // Connect a pipe where the HMTL will come out
```

```
    NSPipe *outPipe = [[NSPipe alloc] init];
    [task setStandardOutput:outPipe];
    [outPipe release];

    // Start the process
    [task launch];

    // Get the data from the text view
    NSData *inData = [[textStorage string] dataUsingEncoding:NSUTF8StringEncoding];

    // Put the data in the pipe and close it
    [[inPipe fileHandleForWriting] writeData:inData];
    [[inPipe fileHandleForWriting] closeFile];

    // Read the data out of the pipe
    NSData *outData = [[outPipe fileHandleForReading] readDataToEndOfFile];

    // All done with the task
    [task release];

    return outData;
}

- (IBAction)renderRest:(id)sender
{
    // Start the spinning so the user feels like waiting
    [progressIndicator startAnimation:nil];

    // Get the html as an NSData
    NSData *htmlData = [self dataForHTML];

    // Put the html in the main WebFrame
    WebFrame *wf = [webView mainFrame];
    [wf loadData:htmlData
        MIMEType:@"text/html"
textEncodingName:@"utf-8"
         baseURL:nil];


    // Stop the spinning so the user feels done
    [progressIndicator stopAnimation:nil];

}



// Triggered by menu item
- (IBAction)startSavePanelForHTML:(id)sender
{
    // Where does it save by default?
    NSString *restPath = [self fileName];
    NSString *directory = [restPath stringByDeletingLastPathComponent];
    NSString *filename = [[[restPath lastPathComponent]
                          stringByDeletingPathExtension]
                          stringByAppendingPathExtension:@"html"];

    // Start the save panel
    NSSavePanel *sp = [NSSavePanel savePanel];
    [sp setRequiredFileType:@"html"];
```

```
        [sp setCanSelectHiddenExtension:YES];
        [sp beginSheetForDirectory:directory
                              file:filename
                    modalForWindow:[editView window]
                     modalDelegate:self
                    didEndSelector:@selector(htmlSavePanel:endedWithCode:context:)
                       contextInfo:NULL];
}

// Called when the save panel is dismissed
- (void)htmlSavePanel:(NSSavePanel *)sp
        endedWithCode:(int)returnCode
              context:(void *)context
{
    // Did the user hit Cancel?
    if (returnCode != NSOKButton) {
        return;
    }

    // Get the chosen filename
    NSString *savePath = [sp filename];

    // Get the HTML data
    NSData *htmlData = [self dataForHTML];

    // Write it to the file
    NSError *writeError;
    BOOL success = [htmlData writeToFile:savePath
                                 options:NSAtomicWrite
                                   error:&writeError];

    // Did the write fail?
    if (!success) {

        // Show the user why
        NSAlert *alert = [NSAlert alertWithError:writeError];
        [alert beginSheetModalForWindow:[editView window]
                          modalDelegate:nil
                         didEndSelector:NULL
                            contextInfo:NULL];
        return;
    }

}

#pragma mark Printing Support

- (NSPrintOperation *)printOperationWithSettings:(NSDictionary *)printSettings
                                           error:(NSError **)outError
{
    // Get the information from Page Setup
    NSPrintInfo *printInfo = [self printInfo];

    // Get the view that displays the whole HTML document
    NSView *docView = [[[webView mainFrame] frameView] documentView];

    // Create a print operation
    return [NSPrintOperation printOperationWithView:docView
                                          printInfo:printInfo];
```

```
        }

    @end
```

While there are a number of alternatives, the specific plain-text format that we're going to suggest here is reStructuredText (also referred to as reST). Here is how the reStructuredText website describes it:

> reStructuredText is an easy-to-read, what-you-see-is-what-you-get plaintext markup syntax and parser system. It is useful for in-line program documentation (such as Python docstrings), for quickly creating simple web pages, and for standalone documents. reStructuredText is designed for extensibility for specific application domains. The reStructuredText parser is a component of Docutils. reStructuredText is a revision and reinterpretation of the StructuredText and Setext lightweight markup systems.

ReST is the preferred format for Python documentation. If you create a Python package of your code and decide to upload it to the PyPI, reStructuredText is the expected documentation format. Many individual Python projects are also using ReST as the primary format for their documentation needs.

So why would you want to use ReST as a documentation format? First, because the format is uncomplicated. Second, there is an almost immediate familiarity with the markup. When you see the structure of a document, you quickly understand what the author intended. Here is an example of a very simple ReST file:

```
=======
Heading
=======
SubHeading
----------
This is just a simple
little subsection. Now,
we'll show a bulleted list:

- item one
- item two
- item three
```

That probably makes some sort of structured sense to you without having to read the documentation about what constitutes a valid reStructuredText file. You might not be able to write a ReST text file, but you can probably follow along enough to read one.

Third, converting from ReST to HTML is simple. And it's that third point that we're going to focus on in this section. We won't try to give a tutorial on reStructuredText here. If you want a quick overview of the markup syntax, visit *http://docutils.source forge.net/docs/user/rst/quickref.html*.

Using the document that we just showed you as an example, we'll walk through the steps converting ReST to HTML:

```
In [2]: import docutils.core

In [3]: rest - '''=======
   ...: Heading
   ...: =======
   ...: SubHeading
   ...: ----------
   ...: This is just a simple
   ...: little subsection. Now,
   ...: we'll show a bulleted list:
   ...:
   ...: - item one
   ...: - item two
   ...: - item three
   ...: '''

In [4]: html =  docutils.core.publish_string(source=rest, writer_name='html')

In [5]: print html[html.find('<body>') + 6:html.find('</body>')]

<div class="document" id="heading">
<h1 class="title">Heading</h1>
<h2 class="subtitle" id="subheading">SubHeading</h2>
<p>This is just a simple
little subsection. Now,
we'll show a bulleted list:</p>
<ul class="simple">
<li>item one</li>
<li>item two</li>
<li>item three</li>
</ul>
</div>
```

This was a simple process. We imported **docutils.core**. Then we defined a string that contained our reStructuredText, and ran the string through **docutils.core.pub lish_string()**, and then told it to format it as HTML. Then we did a string slice and extracted the text between the **<body>** and **</body>** tags. The reason we sliced this **div** area is because docutils, the library we used to convert to HTML, puts an embedded stylesheet in the generated HTML page so that it doesn't look too plain.

Now that you see how simple it is, let's take an example that is slightly more in the realm of system administration. Every good sysadmin needs to keep track of the servers they have and the tasks those servers are being used for. So, here's an example of the way to create a plain-text server list table and convert it to HTML:

```
In [6]: server_list = '''==============   ============   ================
   ...:  Server Name    IP Address     Function
   ...: ==============   ============   ================
   ...: card             192.168.1.2    mail server
   ...: vinge            192.168.1.4    web server
   ...: asimov           192.168.1.8    database server
   ...: stephenson       192.168.1.16   file server
   ...: gibson           192.168.1.32   print server
   ...: ==============   ============   ================'''
```

```
In [7]: print server_list
==============  ===========  ================
  Server Name   IP Address    Function
==============  ===========  ================
card            192.168.1.2   mail server
vinge           192.168.1.4   web server
asimov          192.168.1.8   database server
stephenson      192.168.1.16  file server
gibson          192.168.1.32  print server
==============  ===========  ================

In [8]: html = docutils.core.publish_string(source=server_list,
writer_name='html')

In [9]: print html[html.find('<body>') + 6:html.find('</body>')]

<div class="document">
<table border="1" class="docutils">
<colgroup>
<col width="33%" />
<col width="29%" />
<col width="38%" />
</colgroup>
<thead valign="bottom">
<tr><th class="head">Server Name</th>
<th class="head">IP Address</th>
<th class="head">Function</th>
</tr>
</thead>
<tbody valign="top">
<tr><td>card</td>
<td>192.168.1.2</td>
<td>mail server</td>
</tr>
<tr><td>vinge</td>
<td>192.168.1.4</td>
<td>web server</td>
</tr>
<tr><td>asimov</td>
<td>192.168.1.8</td>
<td>database server</td>
</tr>
<tr><td>stephenson</td>
<td>192.168.1.16</td>
<td>file server</td>
</tr>
<tr><td>gibson</td>
<td>192.168.1.32</td>
<td>print server</td>
</tr>
</tbody>
</table>
</div>
```

Another excellent choice for a plain text markup format is Textile. According to its website, "Textile takes plain text with *simple* markup and produces valid XHTML. It's used in web applications, content management systems, blogging software and online forums." So if Textile is a markup language, why are we writing about it in a book about Python? The reason is that a Python library exists that allows you to process Textile markup and convert it to XHTML. You can write command-line utilities to call the Python library and convert Textile files and redirect the output into XHTML files. Or you can call the Textile conversion module from within some script and programmatically deal with the XHTML that is returned. Either way, the Textile markup and the Textile processing module can be hugely beneficial to your documenting needs.

You can install the Textile Python module, with `easy_install textile`. Or you can install it using your system's packaging system if it's included. For Ubuntu, the package name is `python-textile`, and you can install it with `apt-get install python-textile`. Once Textile is installed, you can start using it by simply importing it, creating a `Textiler` object, and calling a single method on that object. Here is an example of code that converts a Textile bulleted list to XHTML:

```
In [1]: import textile

In [2]: t = textile.Textiler('''* item one
   ...: * item two
   ...: * item three''')

In [3]: print t.process()
<ul>
<li>item one</li>
<li>item two</li>
<li>item three</li>
</ul>
```

We won't try to present a Textile tutorial here. There are plenty of resources on the Web for that. For example, *http://hobix.com/textile/* provides a good reference for using Textile. While we won't get too in-depth into the ins and outs of Textile, we will look at the way Textile works for one of the examples of manually gathered information we described earlier—a server list with corresponding IP addresses and functions:

```
In [1]: import textile

In [2]: server_list = '''|_. Server Name|_. IP Address|_. Function|
   ...: |card|192.168.1.2|mail server|
   ...: |vinge|192.168.1.4|web server|
   ...: |asimov|192.168.1.8|database server|
   ...: |stephenson|192.168.1.16|file server|
   ...: |gibson|192.168.1.32|print server|'''

In [3]: print server_list
|_. Server Name|_. IP Address|_. Function|
|card|192.168.1.2|mail server|
|vinge|192.168.1.4|web server|
|asimov|192.168.1.8|database server|
```

```
|stephenson|192.168.1.16|file server|
|gibson|192.168.1.32|print server|

In [4]: t = textile.Textiler(server_list)

In [5]: print t.process()
<table>
<tr>
<th>Server Name</th>
<th>IP Address</th>
<th>Function</th>
</tr>
<tr>
<td>card</td>
<td>192.168.1.2</td>
<td>mail server</td>
</tr>
<tr>
<td>vinge</td>
<td>192.168.1.4</td>
<td>web server</td>
</tr>
<tr>
<td>asimov</td>
<td>192.168.1.8</td>
<td>database server</td>
</tr>
<tr>
<td>stephenson</td>
<td>192.168.1.16</td>
<td>file server</td>
</tr>
<tr>
<td>gibson</td>
<td>192.168.1.32</td>
<td>print server</td>
</tr>
</table>
```

So you can see that ReST and Textile can both be used effectively to integrate the conversion of plain text data into a Python script. If you do have data, such as server lists and contact lists, that needs to be converted into HTML and then have some action (such as emailing the HTML to a list of recipients or FTPing the HTML to a web server somewhere) taken upon it, then either the docutils or the Textile library could be a useful tool for you.

Information Formatting

The next step in getting your information into the hands of your audience is formatting the data into a medium that is easily read and understood. We think of that medium as being something at least comprehensible to the user, but better yet, it can be something attractive. Technically, ReST and Textile encompass both the data gathering and the data formatting steps of information sharing, but the following examples will focus specifically on converting data that we've already gathered into a more presentable medium.

Graphical Images

The following two examples will continue the example of parsing an Apache logfile for the client IP address and the number of bytes that were transferred. In the previous section, our example generated a shelve file that contained some information that we want to share with other users. So, now, we will create a chart object from the shelve file to make the data easy to read:

```python
#!/usr/bin/env python

import gdchart
import shelve

shelve_file = shelve.open('access.s')
items_list = [(i[1], i[0]) for i in shelve_file.items()]
items_list.sort()
bytes_sent = [i[0] for i in items_list]
#ip_addresses = [i[1] for i in items_list]
ip_addresses = ['XXX.XXX.XXX.XXX' for i in items_list]

chart = gdchart.Bar()
chart.width = 400
chart.height = 400
chart.bg_color = 'white'
chart.plot_color = 'black'
chart.xtitle = "IP Address"
chart.ytitle = "Bytes Sent"
chart.title = "Usage By IP Address"
chart.setData(bytes_sent)
chart.setLabels(ip_addresses)
chart.draw("bytes_ip_bar.png")

shelve_file.close()
```

In this example, we imported two modules, gdchart and shelve. We then opened the shelve file we created in the previous example. Since the shelve object shares the same interface as the builtin dictionary object, we were able to call the Items() method on it. items() returns a list of tuples in which the first element of the tuple is the dictionary key and the second element of the tuple is the value for that key. We are able to use the items() method to help sort the data in a way that will make more sense when it is plotted. We use a list comprehension to reverse the order of the previous tuple. Instead of being tuples of (ip_address, bytes_sent), it is now (bytes_sent, ip_addresses). We then sort this list and since the bytes_sent element is first, the list.sort() method will sort by that field first. We then use list comprehensions again to pull the bytes_sent and the ip_addresses fields. You may notice that we're inserting an

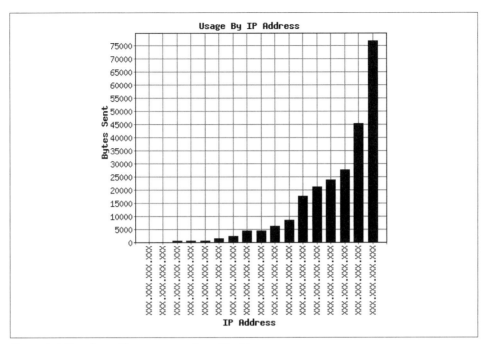

Figure 4-1. Bar chart of bytes requested per IP address

obfuscated XXX.XXX.XXX.XXX for the IP addresses because we've taken these logfiles from a production web server.

After getting the data that is going to feed the chart out of the way, we can actually start using gdchart to make a graphical representation of the data. We first create a gdchart.Bar object. This is simply a chart object for which we'll be setting some attributes and then we'll render a PNG file. We then define the size of the chart, in pixels; we assign colons to use for the background and foreground; and we create titles. We set the data and labels for the chart, both of which we are pulling from the Apache log parsing module. Finally, we draw() the chart out to a file and then close our shelve object. Figure 4-1 shows the chart image.

Here is another example of a script for visually formatting the shelve data, but this time, rather than a bar chart, the program creates a pie chart:

```python
#!/usr/bin/env python

import gdchart
import shelve
import itertools

shelve_file = shelve.open('access.s')
items_list = [(i[1], i[0]) for i in shelve_file.items() if i[1] > 0]
items_list.sort()
bytes_sent = [i[0] for i in items_list]
#ip_addresses = [i[1] for i in items_list]
```

```
ip_addresses = ['XXX.XXX.XXX.XXX' for i in items_list]

chart - gdchart.Pie()
chart.width = 800
chart.height = 800
chart.bg_color = 'white'
color_cycle = itertools.cycle([0xDDDDDD, 0x111111, 0x777777])
color_list = []
for i in bytes_sent:
    color_list.append(color_cycle.next())
chart.color = color_list

chart.plot_color = 'black'
chart.title = "Usage By IP Address"
chart.setData(*bytes_sent)
chart.setLabels(ip_addresses)
chart.draw("bytes_ip_pie.png")

shelve_file.close()
```

This script is nearly identical to the bar chart example, but we did have to make a few variations. First, this script creates an instance of gdchart.Pie rather than gdchart.Bar. Second, we set the colors for the individual data points rather than just using black for all of them. Since this is a pie chart, having all data pieces black would make the chart impossible to read, so we decided to alternate among three shades of grey. We were able to alternate among these three choices by using the cycle() function from the itertools module. We recommend having a look at the itertools module. There are lots of fun functions in there to help you deal with iterable objects (such as lists). Figure 4-2 is the result of our pie graph script.

The only real problem with the pie chart is that the (obfuscated) IP addresses get mingled together toward the lower end of the bytes transferred. Both the bar chart and the pie chart make the data in the shelve file much easier to read, and creating each chart was surprisingly simple. And plugging in the information was startlingly simple.

PDFs

Another way to format information from a data file is to save it in a PDF file. PDF has gone mainstream, and we almost expect all documents to be able to convert to PDF. As a sysadmin, knowing how to generate easy-to-read PDF documents can make your life easier. After reading this section, you should be able to apply your knowledge to creating PDF reports of network utilization, user accounts, and so on. We will also describe the way to embed a PDF automatically in multipart MIME emails with Python.

The 800 pound gorilla in PDF libraries is ReportLab. There is a free version and a commercial version of the software. There are quite a few examples you can look at in the ReportLab PDF library at *http://www.reportlab.com/docs/userguide.pdf*. In addition to reading this section, we highly recommend that you read ReportLab's official

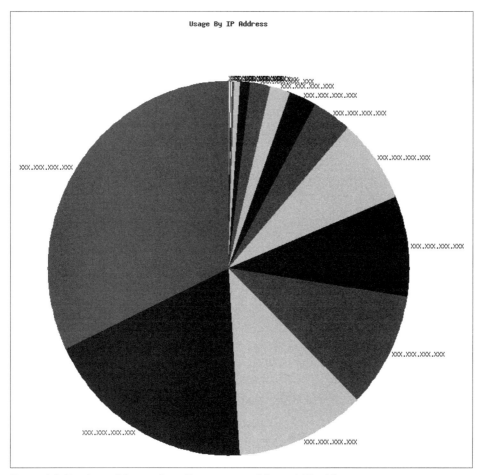

Figure 4-2. Pie chart of the number of bytes requested for each IP address

documentation. To install ReportLab on Ubuntu, you can simply `apt-get install python-reportlab`. If you're not on Ubuntu, you can seek out a package for your operating system. Or, there is always the source distribution to rely on.

Example 4-3 is an example of a "Hello World" PDF created with ReportLab.

Example 4-3. "Hello World" PDF

```
#!/usr/bin/env python
from reportlab.pdfgen import canvas

def hello():
    c = canvas.Canvas("helloworld.pdf")
    c.drawString(100,100,"Hello World")
    c.showPage()
    c.save()
hello()
```

There are a few things you should notice about our "Hello World" PDF creation. First, we creat a canvas object. Next, we use the `drawString()` method to do the equivalent of `file_obj.write()` to a text file. Finally, `showPage()` stops the drawing, and `save()` actually creates the PDF. If you run this code, you will get a big blank PDF with the words "Hello World" at the bottom.

If you've downloaded the source distribution for ReportLab, you can use the tests they've included as example-driven documentation. That is, when you run the tests, they'll generate a set of PDFs for you, and you can compare the test code with the PDFs to see how to accomplish various visual effects with the ReportLab library.

Now that you've seen how to create a PDF with ReportLab, let's see how you can use ReportLab to create a custom disk usage report. Creating a custom disk usage report could be useful. See Example 4-4.

Example 4-4. Disk report PDF

```python
#!/usr/bin/env python
import subprocess
import datetime
from reportlab.pdfgen import canvas
from reportlab.lib.units import inch

def disk_report():
    p = subprocess.Popen("df -h", shell=True,
                        stdout=subprocess.PIPE)
    return p.stdout.readlines()

def create_pdf(input,output="disk_report.pdf"):
    now = datetime.datetime.today()
    date = now.strftime("%h %d %Y %H:%M:%S")
    c = canvas.Canvas(output)
    textobject = c.beginText()
    textobject.setTextOrigin(inch, 11*inch)
    textobject.textLines('''
Disk Capacity Report: %s
''' % date)
    for line in input:
        textobject.textLine(line.strip())
    c.drawText(textobject)
    c.showPage()
    c.save()
report = disk_report()
create_pdf(report)
```

This code will generate a report that displays the current disk usage, with a datestamp and the words, "Disk Capacity Report." For such a small handful of lines of codes, this is quite impressive. Let's look at some of the highlights of this example. First, the `disk_report()` function that simply takes the output of `df -h` and returns it as a list. Next in the `create_pdf()` function, let's create a formatted datestamp. The most important part of this example is the `textobject`.

The `textobject` function is used to create the object that you will place in a PDF. We create a `textobject` by calling `beginText()`. Then we define the way we want the data to pack into the page. Our PDF approximates an 8.5×11–inch document, so to pack our text near the top of the page, we told the text object to set the text origin at 11 inches. After that we created a title by writing out a string to the text object, and then we finished by iterating over our list of lines from the `df` command. Notice that we used `line.strip()` to remove the newline characters. If we didn't do this, we would have seen blobs of black squares where the newline characters were.

You can create much more complex PDFs by adding colors and pictures, but you can figure that out by reading the excellent userguide associated with the ReportLab PDF library. The main thing to take away from these examples is that the text is the core object that holds the data that ultimately gets rendered out.

Information Distribution

After you've gathered and formatted your data, you need to get it to the people who are interested in it. In this chapter, we'll mainly focus on ways to email the documentation to your recipients. If you need to post some documentation to a web server for your users to look at, you can use FTP. We discuss using the Python standard FTP module in the next chapter.

Sending Email

Dealing with email is a significant part of being a sysadmin. Not only do we have to manage email servers, but we often to need come up with ways to generate warning messages and alerts via email. The Python Standard Library has terrific support for sending email, but very little has been written about it. Because all sysadmins should take pride in a carefully crafted automated email, this section will show you how to use Python to perform various email tasks.

Sending basic messages

There are two different packages in Python that allow you to send email. One low level package, smtplib, is an interface that corresponds to the various RFC's for the SMTP protocol. It sends email. The other package, email, assists with parsing and generating emails. Example 4-5 uses `smtplib` to build a string that represents the body of an email message and then uses the email package to send it to an email server.

Example 4-5. Sending messages with SMTP

```
#!/usr/bin/env python

import smtplib
mail_server = 'localhost'
mail_server_port = 25
```

```
from_addr = 'sender@example.com'
to_addr = 'receiver@example.com'

from_header = 'From: %s\r\n' % from_addr
to_header = 'To: %s\r\n\r\n' % to_addr
subject_header = 'Subject: nothing interesting'

body = 'This is a not-very-interesting email.'

email_message = '%s\n%s\n%s\n\n%s' % (from_header, to_header, subject_header, body)

s = smtplib.SMTP(mail_server, mail_server_port)
s.sendmail(from_addr, to_addr, email_message)
s.quit()
```

Basically, we defined the host and port for the email server along with the "to" and "from" addresses. Then we built up the email message by concatenating the header portions together with the email body portion. Finally, we connected to the SMTP server and sent it to to_addr and from from_addr. We should also note that we specifically formatted the From: and To: with \r\n to conform to the RFC specification.

See Chapter 10, specifically the section "Scheduling Python Processes," for an example of code that creates a cron job that sends mail with Python. For now, let's move from this basic example onto some of the fun things Python can do with mail.

Using SMTP authentication

Our last example was pretty simple, as it is trivial to send email from Python, but unfortunately, quite a few SMTP servers will force you to use authentication, so it won't work in many situations. Example 4-6 is an example of including SMTP authentication.

Example 4-6. SMTP authentication

```
#!/usr/bin/env python
import smtplib
mail_server = 'smtp.example.com'
mail_server_port = 465

from_addr = 'foo@example.com'
to_addr = 'bar@exmaple.com'

from_header = 'From: %s\r\n' % from_addr
to_header = 'To: %s\r\n\r\n' % to_addr
subject_header = 'Subject: Testing SMTP Authentication'

body = 'This mail tests SMTP Authentication'

email_message = '%s\n%s\n%s\n\n%s' % (from_header, to_header, subject_header, body)

s = smtplib.SMTP(mail_server, mail_server_port)
s.set_debuglevel(1)
s.starttls()
```

```
s.login("fatalbert", "mysecretpassword")
s.sendmail(from_addr, to_addr, email_message)
s.quit()
```

The main difference with this example is that we specified a username and password, enabled a **debuglevel**, and then started SSL by using the **starttls()** method. Enabling debugging when authentication is involved is an excellent idea. If we take a look at a failed debug session, it will look like this:

```
$ python2.5 mail.py
send: 'ehlo example.com\r\n'
reply: '250-example.com Hello example.com [127.0.0.1], pleased to meet you\r\n'
reply: '250-ENHANCEDSTATUSCODES\r\n'
reply: '250-PIPELINING\r\n'
reply: '250-8BITMIME\r\n'
reply: '250-SIZE\r\n'
reply: '250-DSN\r\n'
reply: '250-ETRN\r\n'
reply: '250-DELIVERBY\r\n'
reply: '250 HELP\r\n'
reply: retcode (250); Msg: example.com example.com [127.0.0.1], pleased to meet you
ENHANCEDSTATUSCODES
PIPELINING
8BITMIME
SIZE
DSN
ETRN
DELIVERBY
HELP
send: 'STARTTLS\r\n'
reply: '454 4.3.3 TLS not available after start\r\n'
reply: retcode (454); Msg: 4.3.3 TLS not available after start
```

In this example, the server with which we attempted to initiate SSL did not support it and sent us out. It would be quite simple to work around this and many other potential issues by writing scripts that included some error handle code to send mail using a cascading system of server attempts, finally finishing at localhost attempt to send mail.

Sending attachments with Python

Sending text-only email is so passé. With Python we can send messages using the MIME standard, which lets us encode attachments in the outgoing message. In a previous section of this chapter, we covered creating PDF reports. Because sysadmins are impatient, we are going to skip a boring diatribe on the origin of MIME and jump straight into sending an email with an attachment. See Example 4-7.

Example 4-7. Sending a PDF attachment email

```
import email
from email.MIMEText import MIMEText
from email.MIMEMultipart import MIMEMultipart
from email.MIMEBase import MIMEBase
```

```
from email import encoders
import smtplib
import mimetypes

from_addr = 'noah.gift@gmail.com'
to_addr = 'jjinux@gmail.com'
subject_header = 'Subject: Sending PDF Attachemt'
attachment = 'disk_usage.pdf'
body = '''
This message sends a PDF attachment created with Report
Lab.
'''

m = MIMEMultipart()
m["To"] = to_addr
m["From"] = from_addr
m["Subject"] = subject_header

ctype, encoding = mimetypes.guess_type(attachment)
print ctype, encoding
maintype, subtype = ctype.split('/', 1)
print maintype, subtype

m.attach(MIMEText(body))
fp = open(attachment, 'rb')
msg = MIMEBase(maintype, subtype)
msg.set_payload(fp.read())
fp.close()
encoders.encode_base64(msg)
msg.add_header("Content-Disposition", "attachment", filename=attachment)
m.attach(msg)

s = smtplib.SMTP("localhost")
s.set_debuglevel(1)
s.sendmail(from_addr, to_addr, m.as_string())
s.quit()
```

So, we used a little magic and encoded our disk report PDF we created earlier and emailed it out.

Trac

Trac is a wiki and issue tracking system. It is typically used for software development, but can really be used for anything that you would want to use a wiki or ticketing system for, and it is written in Python. You can find the latest copy of the Trac documentation and package here: *http://trac.edgewall.org/*. It is beyond the scope of this book to get into too much detail about Trac, but it is a good tool for general trouble tickets as well. One of the other interesting aspects of Trac is that it can be extended via plug-ins.

We're mentioning it last because it really fits into all three of the categories that we've been discussing: information gathering, formatting, and distribution. The wiki portion allows users to create web pages through browsers. The information they put into those passages is rendered in HTML for other users to view through browsers. This is the full cycle of what we've been discussing in this chapter.

Similarly, the ticket tracking system allows users to put in requests for work or to report problems they encounter. You can report on the tickets that have been entered via the web interface and can even generate CSV reports. Once again, Trac spans the full cycle of what we've discussed in this chapter.

We recommend that you explore Trac to see if it meets your needs. You might need something with more features and capabilities or you might want something simpler, but it's worth finding out more about.

Summary

In this chapter, we looked at ways to gather data, in both an automated and a manual way. We also looked at ways to put that data together into a few different, more distributable formats, namely HTML, PDF, and PNG. Finally, we looked at how to get the information out to people who are interested in it. As we said at the beginning of this chapter, documentation might not be the most glamorous part of your job. You might not have even realized that you were signing up to document things when you started. But clear and precise documentation is a critical element of system administration. We hope the tips in this chapter can make the sometimes mundane task of documentation a little more fun.

## CHAPTER 5

Networking

Networking often refers to connecting multiple computers together for the purpose of allowing some communication among them. But, for our purposes, we are less interested in allowing computers to communicate with one another and more interested in allowing processes to communicate with one another. Whether the processes are on the same computer or different computers is irrelevant for the techniques that we're going to show.

This chapter will focus on writing Python programs that connect to other processes using the standard socket library (as well as libraries built on top of socket) and then interacting with those other processes.

Network Clients

While servers sit and wait for a client to connect to them, clients initiate connections. The Python Standard Library contains implementations of many used network clients. This section will discuss some of the more common and frequently useful clients.

socket

The socket module provides a Python interface to your operating system's socket implementation. This means that you can do whatever can be done to or with sockets, using Python. In case you have never done any network programming before, this chapter does provide a brief overview of networking. It should give you a flavor of what kinds of things you can do with the Python networking libraries.

The socket module provides the factory function, socket(). The socket() function, in turn, returns a socket object. While there are a number of arguments to pass to socket() for specifying the kind of socket to create, calling the socket() factory function with no arguments returns a socket object with sensible defaults—a TCP/IP socket:

```
In [1]: import socket

In [2]: s = socket.socket()
```

```
In [3]: s.connect(('192.168.1.15', 80))

In [4]: s.send("GET / HTTP/1.0\n\n")
Out[4]: 16

In [5]: s.recv(200)
Out[5]: 'HTTP/1.1 200 OK\r\n\
Date: Mon, 03 Sep 2007 18:25:45 GMT\r\n\
Server: Apache/2.0.55 (Ubuntu) DAV/2 PHP/5.1.6\r\n\
Content-Length: 691\r\n\
Connection: close\r\n\
Content-Type: text/html; charset=UTF-8\r\n\
\r\n\
<!DOCTYPE HTML P'
In [6]: s.close()
```

This example created a **socket** object called s from the **socket()** factory function. It then connected to a local default web server, indicated by port 80, which is the default port for HTTP. Then, it sent the server the text string **"GET / HTTP/1.0\n\n"** (which is simply an HTTP request). Following the send, it received the first 200 bytes of the server's response, which is a **200 OK** status message and HTTP headers. Finally, we closed the connection.

The **socket** methods demonstrated in this example represent the methods that you are likely to find yourself using most often. **Connect()** establishes a communication channel between your **socket** object and the remote (specifically meaning "not this socket object"). **Send()** transmits data from your **socket** object to the remote end. **Recv()** receives any data that the remote end has sent back. And **close()** terminates the communication channel between the two sockets. This is a really simple example that shows the ease with which you can create **socket** objects and then send and receive data over them.

Now we'll look at a slightly more useful example. Suppose you have a server that is running some sort of network application, such as a web server. And suppose that you are interested in watching this server to be sure that, over the course of a day, you can make a socket connection to the web server. This sort of monitoring is minimal, but it proves that the server itself is still up and that the web server is still listening on some port. See Example 5-1.

Example 5-1. TCP port checker

```
#!/usr/bin/env python

import socket
import re
import sys

def check_server(address, port):
    #create a TCP socket
    s = socket.socket()
    print "Attempting to connect to %s on port %s" % (address, port)
    try:
```

```
        s.connect((address, port))
        print "Connected to %s on port %s" % (address, port)
        return True
    except socket.error, e:
        print "Connection to %s on port %s failed: %s" % (address, port, e)
        return False

if __name__ == '__main__':
    from optparse import OptionParser
    parser = OptionParser()

    parser.add_option("-a", "--address", dest="address", default='localhost',
                        help="ADDRESS for server", metavar="ADDRESS")

    parser.add_option("-p", "--port", dest="port", type="int", default=80,
                        help="PORT for server", metavar="PORT")

    (options, args) = parser.parse_args()
    print 'options: %s, args: %s' % (options, args)
    check = check_server(options.address, options.port)
    print 'check_server returned %s' % check
    sys.exit(not check)
```

All of the work occurs in the check_server() function. Check_server() creates a socket object. Then, it tries to connect to the specified address and port number. If it succeeds, it returns True. If it fails, the socket.connect() call will throw an exception, which is handled, and the function returns False. The main section of the code calls check_server(). This "main" section parses the arguments from the user and puts the user requested arguments into an appropriate format to pass in to check_server(). This whole script prints out status messages as it goes along. The last thing it prints out is the return value of check_server(). The script returns the opposite of the check_server() return code to the shell. The reason that we return the opposite of this return code is to make this script a useful scriptable utility. Typically, utilities like this return 0 to the shell on success and something other than 0 on failure (typically something positive). Here is an example of the piece of code successfully connecting to the web server we connected to earlier:

```
jmjones@dinkgutsy:code$ python port_checker_tcp.py -a 192.168.1.15 -p 80
options: {'port': 80, 'address': '192.168.1.15'}, args: []
Attempting to connect to 192.168.1.15 on port 80
Connected to 192.168.1.15 on port 80
check_server returned True
```

The last output line, which contains check_server returned True, means that the connection was a success.

Here is an example of a connection call that failed:

```
jmjones@dinkgutsy:code$ python port_checker_tcp.py -a 192.168.1.15 -p 81
options: {'port': 81, 'address': '192.168.1.15'}, args: []
Attempting to connect to 192.168.1.15 on port 81
Connection to 192.168.1.15 on port 81 failed: (111, 'Connection refused')
check_server returned False
```

The last log line, which contains `check_server returned False`, means that the connection was a failure. In the penultimate output line, which contains `Connection to 192.168.1.15 on port 81 failed`, we also see the reason, `'Connection refused'`. Just a wild guess here, but it may have something to do with there being nothing running on port 81 of this particular server.

We've created three examples to demonstrate how you can use this utility in shell scripts. First, we give a shell command to run the script and to print out SUCCESS if the script succeeds. We use the `&&` operator in place of an if-then statement:

```
$ python port_checker_tcp.py -a 192.168.1.15 -p 80 && echo "SUCCESS"
options: {'port': 80, 'address': '192.168.1.15'}, args: []
Attempting to connect to 192.168.1.15 on port 80
Connected to 192.168.1.15 on port 80
check_server returned True
SUCCESS
```

This script succeeded, so after executing and printing status results, the shell prints SUCCESS:

```
$ python port_checker_tcp.py -a 192.168.1.15 -p 81 && echo "FAILURE"
options: {'port': 81, 'address': '192.168.1.15'}, args: []
Attempting to connect to 192.168.1.15 on port 81
Connection to 192.168.1.15 on port 81 failed: (111, 'Connection refused')
check_server returned False
```

This script failed, so it never printed FAILURE:

```
$ python port_checker_tcp.py -a 192.168.1.15 -p 81 || echo "FAILURE"
options: {'port': 81, 'address': '192.168.1.15'}, args: []
Attempting to connect to 192.168.1.15 on port 81
Connection to 192.168.1.15 on port 81 failed: (111, 'Connection refused')
check_server returned False
FAILURE
```

This script failed, but we changed the `&&` to `||`. This just means if the script returns a failure result, print FAILURE. So it did.

The fact that a web server allows a connection on port 80 doesn't mean that there is an HTTP server available for the connection. A test that will help us better determine the status of a web server is whether the web server generates HTTP headers with the expected status code for some specific URL. Example 5-2 does just that.

Example 5-2. Socket-based web server checker

```
#!/usr/bin/env python

import socket
import re
import sys


def check_webserver(address, port, resource):
    #build up HTTP request string
    if not resource.startswith('/'):
```

```
    resource = '/' + resource
request_string = "GET %s HTTP/1.1\r\nHost: %s\r\n\r\n" % (resource, address)
print 'HTTP request:'
print '|||%s|||' % request_string

#create a TCP socket
s = socket.socket()
print "Attempting to connect to %s on port %s" % (address, port)
try:
    s.connect((address, port))
    print "Connected to %s on port %s" % (address, port)
    s.send(request_string)
    #we should only need the first 100 bytes or so
    rsp = s.recv(100)
    print 'Received 100 bytes of HTTP response'
    print '|||%s|||' % rsp
except socket.error, e:
    print "Connection to %s on port %s failed: %s" % (address, port, e)
    return False
finally:
    #be a good citizen and close your connection
    print "Closing the connection"
    s.close()
lines = rsp.splitlines()
print 'First line of HTTP response: %s' % lines[0]
try:
    version, status, message = re.split(r'\s+', lines[0], 2)
    print 'Version: %s, Status: %s, Message: %s' % (version, status, message)
except ValueError:
    print 'Failed to split status line'
    return False
if status in ['200', '301']:
    print 'Success - status was %s' % status
    return True
else:
    print 'Status was %s' % status
    return False

if __name__ == '__main__':
    from optparse import OptionParser
    parser = OptionParser()
    parser.add_option("-a", "--address", dest="address", default='localhost',
                    help="ADDRESS for webserver", metavar="ADDRESS")

    parser.add_option("-p", "--port", dest="port", type="int", default=80,
                    help="PORT for webserver", metavar="PORT")

    parser.add_option("-r", "--resource", dest="resource", default='index.html',
                    help="RESOURCE to check", metavar="RESOURCE")

    (options, args) = parser.parse_args()
    print 'options: %s, args: %s' % (options, args)
    check = check_webserver(options.address, options.port, options.resource)
    print 'check_webserver returned %s' % check
    sys.exit(not check)
```

Similar to the previous example where check_server() did all the work, check_web server() does all the work in this example, too. First, check_webserver() builds up the HTTP request string. The HTTP protocol, in case you don't know, is a well-defined way that HTTP clients and servers communicate. The HTTP request that check_web server() builds is nearly the simplest HTTP request possible. Next, check_web server() creates a socket object, connects to the server, and sends the HTTP request to the server. Then, it reads back the response from the server and closes the connection. When there is a socket error, check_webserver() returns False, indicating that the check failed. It then takes what it read from the server, and extracts the status code from it. If the status code is either 200 meaning "OK," or 301, meaning "Moved Permanently," check_webserver() returns True, otherwise, it returns False. The main portion of the script parses the input from the user and calls check_webserver(). After it gets the result back from check_webserver(), it returns the opposite of the return value from check_web server() to the shell. The concept here is similar to what we did with the plain socket checker. We want to be able to call this from a shell script and see if it succeeded or failed. Here is the code in action:

```
$ python web_server_checker_tcp.py -a 192.168.1.15 -p 80 -r apache2-default
options: {'resource': 'apache2-default', 'port': 80, 'address':
'192.168.1.15'}, args: []
HTTP request:
|||GET /apache2-default HTTP/1.1
Host: 192.168.1.15

|||
Attempting to connect to 192.168.1.15 on port 80
Connected to 192.168.1.15 on port 80
Received 100 bytes of HTTP response
|||HTTP/1.1 301 Moved Permanently
Date: Wed, 16 Apr 2008 23:31:24 GMT
Server: Apache/2.0.55 (Ubuntu) |||
Closing the connection
First line of HTTP response: HTTP/1.1 301 Moved Permanently
Version: HTTP/1.1, Status: 301, Message: Moved Permanently
Success - status was 301
check_webserver returned True
```

The last four output lines show that the HTTP status code for /apache2-default on this web server was 301, so this run was successful.

Here is another run. This time, we'll intentionally specify a resource that isn't there to show what happens when the HTTP call is False:

```
$ python web_server_checker_tcp.py -a 192.168.1.15 -p 80 -r foo
options: {'resource': 'foo', 'port': 80, 'address': '192.168.1.15'}, args: []
HTTP request:
|||GET /foo HTTP/1.1
Host: 192.168.1.15

|||
Attempting to connect to 192.168.1.15 on port 80
Connected to 192.168.1.15 on port 80
```

```
Received 100 bytes of HTTP response
|||HTTP/1.1 404 Not Found
Date: Wed, 16 Apr 2008 23:58:55 GMT
Server: Apache/2.0.55 (Ubuntu) DAV/2 PH|||
Closing the connection
First line of HTTP response: HTTP/1.1 404 Not Found
Version: HTTP/1.1, Status: 404, Message: Not Found
Status was 404
check_webserver returned False
```

Just as the last four lines of the previous example showed that the run was successful, the last four lines of this example show that it was unsuccessful. Because there is no /foo on this web server, this checker returned False.

This section showed how to construct low-level utilities to connect to network servers and perform basic checks on them. The purpose of these examples was to introduce you to what happens behind the scenes when clients and servers communicate with one another. If you have an opportunity to write a network component using a higher library than the socket module, you should take it. It is not desirable to spend your time writing network components using a low-level library such as socket.

httplib

The previous example showed how to make an HTTP request using the socket module directly. This example will show how to use the httplib module. When should you consider using the httplib module rather than the socket module? Or more generically, when should you consider using a higher level library rather than a lower level library? A good rule of thumb is any chance you get. Sometimes using a lower level library makes sense. You might need to accomplish something that isn't already in an available library, for example, or you might need to have finer-grained control of something already in a library, or there might be a performance advantage. But in this case, there is no reason not to use a higher-level library such as httplib over a lower-level library such as socket.

Example 5-3 accomplishes the same functionality as the previous example did with the httplib module.

Example 5-3. httplib-based web server checker

```
#!/usr/bin/env python

import httplib
import sys


def check_webserver(address, port, resource):
    #create connection
    if not resource.startswith('/'):
        resource = '/' + resource
    try:
        conn = httplib.HTTPConnection(address, port)
        print 'HTTP connection created successfully'
```

```
        #make request
        req = conn.request('GET', resource)
        print 'request for %s successful' % resource
        #get response
        response = conn.getresponse()
        print 'response status: %s' % response.status
    except sock.error, e:
        print 'HTTP connection failed: %s' % e
        return False
    finally:
        conn.close()
        print 'HTTP connection closed successfully'
    if response.status in [200, 301]:
        return True
    else:
        return False

if __name__ == '__main__':
    from optparse import OptionParser
    parser = OptionParser()
    parser.add_option("-a", "--address", dest="address", default='localhost',
                      help="ADDRESS for webserver", metavar="ADDRESS")
    parser.add_option("-p", "--port", dest="port", type="int", default=80,
                      help="PORT for webserver", metavar="PORT")
    parser.add_option("-r", "--resource", dest="resource", default='index.html',
                      help="RESOURCE to check", metavar="RESOURCE")
    (options, args) = parser.parse_args()
    print 'options: %s, args: %s' % (options, args)
    check = check_webserver(options.address, options.port, options.resource)
    print 'check_webserver returned %s' % check
    sys.exit(not check)
```

In its conception, this example follows the socket example pretty closely. Two of the biggest differences are that you don't have to manually create the HTTP request and that you don't have to manually parse the HTTP response. The httplib connection object has a request() method that builds and sends the HTTP request for you. The connection object also has a getresponse() method that creates a response object for you. We were able to access the HTTP status by referring to the status attribute on the response object. Even if it isn't that much less code to write, it is nice to not have to go through the trouble of keeping up with creating, sending, and receiving the HTTP request and response. This code just feels more tidy.

Here is a run that uses the same command-line parameters the previous successful scenario used. We're looking for / on our web server, and we find it:

```
$ python web_server_checker_httplib.py -a 192.168.1.15 -r /
options: {'resource': '/', 'port': 80, 'address': '192.168.1.15'}, args: []
HTTP connection created successfully
request for / successful
response status: 200
HTTP connection closed successfully
check_webserver returned True
```

And here is a run with the same command-line parameters as the failure scenario earlier. We're looking for /foo, and we don't find it:

```
$ python web_server_checker_httplib.py -a 192.168.1.15 -r /foo
options: {'resource': '/foo', 'port': 80, 'address': '192.168.1.15'}, args: []
HTTP connection created successfully
request for /foo successful
response status: 404
HTTP connection closed successfully
check_webserver returned False
```

As we said earlier, any time you have a chance to use a higher-level library, you should use it. Using httplib rather than using the socket module alone was a simpler, cleaner process. And the simpler you can make your code, the fewer bugs you'll have.

ftplib

In addition to the socket and httplib modules, the Python Standard Library also contains an FTP client module named ftplib. ftplib is a full-featured FTP client library that will allow you to programmatically perform any tasks you would normally use an FTP client application to perform. For example, you can log in to an FTP server, list files in a particular directory, retrieve files, put files, change directories, and logout, all from within a Python script. You can even use one of the many GUI frameworks available in Python and build your own GUI FTP application.

Rather than give a full overview of this library, we'll show you Example 5-4 and then explain how it works.

Example 5-4. FTP URL retriever using ftplib

```python
#!/usr/bin/env python

from ftplib import FTP
import ftplib
import sys
from optparse import OptionParser

parser = OptionParser()

parser.add_option("-a", "--remote_host_address", dest="remote_host_address",
    help="REMOTE FTP HOST.",
    metavar="REMOTE FTP HOST")

parser.add_option("-r", "--remote_file", dest="remote_file",
    help="REMOTE FILE NAME to download.",
    metavar="REMOTE FILE NAME")

parser.add_option("-l", "--local_file", dest="local_file",
    help="LOCAL FILE NAME to save remote file to", metavar="LOCAL FILE NAME")

parser.add_option("-u", "--username", dest="username",
    help="USERNAME for ftp server", metavar="USERNAME")
```

```
parser.add_option("-p", "--password", dest="password",
    help="PASSWORD for ftp server", metavar="PASSWORD")

(options, args) = parser.parse_args()

if not (options.remote_file and
        options.local_file and
        options.remote_host_address):
    parser.error('REMOTE HOST, LOCAL FILE NAME, ' \
            'and REMOTE FILE NAME are mandatory')

if options.username and not options.password:
    parser.error('PASSWORD is mandatory if USERNAME is present')

ftp = FTP(options.remote_host_address)
if options.username:
    try:
        ftp.login(options.username, options.password)
    except ftplib.error_perm, e:
        print "Login failed: %s" % e
        sys.exit(1)
else:
    try:
        ftp.login()
    except ftplib.error_perm, e:
        print "Anonymous login failed: %s" % e
        sys.exit(1)
try:
    local_file = open(options.local_file, 'wb')
    ftp.retrbinary('RETR %s' % options.remote_file, local_file.write)
finally:
    local_file.close()
    ftp.close()
```

The first part of the working code (past all the command-line parsing) creates an FTP object by passing the FTP server's address to FTP's constructor. Alternatively, we could have created an FTP object by passing nothing to the constructor and then calling the connect() method with the FTP server's address. The code then logs into the FTP server, using the username and password if they were provided, or anonymous authentication if they were not. Next, it creates a file object to store the data from the file on the FTP server. Then it calls the retrbinary() method on the FTP object. Retrbinary(), as the name implies, retrieves a binary file from an FTP server. It takes two parameters: the FTP retrieve command and a callback function. You might notice that our callback function is the write method on the file object we created in the previous step. It is important to note that we are not calling the write() method in this case. We are passing the write method in to the retrbinary() method so that retrbinary() can call write(). Retrbinary() will call whatever callback function we pass it with each chunk of data that it receives from the FTP server. This callback function could do anything with the data. The callback function could just log that it received N number of bytes from the FTP server. Passing in a file object's write method causes the script to write the contents of the file from the FTP server to the `file` object. Finally, it closes the `file` object and the FTP connection. We did a little error handling in the process: we set up a `try` block around retrieving the binary file from the FTP server and a `finally` block around the call to close the local file and FTP connection. If anything bad happens, we want to clean up our files before the script terminates. For a brief discussion of callbacks, see the Appendix.

urllib

Moving up the standard library modules to a higher-level library, we arrive at `urllib`. When you think of `urllib`, it's easy to think of HTTP libraries only and forget that FTP resources also can be identified by URLs. Consequently, you might not have considered using `urllib` to retrieve FTP resources, but the functionality is there. Example 5-5 is the same as the `ftplib` example earlier, except it uses `urllib`.

Example 5-5. FTP URL retriever using urllib

```
#!/usr/bin/env python
"""
url retriever

Usage:

url_retrieve_urllib.py URL FILENAME

URL:
If the URL is an FTP URL the format should be:
ftp://[username[:password]@]hostname/filename
If you want to use absolute paths to the file to download,
you should make the URL look something like this:
ftp://user:password@host/%2Fpath/to/myfile.txt
Notice the '%2F' at the beginning of the path to the file.

FILENAME:
absolute or relative path to the filename to save downloaded file as
"""

import urllib
import sys

if '-h' in sys.argv or '--help' in sys.argv:
    print __doc__
    sys.exit(1)

if not len(sys.argv) == 3:
    print 'URL and FILENAME are mandatory'
    print __doc__
    sys.exit(1)
url = sys.argv[1]
filename = sys.argv[2]
urllib.urlretrieve(url, filename)
```

This script is short and sweet. It really shows off the power of urllib. There are actually more lines of usage documentation than code in it. There is even more argument parsing than code, which says a lot because there isn't much of that, either. We decided to go with a very simple argument parsing routine with this script. Since both of the "options" were mandatory, we decided to use positional arguments rather than option switches. Effectively, the only line of code in this example that performs work is this one:

```
urllib.urlretrieve(url, filename)
```

After retrieving the options with sys.argv, this line of code pulls down the specified URL and saves it to the specified local filename. It works with HTTP URLs and FTP URLs, and will even work when the username and password are included in the URL.

A point worth emphasizing here is that if you think that something should be easier than the way you are doing it with another language, it probably is. There is probably some higher-level library out there somewhere that will do what you need to do frequently, and that library will be in the Python Standard Library. In this case, urllib did exactly what we wanted to do, and we didn't have to go anywhere beyond the standard library docs to find out about it. Sometimes, you might have to go outside the Python Standard Library, but you will find other Python resources such as the Python Package Index (PyPI) at *http://pypi.python.org/pypi*.

urllib2

Another high level library is urllib2. Urllib2 contains pretty much the same functionality as urllib, but expands on it. For example, urllib2 contains better authentication support and better cookie support. So if you start using urllib and think it isn't doing everything for you that it should, take a look at urllib2 to see if it meets your needs.

Remote Procedure Call Facilities

Typically, the reason for writing networking code is that you need interprocess communication (IPC). Often, plain IPC, such as HTTP or a plain socket, is good enough. However, there are times when it would be even more useful to execute code in a different process or even on a different computer, as though it were in the same process that the code you are working on is in. If you could, in fact, execute code remotely in some other process from your Python program, you might expect that the return values from the remote calls would be Python objects which you could deal more easily with than chunks of text through which you have to manually parse. The good news is that there are several tools for remote procedure call (RPC) functionality.

XML-RPC

XML-RPC exchanges a specifically formatted XML document between two processes to perform a remote procedure call. But you don't need to worry about XML part; you'll probably never have to know the format of the document that is being exchanged between the two processes. The only thing you really need to know to get started using XML-RPC is that there is an implementation of both the client and the server portions in the Python Standard Library. Two things that might be useful to know are XML-RPC is available for most programming languages, and it is very simple to use.

Example 5-6 is a simple XML-RPC server.

Example 5-6. Simple XML-RPC server

```
#!/usr/bin/env python

import SimpleXMLRPCServer
import os

def ls(directory):
    try:
        return os.listdir(directory)
    except OSError:
        return []

def ls_boom(directory):
    return os.listdir(directory)

def cb(obj):
    print "OBJECT::", obj
    print "OBJECT.__class__::", obj.__class__
    return obj.cb()

if __name__ == '__main__':
    s = SimpleXMLRPCServer.SimpleXMLRPCServer(('127.0.0.1', 8765))
    s.register_function(ls)
    s.register_function(ls_boom)
    s.register_function(cb)
    s.serve_forever()
```

This code creates a new `SimpleXMLRPCServer` object and binds it to port 8765 on 127.0.0.1, the loop back interface, which makes this accessible to processes only on this particular machine. It then registers the functions `ls()`, `ls_boom()`, and `cb()`, which we defined in the code. We'll explain the `cb()` function in a few moments. The `ls()` function will list the contents of the directory passed in using `os.listdir()` and return those results as a list. `ls()` masks any `OSError` exceptions that we may get. `ls_boom()` lets any exception that we hit find its way back to the XML-RPC client. Then, the code enters into the `serve_forever()` loop, which waits for a connection it can handle. Here is an example of this code used in an IPython shell:

```
In [1]: import xmlrpclib

In [2]: x = xmlrpclib.ServerProxy('http://localhost:8765')

In [3]: x.ls('.')
Out[3]:
['.svn',
```

```
'web_server_checker_httplib.py',
....
'subprocess_arp.py',
'web_server_checker_tcp.py']

In [4]: x.ls_boom('.')
Out[4]:
['.svn',
 'web_server_checker_httplib.py',
....
 'subprocess_arp.py',
 'web_server_checker_tcp.py']

In [5]: x.ls('/foo')
Out[5]: []

In [6]: x.ls_boom('/foo')
-----------------------------------------------------------------------------
<class 'xmlrpclib.Fault'>                  Traceback (most recent call last)
...
.
.
<<big nasty traceback>>
.
.
...
    786           if self._type == "fault":
--> 787               raise Fault(**self._stack[0])
    788           return tuple(self._stack)
    789

<class 'xmlrpclib.Fault'>: <Fault 1: "<type 'exceptions.OSError'>
    :[Errno 2] No such file or directory: '/foo'">
```

First, we created a ServerProxy() object by passing in the address of the XML-RPC server. Then, we called .ls('.') to see which files were in the server's current working directory. The server was running in a directory that contains example code from this book, so those are the files you see from the directory listing. The really interesting thing is that on the client side, x.ls('.') returned a Python list. Had this server been implemented in Java, Perl, Ruby, or C#, you could expect the same thing. The language that implements the server would have done a directory listing; created a list, array, or collection of filenames; and the XML-RPC server code would have then created an XML representation of that list or array and sent it back over the wire to your client. We also tried out ls_boom(). Since ls_boom() lacks the exception handling of ls(), we can see that the exception passes from the server back to the client. We even see a traceback on the client.

The interoperability possibilities that XML-RPC opens up to you are certainly interesting. But perhaps more interesting is the fact that you can write a piece of code to run on any number of machines and be able to execute that code remotely whenever you wish.

XML-RPC is not without its limitations, though. Whether you think these limitations are problematic or not is a matter of engineering taste. For example, if you pass in a custom Python object, the XML-RPC library will convert that object to a Python dictionary, serialize it to XML, and pass it across the wire. You can certainly work around this, but it would require writing code to extract your data from the XML version of the dictionary so that you could pass it back into the original object that was dictified. Rather than go through that trouble, why not use your objects directly on your RPC server? You can't with XML-RPC, but there are other options.

Pyro

Pyro is one framework that alleviates XML-RPC shortcomings. Pyro stands for Python Remote Objects (capitalization intentional). It lets you do everything you could do with XML-RPC, but rather than dictifying your objects, it maintains their types when you pass them across. If you do want to use Pyro, you will have to install it separately. It doesn't come with Python. Also be aware that Pyro only works with Python, whereas XML-RPC can work between Python and other languages. Example 5-7 is an implementation of the same ls() functionality from the XML-RPC example.

Example 5-7. Simple Pyro server

```python
#!/usr/bin/env python

import Pyro.core
import os
from xmlrpc_pyro_diff import PSACB

class PSAExample(Pyro.core.ObjBase):

    def ls(self, directory):
        try:
            return os.listdir(directory)
        except OSError:
            return []

    def ls_boom(self, directory):
        return os.listdir(directory)

    def cb(self, obj):
        print "OBJECT:", obj
        print "OBJECT.__class__:", obj.__class__
        return obj.cb()

if __name__ == '__main__':
    Pyro.core.initServer()
    daemon=Pyro.core.Daemon()
    uri=daemon.connect(PSAExample(),"psaexample")

    print "The daemon runs on port:",daemon.port
    print "The object's uri is:",uri
```

```
daemon.requestLoop()
```

The Pyro example is similar to the XML-RPC example. First, we created a `PSAExample` class with `ls()`, `ls_boom()`, and `cb()` methods on it. We then created a daemon from Pyro's internal plumbing. Then, we associated the `PSAExample` with the daemon. Finally, we told the daemon to start serving requests.

Here we access the Pyro server from an IPython prompt:

```
In [1]: import Pyro.core
/usr/lib/python2.5/site-packages/Pyro/core.py:11: DeprecationWarning:
The sre module is deprecated, please import re.
  import sys, time, sre, os, weakref

In [2]: psa = Pyro.core.getProxyForURI("PYROLOC://localhost:7766/psaexample")
Pyro Client Initialized. Using Pyro V3.5

In [3]: psa.ls(".")
Out[3]:
['pyro_server.py',
....
 'subprocess_arp.py',
 'web_server_checker_tcp.py']

In [4]: psa.ls_boom('.')
Out[4]:
['pyro_server.py',
....
 'subprocess_arp.py',
 'web_server_checker_tcp.py']

In [5]: psa.ls("/foo")
Out[5]: []

In [6]: psa.ls_boom("/foo")
---------------------------------------------------------------------------
<type 'exceptions.OSError'>                  Traceback (most recent call last)

/home/jmjones/local/Projects/psabook/oreilly/<ipython console> in <module>()
.
.
...
<<big nasty traceback>>
...
.
.
--> 115                    raise self.excObj
    116         def __str__(self):
    117                   s=self.excObj.__class__.__name__

<type 'exceptions.OSError'>: [Errno 2] No such file or directory: '/foo'
```

Nifty. It returned the same output as the XML-RPC example. We expected as much. But what happens when we pass in a custom object? We're going to define a new class, create an object from it, and then pass it to the XML-RPC cb() function and the Pyro cb() method from the examples above. Example 5-8 shows the piece of code that we are going to execute.

Example 5-8. Differences between XML-RPC and Pyro

```
import Pyro.core
import xmlrpclib

class PSACB:
    def __init__(self):
        self.some_attribute = 1

    def cb(self):
        return "PSA callback"

if __name__ == '__main__':
    cb = PSACB()

    print "PYRO SECTION"
    print "*" * 20
    psapyro = Pyro.core.getProxyForURI("PYROLOC://localhost:7766/psaexample")
    print "-->>", psapyro.cb(cb)
    print "*" * 20

    print "XML-RPC SECTION"
    print "*" * 20
    psaxmlrpc = xmlrpclib.ServerProxy('http://localhost:8765')
    print "-->>", psaxmlrpc.cb(cb)
    print "*" * 20
```

The call to the Pyro and XML-RPC implementation of the cb() function should both call cb() on the object passed in to it. And in both instances, it should return the string PSA callback. And here is what happens when we run it:

```
jmjones@dinkgutsy:code$ python xmlrpc_pyro_diff.py
/usr/lib/python2.5/site-packages/Pyro/core.py:11: DeprecationWarning:
The sre module is deprecated, please import re.
  import sys, time, sre, os, weakref
PYRO SECTION
********************
Pyro Client Initialized. Using Pyro V3.5
-->> PSA callback
********************
XML-RPC SECTION
********************
-->>
Traceback (most recent call last):
  File "xmlrpc_pyro_diff.py", line 23, in <module>
    print "-->>", psaxmlrpc.cb(cb)
  File "/usr/lib/python2.5/xmlrpclib.py", line 1147, in __call__
    return self.__send(self.__name, args)
  File "/usr/lib/python2.5/xmlrpclib.py", line 1437, in __request
    verbose=self.__verbose
  File "/usr/lib/python2.5/xmlrpclib.py", line 1201, in request
```

```
        return self._parse_response(h.getfile(), sock)
    File "/usr/lib/python2.5/xmlrpclib.py", line 1340, in _parse_response
        rcturn u.close()
    File "/usr/lib/python2.5/xmlrpclib.py", line 787, in close
        raise Fault(**self._stack[0])
xmlrpclib.Fault: <Fault 1: "<type 'exceptions.AttributeError'>:'dict' object
    has no attribute 'cb'">
```

The Pyro implementation worked, but the XML-RPC implementation failed and left us a traceback. The last line of the traceback says that a dict object has no attribute of cb. This will make more sense when we show you the output from the XML-RPC server. Remember that the cb() function had some print statements in it to show some information about what was going on. Here is the XML-RPC server output:

```
OBJECT:: {'some_attribute': 1}
OBJECT._class_:: <type 'dict'>
localhost - - [17/Apr/2008 16:39:02] "POST /RPC2 HTTP/1.0" 200 -
```

In dictifying the object that we created in the XML-RPC client, some_attribute was converted to a dictionary key. While this one attribute was preserved, the cb() method was not.

Here is the Pyro server output:

```
OBJECT: <xmlrpc_pyro_diff.PSACB instance at 0x9595a8>
OBJECT._class_: xmlrpc_pyro_diff.PSACB
```

Notice that the class of the object is a PSACB, which is how it was created. On the Pyro server side, we had to include code that imported the same code that the client was using. It makes sense that the Pyro server needs to import the client's code. Pyro uses the Python standard pickle to serialize objects, so it makes sense that Pyro behaves similarly.

In summary, if you want a simple RPC solution, don't want external dependencies, can live with the limitations of XML-RPC, and think that interoperability with other languages could come in handy, then XML-RPC is probably a good choice. On the other hand, if the limitations of XML-RPC are too constraining, you don't mind installing external libraries, and you don't mind being limited to using only Python, then Pyro is probably a better option for you.

SSH

SSH is an incredibly powerful, widely used protocol. You can also think of it as a tool since the most common implementation includes the same name. SSH allows you to securely connect to a remote server, execute shell commands, transfer files, and forward ports in both directions across the connection.

If you have the command-line ssh utility, why would you ever want to script using the SSH protocol? The main reason is that using the SSH protocol gives you the full power of SSH combined with the full power of Python.

The SSH2 protocol is implemented using the Python library called paramkio. From within a Python script, writing nothing but Python code, you can connect to an SSH server and accomplish those pressing SSH tasks. Example 5-9 is an example of connecting to an SSH server and executing a simple command.

Example 5-9. Connecting to an SSH server and remotely executing a command

```
#!/usr/bin/env python

import paramiko

hostname = '192.168.1.15'
port = 22
username = 'jmjones'
password = 'xxxYYYxxx'

if __name__ == "__main__":
    paramiko.util.log_to_file('paramiko.log')
    s = paramiko.SSHClient()
    s.load_system_host_keys()
    s.connect(hostname, port, username, password)
    stdin, stdout, stderr = s.exec_command('ifconfig')
    print stdout.read()
    s.close()
```

As you can see, we import the paramiko module and define three variables. Next, we create an SSHClient object. Then we tell it to load the host keys, which, on Linux, come from the "known_hosts" file. After that we connect to the SSH server. None of these steps is particularly complicated, especially if you're already familiar with SSH.

Now we're ready to execute a command remotely. The call to exec_command() executes the command that you pass in and returns three file handles associated with the execution of the command: standard input, standard output, and standard error. And to show that this is being executed on a machine with the same IP address as the address we connected to with the SSH call, we print out the results of ifconfig on the remote server:

```
jmjones@dinkbuntu:~/code$ python paramiko_exec.py
eth0      Link encap:Ethernet  HWaddr XX:XX:XX:XX:XX:XX
          inet addr:192.168.1.15  Bcast:192.168.1.255  Mask:255.255.255.0
          inet6 addr: xx00::000:x0xx:xx0x:0x00/64 Scope:Link
          UP BROADCAST RUNNING MULTICAST  MTU:1500  Metric:1
          RX packets:9667336 errors:0 dropped:0 overruns:0 frame:0
          TX packets:11643909 errors:0 dropped:0 overruns:0 carrier:0
          collisions:0 txqueuelen:1000
          RX bytes:1427939179 (1.3 GiB)  TX bytes:2940899219 (2.7 GiB)

lo        Link encap:Local Loopback
          inet addr:127.0.0.1  Mask:255.0.0.0
          inet6 addr: ::1/128 Scope:Host
          UP LOOPBACK RUNNING  MTU:16436  Metric:1
          RX packets:123571 errors:0 dropped:0 overruns:0 frame:0
          TX packets:123571 errors:0 dropped:0 overruns:0 carrier:0
```

```
collisions:0 txqueuelen:0
RX bytes:94585734 (90.2 MiB)  TX bytes:94585734 (90.2 MiB)
```

It looks exactly as if we had run `ifconfig` on our local machine, except the IP address is different.

Example 5-10 shows you how to use **paramiko** to SFTP files between a remote machine and your local machine. This particular example only retrieves files from the remote machine using the get() method. If you want to send files to the remote machine, use the put() method.

Example 5-10. Retrieving files from an SSH server

```
#!/usr/bin/env python

import paramiko
import os

hostname = '192.168.1.15'
port = 22
username = 'jmjones'
password = 'xxxYYYxxx'
dir_path = '/home/jmjones/logs'

if __name__ == "__main__":
    t = paramiko.Transport((hostname, port))
    t.connect(username=username, password=password)
    sftp = paramiko.SFTPClient.from_transport(t)
    files = sftp.listdir(dir_path)
    for f in files:
        print 'Retrieving', f
        sftp.get(os.path.join(dir_path, f), f)
    t.close()
```

In case you want to use public/private keys rather than passwords, Example 5-11 is a modification of the remote execution example using an RSA key.

Example 5-11. Connecting to an SSH server and remotely executing a command—private keys enabled

```
#!/usr/bin/env python

import paramiko

hostname = '192.168.1.15'
port = 22
username = 'jmjones'
pkey_file = '/home/jmjones/.ssh/id_rsa'

if __name__ == "__main__":
    key = paramiko.RSAKey.from_private_key_file(pkey_file)
    s = paramiko.SSHClient()
    s.load_system_host_keys()
    s.connect(hostname, port, pkey=key)
    stdin, stdout, stderr = s.exec_command('ifconfig')
```

```
    print stdout.read()
    s.close()
```

And Example 5-12 is a modification of the sftp script using an RSA key.

Example 5-12. Retrieving files from an SSH server

```
#!/usr/bin/env python

import paramiko
import os

hostname = '192.168.1.15'
port = 22
username = 'jmjones'
dir_path = '/home/jmjones/logs'
pkey_file = '/home/jmjones/.ssh/id_rsa'

if __name__ == "__main__":
    key = paramiko.RSAKey.from_private_key_file(pkey_file)
    t = paramiko.Transport((hostname, port))
    t.connect(username=username, pkey=key)
    sftp = paramiko.SFTPClient.from_transport(t)
    files = sftp.listdir(dir_path)
    for f in files:
        print 'Retrieving', f
        sftp.get(os.path.join(dir_path, f), f)
    t.close()
```

Twisted

Twisted is an event-driven networking framework for Python that can tackle pretty much any type of network-related task you need it to. A comprehensive single solution has a price of complexity. Twisted will begin to make sense after you've used it a few times, but understanding it initially can be difficult. Further, learning Twisted is such a large project that finding a beginning point to solve a specific problem can often be daunting.

Despite that, though, we highly recommend that you become familiar with it and see if it fits the way you think. If you can easily tailor your thinking to "the Twisted way," then learning Twisted will be likely to be a valuable investment. *Twisted Network Programming Essentials* by Abe Fettig (O'Reilly) is a good place to get started. This book helps to reduce the negative points we have mentioned.

Twisted is an event-driven network, meaning that rather than focusing on writing code that initiates connections being made and dropped and low-level details of data reception, you focus on writing code that handles those happenings.

What advantage would you gain by using Twisted? The framework encourages, and at times nearly requires, that you break your problems into small pieces. The network connection is decoupled from the logic of what occurs when connections are made.

These two facts gain you some level of automatic re-usability from your code. Another thing that Twisted gains for you is that you won't have to worry so much about lower level connection and error handling with network connections. Your part in writing network code is deciding what happens when certain events transpire.

Example 5-13 is a port checker that we've implemented in Twisted. It is very basic, but will demonstrate the event-driven nature of Twisted as we go through the code. But before we do that, we'll go over a few basic concepts that you'll need to know. The basics include reactors, factory, protocols, and deferreds. Reactors are the heart of a Twisted application's main event loop. Reactors handle event dispatching, network communications, and threading. Factories are responsible for spawning new protocol instances. Each factory instance can spawn one type of protocol. Protocols define what to do with a specific connection. At runtime, a protocol instance is created for each connection. And deferreds are a way of chaining actions together.

Twisted

Most folks who write code have a very strong intuition about the logical flow of a program or script: it's like water running down hill, complete with damns, shunts, etc. As a result, such code is fairly easy to think about, both the writing and the debugging. Twisted code is quite different. Being asynchronous, one might say it's more like drop-lets of water in a low-g environment than a river flowing downhill, but there the analogy really breaks down. A new component has been introduced: the event listener (reactor) and friends. To create and debug Twisted code, one must abandon preconceptions with a Zen-like attitude and begin building an intuition for a different logical flow.

Example 5-13. Port checker implemented in Twisted

```
#!/usr/bin/env python

from twisted.internet import reactor, protocol
import sys

class PortCheckerProtocol(protocol.Protocol):
    def __init__(self):
        print "Created a new protocol"
    def connectionMade(self):
        print "Connection made"
        reactor.stop()

class PortCheckerClientFactory(protocol.ClientFactory):
    protocol = PortCheckerProtocol
    def clientConnectionFailed(self, connector, reason):
        print "Connection failed because", reason
        reactor.stop()

if __name__ == '__main__':
    host, port = sys.argv[1].split(':')
    factory = PortCheckerClientFactory()
```

```
print "Testing %s" % sys.argv[1]
reactor.connectTCP(host, int(port), factory)
reactor.run()
```

Notice that we defined two classes (`PortCheckerProtocol` and `PortCheckerClientFactory`), both of which inherit from Twisted classes. We tied our factory, `PortCheckerClientFactory`, to `PortCheckerProtocol` by assigning `PortCheckerProtocol` to `PortCheckerClientFactory`'s class attribute `protocol`. If a factory attempts to make a connection but fails, the factory's `clientConnectionFailed()` method will be called. `ClientConnectionFailed()` is a method that is common to all Twisted factories and is the only method we defined for our factory. By defining a method that "comes with" the `factory` class, we are overriding the default behavior of the class. When a client connection fails, we want to print out a message to that effect and stop the reactor.

`PortCheckerProtocol` is one of the protocols we discussed earlier. An instance of this class will be created once we have established a connection to the server whose port we are checking. We have only defined one method on `PortCheckerProtocol`: `connectionMade()`. This is a method that is common to all Twisted protocol classes. By defining this method ourselves, we are overriding the default behavior. When a connection is successfully made, Twisted will call this protocol's `connectionMade()` method. As you can see, it prints out a simple message and stops the reactor. (We'll get to the reactor shortly.)

In this example, both `connectionMade()` and `clientConnectionFailed()` demonstrate the "event-driven" nature of Twisted. A connection being made is an event. So also is when a client connection fails to be made. When these events occur, Twisted calls the appropriate methods to handle the events, which are referred to as event handlers.

In the main section of this example, we create an instance of `PortCheckerClientFactory`. We then tell the Twisted reactor to connect to the hostname and port number, which were passed in as command-line arguments, using the specified factory. After telling the reactor to connect to a certain port on a certain host, we tell the reactor to run. If we had not told the reactor to run, nothing would have happened.

To summarize the flow chronologically, we start the reactor after giving it a directive. In this case, the directive was to connect to a server and port and use `PortCheckerClientFactory` to help dispatch events. If the connection to the given host and port fails, the event loop will call `clientConnectionFailed()` on `PortCheckerClientFactory`. If the connection succeeds, the factory creates an instance of the protocol, `PortCheckerProtocol`, and calls `connectionMade()` on that instance. Whether the connection succeeds or fails, the respective event handlers will shut the reactor down and the program will stop running.

That was a very basic example, but it showed the basics of Twisted's event handling nature. A key concept of Twisted programming that we did not cover in this example is the idea of deferreds and callbacks. A deferred represents a promise to execute the requested action. A callback is a way of specifying an action to accomplish. Deferreds can be chained together and pass their results on from one to the next. This point is often difficult to really understand in Twisted. (Example 5-14 will elaborate on deferreds.)

Example 5-14 is an example of using Perspective Broker, an RPC mechanism that is unique to Twisted. This example is another implementation of the remote "ls" server that we implemented in XML-RPC and Pyro, earlier in this chapter. First, we will walk you through the server.

Example 5-14. Twisted Perspective Broker server

```python
import os
from twisted.spread import pb
from twisted.internet import reactor

class PBDirLister(pb.Root):
    def remote_ls(self, directory):
        try:
            return os.listdir(directory)
        except OSError:
            return []

    def remote_ls_boom(self, directory):
        return os.listdir(directory)

if __name__ == '__main__':
    reactor.listenTCP(9876, pb.PBServerFactory(PBDirLister()))
    reactor.run()
```

This example defines one class, PBDirLister. This is the Perspective Broker (PB) class that will act as a remote object when the client connects to it. This example defines only two methods on this class: remote_ls() and remote_ls_boom(). Remote_ls() is, not surprisingly, one of the remote methods that the client will call. This remote_ls() method will simply return a listing of the specified directory. And remote_ls_boom() will do the same thing that remote_ls()will do, except that it won't perform exception handling. In the main section of the example, we tell the Perspective Broker to bind to port 9876 and then run the reactor.

Example 5-15 is not as straightforward; it calls remote_ls().

Example 5-15. Twisted Perspective Broker client

```python
#!/usr/bin/python

from twisted.spread import pb
from twisted.internet import reactor

def handle_err(reason):
    print "an error occurred", reason
    reactor.stop()

def call_ls(def_call_obj):
    return def_call_obj.callRemote('ls', '/home/jmjones/logs')
```

```
def print_ls(print_result):
    print print_result
    reactor.stop()

if __name__ == '__main__':
    factory = pb.PBClientFactory()
    reactor.connectTCP("localhost", 9876, factory)
    d = factory.getRootObject()
    d.addCallback(call_ls)
    d.addCallback(print_ls)
    d.addErrback(handle_err)
    reactor.run()
```

This client example defines three functions, handle_err(), call_ls(), and print_ls().
Handle_err() will handle any errors that occur along the way. Call_ls() will initiate
the calling of the remote "ls" method. Print_ls() will print the results of the "ls" call.
This seems a bit odd that there is one function to initiate a remote call and another to
print the results of the call. But because Twisted is an asynchronous, event-driven network framework, it makes sense in this case. The framework intentionally encourages
writing code that breaks work up into many small pieces.

The main section of this example shows how the reactor knows when to call which
callback function. First, we create a client Perspective Broker factory and tell the reactor to connect to localhost:9876, using the PB client factory to handle requests. Next,
we get a placeholder for the remote object by calling factory.getRootObject(). This is
actually a deferred, so we can pipeline activity together by calling addCallback() to it.

The first callback that we add is the call_ls() function call. Call_ls() calls the call
Remote() method on the deferred object from the previous step. CallRemote() returns
a deferred as well. The second callback in the processing chain is print_ls(). When
the reactor calls print_ls(), print_ls() prints the result of the remote call to
remote_ls() in the previous step. In fact, the reactor passes in the results of the remote
call into print_ls(). The third callback in the processing chain is handle_err(), which
is simply an error handler that lets us know if an error occurred along the way. When
either an error occurs or the pipeline reaches print_ls(), the respective methods shut
the reactor down.

Here is what running this client code looks like:

```
jmjones@dinkgutsy:code$ python twisted_perspective_broker_client.py
['test.log']
```

The output is a list of files in the directory we specified, exactly as we would have
expected.

This example seems a bit complicated for the simple RPC example we laid out here.
The server side seems pretty comparable. Creating the client seemed to be quite a bit
more work with the pipeline of callbacks, deferreds, reactors, and factories. But this

was a very simple example. The structure that Twisted provides really shines when the task at hand is of a higher level of complexity.

Example 5-16 is a slight modification to the Perspective Broker client code that we just demonstrated. Rather than calling ls on the remote side, it calls ls_boom. This will show us how the client and server deal with exceptions.

Example 5-16. Twisted Perspective Broker client—error

```python
#!/usr/bin/python

from twisted.spread import pb
from twisted.internet import reactor

def handle_err(reason):
    print "an error occurred", reason
    reactor.stop()

def call_ls(def_call_obj):
    return def_call_obj.callRemote('ls_boom', '/foo')

def print_ls(print_result):
    print print_result
    reactor.stop()

if __name__ == '__main__':
    factory = pb.PBClientFactory()
    reactor.connectTCP("localhost", 9876, factory)
    d = factory.getRootObject()
    d.addCallback(call_ls)
    d.addCallback(print_ls)
    d.addErrback(handle_err)
    reactor.run()
```

Here is what happens when we run this code:

```
jmjones@dinkgutsy:code$ python twisted_perspective_broker_client_boom.py an
error occurred [Failure instance: Traceback from remote host -- Traceback
unavailable
]
```

And on the server:

```
Peer will receive following PB traceback:
Traceback (most recent call last):
...
<more traceback>
...
    state = method(*args, **kw)
  File "twisted_perspective_broker_server.py", line 13, in remote_ls_boom
    return os.listdir(directory)
exceptions.OSError: [Errno 2] No such file or directory: '/foo'
```

The specifics of the error were in the server code rather than the client. In the client, we only knew that an error had occurred. If Pyro or XML-RPC had behaved like this, we would have considered that to be a bad thing. However, in the Twisted client code, our error handler was called. Since this is a different model of programming from Pyro and XML-RPC (event-based), we expect to have to handle our errors differently, and the Perspective Broker code did what we would have expected it to do.

We gave a less-than-tip-of-the-iceberg introduction to Twisted here. Twisted can be a bit difficult to get started with because it is such a comprehensive project and takes such a different approach than what most of us are accustomed to. Twisted is definitely worth investigating further and having in your toolbox when you need it.

Scapy

If you like writing network code, you are going to love Scapy. Scapy is an incredibly handy interactive packet manipulation program and library. Scapy can discover networks, perform scans, traceroutes, and probes. There is also excellent documentation available for Scapy. If you like this intro, you should buy the book for even more details on Scapy.

The first thing to figure out about Scapy is that, as of this writing, it is kept in a single file. You will need to download the latest copy of Scapy here: *http://hg.secdev.org/scapy/raw-file/tip/scapy.py*. Once you download Scapy, you can run it as a standalone tool or import it and use it as a library. Let's get started by using it as an interactive tool. Please keep in mind that you will need to run Scapy with root privileges, as it needs privileged control of your network interfaces.

Once you download and install Scapy, you will see something like this:

```
Welcome to Scapy (1.2.0.2)
>>>
```

You can do anything you would normally do with a Python interpreter,and there are special Scapy commands as well. The first thing we are going to do is run a Scapy `ls()` function, which lists all available layers:

```
>>> ls()
ARP          : ARP
ASN1_Packet : None
BOOTP        : BOOTP
CookedLinux : cooked linux
DHCP         : DHCP options
DNS          : DNS
DNSQR        : DNS Question Record
DNSRR        : DNS Resource Record
Dot11        : 802.11
Dot11ATIM    : 802.11 ATIM
Dot11AssoReq : 802.11 Association Request
Dot11AssoResp : 802.11 Association Response
Dot11Auth    : 802.11 Authentication
[snip]
```

We truncated the output as it is quite verbose. Now, we'll perform a recursive DNS query of *www.oreilly.com* using Caltech University's public DNS server:

```
>>> sr1(IP(dst="131.215.9.49")/UDP()/DNS(rd=1,qd=DNSQR(qname="www.oreilly.com")))
Begin emission:
Finished to send 1 packets.
...*
Received 4 packets, got 1 answers, remaining 0 packets
IP  version=4L ihl=5L tos=0x0 len=223 id=59364 flags=DF
   frag=0L ttl=239 proto=udp chksum=0xb1e src=131.215.9.49 dst=10.0.1.3 options=''
|UDP  sport=domain dport=domain len=203 chksum=0x843 |
DNS  id=0 qr=1L opcode=QUERY aa=0L tc=0L rd=1L ra=1L z=0L
   rcode=ok qdcount=1 ancount=2 nscount=4 arcount=3 qd=
DNSQR  qname='www.oreilly.com.' qtype=A qclass=IN |>
   an=DNSRR  rrname='www.oreilly.com.' type=A rclass=IN ttl=21600 rdata='208.201.239.36'
[snip]
```

Next, let's perform a traceroute:

```
>>> ans,unans=sr(IP(dst="oreilly.com",
>>> ttl=(4,25),id=RandShort())/TCP(flags=0x2))
Begin emission:
.............*Finished to send 22 packets.
*..........*********.***.***.*.*.*.*.*
Received 54 packets, got 22 answers, remaining 0 packets
>>> for snd, rcv in ans:
...     print snd.ttl, rcv.src, isinstance(rcv.payload, TCP)
...
[snip]
20 208.201.239.37 True
21 208.201.239.37 True
22 208.201.239.37 True
23 208.201.239.37 True
24 208.201.239.37 True
25 208.201.239.37 True
```

Scapy can even do pure packet dumps like tcpdump:

```
>>> sniff(iface="en0", prn=lambda x: x.show())
###[ Ethernet ]###
dst= ff:ff:ff:ff:ff:ff
src= 00:16:cb:07:e4:58
type= IPv4
###[ IP ]###
version= 4L
ihl= 5L
tos= 0x0
len= 78
id= 27957
flags=
frag= 0L
ttl= 64
proto= udp
chksum= 0xf668
src= 10.0.1.3
dst= 10.0.1.255
```

```
    options= ''
  [snip]
```

You can also do some very slick network visualization of traceroutes if you install graphviz and imagemagic. This example is borrowed from the official Scapy documentation:

```
>>> res,unans = traceroute(["www.microsoft.com","www.cisco.com","www.yahoo.com",
  "www.wanadoo.fr","www.pacsec.com"],dport=[80,443],maxttl=20,retry=-2)
Begin emission:
************************************************************************
 Finished to send 200 packets.
******************Begin emission:
*****************************************Finished to send 110 packets.
*********************************************************Begin emission:
Finished to send 5 packets.
Begin emission:
Finished to send 5 packets.

Received 195 packets, got 195 answers, remaining 5 packets
193.252.122.103:tcp443 193.252.122.103:tcp80 198.133.219.25:tcp443 198.133.219.25:tcp80
  207.46.193.254:tcp443 207.46.193.254:tcp80 69.147.114.210:tcp443 69.147.114.210:tcp80
  72.9.236.58:tcp443 72.9.236.58:tcp80
```

You can now create a fancy graph from those results:

```
>>> res.graph()
>>> res.graph(type="ps",target="| lp")
>>> res.graph(target="> /tmp/graph.svg")
```

Now that you've installed graphviz and imagemagic, the network visualization will blow your mind!

The real fun in using Scapy, though, is when you create custom command-line tools and scripts. In the next section, we will take a look at Scapy the library.

Creating Scripts with Scapy

Now that we can build something permanent with Scapy, one interesting thing to show right off the bat is an arping tool. Let's look at a platform-specific arping tool first:

```
#!/usr/bin/env python
import subprocess
import re
import sys

def arping(ipaddress="10.0.1.1"):
    """Arping function takes IP Address or Network, returns nested mac/ip list"""

    #Assuming use of arping on Red Hat Linux
    p = subprocess.Popen("/usr/sbin/arping -c 2 %s" % ipaddress, shell=True,
                         stdout=subprocess.PIPE)
    out = p.stdout.read()
    result = out.split()
```

```
    #pattern = re.compile(":")
    for item in result:
        if ':' in item:
            print item

if __name__ == '__main__':
    if len(sys.argv) > 1:
        for ip in sys.argv[1:]:
            print "arping", ip
            arping(ip)
    else:
        arping()
```

Now let's look at how we can create that exact same thing using Scapy, but in a platform-neutral way:

```
#!/usr/bin/env python
from scapy import srp,Ether,ARP,conf
import sys

def arping(iprange="10.0.1.0/24"):
    """Arping function takes IP Address or Network, returns nested mac/ip list"""

    conf.verb=0
    ans,unans=srp(Ether(dst="ff:ff:ff:ff:ff:ff")/ARP(pdst=iprange),
            timeout=2)

    collection = []
    for snd, rcv in ans:
        result = rcv.sprintf(r"%ARP.psrc% %Ether.src%").split()
        collection.append(result)
    return collection

if __name__ == '__main__':
    if len(sys.argv) > 1:
        for ip in sys.argv[1:]:
            print "arping", ip
            print arping(ip)
    else:
        print arping()
```

As you can see, the information contained in the output is quite handy, as it gives us the Mac and IP addresses of everyone on the subnet:

```
# sudo python scapy_arp.py
[['10.0.1.1', '00:00:00:00:00:10'], ['10.0.1.7', '00:00:00:00:00:12'],
['10.0.1.30', '00:00:00:00:00:11'], ['10.0.1.200', '00:00:00:00:00:13']]
```

From these examples, you should get the impression of how handy Scapy is and how easy it is to use.

## CHAPTER 6

Data

Introduction

The need to control dealing with data, files, and directories is one of the reasons IT organizations need sysadmins. What sysadmin hasn't had the need to process all of the files in a directory tree and parse and replace text? And if you haven't written a script yet that renames all of the files in a directory tree, you probably will at some point in the future. These abilities are the essence of what it means to be a sysadmin, or at least to be a really good sysadmin. For the rest of this chapter, we're going to focus on data, files, and directories.

Sysadmins need to constantly wrangle data from one location to the next. The movement of data on a daily basis is more prevelant in some sysadmin jobs than others. In the animation industry, constantly "wrangling" data from one location to the next is required because digital film production requires terabytes upon terabytes of storage. Also, there are different disk I/O requirements based on the quality and resolution of the image being viewed at any given time. If data needs to be "wrangled" to an HD preview room so that it can be inspected during a digital daily, then the "fresh" un-compressed, or slightly compressed, HD image files will need to be moved. Files need to be moved because there are generally two types of storage in animation. There is cheap, large, slow, safe, storage, and there is fast, expensive storage that is oftentimes a JBOD, or "just a bunch of disks," striped together RAID 0 for speed. A sysadmin in the film industry who primarily deals with data is called a "data wrangler."

A data wrangler needs to be constantly moving and migrating fresh data from location to location. Often the workhorse of moving data is rsync, scp, cp, or mv. These simple and powerful tools can be scripted with Python to do some incredible things.

Using the standard library, it is possible to do some amazing things without shelling out once. The advantage of using the standard library is that your data moving script will work just about anywhere, without having to depend on a platform-specific version of, say, tar.

Let's also not forget backups. There are many custom backup scripts and applications that can be written with a trivial amount of Python code. We will caution that writing extra tests for your backup code is not only wise, but necessary. You should make sure you have both unit, and functional testing in place when you are depending on backup scripts you have written yourself.

In addition, it is often necessary to process data at some point before, after, or during a move. Of course, Python is great for this as well. Creating a deduplication tool, a tool that finds duplicate files, and performs actions upon them can be very helpful for this, so we'll show you how to do it. This is one example of dealing with the constant flow of data that a sysadmin often encounters.

Using the OS Module to Interact with Data

If you have ever struggled with writing cross-platform shell scripts, you will appreciate the fact that the OS module is a portable application programming interface (API) to system services. In Python 2.5, the OS module contains over 200 methods, and many of those methods deal with data. In this section, we will go over many of the methods in that module that systems administrators care about when dealing with data.

Whenever you find yourself needing to explore a new module, IPython is often the right tool for the job, so let's start our journey through the OS module using IPython to execute a sequence of actions that are fairly commonly encountered. Example 6-1 shows you how to do that.

Example 6-1. Exploring common OS module data methods

```
In [1]: import os

In [2]: os.getcwd()
Out[2]: '/private/tmp'

In [3]: os.mkdir("/tmp/os_mod_explore")

In [4]: os.listdir("/tmp/os_mod_explore")
Out[4]: []

In [5]: os.mkdir("/tmp/os_mod_explore/test_dir1")

In [6]: os.listdir("/tmp/os_mod_explore")
Out[6]: ['test_dir1']

In [7]: os.stat("/tmp/os_mod_explore")
Out[7]: (16877, 6029306L, 234881026L, 3, 501, 0, 102L,
1207014425, 1207014398, 1207014398)

In [8]: os.rename("/tmp/os_mod_explore/test_dir1",
"/tmp/os_mod_explore/test_dir1_renamed")

In [9]: os.listdir("/tmp/os_mod_explore")
Out[9]: ['test_dir1_renamed']

In [10]: os.rmdir("/tmp/os_mod_explore/test_dir1_renamed")
```

```
In [11]: os.rmdir("/tmp/os_mod_explore/")
```

As you can see, after we imported the OS module, in line [2] we get the current working directory, then proceed to make a directory in line [3]. We then use os.listdir in line [4] to list the contents of our newly created directory. Next, we do an os.stat, which is very similar to the stat command in Bash, and then rename a directory in line [8]. In line [9], we verify that the directory was created and then we proceed to delete what we created by using the os.rmdir method.

This is by no means an exhaustive look at the OS module. There are methods to do just about anything you would need to do to the data, including changing permissions and creating symbolic links. Please refer to the documentation for the version of Python you are using, or alternately, use IPython with tab completion to view the available methods for the OS module.

Copying, Moving, Renaming, and Deleting Data

Since we talked about data wrangling in the introduction, and you now also have a bit of an idea about how to use the OS module, we can jump right into a higher-level module, called shutil that deals with data on a larger scale. The shutil module has methods for copying, moving, renaming, and deleting data just as the OS module does, but it can perform actions on an entire data tree.

Exploring the shutil module with IPython is a fun way to get acquainted with it. In the example below, we will be using shutil.copytree, but shutil has many other methods that do slightly different things. Please refer to the Python Standard Library documentation to see the differences between shutil copy methods. See Example 6-2.

Example 6-2. Using the shutil module to copy a data tree

```
In [1]: import os

In [2]: os.chdir("/tmp")
In [3]: os.makedirs("test/test_subdir1/test_subdir2")

In [4]: ls -lR
total 0
drwxr-xr-x  3 ngift  wheel  102 Mar 31 22:27 test/

./test:
total 0
drwxr-xr-x  3 ngift  wheel  102 Mar 31 22:27 test_subdir1/

./test/test_subdir1:
total 0
drwxr-xr-x  2 ngift  wheel  68 Mar 31 22:27 test_subdir2/

./test/test_subdir1/test_subdir2:
```

```
In [5]: import shutil

In [6]: shutil.copytree("test", "test-copy")

In [19]: ls -lR
total 0
drwxr-xr-x  3 ngift  wheel  102 Mar 31 22:27 test/
drwxr-xr-x  3 ngift  wheel  102 Mar 31 22:27 test-copy/

./test:
total 0
drwxr-xr-x  3 ngift  wheel  102 Mar 31 22:27 test_subdir1/

./test/test_subdir1:
total 0
drwxr-xr-x  2 ngift  wheel  68 Mar 31 22:27 test_subdir2/

./test/test_subdir1/test_subdir2:

./test-copy:
total 0
drwxr-xr-x  3 ngift  wheel  102 Mar 31 22:27 test_subdir1/

./test-copy/test_subdir1:
total 0
drwxr-xr-x  2 ngift  wheel  68 Mar 31 22:27 test_subdir2/

./test-copy/test_subdir1/test_subdir2:
```

Obviously, this is quite simple, yet incredibly useful, as you can quite easily wrap this type of code into a more sophisticated cross-platform, data mover script. The immediate use for this kind of code sequence that pops into our heads is to move data from one filesystem to another on an event. In an animation environment, it is often necessary to wait for the latest frames to be finished to convert them into a sequence to edit.

We could write a script to watch a directory for "x" number of frames in a cron job. When that cron job sees that the correct number of frames has been reached, it could then migrate that directory into another directory where the frames could be processed, or even just moved so that they are on a faster disk with I/O quick enough to handle playback of uncompressed HD footage.

The shutil module doesn't just copy files though, it also has methods for moving and deleting trees of data as well. Example 6-3 shows a move of our tree, and Example 6-4 shows how to delete it.

Example 6-3. Moving a data tree with shutil

```
In [20]: shutil.move("test-copy", "test-copy-moved")

In [21]: ls -lR
total 0
drwxr-xr-x  3 ngift  wheel  102 Mar 31 22:27 test/
```

```
drwxr-xr-x  3 ngift  wheel  102 Mar 31 22:27 test-copy-moved/

./test:
total 0
drwxr-xr-x  3 ngift  wheel  102 Mar 31 22:27 test_subdir1/

./test/test_subdir1:
total 0
drwxr-xr-x  2 ngift  wheel   68 Mar 31 22:27 test_subdir2/

./test/test_subdir1/test_subdir2:

./test-copy-moved:
total 0
drwxr-xr-x  3 ngift  wheel  102 Mar 31 22:27 test_subdir1/

./test-copy-moved/test_subdir1:
total 0
drwxr-xr-x  2 ngift  wheel   68 Mar 31 22:27 test_subdir2/

./test-copy-moved/test_subdir1/test_subdir2:
```

Example 6-4. Deleting a data tree with shutil

```
In [22]: shutil.rmtree("test-copy-moved")

    In [23]: shutil.rmtree("test-copy")
    In [24]: ll
```

Moving a data tree is a bit more exciting than deleting a data tree, as there is nothing to show after a delete. Many of these simple examples could be combined with other actions in more sophisticated scripts. One kind of script that might be useful is to write a backup tool that copies a directory tree to cheap network storage and then creates a datestamped archive. Fortunately, we have an example of doing just that in pure Python in the backup section of this chapter.

Working with Paths, Directories, and Files

One can't talk about dealing with data without taking into account paths, directories, and files. Every sysadmin needs to be able to, at the very least, write a tool that walks a directory, searches for a condition, and then does something with the result. We are going to cover some interesting ways to do just that.

As always, the Standard Library in Python has some killer tools to get the job done. Python doesn't have a reputation for being "batteries included" for nothing. Example 6-5 shows how to create an extra verbose directory walking script with functions that explicitly return files, directories, and paths.

Example 6-5. Verbose directory walking script

```python
import os
path = "/tmp"

def enumeratepaths(path=path):
    """Returns the path to all the files in a directory recursively"""
    path_collection = []
    for dirpath, dirnames, filenames in os.walk(path):
        for file in filenames:
            fullpath = os.path.join(dirpath, file)
            path_collection.append(fullpath)

    return path_collection

def enumeratefiles(path=path):
    """Returns all the files in a directory as a list"""
    file_collection = []
    for dirpath, dirnames, filenames in os.walk(path):
        for file in filenames:
            file_collection.append(file)

    return file_collection

def enumeratedir(path=path):
    """Returns all the directories in a directory as a list"""
    dir_collection = []
    for dirpath, dirnames, filenames in os.walk(path):
        for dir in dirnames:
            dir_collection.append(dir)

    return dir_collection

if __name__ == "__main__":
    print "\nRecursive listing of all paths in a dir:"
    for path in enumeratepaths():
        print path
    print "\nRecursive listing of all files in dir:"
    for file in enumeratefiles():
        print file
    print "\nRecursive listing of all dirs in dir:"
    for dir in enumeratedir():
        print dir
```

On a Mac laptop, the output of this script looks like this:

```
[ngift@Macintosh-7][H:12022][J:0]# python enumarate_file_dir_path.py

Recursive listing of all paths in a dir:
/tmp/.aksusb
/tmp/ARD_ABJMMRT
/tmp/com.hp.launchport
/tmp/error.txt
/tmp/liten.py
/tmp/LitenDeplicationReport.csv
/tmp/ngift.liten.log
```

```
/tmp/hsperfdata_ngift/58920
/tmp/launch-h36okI/Render
/tmp/launch-qy1S9C/Listeners
/tmp/launch-RTJzTw/:0
/tmp/launchd-150.wDvODl/sock

Recursive listing of all files in dir:
.aksusb
ARD_ABJMMRT
com.hp.launchport
error.txt
liten.py
LitenDeplicationReport.csv
ngift.liten.log
58920
Render
Listeners
:0
sock

Recursive listing of all dirs in dir:
.X11-unix
hsperfdata_ngift
launch-h36okI
launch-qy1S9C
launch-RTJzTw
launchd-150.wDvODl
ssh-YcE2t6PfnO
```

A note about the previous code snippet—os.walk returns a generator object, so if you call pass a value to os.walk, you can walk a tree yourself:

```
In [2]: import os

In [3]: os.walk("/tmp")
Out[3]: [generator object at 0x508e18]
```

This is what it looks like when it is run from IPython. You will notice using a generator gives us the ability to call path.next(). We won't get into the nitty gritty details about generators, but it is important to know that os.walk returns a generator object. Generators are tremendously useful for systems programming. Visit David Beazely's website (http://www.dabeaz.com/generators/) to find out all you need to know about them.

```
In [2]: import os

In [3]: os.walk("/tmp")
Out[3]: [generator object at 0x508e18]

    In [4]: path = os.walk("/tmp")

    In [5]: path.
    path.__class__        path.__init__         path.__repr__         path.gi_running
    path.__delattr__      path.__iter__         path.__setattr__      path.next
    path.__doc__          path.__new__          path.__str__          path.send
    path.__getattribute__ path.__reduce__       path.close            path.throw
```

```
path.__hash__            path.__reduce_ex__        path.gi_frame

In [5]: path.next()
Out[5]:
('/tmp',
['.X11-unix',
'hsperfdata_ngift',
'launch-h36okI',
'launch-qy1S9C',
'launch-RTJzTw',
'launchd-150.wDvODl',
'ssh-YcE2t6PfnO'],
['.aksusb',
'ARD_ABJMMRT',
'com.hp.launchport',
'error.txt',
'liten.py',
'LitenDeplicationReport.csv',
'ngift.liten.log'])
```

In a bit, we will look at generators in more detail, but let's first make a cleaner module that gives us files, directories, and paths in a clean API.

Now that we have walked a very basic directory, let's make this an object-oriented module so that we can easily import and reuse it again. It will take a small amount of work to make a hardcoded module, but a generic module that we can reuse later will certainly make our lives easier. See Example 6-6.

Example 6-6. Creating reusable directory walking module

```
import os

class diskwalk(object):
"""API for getting directory walking collections"""
def __init__(self, path):
    self.path = path

def enumeratePaths(self):
    """Returns the path to all the files in a directory as a list"""
    path_collection = []
    for dirpath, dirnames, filenames in os.walk(self.path):
        for file in filenames:
            fullpath = os.path.join(dirpath, file)
            path_collection.append(fullpath)

    return path_collection

def enumerateFiles(self):
    """Returns all the files in a directory as a list"""
    file_collection = []
    for dirpath, dirnames, filenames in os.walk(self.path):
        for file in filenames:
        file_collection.append(file)

    return file_collection
```

```
def enumerateDir(self):
    """Returns all the directories in a directory as a list"""
    dir_collection = []
    for dirpath, dirnames, filenames in os.walk(self.path):
        for dir in dirnames:
            dir_collection.append(dir)

    return dir_collection
```

As you can see, with a few small modifications, we were able to make a very nice interface for future modifications. One of the nice things about this new module is that we can import it into another script.

Comparing Data

Comparing data is quite important to a sysadmin. Questions you might often ask yourself are, "What files are different between these two directories? How many copies of this same file exist on my system?" In this section, you will find the ways to answer those questions and more.

When dealing with massive quantities of important data, it often is necessary to compare directory trees and files to see what changes have been made. This becomes critical if you start writing large data mover scripts. The absolute doomsday scenario is to write a large data move script that damages critical production data.

In this section, we will first explore a few lightweight methods to compare files and directories and then move on to eventually exploring doing checksum comparisons of files. The Python Standard Library has several modules that assist with comparisons and we will be covering `filecmp` and `os.listdir`.

Using the filecmp Module

The `filecmp` module contains functions for doing fast and efficient comparisons of files and directories. The `filecmp` module will perform a `os.stat` on two files and return a True if the results of `os.stat` are the same for both files or a False if the results are not. Typically, `os.stat` is used to determine whether or not two files use the same inodes on a disk and whether they are the same size, but it does not actually compare the contents.

In order to fully understand how `filecmp` works, we need to create three files from scratch. To do this on computer, change into the */tmp* directory, make a file called *file0.txt*, and place a "0" in the file. Next, create a file called *file1.txt*, and place a "1" in that file. Finally, create a file called *file00.txt*, and place a "0" in it. We will use these files as examples in the following code:

```
In [1]: import filecmp
```

```
In [2]: filecmp.cmp("file0.txt", "file1.txt")
Out[2]: False

In [3]: filecmp.cmp("file0.txt", "file00.txt")
Out[3]: True
```

As you can see, the cmp function returned True in the case of *file0.txt* and *file00.txt*, and False when *file1.txt* was compared with *file0.txt*.

The dircmp function has a number of attributes that report differences between directory trees. We won't go over every attribute, but we have created a few examples of useful things you can do. For this example, we created two subdirectories in the */tmp* directory and copied the files from our previous example into each directory. In *dirB*, we created one extra file named *file11.txt*, into which we put "11":

```
In [1]: import filecmp

In [2]: pwd
Out[2]: '/private/tmp'

In [3]: filecmp.dircmp("dirA", "dirB").diff_files
Out[3]: []

In [4]: filecmp.dircmp("dirA", "dirB").same_files
Out[4]: ['file1.txt', 'file00.txt', 'file0.txt']

In [5]: filecmp.dircmp("dirA", "dirB").report()
diff dirA dirB
Only in dirB : ['file11.txt']
Identical files : ['file0.txt', 'file00.txt', 'file1.txt']
```

You might be a bit surprised to see here that there were no matches for diff_files even though we created a *file11.txt* that has unique information in it. The reason is that diff_files compares only the differences between files with the same name.

Next, look at the output of same_files, and notice that it only reports back files that are identical in two directories. Finally, we can generate a report as shown in the last example. It has a handy output that includes a breakdown of the differences between the two directories. This brief overview is just a bit of what the filecmp module can do, so we recommend taking a look at the Python Standard Library documentation to get a full overview of the features we did not have space to cover.

Using os.list

Another lightweight method of comparing directories is to use os.listdir. You can think of os.listdir as an ls command that returns a Python list of the files found. Because Python supports many interesting ways to deal with lists, you can use os.listdir to determine differences in a directory yourself, quite simply by converting your list into a set and then subtracting one set from another. Here is an example of what this looks like in IPython:

```
In [1]: import os

In [2]: dirA = set(os.listdir("/tmp/dirA"))

In [3]: dirA
Out[3]: set(['file1.txt', 'file00.txt', 'file0.txt'])

In [4]: dirB = set(os.listdir("/tmp/dirB"))

In [5]: dirB
Out[5]: set(['file1.txt', 'file00.txt', 'file11.txt', 'file0.txt'])

In [6]: dirA - dirB
Out[6]: set([])

In [7]: dirB-dirA
Out[7]: set(['file11.txt'])
```

From this example, you can see that we used a neat trick of converting two lists into sets and then subtracting the sets to find the differences. Notice that line [7] returns file11.txt because dirB is a superset of dirA, but in line [6] the results are empty because dirA contains all of the same items as dirB. Using sets makes it easy to create a simple merge of two data structures as well, by subtracting the full paths of one directory against another and then copying the difference. We will discuss merging data in the next section.

This approach has some very large limitations though. The actual name of a file is often misleading, as it is possible to have a file that is 0k that has the same name as a file with 200 GBs. In the next section, we cover a better approach to finding the differences between two directories and merging the contents together.

Merging Data

What can you do when you don't want to simply compare data files, but you would like to merge two directory trees together? A problem often can occur when you want to merge the contents of one tree into another without creating any duplicates.

You could just blindly copy the files from one directory into your target directory, and then deduplicate the directory, but it would be more efficient to prevent the duplicates in the first place. One reasonably simple solution would be to use the filecmp module's dircmp function to compare two directories, and then copy the unique results using the os.listdir technique described earlier. A better choice would be to use MD5 checksums, which we explain in the next section.

MD5 Checksum Comparisons

Performing a MD5 checksum on a file and comparing it to another file is like going target shooting with a bazooka. It is the big weapon you pull out when you want to be sure of what you are doing, although a byte-by-byte comparison is truly 100 percent accurate. Example 6-7 shows how the function takes in a path to a file and returns a checksum.

Example 6-7. Performing an MD5 checksum on files

```
import hashlib

def create_checksum(path):
    """
    Reads in file. Creates checksum of file line by line.
    Returns complete checksum total for file.
    """
    fp = open(path)
    checksum = hashlib.md5()
    while True:
        buffer = fp.read(8192)
        if not buffer:break
        checksum.update(buffer)
    fp.close()
    checksum = checksum.digest()
    return checksum
```

Here is an iterative example that uses this function with IPython to compare two files:

```
In [2]: from checksum import createChecksum

In [3]: if createChecksum("image1") == createChecksum("image2"):
   ...:     print "True"
   ...:
   ...:
True

In [5]: if createChecksum("image1") == createChecksum("image_unique"):
print "True"
   ...:
   ...:
```

In that example, the checksums of the files were manually compared, but we can use the code we wrote earlier that returns a list of paths to recursively compare a directory tree full of files and gives us duplicates. One of the other nice things about creating a reasonable API is that we can now use IPython to interactively test our solution. Then, if it works, we can create another module. Example 6-8 shows the code for finding the duplicates.

Example 6-8. Performing an MD5 checksum on a directory tree to find duplicates

```
In [1]: from checksum import createChecksum

In [2]: from diskwalk_api import diskwalk

In [3]: d = diskwalk('/tmp/duplicates_directory')

In [4]: files = d.enumeratePaths()
```

```
In [5]: len(files)
Out[5]: 12

In [6]: dup = []

In [7]: record = {}

In [8]: for file in files:
    compound_key = (getsize(file),create_checksum(file))
    if compound_key in record:
        dup.append(file)
    else:

            record[compound_key] = file

....:
....:
In [9]: print dup
['/tmp/duplicates_directory/image2']
```

The only portion of this code that we haven't looked at in previous examples is found on line [8]. We create an empty dictionary and then use a key to store the checksum we generate. This can serve as a simple way to determine whether or not that checksum has been seen before. If it has, then we toss the file into a dup list. Now, let's separate this into a piece of code we can use again. After all that is quite useful. Example 6-9 shows how to do that.

Example 6-9. Finding duplicates

```
from checksum import create_checksum
from diskwalk_api import diskwalk
from os.path import getsize

def findDupes(path = '/tmp'):
 dup = []
 record = {}
 d = diskwalk(path)
 files = d.enumeratePaths()
 for file in files:
     compound_key = (getsize(file),create_checksum(file))
     if compound_key in record:
         dup.append(file)
     else:
         #print "Creating compound key record:", compound_key
         record[compound_key] = file
 return dup

if __name__ == "__main__":
dupes = findDupes()
for dup in dupes:
    print "Duplicate: %s" % dup
```

When we run that script, we get the following output:

```
[ngift@Macintosh-7][H:10157][J:0]# python find_dupes.py
Duplicate: /tmp/duplicates_directory/image2
```

We hope you can see that this shows what even a little bit of code reuse can accomplish. We now have a generic module that will take a directory tree and return a list of all the duplicate files. This is quite handy in and of itself, but next we can take this one step further and automatically delete the duplicates.

Deleting files in Python is simple, as you can use os.remove (file). In this example, we have a number of 10 MB files in our */tmp* directory; let's try to delete one of them using os.remove (file):

```
In [1]: import os

In [2]: os.remove("10
10mbfile.0  10mbfile.1  10mbfile.2  10mbfile.3  10mbfile.4
10mbfile.5  10mbfile.6  10mbfile.7  10mbfile.8

In [2]: os.remove("10mbfile.1")

In [3]: os.remove("10
10mbfile.0  10mbfile.2  10mbfile.3  10mbfile.4  10mbfile.5
10mbfile.6  10mbfile.7  10mbfile.8
```

Notice that tab completion in IPython allows us to see the matches and fills out the names of the image files for us. Be aware that the os.remove (file) method is silent and permanent, so this might or might not be what you want to do. With that in mind, we can implement an easy method to delete our duplicates, and then enhance it after the fact. Because it is so easy to test interactive code with IPython, we are going to write a test function on the fly and try it:

```
In [1]: from find_dupes import findDupes

In [2]: dupes = findDupes("/tmp")

In [3]: def delete(file):
              import os
   ...:     print "deleting %s" % file
   ...:     os.remove(file)
   ...:
   ...:

In [4]: for dupe in dupes:
   ...:     delete(dupe)
   ...:
   ...:
In [5]: for dupe in dupes:
delete(dupe)
   ...:
   ...:
deleting /tmp/10mbfile.2
deleting /tmp/10mbfile.3
deleting /tmp/10mbfile.4
deleting /tmp/10mbfile.5
```

```
deleting /tmp/10mbfile.6
deleting /tmp/10mbfile.7
deleting /tmp/10mbfile.8
```

In this example, we added some complexity to our delete method by including a print statement of the files we automatically deleted. Just because we created a whole slew of reusable code, it doesn't mean we need to stop now. We can create another module that does fancy delete-related things when it is a `file` object. The module doesn't even need to be tied to duplicates, it can be used to delete anything. See Example 6-10.

Example 6-10. Delete module

```python
#!/usr/bin/env python
import os

class Delete(object):
"""Delete Methods For File Objects"""

def __init__(self, file):
    self.file = file

def interactive(self):
    """interactive deletion mode"""

    input = raw_input("Do you really want to delete %s [N]/Y" % self.file)
    if input.upper():
        print "DELETING:  %s" % self.file
        status = os.remove(self.file)
    else:
        print "Skipping:  %s" % self.file
    return
def dryrun(self):
    """simulation mode for deletion"""

    print "Dry Run:  %s [NOT DELETED]" % self.file
    return

def delete(self):

    """Performs a delete on a file, with additional conditions
    """

    print "DELETING:  %s" % self.file
    try:
        status = os.remove(self.file)
    except Exception, err:
        print err
        return status

if __name__ == "__main__":
    from find_dupes import findDupes
    dupes = findDupes('/tmp')

    for dupe in dupes:
        delete = Delete(dupe)
```

```
#delete.dryrun()
#delete.delete()
#delete.interactive()
```

In this module, you will see three different types of deletes. The interactive delete method prompts the user to confirm each file he is going to delete. This can seem a bit annoying, but it is good protection when other programmers will be maintaining and updating the code.

The dry run method simulates a deletion. And, finally, there is an actual delete method that will permanently delete your files. At the bottom of the module, you can see that there is a commented example of the ways to use each of these three different methods. Here is an example of each method in action:

- Dry run

```
ngift@Macintosh-7][H:10197][J:0]# python delete.py
Dry Run:  /tmp/10mbfile.1 [NOT DELETED]
Dry Run:  /tmp/10mbfile.2 [NOT DELETED]
Dry Run:  /tmp/10mbfile.3 [NOT DELETED]
Dry Run:  /tmp/10mbfile.4 [NOT DELETED]
Dry Run:  /tmp/10mbfile.5 [NOT DELETED]
Dry Run:  /tmp/10mbfile.6 [NOT DELETED]
Dry Run:  /tmp/10mbfile.7 [NOT DELETED]
Dry Run:  /tmp/10mbfile.8 [NOT DELETED]
```

- Interactive

```
ngift@Macintosh-7][H:10201][J:0]# python delete.py
Do you really want to delete /tmp/10mbfile.1 [N]/YY
DELETING:  /tmp/10mbfile.1
Do you really want to delete /tmp/10mbfile.2 [N]/Y
Skipping:  /tmp/10mbfile.2
Do you really want to delete /tmp/10mbfile.3 [N]/Y
```

- Delete

```
[ngift@Macintosh-7][H:10203][J:0]# python delete.py
DELETING:  /tmp/10mbfile.1
DELETING:  /tmp/10mbfile.2
DELETING:  /tmp/10mbfile.3
DELETING:  /tmp/10mbfile.4
DELETING:  /tmp/10mbfile.5
DELETING:  /tmp/10mbfile.6
DELETING:  /tmp/10mbfile.7
DELETING:  /tmp/10mbfile.8
```

You might find using encapsulation techniques like this very handy when dealing with data because you can prevent a future problem by abstracting what you are working on enough to make it nonspecific to your problem. In this situation, we wanted to automatically delete duplicate files, so we created a module that generically finds file-names and deletes them. We could make another tool that generically takes file objects and applies some form of compression as well. We are actually going to get to that example in just a bit.

Pattern Matching Files and Directories

So far you have seen how to process directories and files, and perform actions such as finding duplicates, deleting directories, moving directories, and so on. The next step in mastering the directory tree is to use pattern matching, either alone or in combination with these previous techniques. As just about everything else in Python, performing a pattern match for a file extension or filename is simple. In this section, we will demonstrate a few common pattern matching problems and apply the techniques used earlier to create simple, yet powerful reusable tools.

A fairly common problem sysadmins need to solve is that they need to track down and delete, move, rename, or copy a certain file type. The most straightforward approach to doing this in Python is to use either the fnmatch module or the glob module. The main difference between these two modules is that fnmatch returns a True or False for a Unix wildcard, and glob returns a list of pathnames that match a pattern. Alternatively, regular expressions can be used to create more sophisticated pattern matching tools. Please refer to Chapter 3 to get more detailed instructions on using regular expressions to match patterns.

Example 6-11 will look at how fnmatch and glob can be used. We will reuse the code we've been working on by importing diskwalk from the diskwalk_api module.

Example 6-11. Interactively using fnmatch and glob to search for file matches

```
In [1]: from diskwalk_api import diskwalk

In [2]: files = diskwalk("/tmp")

In [3]: from fnmatch import fnmatch

In [4]: for file in files:
   ...:       if fnmatch(file,"*.txt"):
   ...:           print file
   ...:
   ...:
/tmp/file.txt

In [5]: from glob import glob

In [6]: import os

In [7]: os.chdir("/tmp")

In [8]: glob("*")
Out[8]: ['file.txt', 'image.iso', 'music.mp3']
```

In the previous example, after we reused our previous diskwalk module, we received a list of all of the full paths located in the */tmp* directory. We then used fnmatch to determine whether each file matched the pattern "*.txt". The glob module is a bit different, in that it will literally "glob," or match a pattern, and return the full path. Glob is a much higher-level function than `fnmatch`, but both are very useful tools for slightly different jobs.

The `fnmatch` function is particularly useful when it is combined with other code to create a filter to search for data in a directory tree. Often, when dealing with directory trees, you will want to work with files that match certain patterns. To see this in action, we will solve a classic sysadmin problem by renaming all of the files that match a pattern in a directory tree. Keep in mind that it is just as simple to rename files as it is to delete, compress, or process them. There is a simple pattern here:

1. Get the path to a file in a directory.
2. Perform some optional layer of filtering; this could involve many filters, such as filename, extension, size, uniqueness, and so on.
3. Perform an action on them; this could be copying, deleting, compressing, reading, and so on. Example 6-12 shows how to do this.

Example 6-12. Renaming a tree full of MP3 files to text files

```
In [1]: from diskwalk_api import diskwalk

In [2]: from shutil import move

In [3]: from fnmatch import fnmatch

In [4]: files = diskwalk("/tmp")

In [5]: for file in files:
            if fnmatch(file, "*.mp3"):
                #here we can do anything we want, delete, move, rename...hmmm rename
                move(file, "%s.txt" % file)
In [6]: ls -l /tmp/
total 0
-rw-r--r--  1 ngift  wheel  0 Apr  1 21:50 file.txt
-rw-r--r--  1 ngift  wheel  0 Apr  1 21:50 image.iso
-rw-r--r--  1 ngift  wheel  0 Apr  1 21:50 music.mp3.txt
-rw-r--r--  1 ngift  wheel  0 Apr  1 22:45 music1.mp3.txt
-rw-r--r--  1 ngift  wheel  0 Apr  1 22:45 music2.mp3.txt
-rw-r--r--  1 ngift  wheel  0 Apr  1 22:45 music3.mp3.txt
```

Using code we already wrote, we used four lines of very readable Python code to rename a tree full of mp2 files to text files. If you are one of the few sysadmins who has not read at least one episode of BOFH, or Bastard Operator From Hell, it might not be immediately obvious what we could do next with our bit of code.

Imagine you have a production file server that is strictly for high-performance disk I/O storage, and it has a limited capacity. You have noticed that it often gets full because one or two abusers place hundreds of GBs of MP3 files on it. You could put a quota on the amount of file space each user can access, of course, but often that is more trouble than it is worth. One solution would be to create a cron job every night that finds these MP3 files, and does "random" things to them. On Monday it could rename them to text files, on Tuesday it could compress them into ZIP files, on Wednesday it could move them all into the */tmp* directory, and on Thursday it could delete them, and send the owner of the file an emailed list of all the MP3 files it deleted. We would not suggest doing this unless you own the company you work for, but for the right BOFH, the earlier code example is a dream come true.

Wrapping Up rsync

As you might well already know, `rsync` is a command-line tool that was originally written by Andrew Tridgell and Paul Mackerra. Late in 2007, rsync version 3 was released for testing and it includes an even greater assortment of options than the original version.

Over the years, we have found ourselves using rsync as the primary tool to move data from point A to point B. The manpage and options are staggering works, so we recommend that you read through them in detail. Rsync may just be the single most useful command-line tool ever written for systems administrators.

With that being said, there are some ways that Python can help control, or glue rsync's behavior. One problem that we have encountered is ensuring that data gets copied at a scheduled time. We have been in many situations in which we needed to synchronize TBs of data as quickly as possible between one file server and another, but we did not want to monitor the process manually. This is a situation in which Python really makes a lot of sense.

With Python you can add a degree of artificial intelligence to rsync and customize it to your particular needs. The point of using Python as glue code is that you make Unix utilities do things they were never intended to do, and so you make highly flexible and customizable tools. The limit is truly only your imagination. Example 6-13 shows a very simple example of how to wrap rsync.

Example 6-13. Simple wrap of rsync

```
#!/usr/bin/env python
#wraps up rsync to synchronize two directories
from subprocess import call
import sys

source = "/tmp/sync_dir_A/" #Note the trailing slash
target = "/tmp/sync_dir_B"
rsync = "rsync"
arguments = "-a"
cmd = "%s %s %s %s" % (rsync, arguments, source, target)


def sync():

ret = call(cmd, shell=True)
if ret !=0:
```

```
    print "rsync failed"
    sys.exit(1)
sync()
```

This example is hardcoded to synchronize two directories and to print out a failure message if the command does not work. We could do something a bit more interesting, though, and solve a problem that we have frequently run into. We have often found that we are called upon to synchronize two very large directories, and we don't want to monitor data synchronization overnight. But if you don't monitor the synchronization, you can find that it disrupted partway through the process, and quite often the data, along with a whole night, is wasted, and the process needs to start again the next day. Using Python, you can create a more aggressive, highly motivated rsync command.

What would a highly motivated rsync command do exactly? Well, it would do what you would do if you were monitoring the synchronization of two directories: it would continue trying to synchronize the directories until it finished, and then it would send an email saying it was done. Example 6-14 shows the rsync code of our little over achiever in action.

Example 6-14. An rsync command that doesn't quit until the job is finished

```
#!/usr/bin/env python
#wraps up rsync to synchronize two directories
from subprocess import call
import sys
import time

"""this motivated rsync tries to synchronize forever"""

source = "/tmp/sync_dir_A/" #Note the trailing slash
target = "/tmp/sync_dir_B"
rsync = "rsync"
arguments = "-av"
cmd = "%s %s %s %s" % (rsync, arguments, source, target)

def sync():
while True:
    ret = call(cmd, shell=True)
    if ret !=0:
        print "resubmitting rsync"
        time.sleep(30)
    else:
        print "rsync was succesful"
        subprocess.call("mail -s 'jobs done' bofh@example.com", shell=True)
        sys.exit(0)
sync()

        </literallayout>
</example>
```

This is overly simplified and contains hardcoded data, but it is an example of the kind of useful tool you can develop to automate something you normally need to monitor manually. There are some other features you can include, such as the ability to set the retry interval and limit as well as the ability to check for disk usage on the machine to which you are connecting and so on.

Metadata: Data About Data

Most systems administrators get to the point where they start to be concerned, not just about data, but about the data about the data. Metadata, or data about data, can often be more important than the data itself. To give an example, in film and television, the same data often exists in multiple locations on a filesystem or even on several filesystems. Keeping track of the data often involves creating some type of metadata management system.

It is the data about how those files are organized and used, though, that can be the most critical to an application, to an animation pipeline, or to restore a backup. Python can help here, too, as it is easy to both use metadata and write metadata with Python.

Let's look at using a popular ORM, SQLAlchemy, to create some metadata about a filesystem. Fortunately, the documentation for SQLAlchemy is very good, and SQLAlchemy works with SQLite. We think this is a killer combination for creating custom metadata solutions.

In the examples above, we walked a filesystem in real time and performed actions and queries on paths that we found. While this is incredibly useful, it is also time-consuming to search a large filesystem consisting of millions of files to do just one thing. In Example 6-15, we show what a very basic metadata system could look like by combining the directory walking techniques we have just mastered with an ORM.

Example 6-15. Creating metadata about a filesystem with SQLAlchemy

```
#!/usr/bin/env python
from sqlalchemy import create_engine
from sqlalchemy import Table, Column, Integer, String, MetaData, ForeignKey
from sqlalchemy.orm import mapper, sessionmaker
import os

#path
path = " /tmp"

#Part 1:  create engine
engine = create_engine('sqlite:///:memory:', echo=False)

#Part 2:  metadata
metadata = MetaData()

filesystem_table = Table('filesystem', metadata,
    Column('id', Integer, primary_key=True),
    Column('path', String(500)),
    Column('file', String(255)),
)
```

```
metadata.create_all(engine)

#Part 3:  mapped class
class Filesystem(object):

    def __init__(self, path, file):
        self.path = path
        self.file = file

    def __repr__(self):
        return "[Filesystem('%s','%s')]" % (self.path, self.file)

#Part 4:  mapper function
mapper(Filesystem,filesystem_table)

#Part 5:  create session
Session = sessionmaker(bind=engine, autoflush=True, transactional=True)
session = Session()

#Part 6:  crawl file system and populate database with results
for dirpath, dirnames, filenames in os.walk(path):
    for file in filenames:
        fullpath = os.path.join(dirpath, file)
        record = Filesystem(fullpath, file)
        session.save(record)

#Part 7:  commit to the database
session.commit()

#Part 8:  query
for record in session.query(Filesystem):
    print "Database Record Number: %s, Path: %s , File: %s " \
    % (record.id,record.path, record.file)
```

It would be best to think about this code as a set of procedures that are followed one after another. In part one, we create an engine, which is really just a fancy way of defining the database we are going to use. In part two, we define a metadata instance, and create our database tables. In part three, we create a class that will map to the tables in the database that we created. In part four, we call a mapper function that puts the ORM; it actually maps this class to the tables. In part five, we create a session to our database. Notice that there are a few keyword parameters that we set, including autoflush and transactional.

Now that we have the very explicit ORM setup completed, in part six, we do our usual song and dance, and grab the filenames and complete paths while we walk a directory tree. There are a couple of twists this time, though. Notice that we create a record in the database for each fullpath and file we encounter, and that we then save each newly created record as it is created. We then commit this transaction to our "in memory" SQLite database in part seven.

Finally, in part eight, we perform a query, in Python, of course, that returns the results of the records we placed in the database. This example could potentially be a fun way to experiment with creating custom SQLAlchemy metadata solutions for your company or clients. You could expand this code to do something interesting, such as perform relational queries or write results out to a file, and so on.

Archiving, Compressing, Imaging, and Restoring

Dealing with data in big chunks is a problem that sysadmins have to face every day. They often use tar, dd, gzip, bzip, bzip2, hdiutil, asr, and other utilities to get their jobs done.

Believe it or not, the "batteries included" Python Standard Library has built-in support for TAR files, zlib files, and gzip files. If compression and archiving is your goal, then you will not have any problem with the rich tools Python has to offer. Let's look at the grandaddy of all archive packages: tar; and we we'll see how the standard library implements tar.

Using tarfile Module to Create TAR Archives

Creating a TAR archive is quite easy, almost too easy in fact. In Example 6-16, we create a very large file as an example. Note, the syntax is much more user friendly than even the tar command itself.

Example 6-16. Create big text file

```
In [1]: f = open("largeFile.txt", "w")

In [2]: statement = "This is a big line that I intend to write over and over again."
ln [3]: x = 0
In [4]: for x in xrange(20000):
....:     x += 1
....:     f.write("%s\n" % statement)
....:
....:
In [4]: ls -l
-rw-r--r-- 1 root root 1236992 Oct 25 23:13 largeFile.txt
```

OK, now that we have a big file full of junk, let's TAR that baby up. See Example 6-17.

Example 6-17. TAR up contents of file

```
In [1]: import tarfile

In [2]: tar = tarfile.open("largefile.tar", "w")

In [3]: tar.add("largeFile.txt")

In [4]: tar.close()
```

```
In [5]: ll

-rw-r--r-- 1 root root 1236992 Oct 25 23:15 largeFile.txt
-rw-r--r-- 1 root root 1236992 Oct 26 00:39 largefile.tar
```

So, as you can see, this makes a vanilla TAR archive in a much easier syntax than the
regular `tar` command. This certainly makes the case for using the IPython shell to do
all of your daily systems administration work.

While it is handy to be able to create a TAR file using Python, it is almost useless to
TAR up only one file. Using the same directory walking pattern we have used numerous
times in this chapter, we can create a TAR file of the whole *tmp* directory by walking
the tree and then adding each file to the contents of the *tmp* directory TAR. See Example 6-18.

Example 6-18. TAR up contents of a directory tree

```
In [27]: import tarfile

In [28]: tar = tarfile.open("temp.tar", "w")

In [29]: import os

In [30]: for root, dir, files in os.walk("/tmp"):
   ....:     for file in filenames:
   ....:
KeyboardInterrupt

In [30]: for root, dir, files in os.walk("/tmp"):
for file in files:
   ....:             fullpath = os.path.join(root,file)
   ....:             tar.add(fullpath)
   ....:
   ....:

In [33]: tar.close()
```

It is quite simple to add the contents of a directory tree by walking a directory, and it
is a good pattern to use, because it can be combined with some of the other techniques
we have covered in this chapter. Perhaps you are archiving a directory full of media
files. It seems silly to archive exact duplicates, so perhaps you want to replace duplicates
with symbolic links before you create a TAR file. With the information in this chapter,
you can easily build the code that will do just that and save quite a bit of space.

Since doing a generic TAR archive is a little bit boring, let's spice it up a bit and add
bzip2 compression, which will make your CPU whine and complain at how much you
are making it work. The bzip2 compression algorithm can do some really funky stuff.
Let's look at an example of how impressive it can truly be.

Then get real funky and make a 60 MB text file shrink down to 10 K! See Example 6-19.

Example 6-19. Creating bzip2 TAR archive

```
In [1: tar = tarfile.open("largefilecompressed.tar.bzip2", "w|bz2")

In [2]: tar.add("largeFile.txt")

In [3]: ls -h
foo1.txt fooDir1/ largeFile.txt largefilecompressed.tar.bzip2*
foo2.txt fooDir2/ largefile.tar

ln [4]: tar.close()

In [5]: ls -lh

-rw-r--r-- 1 root root 61M Oct 25 23:15 largeFile.txt
-rw-r--r-- 1 root root 61M Oct 26 00:39 largefile.tar
-rwxr-xr-x 1 root root 10K Oct 26 01:02 largefilecompressed.tar.bzip2*
```

What is amazing is that bzip2 was able to compress our 61 M text file into 10 K, although we did cheat quite a bit using the same data over and over again. This didn't come at zero cost of course, as it took a few minutes to compress this file on a dual core AMD system.

Let's go the whole nine yards and do a compressed archive with the rest of the available options, starting with gzip next. The syntax is only slightly different. See Example 6-20.

Example 6-20. Creating a gzip TAR archive

```
In [10]: tar = tarfile.open("largefile.tar.gzip", "w|gz")

In [11]: tar.add("largeFile.txt")

ln [12]: tar.close()

In [13]: ls -lh

-rw-r--r-- 1 root root  61M Oct 26 01:20 largeFile.txt
-rw-r--r-- 1 root root  61M Oct 26 00:39 largefile.tar
-rwxr-xr-x 1 root root 160K Oct 26 01:24 largefile.tar.gzip*
```

A gzip archive is still incredibly small, coming in at 160 K, but on my machine it was able to create this compressed TAR file in seconds. This seems like a good trade-off in most situations.

Using a tarfile Module to Examine the Contents of TAR Files

Now that we have a tool that creates TAR files, it only makes sense to examine the TAR file's contents. It is one thing to blindly create a TAR file, but if you have been a systems administrator for any length of time, you have probably gotten burned by a bad backup, or have been accused of making a bad backup.

To put this situation in perspective and highlight the importance of examining TAR archives, we will share a story about a fictional friend of ours, let's call it *The Case of the Missing TAR Archive*. Names, identities, and facts, are fictional; if this story resembles reality, it is completely coincidental.

OUr friend worked at a major television studio as a systems administrator and was responsible for supporting a department led by a real crazy man. This man had a reputation for not telling the truth, acting impulsively, and well, being crazy. If a situation arose where the crazy man was at fault, like he missed a deadline with a client, or didn't produce a segment according to the specifications he was given, he would gladly just lie and blame it on someone else. Often times, that someone else was our friend, the systems administrator.

Unfortunately, our friend, was responsible for maintaining this lunatic's backups. His first thought was it was time to look for a new job, but he had worked at this studio for many years, and had many friends, and didn't want to waste all that on this temporarily bad situation. He needed to make sure he covered all of his bases and so instituted a logging system that categorized the contents of all of the automated TAR archives that were created for the crazy man, as he felt it was only a matter of time before he would get burned when the crazy man missed a deadline, and needed an excuse.

One day our friend, William, gets a call from his boss, "William I need to see you in my office immediately, we have a situation with the backups." William, immediately walked over to his office, and was told that the crazy man, Alex, had accused William of damaging the archive to his show, and this caused him to miss a deadline with his client. When Alex missed deadlines with his client, it made Alex's boss Bob, very upset.

William was told by his boss that Alex had told him the backup contained nothing but empty, damaged files, and that he had been depending on that archive to work on his show. William then told his boss, he was certain that he would eventually be accused of messing up an archive, and had secretly written some Python code that inspected the contents of all the TAR archives he had made and created extended information about the attributes of the files before and after they were backed up. It turned out that Alex had never created a show to begin with and that there was an empty folder being archived for months.

When Alex was confronted with this information, he quickly backpeddled and looked for some way to shift attention onto a new issue. Unfortunately for Alex, this was the last straw and a couple of months later, he never showed up to work. He may have either left or been fired, but it didn't matter, our friend, William had solved, *The Case of the Missing TAR Archive*.

The moral of this story is that when you are dealing with backups, treat them like nuclear weapons, as backups are fraught with danger in ways you might not even imagine.

Here are several methods to examine the contents of the TAR file we created earlier:

```
In [1]: import tarfile

In [2]: tar = tarfile.open("temp.tar","r")

In [3]: tar.list()
-rw-r--r-- ngift/wheel             2 2008-04-04 15:17:14 tmp/file00.txt
-rw-r--r-- ngift/wheel             2 2008-04-04 15:15:39 tmp/file1.txt
-rw-r--r-- ngift/wheel             0 2008-04-04 20:50:57 tmp/temp.tar
-rw-r--r-- ngift/wheel             2 2008-04-04 16:19:07 tmp/dirA/file0.txt
-rw-r--r-- ngift/wheel             2 2008-04-04 16:19:07 tmp/dirA/file00.txt
-rw-r--r-- ngift/wheel             2 2008-04-04 16:19:07 tmp/dirA/file1.txt
-rw-r--r-- ngift/wheel             2 2008-04-04 16:19:52 tmp/dirB/file0.txt
-rw-r--r-- ngift/wheel             2 2008-04-04 16:19:52 tmp/dirB/file00.txt
-rw-r--r-- ngift/wheel             2 2008-04-04 16:19:52 tmp/dirB/file1.txt
-rw-r--r-- ngift/wheel             3 2008-04-04 16:21:50 tmp/dirB/file11.txt

In [4]: tar.name
Out[4]: '/private/tmp/temp.tar'

In [5]: tar.getnames()
Out[5]:
['tmp/file00.txt',
 'tmp/file1.txt',
 'tmp/temp.tar',
 'tmp/dirA/file0.txt',
 'tmp/dirA/file00.txt',
 'tmp/dirA/file1.txt',
 'tmp/dirB/file0.txt',
 'tmp/dirB/file00.txt',
 'tmp/dirB/file1.txt',
 'tmp/dirB/file11.txt']

In [10]: tar.members
Out[10]:
[<TarInfo 'tmp/file00.txt' at 0x109eff0>,
 <TarInfo 'tmp/file1.txt' at 0x109ef30>,
 <TarInfo 'tmp/temp.tar' at 0x10a4310>,
 <TarInfo 'tmp/dirA/file0.txt' at 0x10a4350>,
 <TarInfo 'tmp/dirA/file00.txt' at 0x10a43b0>,
 <TarInfo 'tmp/dirA/file1.txt' at 0x10a4410>,
 <TarInfo 'tmp/dirB/file0.txt' at 0x10a4470>,
 <TarInfo 'tmp/dirB/file00.txt' at 0x10a44d0>,
 <TarInfo 'tmp/dirB/file1.txt' at 0x10a4530>,
 <TarInfo 'tmp/dirB/file11.txt' at 0x10a4590>]
```

Those examples show how to examine the names of the files in the TAR archive, which could be validated in data verification script. Extracting files is not much more work. If you want to extract a whole TAR archive to the current working directory, you can simply use the following:

```
In [60]: tar.extractall()

drwxrwxrwx  7 ngift  wheel     238 Apr  4 22:59 tmp/
```

If you are extremely paranoid, and you should be, then you could also include a step that extracts the contents of the archives and performs random MD5 checksums on files from the archive and compare them against MD5 checksums you made on the file before it was backed up. This could be a very effective way to monitor whether the integrity of the data is what you expect it to be.

No sane archiving solution should just trust that an archive was created properly. At the very least, random spot checking of archives needs to be done automatically. At best, every single archive should be reopened and checked for validity after it has been created.

## CHAPTER 7

SNMP

Introduction

SNMP can change your life as a sysadmin. The rewards of using SNMP are not as instantaneous as writing a few lines of Python to parse a logfile, for example, but when an SNMP infrastructure has been setup, it is amazing to work with.

In this chapter, we will be covering these aspects of SNMP: autodiscovery, polling/ monitoring, writing agents, device control, and finally enterprise SNMP integration. Of course, all of these things are going to be done with Python.

If you are unfamiliar with SNMP or need to brush up on SNMP, we highly recommend reading *Essential SNMP* by Douglas Mauro and Kevin Schmidt (O'Reilly), or at least keeping it handy. A good SNMP reference book is essential to truly understanding SNMP and what it can do. We will go over a few of the basics of SNMP in the next section, but going into much detail is beyond the scope of this book. In fact, there is more than enough material for a complete book on using Python with SNMP.

Brief Introduction to SNMP

SNMP Overview

The 10,000 foot view of SNMP is that it is a protocol for managing devices on an IP network. Typically, this is done via UDP ports 161 and 162, although it is possible, but rare, to use TCP as well. Just about any modern device in a data center supports SNMP; this means it is possible to manage not only switches and routers, but servers, printers, UPSs, storage, and more.

The basic use for SNMP is to send UDP packets to hosts and to wait for a response. This is how monitoring of devices occurs on a very simple level. It is also possible to do other things with the SNMP protocol, though, such as control devices and write agents that respond to conditions.

Some typical things you would do with SNMP are monitor the CPU load, disk usage, and free memory. You may also use it to manage and actually control switches, perhaps even going so far as to reload a switch configuration via SNMP. It is not commonly known that you can monitor software as well, such as web applications and databases. Finally, there is support for Remote Monitoring in the RMON MIB, which supports "flow-based" monitoring; this is different than regular SNMP monitoring, which is "device-based."

Because we have mentioned the acronym MIB, it is about time to bring this up. SNMP is just a protocol, and it makes no assumptions about the data. On devices that are being monitored, they run an agent, snmpd, that has a list of objects that it keeps track of. The actual list of objects is controlled by MIBs, or management information bases. Every agent implements at least one MIB, and that is MIB-II, which is defined in RFC 1213. One way of thinking of an MIB is as a file that translates names to numbers, just like DNS, although it is slightly more complicated.

Inside this file is where the definitions of these managed objects live. Every object has three attributes: name, type and syntax, and encoding. Of these, name is the one you will need to know the most about. Name is often referred to as an OID, or object identifier. This OID is how you tell the agent what you want to get. The names come in two forms: numeric and "human-readable." Most often you want to use the human-readable OID name, as the numeric name is very long and difficult to remember. One of the most common OIDs is sysDescr. If you use the command-line tool snmpwalk to determine the value of the sysDescr OID, you can do it by name or number:

```
[root@rhel][H:4461][J:0]# snmpwalk -v 2c -c public localhost .1.3.6.1.2.1.1.1.0
SNMPv2-MIB::sysDescr.0 = STRING: Linux localhost
   2.6.18-8.1.15.el5 #1 SMP Mon Oct 22 08:32:04 EDT 2007 i686

[root@rhel][H:4461][J:0]# snmpwalk -v 2c -c public localhost sysDescr
SNMPv2-MIB::sysDescr.0 = STRING: Linux localhost
   2.6.18-8.1.15.el5 #1 SMP Mon Oct 22 08:32:04 EDT 2007 i686
```

At this point, we have dropped a pile of acryonyms, and an RFC, so fight the urge to get up and walk away or fall asleep. We promise it gets better very soon, and you will be writing code in a few minutes.

SNMP Installation and Configuration

For simplicity's sake, we will only be dealing with Net-SNMP and the corresponding Python bindings to Net-SNMP. This does not discount some of the other Python-based SNMP libraries out there though, including PySNMP, which both TwistedSNMP and Zenoss utilize. In both Zenoss and TwistedSNMP, PySNMP is used in an asynchronous style. It is a very valid approach, and it is worth looking at as well; we just don't have room to cover both in this chapter.

In terms of Net-SNMP itself, we will be dealing with two different APIs. Method one is to use the subprocess module to wrap up Net-SNMP command-line tools, and method two is to use the new Python bindings. Each method has advantages and disadvantages depending on what environment they are implemented in.

Finally, we also discuss Zenoss, which is an impressive all-Python, open source, enterprise SNMP monitoring solution. With Zenoss, you can avoid having to write an SNMP management solution from scratch and can instead communicate with it via its public APIs. It is also possible to write plug-ins for Zenoss, contribute patches, and finally extend Zenoss itself.

In order to do anything useful with SNMP, specifically Net-SNMP, you must actually have it installed. Fortunately, most Unix and Linux operating systems already come installed with Net-SNMP, so if you need to monitor a device, usually it just involves adjusting the *snmpd.conf* file to fit your needs and starting the daemon. If you plan on developing with Net-SNMP with Python bindings, which is what we cover in this chapter, you will need to compile from source to install the Python bindings. If you just plan on wrapping up Net-SNMP command-line tools—such as snmpget, snmpwalk, snmpdf, and others—then you don't need to do anything if Net-SNMP is already installed.

One option is to download a virtual machine with the source code for this book in it at *http://www.oreilly.com/9780596515829*. You can also refer to *www.py4sa.com*, the companion site for the book, as it will have the latest information on how to run examples in this section.

We have also configured this virtual machine with Net-SNMP and the Python bindings installed. You can then run all of the examples just by using this virtual machine. If you have beefy enough hardware at your disposal, you can also make a few copies of the virtual machine and simulate some of the other code in this chapter that talks to many machines at the same time.

If you do decide to install the Python bindings, you will need to download the Net-SNMP from sourceforge.net and get a version of Net-SNMP of 5.4.x or higher. The bindings are not built by default, so you should carefully follow the build instructions in the Python/README directory. In a nutshell though, you will first need to compile this version of Net-SNMP and then run the setup.py script in the Python directory. We have found the least painful installation method is on Red Hat, and there is a source RPM available. If you decide to compile, you might want to first try it out on Red Hat to see what a successful build looks like, and then venture out to AIX, Solaris, OS X, HPUX, etc. Finally, if you get stuck, just use the virtual machine to run the examples and figure out how to get it to compile later.

One final note on compiling yourself: make sure you run the Python setup.py build and the python setup.py test. You should find out right away if Net-SNMP works with Python. One tip if you have trouble compiling with Python is to manually run ldcon fig like this:

```
ldconfig -v /usr/local/lib/
```

In terms of configuration, if you happen to be installing Net-SNMP on a client you want to monitor, you should compile Net-SNMP with the Host Resources MIB. Typically, you can do this as follows:

```
./configure -with-mib-modules=host
```

Note that when you run configure, it attempts to run an auto-configure script. You don't need to do this if you don't want. Often, it is much easier to just create a custom configuration file yourself. The configuration file on Red-Hat-based systems usually lives in */etc/snmp/snmpd.conf*, and it can be as simple as this:

```
syslocation "O'Reilly"
syscontact bofh@oreilly.com
rocommunity public
```

Just this simple configuration file is enough for the rest of this chapter, and non-SNMPv3 queries. SNMPv3 is a bit tougher to configure and slightly out of scope for most of this chapter, although we do want to mention that for device control in a production environment, it is highly recommended to use SNMPv3, as v2 and v1 transmit in the clear. For that matter, you should never do SNMP v2 or v1 queries across the Internet, as you may have traffic intercepted. There have been some high-profile break-ins that have occurred as a result of doing just this.

IPython and Net-SNMP

If you haven't done any SNMP development before, you may have gotten the impression that it is a bit nasty. Well, to be honest, it is. Dealing with SNMP is a bit of a pain, as it involves a very complex protocol, lots of RFCs to read, and a high chance for many things to go wrong. One way to diminish much of the initial pain of getting started with development is to use IPython to explore the SNMP code you will write and to get comfortable with the API.

Example 7-1 is a very brief snippet of live code to run on a local machine.

Example 7-1. Using IPython and Net-SNMP with Python bindings

```
In [1]: import netsnmp

In [2]: oid = netsnmp.Varbind('sysDescr')

In [3]: result = netsnmp.snmpwalk(oid,
   ...:                           Version = 2,
   ...:                           DestHost="localhost",
   ...:                           Community="public")

Out[4]: ('Linux localhost 2.6.18-8.1.14.el5 #1 SMP Thu Aug 27 12:51:54 EDT 2008 i686',)
```

Using tab completion when exploring a new library is very refreshing. In this example, we made full use of IPython's tab completion capabilities and then made a basic SNMP v2 query. As a general note, sysDescr, as we mentioned earlier, is a very important OID query to perform some basic level of identification on a machine. In the output of this example, you will see that it is quite similar, if not identical, to the output of uname -a.

As we will see later in this chapter, parsing the response from a sysDescr query is an important part of initially discovering a data center. Unfortunately, like many parts of SNMP, it is not an exact science. Some equipment may not return any response, some may return something helpful but not complete like "Fibre Switch," and others will return a vendor identification string. We don't have space to get into too much detail in solving this problem, but dealing with these differences in responses is where the big boys earn their money.

As you learned in the IPython chapter, you can write out a class or function to a file while inside of IPython by switching to Vim, by typing the following:

```
ed some_filename.py
```

Then when you quit Vim, you will get that module's attributes in your namespace, and you can see them by typing in who. This trick is very helpful for working Net-SNMP, as iterative coding is a natural fit for this problem domain. Let's go ahead and write this code below out to a file named *snmp.py* by typing the following:

```
ed snmp.py
```

Example 7-2 shows a simple module that allows us to abstract away the boilerplate code associated with creating a session with Net-SNMP.

Example 7-2. Basic Net-SNMP session module

```python
#!/usr/bin/env python
import netsnmp

class Snmp(object):
    """A basic SNMP session"""
    def __init__(self,
                 oid = "sysDescr",
                 Version = 2,
                 DestHost = "localhost",
                 Community = "public"):
        self.oid = oid
        self.version = Version
        self.destHost = DestHost
        self.community = Community

    def query(self):
        """Creates SNMP query session"""
        try:
            result = netsnmp.snmpwalk(self.oid,
                                      Version = self.version,
                                      DestHost = self.destHost,
                                      Community = self.community)
        except Exception, err:
            print err
```

```
        result = None
    return result
```

When you save this file in IPython and type in who, you will see something like this:

```
In [2]: who
Snmp netsnmp
```

Now that we have an object-oriented interface to SNMP, we can begin using it to query our local machine:

```
In [3]: s = snmp()
```

```
In [4]: s.query()
Out[4]: ('Linux localhost 2.6.18-8.1.14.el5 #1 SMP Thu Sep 27 18:58:54 EDT 2007 i686',)
```

```
In [5]: result = s.query()
```

```
In [6]: len(result)
Out[6]: 1
```

As you can tell, it is quite easy to get results using our module, but we are basically just running a hardcoded script, so let us change the value of the OID object to walk the entire system subtree:

```
In [7]: s.oid
Out[7]: 'sysDescr'
```

```
In [8]: s.oid = ".1.3.6.1.2.1.1"
```

```
In [9]: result = s.query()
```

```
In [10]: print result
('Linux localhost 2.6.18-8.1.14.el5 #1 SMP Thu Sep 27 18:58:54 EDT 2007 i686',
 '.1.3.6.1.4.1.8072.3.2.10', '121219', 'me@localhost.com', 'localhost', '"My Local Machine"',
 '0', '.1.3.6.1.6.3.10.3.1.1', '.1.3.6.1.6.3.11.3.1.1', '.1.3.6.1.6.3.15.2.1.1',
   '.1.3.6.1.6.3.1',
 '.1.3.6.1.2.1.49', '.1.3.6.1.2.1.4', '.1.3.6.1.2.1.50', '.1.3.6.1.6.3.16.2.2.1',
   'The SNMP Management Architecture MIB.',
 'The MIB for Message Processing and Dispatching.', 'The management information definitions
   for the SNMP User-based Security Model.',
 'The MIB module for SNMPv2 entities', 'The MIB module for managing TCP implementations',
 'The MIB module for managing IP and ICMP implementations', 'The MIB module for
   managing UDP [snip]',
 'View-based Access Control Model for SNMP.', '0', '0', '0', '0', '0', '0', '0', '0')
```

This style of interactive, investigative programming makes dealing with SNMP quite pleasant. At this point, if you feel inclined, you can start investigating various queries with other OIDs, or you can even walk a full MIB tree. Walking a full MIB tree can take quite some time though, as queries will need to occur for the multitude of OIDs; so often, this is not the best practice in a production environment, as it will consume resources on the client machine.

Remember that MIB-II is just a file full of OIDs, and it is included with most systems that support SNMP. Other vendor-specific MIBs are additional files that an agent can refer to and give responses to. You will need to look up vendor-specific documentation to determine what OID in what MIB to query if you want to take this to the next level.

Next, we are going to use an IPython-specific feature that lets you send jobs to the background:

```
In [11]: bg s.query()
Starting job # 0 in a separate thread.

In [12]: jobs[0].status
Out[12]: 'Completed'

In [16]: jobs[0].result
Out[16]:
('Linux localhost 2.6.18-8.1.14.el5 #1 SMP Thu Sep 27 18:58:54 EDT 2007 i686',
 '.1.3.6.1.4.1.8072.3.2.10', '121219', 'me@localhost.com', 'localhost',
   '"My Local Machine"',
 '0', '.1.3.6.1.6.3.10.3.1.1', '.1.3.6.1.6.3.11.3.1.1', '.1.3.6.1.6.3.15.2.1.1',
   '.1.3.6.1.6.3.1',
 '.1.3.6.1.2.1.49', '.1.3.6.1.2.1.4', '.1.3.6.1.2.1.50', '.1.3.6.1.6.3.16.2.2.1',
 'The SNMP Management Architecture MIB.', 'The MIB for Message Processing and
   Dispatching.',
 'The management information definitions for the SNMP User-based Security Model.',
 'The MIB module for SNMPv2 entities', 'The MIB module for managing TCP implementations',
 'The MIB module for managing IP and ICMP implementations', 'The MIB module for
   managing UDP implementations',
 'View-based Access Control Model for SNMP.', '0', '0', '0', '0', '0', '0', '0', '0')
```

Before you get too excited, let us tell you that while background threading works like a charm in IPython, it only works with libraries that support asynchronous threading. The Python bindings for Net-SNMP are synchronous. In a nutshell, you cannot write multithreaded code as the underlying C code blocks waiting for a response.

Fortunately, as you found out in the processes and concurrency chapter, it is trivial to use the processing module to fork processes that handle parallel SNMP queries. In the next section, we will address this when we write a sample tool to automatically discover a data center.

Discovering a Data Center

One of the more useful things SNMP is used for is discovery of a data center. In simplistic terms, discovery gathers an inventory of devices on a network and information about those devices. More advanced forms of discovery can be used to make correlations about the data gathered, such as the exact Mac address that a server lives in on a Cisco switch, or what the storage layout is for a Brocade fibre switch.

In this section, we will create a basic discovery script that will gather valid IP addresses, Mac addresses, basic SNMP information, and place that in a record. This can serve as a useful base to implement data center discovery applications at your facility. We will be drawing on information we covered in other chapters to accomplish this.

There are a few different discovery algorithms that we have come across, but we will present this one, as it is one of the more simple. A one-sentence description of the algorithm: send out a bunch of ICMP pings; for each device that responds, send out a basic SNMP query; parse that output; and then do further discovery based on the results. Another algorithm could involve just sending out SNMP queries in a shotgun style and then having another process just collect the responses, but, as we mentioned, we will be focusing on the first algorithm. See Example 7-3.

 Just a note about the code below: because the Net-SNMP library is synchronous, we are forking a call to subprocess.call. This gets us around the blocking that occurs. For the ping portion we could have just used subprocess.Popen, but to keep the code consistent, we are using the same pattern for SNMP and ping.

Example 7-3. Basic data center discovery

```python
#!/usr/bin/env python
from processing import Process, Queue, Pool
import time
import subprocess
import sys
from snmp import Snmp

q = Queue()
oq = Queue()
#ips = IP("10.0.1.0/24")
ips = ["192.19.101.250", "192.19.101.251", "192.19.101.252","192.19.101.253",
"192.168.1.1"]
num_workers = 10

class HostRecord(object):
    """Record for Hosts"""
    def __init__(self, ip=None, mac=None, snmp_response=None):
        self.ip = ip
        self.mac = mac
        self.snmp_response = snmp_response
    def __repr__(self):
        return "[Host Record('%s','%s','%s')]" % (self.ip,
                                                  self.mac,
                                                  self.snmp_response)

def f(i,q,oq):
    while True:
        time.sleep(.1)
        if q.empty():
            sys.exit()
```

```
                print "Process Number: %s Exit" % i
            ip = q.get()
            print "Process Number: %s" % i
            ret = subprocess.call("ping -c 1 %s" % ip,
                            shell=True,
                            stdout=open('/dev/null', 'w'),
                            stderr=subprocess.STDOUT)
            if ret == 0:
                print "%s: is alive" % ip
                oq.put(ip)
            else:
                print "Process Number: %s didn't find a response for %s " % (i, ip)
                pass

def snmp_query(i,out):
    while True:
        time.sleep(.1)
        if out.empty():
            sys.exit()
            print "Process Number: %s" % i
        ipaddr = out.get()
        s = Snmp()
        h = HostRecord()
        h.ip = ipaddr
        h.snmp_response = s.query()
        print h
        return h
try:
    q.putmany(ips)

finally:
    for i in range(num_workers):
        p = Process(target=f, args=[i,q,oq])
        p.start()
    for i in range(num_workers):
        pp = Process(target=snmp_query, args=[i,oq])
        pp.start()

print "main process joins on queue"
p.join()
#while not oq.empty():
#    print "Validated", oq.get()


print "Main Program finished"
```

If we run this script, we get output that looks something like this:

```
[root@giftcsllc02][H:4849][J:0]> python discover.py
Process Number: 0
192.19.101.250: is alive
Process Number: 1
192.19.101.251: is alive
Process Number: 2
Process Number: 3
Process Number: 4
```

```
main process joins on queue
192.19.101.252: is alive
192.19.101.253: is alive
Main Program finished
[Host Record('192.19.101.250','None','('Linux linux.host 2.6.18-8.1.15.el5
    #1 SMP Mon Oct 22 08:32:04 EDT 2007 i686',)')]
[Host Record('192.19.101.252','None','('Linux linux.host 2.6.18-8.1.15.el5
    #1 SMP Mon Oct 22 08:32:04 EDT 2007 i686',)')]
[Host Record('192.19.101.253','None','('Linux linux.host 2.6.18-8.1.15.el5
    #1 SMP Mon Oct 22 08:32:04 EDT 2007 i686',)')]
[Host Record('192.19.101.251','None','('Linux linux.host 2.6.18-8.1.15.el5
    #1 SMP Mon Oct 22 08:32:04 EDT 2007 i686',)')]
Process Number: 4 didn't find a response for 192.168.1.1
```

Looking at the output of this code, we see the beginnings of an interesting algorithm to discover a data center. There are a few things to fix, like adding a Mac address to the Host Record object, and making the code more object-oriented, but that could turn into a whole other book. In fact, that could turn into a whole company. On that note we turn to the next section.

Retrieving Multiple-Values with Net-SNMP

Getting just one value from SNMP is toy code, although it can be very useful to test out responses or to perform an action based on a specific value, like the OS type of a machine. In order to do something more meaningful, we need to get a few values and do something with them.

A very common task is to do an inventory of your data center, or department, to figure out some set of parameters across all of your machines. Here is one hypothetical situation: you are preparing for a major software upgrade, and you have been told all systems will need to have at least 1 GB of RAM. You seem to remember that most of the machines have at least 1 GB of RAM, but there are a few of the thousands of machines you support that do not.

You obviously have some tough decisions to make. Let's go over some of the options:

Option 1
> Physically walk up to every one of your machines and check how much RAM is installed by running a command, or opening the box. This is obviously not a very appealing option.

Option 2
> Shell into every box and run a command to determine how much RAM it has. There are quite a few problems with this approach, but at least it could be theoretically scripted via ssh keys. One of the obvious problems is that a cross-platform script would need to be written, as every OS is slightly different. Another problem is that this method depends on knowing where all of the machines live.

Option 3

Write a small script that travels and asks every device on your network how much memory it has via SNMP.

Using option 3 via SNMP, it is easy to generate an inventory report, which shows just the machines that do not have at least 1 GB of RAM. The exact OID name we will need to query is "hrMemorySize." SNMP is something that can always benefit from being concurrent, but it is best not to optimize until it is absolutely necessary. On that note, let's dive right into something quick.

We can reuse our code from the earlier example to run a very quick test.

Getting memory value from SNMP:

```
In [1]: run snmpinput

In [2]: who
netsnmp Snmp

In [3]: s = Snmp()

In [4]: s.DestHost = "10.0.1.2"

In [5]: s.Community = "public"

In [6]: s.oid = "hrMemorySize"

In [7]: result = int(s.query()[0])
   hrMemorySize   = None ( None )

In [27]: print result
2026124
```

As you can see, this is a very straightforward script to write. The result comes back as a tuple, in line [6], so we extracted the index 0 and converted it to an integer. The result is now an integer consisting of KB. One thing to keep in mind is that different machines will calculate RAM in different ways. It is best to account for this by using rough parameters and not hardcoding an absolute value, as you may get results that are different than what you expect. For example you may want to look for a range of value that is slightly below 1 GB of RAM, say 990 MB.

In this case, we can do the math in our heads to estimate that this corresponds to roughly 2 GB of RAM. Having this information, you are now informed by your boss that you need to determine which machines in your data center contain under 2 GBs of RAM, as a new application will need to be installed that requires at least 2 GBs of RAM.

With that bit of information, we can now automate determining memory. What makes the most sense is to query each machine and figure out if it does not contain 2 GBs of RAM and then to put that information into a CSV file so that it can easily be imported into Excel or Open Office Calc.

Next you can write a command-line tool that takes a subnet range as input and an optional OID keyword value but will default to using "hrMemorySize." We will also want to iterate a range of IP addresses in a subnet.

As always, as a sysadmin writing code, you are faced with some tough decisions. Should you spend a few hours, or a day, writing a really long script that you can reuse for other things, because it is object-oriented, or should you just whip out something quick and dirty? We think in most cases it is safe to say you can do both. If you use IPython, you can log scripts you write and then later turn them into more polished scripts. In general though, it is a good idea to write reusable code, as it becomes like a snowball and soon reaches its own inertia.

Hopefully you now understand the power of SNMP if you didn't already. Let's go write our script...

Finding Memory

In this next example, we write a command-line tool to calculate the memory installed on machines via SNMP:

```python
#!/usr/bin/env python
#A command line tool that will grab total memory in a machine

import netsnmp
import optparse
from IPy import IP

class SnmpSession(object):
    """A Basic SNMP Session"""
    def __init__(self,
                    oid="hrMemorySize",
                    Version=2,
                    DestHost="localhost",
                    Community="public"):

        self.oid = oid
        self.Version = Version
        self.DestHost = DestHost
        self.Community = Community


    def query(self):
        """Creates SNMP query session"""
        try:
            result = netsnmp.snmpwalk(self.oid,
                                    Version = self.Version,
                                    DestHost = self.DestHost,
                                    Community = self.Community)
        except:
            #Note this is toy code, but let's us know what exception is raised
            import sys
            print sys.exc_info()
```

```
        result = None

    return result

class SnmpController(object):
    """Uses optparse to Control SnmpSession"""

    def run(self):
        results = {}    #A place to hold and collect snmp results
        p = optparse.OptionParser(description="A tool that determines
                                      memory installed",
                                  prog="memorator",
                                  version="memorator 0.1.0a",
                                  usage="%prog [subnet range] [options]")
        p.add_option('--community', '-c',help='community string',
          default='public')
        p.add_option('--oid', '-o', help='object identifier',
          default='hrMemorySize')
        p.add_option('--verbose', '-v', action='store_true',
          help='increase verbosity')
        p.add_option('--quiet', '-q', action='store_true',help='
                    suppresses most messages')
        p.add_option('--threshold', '-t', action='store', type="int",
                    help='a number to filter queries with')

        options, arguments = p.parse_args()
            if arguments:
            for arg in arguments:
                try:
                    ips = IP(arg)    #Note need to convert instance to str
                except:
                    if not options.quiet:
                        print 'Ignoring %s, not a valid IP address' % arg
                    continue

                for i in ips:
                    ipAddr = str(i)
                    if not options.quiet:
                        print 'Running snmp query for: ', ipAddr

                    session = SnmpSession(options.oid,
                                            DestHost = ipAddr,
                                            Community = options.community)

                    if options.oid == "hrMemorySize":
                        try:
                            memory = int(session.query()[0])/1024
                        except:
                            memory = None
                        output = memory

                    else:
                        #Non-memory related SNMP query results
                        output = session.query()
```

```
                    if not options.quiet:
                        print "%s returns %s" % (ipAddr,output)

                #Put everything into an IP/result dictionary
                #But only if it is a valid response
                if output != None:
                    if options.threshold:    #ensures a specific threshold
                        if output < options.threshold:
                            results[ipAddr] = output
                            #allow printing to standard out
                            if not options.quiet:
                                print "%s returns %s" % (ipAddr,output)

                else:
                    results[ipAddr] = output
                    if not options.quiet:
                        print output

        print "Results from SNMP Query %s for %s:\n" % (options.oid,
            arguments), results


    else:
        p.print_help() #note if nothing is specified on the
    command line, help is printed

def _main():
    """
    Runs memorator.
    """
    start = SnmpController()
    start.run()


if __name__ =='__main__':
    try:
        import IPy
    except:
        print "Please install the IPy module to use this tool"
    _main()
```

OK, let's step through this code a bit and see what it does. We took the whole class from the previous example and placed it into a new module. We next made a controller class that handles option handling via the optparse module. The IPy module, which we refer to over and over again, handles the IP address arguments automatically. We can now place several IP addresses or a subnet range, and our module will look for an SNMP query and return the result as a collected dictionary of IP addresses and SNMP values.

One of the trickier things we did was to create some logic at the end that does not return empty results, and which additionally listens to a threshold number. This means that we set it to return only values under a specific threshold. By using a threshold we can return meaningful results for us and allow for some discrepancies with how different machines handle memory calculations.

Let's look at an example of the output of this tool in action:

```
[ngift@ng-lep-lap][H:6518][J:0]> ./memory_tool_netsnmp.py 10.0.1.2 10.0.1.20
Running snmp query for:   10.0.1.2
   hrMemorySize  = None ( None )
1978
Running snmp query for:   10.0.1.20
   hrMemorySize  = None ( None )
372
Results from SNMP Query hrMemorySize for ['10.0.1.2', '10.0.1.20']:
{'10.0.1.2': 1978, '10.0.1.20': 372}
```

As you can see, the results come back from machines on the 10.0.1.0/24 subnet. Let's now use the threshold flag to simulate looking for machines that do not contain at least 2 GBs of RAM. As we mentioned earlier, there are some differences in how machines calculate RAM, so let's be safe and put in the number 1800, which would correspond roughly to 1800 MBs of RAM. If a machine does not contain at least 1800 MBs or roughly 2GBs of RAM, we will get this in our report.

Here is the output from that query:

```
[ngift@ng-lep-lap][H:6519][J:0]>
    ./memory_tool_netsnmp.py --threshold 1800 10.0.1.2 10.0.1.20
Running snmp query for:   10.0.1.2
   hrMemorySize  = None ( None )
Running snmp query for:   10.0.1.20
   hrMemorySize  = None ( None )
10.0.1.20 returns 372
Results from SNMP Query hrMemorySize for ['10.0.1.2', '10.0.1.20']:
{'10.0.1.20': 372}
```

Although our script does its job, there are a couple of things we can do to optimize the tool. If you need to query thousands of machines, then this tool might take a day to run or more. This might be OK, but if you need the results quickly, you will need to add concurrency and fork each query using a third-party library. The other improvement we could make is to generate a CSV report automatically from our dictionary.

Before we get to automating those tasks, let me show you one additional benefit that you may not have noticed. The code was written in a way to allow any OID to be queried, not just one specific to memory calculation. This comes in very handy because we now have both a tool that calculates memory and a general-purpose tool to perform SNMP queries.

Let's take a look at an example of what we mean:

```
[ngift@ng-lep-lap][H:6522][J:0]> ./memory_tool_netsnmp.py -o sysDescr 10.0.1.2 10.0.1.20
Running snmp query for:   10.0.1.2
   sysDescr  = None ( None )
10.0.1.2 returns ('Linux cent 2.6.18-8.1.14.el5 #1 SMP
  Thu Sep 27 19:05:32 EDT 2007 x86_64',)
('Linux cent 2.6.18-8.1.14.el5 #1 SMP Thu Sep 27 19:05:32 EDT 2007 x86_64',)
```

```
Running snmp query for:   10.0.1.20
    sysDescr  = None ( None )
10.0.1.20 returns ('Linux localhost.localdomain 2.6.18-8.1.14.el5 #1 SMP
 Thu Sep 27 19:05:32 EDT 2007 x86_64',)
('Linux localhost.localdomain 2.6.18-8.1.14.el5 #1 SMP
  Thu Sep 27 19:05:32 EDT 2007 x86_64',)
Results from SNMP Query sysDescr for ['10.0.1.2', '10.0.1.20']:
{'10.0.1.2': ('Linux cent 2.6.18-8.1.14.el5 #1 SMP
Thu Sep 27 19:05:32 EDT 2007 x86_64',), '10.0.1.20':
('Linux localhost.localdomain 2.6.18-8.1.14.el5 #1 SMP
    Thu Sep 27 19:05:32 EDT 2007 x86_64',)}
```

It is good to keep this fact in mind when writing what could be a one-off tool. Why not spend an extra 30 minutes and make it generic? As a result, you may have a tool that you find yourself using over and over again, and that 30 minutes becomes a drop in the bucket compared to how much time you saved in the future.

Creating Hybrid SNMP Tools

Since we have shown a few examples of separate tools, it's good to note that these techniques can be combined to create some very sophisticated tools. Let's start by creating a whole slew of one-off tools, and then later we can make sure of these in bigger scripts.

There is a useful tool called snmpstatus that grabs a few different snmp queries and combines them into a "status":

```python
import subprocess

class Snmpdf(object):
    """A snmpstatus command-line tool"""
    def __init__(self,
                    Version="-v2c",
                    DestHost="localhost",
                    Community="public",
                    verbose=True):

        self.Version = Version
        self.DestHost = DestHost
        self.Community = Community
        self.verbose = verbose

    def query(self):
        """Creates snmpstatus query session"""
        Version = self.Version
        DestHost = self.DestHost
        Community = self.Community
        verbose = self.verbose

        try:
            snmpstatus = "snmpstatus %s -c %s %s" % (Version, Community, DestHost)
            if verbose:
                print "Running: %s" % snmpstatus
```

```
            p = subprocess.Popen(snmpstatus,
                                 shell=True,
                                 stdout=subprocess.PIPE)

            out = p.stdout.read()
            return out

        except:
            import sys
            print >> sys.stderr, "error running %s" % snmpstatus


def _main():
    snmpstatus = Snmpdf()
    result = snmpstatus.query()
    print result
if __name__ == "__main__":
    _main()
```

We hope you are paying attention to the fact that this script has very few differences from the snmpdf command, with the exception of things being named differently. This is a perfect example of when it becomes a good idea to create another level of abstraction and then resuse common components. If we created a module to handle all of the boilerplate code, our new script would be only a few lines long. Keep this in mind; we will revist this later.

Another tool, related to SNMP, is ARP, which uses the ARP protocol. By using ARP protocol, it is possible to obtain Mac addresses of devices based on their IP address if you are physically located on the same network. Let's write one of those tools too. This one-off tool will come in handy a little later.

ARP is so easy to wrap up into a script that it is better to just show an example by using IPython interactively. Go ahead and fire up IPython, and try this out:

```
import re
import subprocess

#some variables
ARP = "arp"
IP = "10.0.1.1"
CMD = "%s %s " % (ARP, IP)
macPattern = re.compile(":")

def getMac():
    p = subprocess.Popen(CMD, shell=True, stdout=subprocess.PIPE)
    out = p.stdout.read()
    results = out.split()
    for chunk in results:
        if re.search(macPattern, chunk):
            return chunk

if __name__ == "__main__":
    macAddr = getMac()
    print macAddr
```

This snippet of code is not a reusable tool yet, but you could easily take this idea and use it as part of a general data center discovery library.

Extending Net-SNMP

As we have discussed earlier, Net-SNMP is installed as an agent on most *nix machines. There is a default set of information that an agent can return, but it is also possible to extend an agent on a machine. It is reasonably straightforward to write an agent that collects just about anything and then returns the results via the SNMP protocol.

The *EXAMPLE.conf* file is one of the best sources for information on extending Net-SNMP, and it is included with Net-SNMP. Doing a man on snmpd.conf is also useful for more verbose information that documents the API. Both of these would be good sources of information to reference if you are interested in further study on extending native agents.

For a Python programmer, extending Net-SNMP is one of the most exciting aspects of working with SNMP, as it allows a developer to write code to monitor whatever they see fit, and to additionally have the agent internally respond to conditions that you have assigned to it.

Net-SNMP offers quite a few ways to extend its agent, but to get started we are going to write a Hello World program that we will query from snmp. The first step is to create a very simple *snmpd.conf* file that executes our Hello World program in Python. Example 7-4 shows what that looks like on a Red Hat machine.

Example 7-4. SNMP configuration file with Hello World

```
syslocation "O'Reilly"
syscontact bofh@oreilly.com
rocommunity public
exec helloworld /usr/bin/python -c "print 'hello world from Python'"
```

Next we need to tell snmpd to re-read the configuration file. We can do that three different ways. On Red Hat you can use:

```
service snmpd reload
```

or you can also do:

```
ps -ef | grep snmpd
root     12345     1  0 Apr14 ?
00:00:30 /usr/sbin/snmpd -Lsd -Lf /dev/null -p /var/run/snmpd.pid -a
```

Then you can send it:

```
kill -HUP 12345
```

Finally, the snmpset command can assign an integer (1) to UCD-SNMP-MIB::versionUpdateConfig.0, which will tell snmpd to reread the configuration file.

Now that we have modified the *snmpd.conf* file and told snmpd to reread the configuration file, we can go ahead and query our machine by using either the snmpwalk command-line tool or the Net-SNMP binding with IPython. Here is what it looks like from the snmpwalk command:

```
[root@giftcsllc02][H:4904][J:0]> snmpwalk -v 1 -c public localhost .1.3.6.1.4.1.2021.8
UCD-SNMP-MIB::extIndex.1 = INTEGER: 1
UCD-SNMP-MIB::extNames.1 = STRING: helloworld
UCD-SNMP-MIB::extCommand.1 = STRING: /usr/bin/python
  -c "print 'hello world from Python'"
UCD-SNMP-MIB::extResult.1 = INTEGER: 0
UCD-SNMP-MIB::extOutput.1 = STRING: hello world from Python
UCD-SNMP-MIB::extErrFix.1 = INTEGER: noError(0)
UCD-SNMP-MIB::extErrFixCmd.1 = STRING:
```

This query bears some explanation, as the observant reader may wonder where we got it. 1.3.6.1.4.1.2021.8 from. This OID is the ucdavis.extTable. When you create an extension to snmpd.conf, it will assign it to this OID. Things get slightly more complicated if you would like to query a custom OID that you create. The proper way to do this is to fill out a request with iana.org and to get an enterprise number. You can then use that number to create custom queries to an agent. The main reason for this is to keep a uniform namespace that avoids collisions with other future vendor numbers you may run into.

Getting output from one-liners isn't really Python's strength, and it is kind of silly. Here is an example of a script that parses the total number of Firefox hits in an Apache log and then returns the number for a custom enterprise number. Let's start backward this time and see what it looks like when we query it:

```
snmpwalk -v 2c -c public localhost .1.3.6.1.4.1.2021.28664.100
UCD-SNMP-MIB::ucdavis.28664.100.1.1 = INTEGER: 1
UCD-SNMP-MIB::ucdavis.28664.100.2.1 = STRING: "FirefoxHits"
UCD-SNMP-MIB::ucdavis.28664.100.3.1 = STRING:
 "/usr/bin/python /opt/local/snmp_scripts/agent_ext_logs.py"
UCD-SNMP-MIB::ucdavis.28664.100.100.1 = INTEGER: 0
UCD-SNMP-MIB::ucdavis.28664.100.101.1 = STRING:
   "Total number of Firefox Browser Hits: 15702"
UCD-SNMP-MIB::ucdavis.28664.100.102.1 = INTEGER: 0
UCD-SNMP-MIB::ucdavis.28664.100.103.1 = ""
```

If you look at the value of 100.101.1, you will see the output of a script that uses a generator pipeline to parse an Apache log and look for all Firefox hits in the log. It then sums them and returns the output via SNMP. Example 7-5 is the script that gets run when we query this OID.

Example 7-5. Generator pipeline to look for total firefox hits in Apache logfile

```
import re

"""Returns Hit Count for Firefox"""

def grep(lines,pattern="Firefox"):
```

```
        pat = re.compile(pattern)
        for line in lines:
            if pat.search(line): yield line

def increment(lines):
    num = 0
    for line in lines:
        num += 1
    return num

wwwlog = open("/home/noahgift/logs/noahgift.com-combined-log")
column = (line.rsplit(None,1)[1] for line in wwwlog)
match  = grep(column)
count = increment(match)
print "Total Number of Firefox Hits: %s" % count
```

In order for our query to work in the first place, we needed to tell snmpd.conf about this script, and here is what that section looks like:

```
syslocation "O'Reilly"
syscontact bofh@oreilly.com
rocommunity public
exec helloworld /usr/bin/python -c "print 'hello world from Python'"
exec .1.3.6.1.4.1.2021.28664.100 FirefoxHits /usr/bin/python
  /opt/local/snmp_scripts/agent_ext_logs.py
```

The magic portion is the last line, in which .1.3.6.1.4.1.2021 is the ucdavis enterprise number, 28664 our enterprise number, and 100 is some contrived value that we decided we wanted to use. It is really important to follow best practices and use your our enterprise number if you plan on extending SNMP. The main reason is that you will avoid causing havoc if you decide to use a range already occupied by someone else and then make changes via snmpset.

We would like to close with the fact that this is one of the more exciting topics in the book, and SNMP is still a very untouched playground. There are many things that customizing Net-SNMP can be useful for, and if you are careful to use SNMP v3, you can do some incredible things that are most easily accomplished through the SNMP protocol; and that ssh or sockets would be the most natural choice.

SNMP Device Control

One of the more interesting things SNMP can do is control a device through the SNMP protocol. Obviously, this creates a significant advantage over using something like Pyexpect (*http://sourceforge.net/projects/pexpect/*) to control a router, as it is much more straightforward.

For brevity's sake, we will only cover SNMP v1 in the example, but if you are communicating with a device over an insecure network, it should be done via SNMP v3. For this section, it would be good to reference *Essential SNMP* and *Cisco IOS Cookbook* by Kevin Dooley and Ian J. Brown (O'Reilly) if you have a Safari account or have bought those books. They include some excellent information about both talking to Cisco devices via SNMP and basic configuration.

Because reloading a Cisco configuration via SNMP is plain cool, it seems like a perfect choice to talk about device control. For this example it is necessary to have a running TFTP server from which the router will pull the IOS file, and the router must be configured to allow read/write access for SNMP. Example 7-6 is what the Python code looks like.

Example 7-6. Upload new switch configuration Cisco router

```
import netsnmp

vars = netsnmp.Varbind(netsnmp.VarList(netsnmp.Varbind(".1.2.6.1.4.1.9.2.10.6.0", "1"),
        (netsnmp.Varbind("cisco.example.com.1.3.6.1.4.1.9.2.10.12.172.25.1.1",
                        "iso-config.bin")

result = netsnmp.snmpset(vars,
                        Version = 1,
                        DestHost='cisco.example.com',
                        Community='readWrite')
```

In this example, we used Net-SNMP's VarList to assign the instruction to first erase the flash for the switch and second load a new IOS image file. This could be the basis for a script that upgrades the IOS of every switch at once in a data center. As with all code in this book, you should test this out in a nonproduction environment before just seeing what happens.

One final thing to point out is that SNMP is often not thought of in terms of device control, but it is a powerful way to programmatically control devices in a data center, as it serves as a uniform specification for device control that has been under development since 1988. The future probably holds a very interesting story for SNMP v3.

Enterprise SNMP Integration with Zenoss

Zenoss is a fascinating new option for enterprise SNMP management systems. Not only is Zenoss a completely open source application, it is also written in pure Python. Zenoss is a new breed of enterprise application that is both incredibly powerful and extendable via an XML-RPC or ReST API. For more information on ReST, take a look at *RESTful Web Services* by Leonard Richardson and Sam Ruby (O'Reilly).

Finally, if you want to help develop Zenoss, you can contribute patches.

Zenoss API

For the latest information on the Zenoss API, please visit *http://www.zenoss.com/community/docs/howtos/send-events/*.

Using Zendmd

Not only does Zenoss come with a robust SNMP monitoring and discovery system, it also includes a high-level API called zendmd. You can open up a customized shell and run commands directly against Zenoss.

Using zendmd:

```
>>> d = find('build.zenoss.loc')
>>> d.os.interfaces.objectIds()
['eth0', 'eth1', 'lo', 'sit0', 'vmnet1', 'vmnet8']
>>> for d in dmd.Devices.getSubDevices():
>>>     print d.id, d.getManageIp()
```

Device API

You can also communicate directly with Zenoss via an XML-RPC API and add or remove devices. Below are two examples.

Using ReST:

```
[zenos@zenoss $]
wget 'http://admin:zenoss@MYHOST:8080/zport/dmd
/ZenEventManager/manage_addEvent?device=MYDEVICE&component=MYCOMPONENT&summary=↴
    MYSUMMARY&severity=4&eclass=EVENTCLASS&eventClassKey=EVENTCLASSKEY
```

Using XML-RPC:

```
>>> from xmlrpclib import ServerProxy
>>> serv = ServerProxy('http://admin:zenoss@MYHOST:8080/zport/dmd/ZenEventManager')
>>> evt = {'device':'mydevice', 'component':'eth0',
'summary':'eth0 is down','severity':4, 'eventClass':'/Net'}
>>> serv.sendEvent(evt)
```

## CHAPTER 8

OS Soup

Introduction

Being a sysadmin often means that you get thrown to the wolves. Rules, a predictable schedule, or even choice of an operating system is often out of your control. To be even a marginally effective sysadmin nowadays, you need to know it all, and we mean all the operating systems. From Linux, to Solaris, to OS X, to FreeBSD, it needs to be in your toolbelt. Although only time will tell, it does seem as if the proprietary operating systems, such as AIX and HP-UX, won't last forever, but they still are necessary to know for many people.

Fortunately, Python comes to the rescue yet again—we hope you are noticing a trend here—by offering a mature standard library that has just about anything a multi-OS systems administrator needs. Python's massive standard library has a module that deals with just about anything a sysadmin could want to do, from tarring up a directory, to comparing files and directories, to parsing config files. Python's maturity, coupled with its elegance and readability, is why it is the 800 pound gorilla of systems administration.

Many complex systems administration facilities, such as animation pipelines and data centers, are switching away from Perl to Python because it offers much more readable and elegant code. While Ruby is an interesting language that shares many of the positive features of Python, when one compares the standard library and maturity of the language, Ruby lacks in comparison to Python for a systems administration language.

Since this chapter is going to be a mixture of many different operating systems, we won't have time to explore any of them in great depth, but we will explore them enough to demonstrate how Python can act in as both a generic, cross-platform scripting language and a unique weapon for each operating system. Finally, there is a new "operating system" on the horizon, and it comes in the form of a data center. Some people refer to this new platform as Cloud Computing, and we will talk about Amazon's and Google's offerings.

Enough of the idle banter, something smells delicious in the kitchen...is that OS soup?

Cross-Platform Unix Programming in Python

While there are some significant differences between *nix operating systems, there is much more in common that not. One way to bring the different versions of *nix back together is to write cross-platform tools and libraries that bridge the divide between the operating system differences. One of the most basic ways to accomplish this is to write conditional statements that check for the operating systems, platform, and version in code that you write.

Python takes the "batteries included" philosophy quite seriously, and includes a tool for just about any problem you could think of. For the problem of determing what platform your code is running on, there is the platform module. Let's look at the essentials of using the platform module.

An easy way to get comfortable with the platform module is to create a tool the prints out all available information about a system. See Example 8-1.

Example 8-1. Using the platform module to print a system report

```
#!/usr/bin/env python
import platform

profile = [
platform.architecture(),
platform.dist(),
platform.libc_ver(),
platform.mac_ver(),
platform.machine(),
platform.node(),
platform.platform(),
platform.processor(),
platform.python_build(),
platform.python_compiler(),
platform.python_version(),
platform.system(),
platform.uname(),
platform.version(),
]

for item in profile:
  print item
```

Here is the output of that script on OS X Leopard 10.5.2:

```
[ngift@Macintosh-6][H:10879][J:0]% python cross_platform.py
('32bit', '')
('', '', '')
('', '')
('10.5.2', ('', '', ''), 'i386')
i386
Macintosh-6.local
Darwin-9.2.0-i386-32bit
i386
```

```
('r251:54863', 'Jan 17 2008 19:35:17')
GCC 4.0.1 (Apple Inc. build 5465)
2.5.1
Darwin
('Darwin', 'Macintosh-6.local', '9.2.0', 'Darwin Kernel Version 9.2.0:
Tue Feb  5 16:13:22 PST 2008; root:xnu-1228.3.13~1/RELEASE_I386', 'i386', 'i386')
Darwin Kernel Version 9.2.0: Tue Feb  5 16:13:22 PST 2008;
root:xnu-1228.3.13~1/RELEASE_I386
```

This gives us some idea of the kind of information we can gather. The next step on the road to writing cross-platform code is to create a fingerprint module that will "fingerprint" which platform and version we are running on. In this example, we will finger-print the following operating systems: Mac OS X, Ubuntu, Red Hat/Cent OS, FreeBSD, and SunOS. See Example 8-2.

Example 8-2. Fingerprinting an operating system type

```
#!/usr/bin/env python
import platform

"""

Fingerprints the following Operating Systems:

* Mac OS X
* Ubuntu
* Red Hat/Cent OS
* FreeBSD
* SunOS

"""
class OpSysType(object):
    """Determins OS Type using platform module"""

    def __getattr__(self, attr):
        if attr == "osx":
            return "osx"
        elif attr == "rhel":
            return "redhat"
        elif attr == "ubu":
            return "ubuntu"
        elif attr == "fbsd":
            return "FreeBSD"
        elif attr == "sun":
            return "SunOS"
        elif attr == "unknown_linux":
            return "unknown_linux"
        elif attr == "unknown":
            return "unknown"
        else:
            raise AttributeError, attr

    def linuxType(self):
        """Uses various methods to determine Linux Type"""

        if platform.dist()[0] == self.rhel:
```

```
      return self.rhel
    elif platform.uname()[1] == self.ubu:
      return self.ubu
    else:
      return self.unknown_linux

  def queryOS(self):
    if platform.system() == "Darwin":
      return self.osx
    elif platform.system() == "Linux":
      return self.linuxType()
    elif platform.system() == self.sun:
      return self.sun
    elif platform.system() == self.fbsd:
          return self.fbsd

  def fingerprint():
    type = OpSysType()
    print type.queryOS()

  if __name__ == "__main__":
    fingerprint()
```

Let's take a look at this output when we run it on the various platforms.

Red Hat:

```
[root@localhost]/# python fingerprint.py
redhat
```

Ubuntu:

```
root@ubuntu:/# python fingerprint.py
ubuntu
```

Solaris 10 or SunOS:

```
bash-3.00# python fingerprint.py
SunOS
```

FreeBSD

```
# python fingerprint.py
FreeBSD
```

While the output of the command is not tremendously interesting, it does do a very powerful thing for us. This simple module allows us to write cross-platform code, as we can, perhaps, query a dictionary for these operating system types, and if they match, run the appropriate platform-specific code. One of the ways the benefits of cross-platform APIs are most tangible is writing scripts that manage a network via ssh keys. Code can run simultaneously on many platforms yet provide consistent results.

Using SSH Keys, NFS-Mounted Source Directory, and Cross-Platform Python to Manage Systems

One way to manage a diverse infrastructure of *nix machines is to use a combination of ssh keys, a commonly shared NFS-mounted src directory, and cross-platform Python code. Breaking this process into steps will make it clearer.

Step 1: create a public ssh key on the system from which you will manage machines. Note that this can vary by platform. Please consult your operating system documentation or do a man on ssh for details. See Example 8-3.

 One thing to point out in the example below is that for demonstration we are creating ssh keys for the root user, but perhaps a better security strategy would be to create a user account that has sudo privileges to run only this script.

Example 8-3. Creating a public ssh key

```
[ngift@Macintosh-6][H:11026][J:0]% ssh-keygen -t rsa
Generating public/private rsa key pair.
Enter file in which to save the key (/root/.ssh/id_rsa):
Enter passphrase (empty for no passphrase):
Enter same passphrase again:
Your identification has been saved in /root/.ssh/id_rsa.
Your public key has been saved in /root/.ssh/id_rsa.pub.
The key fingerprint is:
6c:2f:6e:f6:b7:b8:4d:17:05:99:67:26:1c:b9:74:11 root@localhost.localdomain
[ngift@Macintosh-6][H:11026][J:0]%
```

Step 2: SCP the public key to the host machines and create an *authorized_keys* file. See Example 8-4.

Example 8-4. Distributing ssh key

```
[ngift@Macintosh-6][H:11026][J:0]% scp id_leop_lap.pub root@10.0.1.51:~/.ssh/
root@10.0.1.51's password:
id_leop_lap.pub
  100%  403     0.4KB/s   00:00
[ngift@Macintosh-6][H:11027][J:0]% ssh root@10.0.1.51
root@10.0.1.51's password:
Last login: Sun Mar  2 06:26:10 2008
[root@localhost]~# cd .ssh
[root@localhost]~/.ssh# ll
total 8
-rw-r--r-- 1 root root  403 Mar  2 06:32 id_leop_lap.pub
-rw-r--r-- 1 root root 2044 Feb 14 05:33 known_hosts
[root@localhost]~/.ssh# cat id_leop_lap.pub > authorized_keys
[root@localhost]~/.ssh# exit

Connection to 10.0.1.51 closed.
[ngift@Macintosh-6][H:11028][J:0]% ssh root@10.0.1.51
```

```
Last login: Sun Mar  2 06:32:22 2008 from 10.0.1.3
[root@localhost]~#
```

Step 3: mount a common NFS src directory that contains the modules you need clients to run. Often, the easiest way to accomplish this is to use autofs and then make a symbolic link. Alternately, this could be done via a version control system, in which a command is issued via ssh to tell the remote hosts to update their local svn repository full of code. Next, the script would run the newest module. For example, on a Red Hat-based system, you might do something like this:

```
ln -s /net/nas/python/src /src
```

Step 4: write a dispatcher to run code against a network of machines. This is a fairly simple task now that we have ssh keys and a common NFS-mounted src directory, or version control-monitored src directory. As usual, let's start with the simplest possible example of a ssh-based dispatch system. If you have never done this before, you will slap yourself thinking how easy it is to do incredibly powerful things. In Example 8-5, we run a simple uname command.

Example 8-5. Simple ssh-based dispatcher

```
#!/usr/bin/env python
import subprocess

"""

A ssh based command dispatch system

"""

machines = ["10.0.1.40",
"10.0.1.50",
"10.0.1.51",
"10.0.1.60",
"10.0.1.80"]

cmd = "uname"
for machine in machines:
    subprocess.call("ssh root@%s %s" % (machine, cmd), shell=True)
```

Running that script on those five IP addresses, which are a mixture of CentOS 5, FreeBSD 7, Ubuntu 7.1, and Solaris 10, gives the following:

```
[ngift@Macintosh-6][H:11088][J:0]% python dispatch.py
Linux
Linux
Linux
SunOS
FreeBSD
```

Since we wrote a more accurate operating system fingerprint script, let's use that to get xx a more accurate description of the host machines to which we're dispatching commands in order to temporarily create src directory on the remote machines and copy our code to each machine. Of course, since we have a dispatch script, it is becoming

---

painfully obvious we need a robust CLI to our tool, as we have to change the script each time we want to do anything different such as the following:

```
cmd = "mkdir /src"
or:
cmd = "python /src/fingerprint.py"
or even:
subprocess.call("scp fingerprint.py root@%s:/src/" % machine, shell=True)
```

We will change that right after we get our `fingerprint.py` script to run, but let's look at the new cmd first:

```
#!/usr/bin/env python
import subprocess


"""

A ssh based command dispatch system

"""

machines = ["10.0.1.40",
"10.0.1.50",
"10.0.1.51",
"10.0.1.60",
"10.0.1.80"]

cmd = "python /src/fingerprint.py"
for machine in machines:
    subprocess.call("ssh root@%s %s" % (machine, cmd), shell=True)
```

Now, let's look at the new output:

```
[ngift@Macintosh-6][H:11107][J:0]# python dispatch.py
redhat
ubuntu
redhat
SunOS
FreeBSD
```

This is much better thanks to our `fingerprint.py` module. Of course, our few lines of dispatch code need a major overhaul to be considered useful, as we have to change things by editing the script. We need a better tool, so let's make one.

Creating a Cross-Platform, Systems Management Tool

Using ssh keys with a simple ssh-based dispatch system was marginally useful, but hardly extensible or reusable. Let's make a list of problems with our previous tool, and then a list of requirements to fix those problems. Problems: the list of machines is hardcoded into our script; the command we dispatch is hardcoded into our script; we can only run one command at a time; we have to run the same list of commands to all machines, we cannot pick and choose; and our dispatch code blocks waiting for each command to respond. Requirements: we need a command-line tool that reads in a config file with IP addresses and commands to run; we need a CLI interface with options to send a command(s) to machine(s); and we need to run dispatch in a separate thread pool so the processes do not block.

It seems like we can get away with creating a very basic configuration file syntax to parse, with a section for machines, and a section for commands. See Example 8-6.

Example 8-6. Dispatch config file

```
[MACHINES]
CENTOS: 10.0.1.40
UBUNTU: 10.0.1.50
REDHAT: 10.0.1.51
SUN: 10.0.1.60
FREEBSD: 10.0.1.80
[COMMANDS]
FINGERPRINT : python /src/fingerprint.py
```

Next, we need to write a function that reads the config file and splits the MACHINES and COMMANDS up so we can iterate over them one at a time. See Example 8-7.

 One thing to note is that our commands will be imported from the config file randomly. In many cases, this is a showstopper, and it would be better to just write a Python file and use that as a configuration file.

Example 8-7. Advanced ssh dispatcher

```
#!/usr/bin/env python
import subprocess
import ConfigParser

"""

A ssh based command dispatch system

"""

def readConfig(file="config.ini"):
    """Extract IP addresses and CMDS from config file and returns tuple"""
    ips = []
    cmds = []
    Config = ConfigParser.ConfigParser()
    Config.read(file)
    machines = Config.items("MACHINES")
    commands = Config.items("COMMANDS")
    for ip in machines:
        ips.append(ip[1])
    for cmd in commands:
        cmds.append(cmd[1])
    return ips, cmds

ips, cmds = readConfig()

#For every ip address, run all commands
```

```
for ip in ips:
  for cmd in cmds:
    subprocess.call("ssh root@%s %s" % (ip, cmd), shell=True)
```

This trivial piece of code is fun to use. We can arbitrarily assign a list of commands and machines and run them at once. If we look at the output of the command, we can see if it looks the same:

```
[ngift@Macintosh-6][H:11285][J:0]# python advanced_dispatch1.py
redhat
redhat
ubuntu
SunOS
FreeBSD
```

Even though we have a fairly sophisticated tool, we still have not met our original requirements specification of running dispatched commands in a separate thread pool. Fortunately, we can use some of the tricks from the processes chapter to create a thread pool for our dispatcher quite easily. Example 8-8 shows what adding threading can do.

Example 8-8. Multithreaded command dispatch tool

```
#!/usr/bin/env python
import subprocess
import ConfigParser
from threading import Thread
from Queue import Queue
import time
"""

A threaded ssh-based command dispatch system

"""
start = time.time()
queue = Queue()

def readConfig(file="config.ini"):
    """Extract IP addresses and CMDS from config file and returns tuple"""
    ips = []
    cmds = []
    Config = ConfigParser.ConfigParser()
    Config.read(file)
    machines = Config.items("MACHINES")
    commands = Config.items("COMMANDS")
    for ip in machines:
        ips.append(ip[1])
    for cmd in commands:
        cmds.append(cmd[1])
    return ips, cmds

def launcher(i,q, cmd):
    """Spawns command in a thread to an ip"""
    while True:
        #grabs ip, cmd from queue
        ip = q.get()
        print "Thread %s: Running %s to %s" % (i, cmd, ip)
```

```
            subprocess.call("ssh root@%s %s" % (ip, cmd), shell=True)
            q.task_done()

#grab ips and cmds from config
ips, cmds = readConfig()

#Determine Number of threads to use, but max out at 25
if len(ips) < 25:
    num_threads = len(ips)
else:
    num_threads = 25

#Start thread pool
for i in range(num_threads):
    for cmd in cmds:
        worker = Thread(target=launcher, args=(i, queue,cmd))
        worker.setDaemon(True)
        worker.start()

print "Main Thread Waiting"
for ip in ips:
    queue.put(ip)
queue.join()
end = time.time()
print "Dispatch Completed in %s seconds" % end - start
```

If we look at the output of our new threaded dispatch engine, we can see that the commands were dispatched and returned in about 1.2 seconds. To really see the speed difference, we should add a timer to our original dispatcher and compare the results:

```
[ngift@Macintosh-6][H:11296][J:0]# python threaded_dispatch.py
Main Thread Waiting
Thread 1: Running python /src/fingerprint.py to 10.0.1.51
Thread 2: Running python /src/fingerprint.py to 10.0.1.40
Thread 0: Running python /src/fingerprint.py to 10.0.1.50
Thread 4: Running python /src/fingerprint.py to 10.0.1.60
Thread 3: Running python /src/fingerprint.py to 10.0.1.80
redhat
redhat
ubuntu
SunOS
FreeBSD
Dispatch Completed in 1 seconds
```

By adding some simple timing code to our original dispatcher, we get this new output:

```
[ngift@Macintosh-6][H:11305][J:0]# python advanced_dispatch1.py
redhat
redhat
ubuntu
SunOS
FreeBSD
Dispatch Completed in 3 seconds
```

From this sample test, we can tell our threaded version is roughly three times quicker. If we were using our dispatch tool to monitor a network full of machines, say 500 machines, and not 5, it would make a substantial difference in performance. So far, our cross-platform systems management tool is proceeding nicely, so let's step it up another notch and use it to create a cross-platform build network.

 We should note that another, perhaps even better, solution would be to implement this using the parallel version of IPython. See *http://ipython.scipy.org/moin/Parallel_Computing*.

Creating a Cross-Platform Build Network

Since we know how to distribute jobs in parallel to a list full of machines, identify what operating system they are running, and finally, create a uniform manifest with EPM that can create a vendor-specific package, doesn't it make sense to put all of this together? We can use these three techniques to quite easily build a cross-platform build network.

With the advent of virtual machines technology, it is quite easy to create a virtual machine for any nonproprietary *nix operating system, such as Debian/Ubuntu, Red Hat/CentOS, FreeBSD, and Solaris. Now, when you create a tool you need to share to the world, or just the people at your company, you can quite easily create a "build farm," perhaps even running on your laptop, in which you run a script, and then instantly create a vendor package for it.

So how would that work? The most automated way to accomplish this would be to create a common NFS-mounted package build tree, and give all of your build servers access to this mount point. Then, use the tools we created earlier to have the build servers spawn package builds into the NFS-mounted directory. Because EPM allows you to create a simple manifest or "list" file, and because we have created a "fingerprint" script, all the hard work is done. OK, let's write that code to do just that.

Here is an example of what a build script could look like:

```python
#!/usr/bin/env python
from fingerprint import fingerprint
from subprocess import call

os = fingerprint()

#Gets epm keyword correct
epm_keyword = {"ubuntu":"dpkg", "redhat":"rpm", "SunOS":"pkg", "osx":"osx"}

try:
    epm_keyword[os]
except Exception, err:
  print err
```

```
subprocess.call("epm -f %s helloEPM hello_epm.list" % platform_cmd, shell=True)
```

Now, with that out of the way, we can edit our *config.ini* file and change it to run our new script.

```
[MACHINES]
CENTOS: 10.0.1.40
UBUNTU: 10.0.1.50
REDHAT: 10.0.1.51
SUN: 10.0.1.60
FREEBSD: 10.0.1.80
[COMMANDS]
FINGERPRINT = python /src/create_package.py
```

Now, we just run our threaded version distribution tool, and eureka, we have packages built for CentOS, Ubuntu, Red Hat, FreeBSD, and Solaris in seconds. This example isn't what we could consider production code, as there needs to be error handling in place, but it is a great example of what Python can whip up in a matter of a few minutes or a few hours.

PyInotify

If you have the privilege of working with GNU/Linux platforms, then you will appreciate PyInotify. According to the documentation, it is "a Python module for watching filesystem changes." The official project page is here: *http://pyinotify.sourceforge.net*.

Example 8-9 shows how it could work.

Example 8-9. Event-monitoring Pyinotify script

```
import os
import sys
from pyinotify import WatchManager, Notifier, ProcessEvent, EventsCodes

class PClose(ProcessEvent):
    """
    Processes on close event
    """

    def __init__(self, path):
        self.path = path
        self.file = file

    def process_IN_CLOSE(self, event):
        """
        process 'IN_CLOSE_*' events
        can be passed an action function
        """
        path = self.path
        if event.name:
            self.file = "%s" % os.path.join(event.path, event.name)
        else:
```

```
            self.file = "%s" % event.path
        print "%s Closed" % self.file
        print "Performing pretend action on %s...." % self.file
        import time
        time.sleep(2)
        print "%s has been processed" % self.file

class Controller(object):

    def __init__(self, path='/tmp'):
        self.path = path

    def run(self):
        self.pclose = PClose(self.path)
        PC = self.pclose
        # only watch these events
        mask = EventsCodes.IN_CLOSE_WRITE | EventsCodes.IN_CLOSE_NOWRITE

        # watch manager instance
        wm = WatchManager()
        notifier = Notifier(wm, PC)

        print 'monitoring of %s started' % self.path

        added_flag = False
        # read and process events
        while True:
            try:
                if not added_flag:
                    # on first iteration, add a watch on path:
                    # watch path for events handled by mask.
                    wm.add_watch(self.path, mask)
                    added_flag = True
                notifier.process_events()
                if notifier.check_events():
                    notifier.read_events()
            except KeyboardInterrupt:
                # ...until c^c signal
                print 'stop monitoring...'
                # stop monitoring
                notifier.stop()
                break
            except Exception, err:
                # otherwise keep on watching
                print err

def main():
    monitor = Controller()
    monitor.run()

if __name__ == '__main__':
    main()
```

If we run this script, it will "pretend" to do things when something is placed in the *tmp* directory. This should give you some idea of how to actually do something useful, such as adding a callback that performs an action. Some of the code in the data section could be useful for doing something that finds duplicates and deletes them automatically, or performs a TAR archive if they match a fnmatch expression you defined. All in all, it is fun and useful that the Python module works on Linux.

OS X

OS X is a weird beast to say the least. On one hand, it has, arguably, the world's finest user interface in Cocoa; on the other hand, as of Leopard, it has a completely POSIX-compliant Unix operating system. OS X accomplished what every Unix operating system vendor tried to do and failed: it brought Unix to the mainstream. With Leopard, OS X included Python 2.5.1, Twisted, and many other Python goodies.

OS X also follows a somewhat strange paradigm of offering a server and regular version of its operating system. For all the things Apple has done right, it might need to rethink that dinosaur-era thinking, but we can get into the one-OS, one-price discussion later. The server version of the operating system offers some better command-line tools for administration, and a few Apple-specific goodies, such as the ability to NetBoot machines, run LDAP Directory Servers, and more.

Scripting DSCL or Directory Services Utility

DSCL stands for Directory Services Command Line, and it is a convenient hook into OS X's directory services API. DSCL will let you read, create and delete records, so Python is a natural fit. Example 8-10 shows using IPython to script DSCL to read Open Directory attributes and their values.

 Note in the example we read only attributes, but it easy enough to modify them as well using the same technique.

Example 8-10. Getting user record interactively with DSCL and IPython

```
In [42]: import subprocess

In [41]: p = subprocess.Popen("dscl . read /Users/ngift", shell=True,stdout=subprocess.PIPE)

In [42]: out = p.stdout.readlines()

In [43]: for line in out:
line.strip().split()


Out[46]: ['NFSHomeDirectory:', '/Users/ngift']
Out[46]: ['Password:', '********']
Out[46]: ['Picture:']
```

```
Out[46]: ['/Library/User', 'Pictures/Flowers/Sunflower.tif']
Out[46]: ['PrimaryGroupID:', '20']
Out[46]: ['RealName:', 'ngift']
Out[46]: ['RecordName:', 'ngift']
Out[46]: ['RecordType:', 'dsRecTypeStandard:Users']
Out[46]: ['UniqueID:', '501']
Out[46]: ['UserShell:', '/bin/zsh']
```

It is good to point out that Apple has centralized both local and LDAP/Active Directory account management to use the `dscl` command. The `dscl` utility is a wonderful breath of fresh air when dealing with it in comparison to other LDAP management tools, even if you take Python out of the equation. Although we don't have the space to go into the details, it is quite easy to script the `dscl` utility with Python to programatically manage accounts either on a local database or a LDAP database such as Open Directory, and the previous code should give you an idea of where to start if you choose to do this.

OS X Scripting APIs

Often, with OS X it is a requirement for a sysadmin to know a bit about high-level scripting that interacts with the actual UI itself. With OS X Leopard, Python, and Ruby, we're given first-class access to the Scripting Bridge. Refer to this documentation for more information: *http://developer.apple.com/documentation/Cocoa/Conceptual/Ruby PythonCocoa/Introduction/Introduction.html.*

One of the options for accessing the OSA, or Open Scripting Architecture, is py-appscript, which has a project page here: *http://sourceforge.net/projects/appscript.*

Using `py-appscript` is quite fun and powerful, as it gives Python the ability to interact with the very rich OSA architecture. Before we dig into it, though, let's build a simple `osascript` command-line tool that shows you how the scripting API works. With Leopard, it is now possible to write `osascript` command-line tools and execute them like Bash or Python scripts. Let's build this script below, call it `bofh.osa`, and then make it executable. See Example 8-11.

Example 8-11. Hello, Bastard Operator From Hell osascript

```
#!/usr/bin/osascript
say "Hello, Bastard Operator From Hell" using "Zarvox"
```

If we run this from the command line, an alien-sounding voice says hello to us. This was a bit silly, but hey, this is OS X; you are supposed to do things like this.

Now, let's dig into using appscript to access this same API, in Python, but let's do this with IPython interactively. Here is an interactive version of an example included with the source code of `appscript` that prints out all of the running processes in alphabetical order:

```
In [4]: from appscript import app

In [5]: sysevents = app('System Events')
```

```
In [6]: processnames = sysevents.application_processes.name.get()

In [7]: processnames.sort(lambda x, y: cmp(x.lower(), y.lower()))

In [8]: print '\n'.join(processnames)
Activity Monitor
AirPort Base Station Agent
AppleSpell
Camino
DashboardClient
DashboardClient
Dock
Finder
Folder Actions Dispatcher
GrowlHelperApp
GrowlMenu
iCal
iTunesHelper
JavaApplicationStub
loginwindow
mdworker
PandoraBoy
Python
quicklookd
Safari
Spotlight
System Events
SystemUIServer
Terminal
TextEdit
TextMate
```

If you happen to need to perform work-flow automation tasks with OS X-specific applications, appscript can be a godsend, as it can also do things in Python that were commmonly done via Applescript. Noah wrote an article that goes into some of this: *http://www.macdevcenter.com/pub/a/mac/2007/05/08/using-python-and-applescript-to-get-the-most-out-of-your-mac.html*.

Some of the things that a sysadmin might do are script Final Cut Pro and create batch operations that interact with, say, Adobe After Effects. One final point of advice is that a very quick-and-dirty way to create GUIs in Python on OS X can be done through Applescript Studio and calls via "do shell script" to Python. A little-known fact is that the original versions of Carbon Copy Cloner were written in Applescript Studio. If you have some time, it is worth exploring.

Automatically Re-Imaging Machines

Yet another revolutionary tool OS X has developed that is ahead of its time is the ASR command-line tool. This tool is a key component in a very popular freeware cloning utility called Carbon Copy Cloner, and it has played a role in automating many environments. Noah used the `asr` utility in tandom with Netboot to automatically re-image machines; in fact, he fully automated at one place he worked. A user would just need to reboot his machine and hold down the "N" key for a netboot, and it was "game over," or the machine would fix itself.

Please don't tell anyone, though, as they still think he works there. Here is a hardcoded and simplistic version of an automated startup script that could be run on a netboot image to automatically re-image a machine, or alternately, it could be run from a second partition on a hard drive. In terms of setup, the */Users* directory and any other important directory should be symbolically linked to another partition or should live on the network, which is even better. See Example 8-12.

Example 8-12. Automatically re-image a partition on OS X and show progress with WXPython progress widget

```
#!/usr/bin/env pythonw
#automatically reimages partition

import subprocess
import os
import sys
import time
from wx import PySimpleApp, ProgressDialog, PD_APP_MODAL, PD_ELAPSED_TIME

#commands to rebuild main partition using asr utility
asr = '/usr/sbin/asr -source '

#path variables
os_path = '/Volumes/main'
ipath = '/net/server/image.dmg '
dpath = '-target /Volumes/main -erase -noprompt -noverify &'
reimage_cmd = "%s%s%s" % (asr,ipath, dpath)

#Reboot Variables
reboot = 'reboot'
bless = '/usr/sbin/bless -folder /Volumes/main/System/Library/CoreServices -setOF'

#wxpython portion
application = PySimpleApp()
dialog = ProgressDialog ('Progress', 'Attempting Rebuild of Main Partition',
                    maximum = 100, style = PD_APP_MODAL | PD_ELAPSED_TIME)

def boot2main():
    """Blesses new partition and reboots"""
    subprocess.call(bless, shell=True)
    subprocess.call(reboot, shell=True)

def rebuild():
    """Rebuilds Partition"""
    try:
        time.sleep(5)   #Gives dialog time to run
        subprocess.call(reimage_cmd)
    except OSError:
```

```
            print "CMD: %s [ERROR:  invalid path]" % reimage_cmd
            sys.exit(1)
    time.sleep(30)
    while True:
        if os.path.exists(os_path):
            x = 0
            wxSleep(1)
            dialog.Update ( x + 1, "Rebuild is complete...\n rebooting to main partition\n
                                    ...in 5 seconds..")
            wxSleep(5)
            print "repaired volume.." + os_path
            boot2main()         #calls reboot/bless function
            break
        else:
            x = 0
            wxSleep(1)
            dialog.Update ( x + 1, 'Reimaging.... ')

def main():
    if os.path.exists(os_path):
        rebuild()
    else:
        print "Could not find valid path...FAILED.."
        sys.exit(1)
if __name__ == "__main__":
    main()
```

To review the code, the script attempts to re-image a partition and pops up a WXPython progress bar. If the path is set correctly, and there are no errors, it then proceeds to re-image the hard drive with the ASR command and a self-updating progress bar, "blesses" the partition that was re-imaged to become the boot volume again, and then tells the machine to reboot.

This script could quite easily become the basis for an enterprise software distribution and management system, as it could be told to distribute different images based on a fingerprint of the hardware, or even by looking at the "old" name of the hard drive. Next, software packages could be distributed programatically using OS X's package management system, or using the open source tool radmind. One interesting scenario in which Noah has deployed OS X was to first automatically re-image a fresh installation of OS X with a base operating system, and then to finish of the rest of the installation with radmind.

If you are doing any serious OS X systems administration, it would be worth taking a look at radmind. Radmind is a type of tripwire system that detects changes in a file-system and is able to restore machines based on this changeset. You can refer to *http://rsug.itd.umich.edu/software/radmind/* if you would like more information. Although radmind is not written in Python, it can be scripted in Python quite easily.

Managing Plist Files from Python

In Chapter 3, we parsed an XML stream generated from the `system_profiler` with ElementTree, but Python on OS X comes bundled with `plistlib`, which allows you to parse and create Plist files. The name of the module itself is `plistlib`. We won't have time to get into a use case for it, but it is worth exploring on your own.

Red Hat Linux Systems Administration

Red Hat is doing a whole slew of things with Python as a company and as an operating system. Some of the most interesting new uses of Python at Red Hat are coming from the Emerging Technologies group: *http://et.redhat.com/page/Main_Page*. Here is a list of some of the projects using Python:

- Libvert, the virtualization API virtual machine manager
- A Python + PyGTK management application built with libvirt VirtInst
- A Python library for simplifying provisioning of guest VMs with libvirt
- Cobbler, which sets up fully automated network boot servers for PXE and virtualization
- Virt-Factory: web-based virtualization management with an application focus
- FUNC (Fedora Unified Network Controller)

Ubuntu Administration

Of all of the mainstream Linux distributions, you could say that Ubuntu is perhaps the one most enamored with Python. Part of this could be that Mark Shuttleworth, the founder, is a long-time Python hacker, going back to the early '90s. One good source for Python packages on Ubuntu is Launchpad: *https://launchpad.net/*.

Solaris Systems Administration

From the late '90s to the early 2000s Solaris was a preferred, "Big Iron" distribution of Unix. Linux's metioric rise in the early 2000s rapidly cut into Solaris' and Sun was in some real trouble. However, recently, a lot of sysadmins, developers, and enterprises are talking about Sun again.

Some of the interesting developments in Sun's future are a 6-month release cycle, just like Ubuntu, with a 18-month support window. It is also copying the single CD approach of Ubuntu as well and ditching the big DVD distribution. Finally, it is mixing some of the ideas from Red Hat and Fedora by having a community-developed version of Solaris mixed. You can know download a live CD or order one here: *http://www.open solaris.com*.

What does all this mean for a sysadmin who uses Python? Sun is suddenly exciting, and it has a slew of interesting technologies from ZFS, to Containers, to LDOMs which are equivalent to VMware virtual machines in some respects. There is even a correlation to this book. Python works just fine on Solaris, and it is even used quite heavily in its developing package management system.

Virtualization

On August 14, 2007, VMware went public in an IPO that raised billions of dollars and solidified "virtualization" as the next big thing for data centers and systems administrators everywhere. Predicting the future is always a dicey bet, but the words "data center operating system," are being tossed around by large companies, and everyone from Microsoft to Red Hat to Oracle are jumping on the virtualization bandwagon. It is safe to say that virtualization is going to completely change the data center and the job of systems administration. Virtualization is a no-brainer example of the often overused phrase, "distruptive technology."

Virtualization is a double-edged sword for systems administrators, as on one hand, it creates the ability to easily test configurations and applications, but on the other hand, it dramatically increases the complexity of administration. No longer does one machine hold one operating system, one machine could hold a hold small business, or a large chunk of a data center. All of the efficiency has to come at some cost, and it does, right out of the hide of the average systems administrator.

You might be at home reading this right now thinking: what could this possibly have to do with Python? Well, quite a bit. Noah's recent employer Racemi has written a comprehensive data center management application in Python that deals with virtualization. Python can and does interact with virtualization in a very fundamental way, from controlling virtual machines, to moving physical machines to virtual machines via Python APIs. Python is right at home in this new virtualized world, and it is a safe bet it will play a big role in whatever future the data center operating system has.

VMware

VMware as, we mentioned earlier, is the current powerhouse in virtualization. Having full control programatically over a virtual machine is obviously the Holy Grail. Luckily, there are several APIs to look at: Perl, XML-RPC, Python, and C. As of this writing, some of the Python implementations are somewhat limited, but that could change. The new direction for VMware appears to be in terms of the XML-RPC API.

VMware has a few different products with a few different APIs. Some of the products you may want to consider scripting are VMware Site Recovery Manager, VMware ESX Server, VMware Server, and VMware Fusion.

We won't have room to cover scripting these technologies, as they fall outside the scope of this book, but it would pay to closely monitor these products and examine what role Python will play.

Cloud Computing

Just when the buzz was settling from virtualization, suddenly cloud computing is raising the buzz yet again. Simply put, "cloud computing" is about using resources that respond on demand to workload requirements. The two big players in cloud computing are Amazon and Google. Google just literally dropped the "C" bomb just a few weeks before this book went to the publisher. Google offered an interesting twist in it that only currently supports Python. This being a book on Python programming, we are sure this doesn't disappoint you too much. For some reason, this whole ordeal with Google offering only Python reminds us of an American Express commercial.

In this section, we go into some of the available APIs that you may need to deal with for both Amazon and Google App Engine. Finally, we talk about how this may impact systems administration.

Amazon Web Services with Boto

An exciting option for dealing with Amazon's cloud computing infrastructure is Boto. With Boto, you can do the following things: Simple Storage Service, Simple Queue Service, Elastic Compute Cloud, Mechanical Turk, SimpleDB. Because this is a very new yet powerful API, we recommend that you just take a look at the project home page yourself: *http://code.google.com/p/boto/*. This will give you the latest information better than we can give you in dead tree format.

Here is a brief example though of how it works with SimpleDB:

Initial connection:

```
In [1]: import boto
In [2]: sdb = boto.connect_sdb()
```

Create a new domain:

```
In [3]: domain = sdb.create_domain('my_domain')
```

Adding a new item:

```
In [4]: item = domain.new_item('item')
```

This is the feel for how the API works currently, but you should take a look at the tests in svn repository to get a real idea of how things work: *http://code.google.com/p/boto/ source/browse*. On a side note, looking at tests is one of the best ways to understand how a new library works.

Google App Engine

Google App Engine was released as a beta service, and it was massively buzzworthy from the day it was announced. It lets you run your application on Google's infrastructure for free. App Engine applications have a strictly Python API for now, but that could change at some point. One of the other interesting things about App Engine is that it also integrates with Google's other services.

One of the ways this affects a systems administrator is that it is increasingly becoming feasible to host major portions of what used to live in your data center into another data center. Knowing how to interact with Google App Engine could be the killer new skill for sysadmins, so it makes sense to investigate it a bit.

We interviewed several people from the App Engine Team and talked to them about how this would affect a systems administrator. They mentioned the following tasks:

1. Bulk Data Uploader: *http://code.google.com/appengine/articles/bulkload.html*.

   Sysadmins often deal with moving large chunks of data around, and this is a tool for doing that in the context of an app on Google App Engine.

2. Logging: *http://code.google.com/appengine/articles/logging.html*.

3. Mail API: send_mail_to_admins() function: *http://code.google.com/appengine/docs/mail/functions.html*.

   In a sysadmin context, this could be useful for monitoring. For important exceptions or key actions, you could automatically send an email to the app's admins.

4. Cron jobs for regular tasks.

   This is something that is not directly a part of Google App Engine, but you could use cron on your own servers to send requests to your app at regular intervals. For example, you could have a cron job that hit *http://yourapp.com/emailsummary* every hour, which triggered an email to be sent to admins with a summary of important events over the last hour.

---

5. Version management: *http://code.google.com/appengine/docs/configuringa napp.html#Required_Elements*.

One of the required fields you set for your app is the "version." Each time you upload an app with the same version ID, it replaces it with the new code. If you change the version ID, you can have multiple versions of your app running in production and use the admin console to select which version receives life traffic.

Building a sample Google App Engine application

To get started with building a Google App Engine application, you will need to first download the SDK for Google app engine here: *http://code.google.com/appengine/down loads.html*. You also might do well to go through the excellent tutorial for Google App Engine: *http://code.google.com/appengine/docs/gettingstarted/*.

In this section, we offer a reverse tutorial on Google App Engine, as there is already an excellent tutorial. If you go to *http://greedycoin.appspot.com/*, you can test out a running version of what we are going to cover, along with the latest version of the source code. The application takes change as an input, stores it in the database, and then returns proper change. It also has the ability to log in via Google's authentication API and perform a recent actions query. See Example 8-13.

Example 8-13. Greedy coin web application

```python
#!/usr/bin/env python2.5
#Noah Gift

import decimal
import wsgiref.handlers
import os

from google.appengine.api import users
from google.appengine.ext import webapp
from google.appengine.ext import db
from google.appengine.ext.webapp import template

class ChangeModel(db.Model):
    user = db.UserProperty()
    input = db.IntegerProperty()
    date = db.DateTimeProperty(auto_now_add=True)

class MainPage(webapp.RequestHandler):
    """Main Page View"""

    def get(self):
        user = users.get_current_user()

        if users.get_current_user():
            url = users.create_logout_url(self.request.uri)
            url_linktext = 'Logout'
        else:
            url = users.create_login_url(self.request.uri)
```

```python
        url_linktext = 'Login'

    template_values = {
    'url': url,
    'url_linktext': url_linktext,
    }
    path = os.path.join(os.path.dirname(__file__), 'index.html')
    self.response.out.write(template.render(path, template_values))

class Recent(webapp.RequestHandler):
    """Query Last 10 Requests"""

    def get(self):

        #collection
        collection = []
        #grab last 10 records from datastore
        query = ChangeModel.all().order('-date')
        records = query.fetch(limit=10)

        #formats decimal correctly
        for change in records:
            collection.append(decimal.Decimal(change.input)/100)

        template_values = {
        'inputs': collection,
        'records': records,
        }

        path = os.path.join(os.path.dirname(__file__), 'query.html')
        self.response.out.write(template.render(path,template_values))

class Result(webapp.RequestHandler):
    """Returns Page with Results"""
    def __init__(self):
        self.coins = [1,5,10,25]
        self.coin_lookup = {25: "quarters", 10: "dimes", 5: "nickels", 1: "pennies"}

    def get(self):
        #Just grab the latest post
        collection = {}

        #select the latest input from the datastore
        change = db.GqlQuery("SELECT * FROM ChangeModel ORDER BY date DESC LIMIT 1")
        for c in change:
            change_input = c.input

        #coin change logic
        coin = self.coins.pop()
        num, rem  = divmod(change_input, coin)
        if num:
            collection[self.coin_lookup[coin]] = num
        while rem > 0:
            coin = self.coins.pop()
            num, rem = divmod(rem, coin)
```

```
            if num:
                collection[self.coin_lookup[coin]] = num

        template_values = {
        'collection': collection,
        'input': decimal.Decimal(change_input)/100,
        }

        #render template
        path = os.path.join(os.path.dirname(__file__), 'result.html')
        self.response.out.write(template.render(path, template_values))

class Change(webapp.RequestHandler):

    def post(self):
        """Printing Method For Recursive Results and While Results"""
        model = ChangeModel()
        try:
            change_input = decimal.Decimal(self.request.get('content'))
            model.input = int(change_input*100)
            model.put()
            self.redirect('/result')
        except decimal.InvalidOperation:
            path = os.path.join(os.path.dirname(__file__), 'submit_error.html')
            self.response.out.write(template.render(path,None))

def main():
    application = webapp.WSGIApplication([('/', MainPage),
                                         ('/submit_form', Change),
                                         ('/result', Result),
                                         ('/recent', Recent)],
                                         debug=True)
    wsgiref.handlers.CGIHandler().run(application)

if __name__ == "__main__":
    main()
```

As a reverse tutorial, let's start by looking at the version running at *http://greedy coin.appspot.com/*, or your development version at *http://localhost:8080/*. There is a pumpkin-colored theme that has two floating boxes; on the left is a form that lets you input change, and on the right there is a navigation box. These pretty, or ugly, colors and layout are just a combination of Django templating and CSS. The Django templates can be found in the main directory, and the CSS we used is found in stylesheets. This really has little to do with Google App Engine, so we will just refer you to the Django templating reference material for more: *http://www.djangoproject.com/documentation/ templates/*.

Now that we have covered this, let's actually get into some Google App Engine specifics. If you notice the "Login" link in the right navigation box, it is made possible by the clever user authentication API. Here is what that actual code looks like:

```
class MainPage(webapp.RequestHandler):
    """Main Page View"""
```

```
def get(self):
    user = users.get_current_user()

    if users.get_current_user():
        url = users.create_logout_url(self.request.uri)
        url_linktext = 'Logout'
    else:
        url = users.create_login_url(self.request.uri)
        url_linktext = 'Login'

    template_values = {
    'url': url,
    'url_linktext': url_linktext,
    }
    path = os.path.join(os.path.dirname(__file__), 'index.html')
    self.response.out.write(template.render(path, template_values))
```

There is a class that inherits from webapp.RequestHandler, and if you define a get
method, you can make a page that checks to see if a user is logged in or not. If you
notice the few lines at the bottom, you will see that the user information gets tossed
into the template system and then gets rendered to the Django template file *in
dex.html.* What is incredibly powerful is that it is trivial to leverage the Google User
Accounts database to create authorization for pages. If you look at the previous code,
it is as simple as saying:

```
user = users.get_current_user()

if users.get_current_user():
```

At this point, we would suggest fiddling around with this code and trying to add code
that only shows up for authenticated users. You don't even need to understand how
things work; you could just use the existing conditional statements to do something.

Now that we have a vague understanding of authentication, let's get into the powerful
stuff. The datastore API lets you store persistent data and then retrieve it throughout
your application. In order to do this, you need to import the datastore, as shown in the
previous code, and then also define a model like this:

```
class ChangeModel(db.Model):
    user = db.UserProperty()
    input = db.IntegerProperty()
    date = db.DateTimeProperty(auto_now_add=True)
```

With that simple class, we can now create and use persistent data. Here is a class in
which we use Python API to the datastore to retrieve the last 10 changes made to the
database, and then display them:

```
class Recent(webapp.RequestHandler):
    """Query Last 10 Requests"""

    def get(self):

        #collection
```

```
collection = []
#grab last 10 records from datastore
query = ChangeModel.all().order('-date')
records = query.fetch(limit=10)

#formats decimal correctly
for change in records:
    collection.append(decimal.Decimal(change.input)/100)

template_values = {
'inputs': collection,
'records': records,
}

path = os.path.join(os.path.dirname(__file__), 'query.html')
self.response.out.write(template.render(path,template_values))
```

The two most important lines are:

```
query = ChangeModel.all().order('-date')
records = query.fetch(limit=10)
```

These pull the results out of the datastore and then "fetch" 10 records in a query. At this point, a simple thing to do for fun would be to experiment with this code and to try to fetch more records, or to sort them in a different way. This should give you some immediate and fun feedback.

Finally, if we look closely at the code below, we might be able to guess that each of the URLs corresponds to a class we defined in our *change.py* file. At this point, we would recommend trying to tweak the names of URLs by changing the parts of the application that depend on a URL; this will give you a good idea of how things get routed around.

```
def main():
    application = webapp.WSGIApplication([('/', MainPage),
    ('/submit_form', Change),
    ('/result', Result),
    ('/recent', Recent)],
    debug=True)
    wsgiref.handlers.CGIHandler().run(application)
```

This is the end of this reverse tutorial on Google App Engine, but it should give you some ideas on how you could implement a more sysadmin-like tool on your own. If you are interested in writing more applications, you should also take a look a Guido's source code for his Google App Engine application: *http://code.google.com/p/rietveld/source/browse*.

Using Zenoss to Manage Windows Servers from Linux

If you have the unfortunate task of managing one or more Windows servers, the task just became a little less unpleasant. Zenoss is an amazing tool that will help us out here. We talk about Zenoss in the Chapter 7, SNMP. In addition to being an industry-leading SNMP tool, Zenoss also provides the tools to talk to a Windows server via WMI—from

Linux! We still get the giggles when thinking about the practical implications of this as well as the technology used to make it possible. From a discussion that we had with the good folks at Zenoss, they push WMI messages down to Samba (or possibly CIFS now) on a Linux box and send them over to your Windows server. And possibly the most interesting part of this (at least for readers of this book, anyway) is that you can script this WMI connection with Python.

 A discussion of the syntax and features of WMI is beyond the scope of this book.

Currently, the Zenoss documentation is pretty light on the WMI-from-Linux-using-Python functionality. However, the examples that we are about to review should provide a good foundation for you to build on. First off, let's look at a non-Python tool for talking WMI to a Windows server from Linux. wmic. wmic is a simple command-line utility that takes username, password, server address, and WMI query as command-line parameters, connects to the appropriate server with the given credentials, passes the query to the server, and displays the result to standard output. The syntax for using the utility is something like this:

```
wmic -U username%password //SERVER_IP_ADDRESS_OR_HOSTNAME "some WMI query"
```

And here is an example of connecting to a server with an IP address of 192.168.1.3 as Administrator and asking for its event logs:

```
wmic -U Administrator%password //192.168.1.3 "SELECT * FROM Win32_NTLogEvent"
```

And here is part of the result of running that command:

```
CLASS: Win32_NTLogEvent
Category|CategoryString|ComputerName|Data|EventCode|EventIdentifier|
    EventType|InsertionStrings|Logfile|Message|RecordNumber|SourceName|
    TimeGenerated|TimeWritten|Type|User
...
|3|DCOM|20080320034341.000000+000|20080320034341.000000+000|Information|(null)
0|(null)|MACHINENAME|NULL|6005|2147489653|3|(,,,,14,0,0 )|System|The Event log
service was started.
|2|EventLog|20080320034341.000000+000|20080320034341.000000+000|Information|(null)
0|(null)|MACHINENAME|NULL|6009|2147489657|3|(5.02.,3790,Service Pack
2,Uniprocessor Free)|System|Microsoft (R) Windows (R) 5.02. 3790 Service Pack 2
Uniprocessor Free.
|1|EventLog|20080320034341.000000+000|20080320034341.000000+000|Information|(null)
```

In order to write a similar Python script, we first have to set up our environment. For the following examples, we used the Zenoss v2.1.3 VMware appliance. In this appliance, some of the Zenoss code is located in the home directory of the zenoss user. The biggest part of that is to add the directory where the wmiclient.py module lives to your PYTHONPATH. We prepended the directory to our already existing PYTHONPATH like this:

```
export PYTHONPATH=~/Products/ZenWin:$PYTHONPATH
```

Once we have access to the needed libraries in Python, we can execute a script something like the following:

```python
#!/usr/bin/env python

from wmiclient import WMI

if __name__ == '__main__':
    w = WMI('winserver', '192.168.1.3', 'Administrator', passwd='foo')
    w.connect()
    q = w.query('SELECT * FROM Win32_NTLogEvent')
    for l in q:
        print "l.timewritten::", l.timewritten
        print "l.message::", l.message
```

Rather than printing out all fields as the wmic example did, this script prints only out the timestamp and the body of the log message. This script connects to the server 192.168.1.3 as Administrator with the password foo. Then, it executes the WMI query 'SELECT * FROM Win32_NTLogEvent'. It then iterates over the results of the query and prints the timestamp and the log message body. It really couldn't get much easier than that.

Here is some of the output from running this script:

```
l.timewritten:: 20080320034359.000000+000
l.message:: While validating that \Device\Serial1 was really a serial port, a
fifo was detected. The fifo will be used.

l.timewritten:: 20080320034359.000000+000
l.message:: While validating that \Device\Serial0 was really a serial port, a
fifo was detected. The fifo will be used.

l.timewritten:: 20080320034341.000000+000
l.message:: The COM sub system is suppressing duplicate event log entries for a
duration of 86400 seconds. The suppression timeout can be controlled by a
REG_DWORD value named SuppressDuplicateDuration under the following registry
key: HKLM\Software\Microsoft\Ole\EventLog.

l.timewritten:: 20080320034341.000000+000
l.message:: The Event log service was started.

l.timewritten:: 20080320034341.000000+000
l.message:: Microsoft (R) Windows (R) 5.02. 3790 Service Pack 2 Uniprocessor
Free.
```

But how did we know to use the timewritten and message attributes for these records? It took just a bit of hacking to find that information. Here is a script that we ran to help us find which attributes we needed to use:

```python
#!/usr/bin/env python

from wmiclient import WMI
```

```
if __name__ == '__main__':
    w = WMI('winserver', '192.168.1.3', 'Administrator', passwd='foo')
    w.connect()
    q = w.query('SELECT * FROM Win32_NTLogEvent')
    for l in q:
        print "result set fields::->", l.Properties_.set.keys()
        break
```

You may notice that this script looks quite similar to the other WMI script. The two differences between this script and the other WMI script are rather than printing out the timestamp and the log message body, this script prints out l.Properties_.set.keys(), and this script breaks after the first result. The set object that we call keys() on is actually a dictionary. (Which makes sense, because keys() is a dictionary method.) Each resulting record from the WMI query should have a set of attributes that correspond to these keys. So, here is the output from running the script that we just discussed:

```
result set fields::-> ['category', 'computername', 'categorystring',
'eventidentifier', 'timewritten', 'recordnumber', 'eventtype', 'eventcode',
'timegenerated', 'sourcename', 'insertionstrings', 'user', 'type', 'message',
'logfile', 'data']
```

The two attributes that we chose to pull from in the first WMI script, 'message' and 'timewritten', are both in this list of keys.

While we aren't huge fans of working with Windows, we recognize that sometimes the job dictates the technology that we use. This tool from Zenoss can make that task a lot less painful. Plus, it's just cool to be able to run a WMI query from Linux. If you have to do much work with Windows, then Zenoss could easily find a prominent place in your toolbox.

## CHAPTER 9

Package Management

Introduction

Package management is a one of the most critical factors in the success of a software development project. Package management can be thought of as the shipping company in an e-commerce business, such as Amazon. If there were no shipping companies, Amazon would not exist. Likewise, if there is not a functional, simple, robust package management system for an operating system or language, then it will be limited to some degree.

When we mention "package management," your first thoughts are probably drawn toward *.rpm* files and yum, or *.deb* files and apt or some other operating system level package management system. We'll get into that in this chapter, but the primary focus is on packaging and managing Python code and your Python environment. Python has always had ways to make Python code universally accessible to the entire system. Recently, though, there have been some projects which have improved the flexibility and usability of packaging, managing, and deploying Python code.

Some of these recent projects include setuptools, Buildout, and virtualenv. Buildout, setuptools, and virtualenv are often about development, development libraries, and dealing with development environments. But at their heart, they are mostly about using Python to deploy Python code in operating system-agnostic ways. (Note that we did say "mostly" here.)

Another deployment scenario involves creating operating system-specific packages and deploying them to an end user's machine. Sometimes, these are two completely different problems, although there is some degree of overlap. We will be discussing an open source tool called EPM that generates native platform packages for AIX, Debian/Ubuntu, FreeBSD, HP-UX, IRIX, Mac OS X, NetBSD, OpenBSD, Red Hat, Slackware, Solaris, and Tru64 Unix.

Package mangement isn't good just for software developers. It is critical for system administrators as well. In fact, a system administrator is often the person with whom the buck stops for package management. Understanding the latest techniques in package management for Python and for other operating systems is one way to make yourself an invaluable resource. Hopefully, this chapter will help you in that regard. A very valuable reference for the topics we cover in this chapter can also be found here: *http://wiki.python.org/moin/buildout/pycon2008_tutorial*.

Setuptools and Python Eggs

According the official documentation, "setuptools is a collection of enhancements to the Python distutils (for Python 2.3.5 on most platforms, although 64-bit platforms require a minimum of Python 2.4) that allow you to more easily build and distribute packages, especially ones that have dependencies on other packages."

Until the creation of setuptools, distutils was the primary way of creating installable Python packages. setuptools is a library that enhances distutils. "Eggs" refers to the final bundle of Python packages and modules, much like an *.rpm* or *.deb* file. They are typically distributed in a zipped format and installed in either the zipped format or are unzipped so that you can navigate the package contents. Eggs is a feature of the setuptools library that works with `easy_install`. According to the official documentation, "Easy Install is a python module (`easy_install`) bundled with `setuptools` that let's you automatically download, build, install and manage Python packages." While it is a module, it is most often thought of and interacted with as a command-line tool. In this section, we will cover and explain `setuptools`, `easy_install`, and `eggs`, and clear up any confusion about what each provides.

We'll outline what we feel are the most useful features of setuptools and easy_install in this chapter. However, to get the full set of documentation on them, you can visit *http://peak.telecommunity.com/DevCenter/setuptools* and *http://peak.telecommunity.com/DevCenter/EasyInstall*, respectively.

Complex tools that do amazing things are often hard to understand. Parts of `setuptools` are difficult to grasp as a direct result of the amazing things it can do. With this section acting as a quickstart guide, and then later referring to the manual, you should be able to get a handle on using setuptools, easy_install, and Python eggs as a user and developer.

Using easy_install

The basics of understanding and using `easy_install` are very easy to grasp. The majority of people reading this book have very likely used rpm, yum, apt-get, fink, or a similar package management tool at some point. The phrase "Easy Install," often refers to the use of a command-line tool named `easy_install` to do similar things as yum on Red Hat-based systems, and `apt-get` on Debian-based systems, but for Python packages.

The `easy_install` tool can be installed by running a "bootstrap" script named `ez_setup.py` with the version of Python you wish `easy_install` to work with.

ez_setup.py grabs the latest version of setuptools and then automatically installs easy_install as a script to the default "scripts" location, which on *nixes is typically the same directory that your python binary lives in. Let's take a look at how "easy" that is. See Example 9-1.

Example 9-1. Bootstrapping easy_install

```
$ curl http://peak.telecommunity.com/dist/ez_setup.py
> ez_setup.py
% Total    % Received % Xferd  Average Speed   Time    Time     Time  Current
Dload  Upload   Total   Spent    Left  Speed
100  9419  100  9419    0     0    606      0  0:00:15  0:00:15 --:--:-- 83353
$ ls
ez_setup.py
$ sudo python2.5 ez_setup.py
Password:
Searching for setuptools
Reading http://pypi.python.org/simple/setuptools/
Best match: setuptools 0.6c8
Processing setuptools-0.6c8-py2.5.egg
setuptools 0.6c8 is already the active version in easy-install.pth
Installing easy_install script to /usr/local/bin
Installing easy_install-2.5 script to /usr/local/bin

Using /Library/Python/2.5/site-packages/setuptools-0.6c8-py2.5.egg
Processing dependencies for setuptools
Finished processing dependencies for setuptools
$
```

In this situation, easy_install was placed into */usr/local/bin* under two different names.

```
$ ls -l /usr/local/bin/easy_install*
-rwxr-xr-x  1 root  wheel  364 Mar  9 18:14 /usr/local/bin/easy_install
-rwxr-xr-x  1 root  wheel  372 Mar  9 18:14 /usr/local/bin/easy_install-2.5
```

This has been a convention that Python itself has used for quite a while: when installing an executable, install one with a version number denoting the version of Python and one without the version number. This means that the one that doesn't have the version number will be used by default when a user doesn't explicitly reference the versioned script. This also means that the last-installed version will become the default. It is convenient, though, that the older version still sticks around.

Here are the contents of the newly installed */usr/local/bin/easy_install*:

```
#!/System/Library/Frameworks/Python.framework/Versions/2.5/Resources/Python.app/
    Contents/MacOS/Python
# EASY-INSTALL-ENTRY-SCRIPT: 'setuptools==0.6c8','console_scripts','easy_install'
__requires__ = 'setuptools==0.6c8'
import sys
from pkg_resources import load_entry_point

sys.exit(
load_entry_point('setuptools==0.6c8', 'console_scripts', 'easy_install')()
)
```

The main point here is that when you install setuptools, it installs a script for you named easy_install that you can use to install and manage Python code. A secondary point here that we were making by showing the contents of the easy_install script is that this is the type of script that is automatically created for you when you use "entry points" when defining packages. Don't worry right now about the contents of this script or entry points or how to create scripts like this. We'll get to all of that later in this chapter.

Now that we have easy_install, we can install any package that is located in the central repository for uploaded Python Modules, commonly referred to as PyPI (Python Package Index), or the "Cheeseshop": *http://pypi.python.org/pypi*.

To install IPython, the shell we use exclusively in examples throughout the book, we can just issue this command:

```
sudo easy_install ipython
```

Notice that easy_install required sudo privileges in this setup, as it installed packages to the global Python site-pacakges directory. It also placed scripts in the default scripts directory of the operating system, which is the same directory that the python executable lives in. Basically, easy_installing a package requires permissions to write files to the *site-packages* directory and the script directory for you Python installation. If this is a problem, you should refer to the section of this chapter where we discuss using virtualenv and setuptools. Alternatively, you could even compile and install Python in a directory that you own, such as your home directory.

Before we get into advanced use of the easy_install tool, here's a quick summary for basic use of easy_install:

1. Download the ez_setup.py bootstrap script.
2. Run ez_setup.py with the version of Python you wish to install packages with.
3. Explicitly run easy_install with the version of python that installed it if you have several versions of Python running on your system.

---

easy_install Advanced Features

For most casual users, using `easy_install` and passing it only one command-line argument without any additional options will fit all of their needs. (By the way, giving `easy_install` only one argument, a package name, will simply download and install that package, as in the previous example with IPython.) There are cases, though, where it is nice to have more power under the hood to do various things other than just download eggs from the Python Package Index. Fortunately, `easy_install` has quite a few tricks up its sleeve and is flexible enough to do a whole assortment of advanced miscellanea.

Search for Packages on a Web Page

As we saw earlier, `easy_install` can automatically search the central repository for packages and automatically install them. It can also install packages in just about any way you can think of. Following is an example of how to search a web page and install or upgrade package by name and version:

```
$ easy_install -f http://code.google.com/p/liten/ liten
Searching for liten
Reading http://code.google.com/p/liten/
Best match: liten 0.1.3
Downloading http://liten.googlecode.com/files/liten-0.1.3-py2.4.egg
[snip]
```

In this situation, there is a Python2.4 and a Python2.5 egg at *http://code.google.com/p/liten/*. `easy_install -f` specifies a location to look for eggs. It found both eggs and then installed the Python2.4 egg, as it was the best match. Obviously, this is quite powerful, as `easy_install` not only found the egg link to begin with, but also found the correct egg version.

Install Source Distribution from URL

Now, we'll automatically install a source distribution from a URL:

```
% easy_install http://superb-west.dl.sourceforge.net/sourceforge
        /sqlalchemy/SQLAlchemy-0.4.3.tar.gz

Downloading http://superb-west.dl.sourceforge.net/sourceforge
/sqlalchemy/SQLAlchemy-0.4.3.tar.gz
Processing SQLAlchemy-0.4.3.tar.gz
Running SQLAlchemy-0.4.3/setup.py -q bdist_egg --dist-dir
  /var/folders/LZ/LZFo5h8JEW4Jzr+ydkXfI++++TI/-Tmp-/
   easy_install-Gw2Xq3/SQLAlchemy-0.4.3/egg-dist-tmp-Mf4jir
zip_safe flag not set; analyzing archive contents...
sqlalchemy.util: module MAY be using inspect.stack
sqlalchemy.databases.mysql: module MAY be using inspect.stack
Adding SQLAlchemy 0.4.3 to easy-install.pth file
```

```
Installed /Users/ngift/src/py24ENV/lib/python2.4/site-packages/SQLAlchemy-0.4.3-py2.4.egg
Processing dependencies for SQLAlchemy==0.4.3
Finished processing dependencies for SQLAlchemy==0.4.3
```

We passed the URL of a gzipped tarball to `easy_install`. It was able to figure out that it should install this source distribution without being explicitly told to do so. This is a neat trick, but the source must include a *setup.py* file at the root level for it to work. For example, at the time of this writing, if someone nested their package several levels deep into empty folders, then this will fail.

Install Egg Located on Local or Network Filesystem

Here is an example of how to install an egg located on a filesystem or NFS-mounted storage:

```
easy_install /net/src/eggs/convertWindowsToMacOperatingSystem-py2.5.egg
```

You can also install eggs from an NFS-mounted directory or a local partition. This can be a very efficient to distribute packages in a *nix environment, especially across a number of machines you'd like to keep in sync with one another regarding the versions of code they are running. Some of the other scripts in this book could help with creating a polling daemon. Each client could run such a daemon to check for updates to the centralized repository of eggs. If there is a new version, then it could automatically update itself.

Upgrading Packages

Another way of using `easy_install` is by getting it to upgrade packages. In the next few examples, we'll walk through installing and then upgrading the CherryPy package.

First, we'll install version 2.2.1 of CherryPy:

```
$ easy_install cherrypy==2.2.1
Searching for cherrypy==2.2.1
Reading http://pypi.python.org/simple/cherrypy/
....
Best match: CherryPy 2.2.1
Downloading http://download.cherrypy.org/cherrypy/2.2.1/CherryPy-2.2.1.tar.gz
....
Processing dependencies for cherrypy==2.2.1
Finished processing dependencies for cherrypy==2.2.1
```

Now, we'll show you what happens when you try to `easy_install` something that has already been installed:

```
$ easy_install cherrypy
Searching for cherrypy
Best match: CherryPy 2.2.1
Processing CherryPy-2.2.1-py2.5.egg
CherryPy 2.2.1 is already the active version in easy-install.pth

Using /Users/jmjones/python/cherrypy/lib/python2.5/site-packages/CherryPy-2.2.1-py2.5.egg
```

```
Processing dependencies for cherrypy
Finished processing dependencies for cherrypy
```

After you've installed some version of a package, you can upgrade to a newer version of the same package by explicitly declaring which version to download and install:

```
$ easy_install cherrypy==2.3.0 Searching for
cherrypy==2.3.0
Reading http://pypi.python.org/simple/cherrypy/
....
Best match: CherryPy 2.3.0
Downloading http://download.cherrypy.org/cherrypy/2.3.0/CherryPy-2.3.0.zip
....
Processing dependencies for cherrypy==2.3.0
Finished processing dependencies for cherrypy==2.3.0
```

Notice that we didn't use the --upgrade flag in this particular example. You only really ever need to use --upgrade if you already have some version of a package installed and want to update it to the latest version of that package.

Next, we upgrade to CherryPy 3.0.0 using the --upgrade flag. Here, --upgrade was purely unnecessary:

```
$ easy_install --upgrade cherrypy==3.0.0
Searching for cherrypy==3.0.0
Reading http://pypi.python.org/simple/cherrypy/
....
Best match: CherryPy 3.0.0
Downloading http://download.cherrypy.org/cherrypy/3.0.0/CherryPy-3.0.0.zip
....
Processing dependencies for cherrypy==3.0.0
Finished processing dependencies for cherrypy==3.0.0
```

Giving the --upgrade flag without specifying a version upgrades the package to the latest version. Notice that this is different from specifying easy_install cherrypy. With easy_install cherrypy, there already existed some version of the CherryPy package, so no action was taken. In the following example, CherryPy will be upgraded to the most current version:

```
$ easy_install --upgrade cherrypy
Searching for cherrypy
Reading http://pypi.python.org/simple/cherrypy/
....
Best match: CherryPy 3.1.0beta3
Downloading http://download.cherrypy.org/cherrypy/3.1.0beta3/CherryPy-3.1.0beta3.zip
....
Processing dependencies for cherrypy
Finished processing dependencies for cherrypy
```

Now, CherryPy is at 3.1.0b3. If we specify to upgrade to something greater than 3.0.0, no action will be taken, since it is already there:

```
$ easy_install --upgrade cherrypy>3.0.0
$
```

Install an Unpacked Source Distribution in Current Working Directory

Although this looks trivial, it can be useful. Rather than going through the `python setup.py install` routine, you can just type the following (it's a few less characters to type, so it's definitely a tip for the lazy):

```
easy_install
```

Extract Source Distribution to Specified Directory

You can use the following example to find either a source distribution or checkout URL for a package and then either extract it or check it out to a specified directory:

```
easy_install --editable --build-directory ~/sandbox liten
```

This is handy, as it allows `easy_install` to take a source distribution and put it in the directory you specify. Since installing a package with `easy_install` doesn't always install everything (such as documentation or code examples), this is a good way to look at everything included in the source distribution. `easy_install` will only pull down the package source. If you need to install the package, you will need to run `easy_install` again.

Change Active Version of Package

This example assumes that you have `liten` version 0.1.3 and some other version of `liten` installed. It also assumes that the other version is the "active version." This is how you would reactivate 0.1.3:

```
easy_install liten=0.1.3
```

This will work whether you need to downgrade to an older package or if you need to get back to a more current version of a package.

Changing Standalone .py File into egg

Here is how you convert a regular standalone Python package into an egg (note the `-f` flag):

```
easy_install -f "http://svn.colorstudy.com/virtualenv/
        trunk/virtualenv.py#egg=virtualenv-1.0" virtualenv
```

This is useful when you want to package a single *.py* file as an egg. Sometimes, using this method is your best choice if you want to use a previously unpackaged standalone Python filesystem-wide. Your other alternative is to set your PYTHONPATH whenever you want to use that standalone module. In this example, we are packaging the `virtua lenv.py` script from that project's trunk and putting our own version and name label on it. In the URL string, the `#egg=virtualenv-1.0` simply specifies the package name and version number we are choosing to give this script. The argument that we give after the URL string is the package name we are looking for. It makes sense to use the

---

consistent names between the URL string and the standalone package name argument, because we are telling `easy_install` to install a package with the same name as what we just created. While it makes sense to keep these two in sync, you shouldn't feel constrained to keep the package name in sync with the name of the module. For example:

```
easy_install -f "http://svn.colorstudy.com/virtualenv/
    trunk/virtualenv.py#egg=foofoo-1.0" foofoo
```

This does exactly the same thing as the previous example, except that it creates a package named foofoo rather than virtualenv. What you choose to name these types of packages is entirely up to you.

Authenticating to a Password Protected Site

There may be cases where you need to install an egg from a website that requires authentication before allowing you to pull down any files. In that case, you can use this syntax for a URL to specify a username and password:

```
easy_install -f http://uid:passwd@example.com/packages
```

You may have a secret skunkworks project you are developing at work that you don't want your coworkers to find out about. (Isn't everyone doing this?) One way to distribute your packages to coworkers "behind the scenes," is to create a simple .htaccess file and then tell `easy_install` to do an authenticated update.

Using Configuration Files

`easy_install` has yet another trick for power users. You can specify default options using config files that are formatted using `.ini` syntax. For systems administrators, this is a godsend of a feature, as it allows a declarative configuration of clients who use `easy_install`. `easy_install` will look for config files in the following places, in this order: *current_working_directory/setup.cfg*, *~/.pydistutils.cfg*, and *distutils.cfg* in the distutils package directory.

So, what can you put in this configuration file? Two of the most common items to set are a default intranet site(s) for package downloads, and a custom install directory for the packages. Here is what a sample `easy_install` configuration file could look like:

```
[easy_install]

#Where to look for packages
find_links = http://code.example.com/downloads

#Restrict searches to these domains
allow_hosts = *.example.com

#Where to install packages. Note, this directory has to be on the PYTHONPATH
install_dir = /src/lib/python
```

This configuration file, which we could call ~/.pydistutils.cfg, defines a specific URL to search for packages, allows only searches for packages to come from example.com (and subdomains), and finally places packages into a custom python package directory.

Easy Install Advanced Features Summary

This was not meant to be a replacement for the comprehensive official documentation for easy_install, but it was meant to highlight some of the key features of the tool for power users. Because easy_install is still in active development, it would be a good idea to frequently check *http://peak.telecommunity.com/DevCenter/EasyInstall* for updates to the documentation. There is also a mailing list called the distutils-sig (sig stands for special interest group) that discusses all things Python distribution-related. Sign up at *http://mail.python.org/mailman/listinfo/distutils-sig*, and you can report bugs and get help for easy_install there, too.

Finally, by doing a simple easy_install --help, you will find even more options that we did not discuss. Chances are very good that something you want to do has already been included as a feature in easy_install.

Creating Eggs

We mentioned earlier that an egg is a bundle of Python modules, but we didn't give a much better definition at the time than that. Here is a definition of "egg" from the setuptools website:

> Python Eggs are the preferred binary distribution format for EasyInstall, because they are cross-platform (for "pure" packages), directly importable, and contain project metadata including scripts and information about the project's dependencies. They can be simply downloaded and added to sys.path directly, or they can be placed in a directory on sys.path and then automatically discovered by the egg runtime system.

And we certainly didn't give any reason why a system administrator would be interested in creating eggs. If all that you do is write one-off scripts, eggs won't help you much. But if you start to recognize patterns and common tasks you find your self reinventing frequently, eggs could save you a lot of trouble. If you create a little library of common tasks that you use, you could bundle them as an egg. And if you do that, you've not only saved yourself time in writing code by reusing it, but you've also made it easy to install on multiple machines.

Creating Python eggs is an incredibly simple process. It really involves just four steps:

1. Install setuptools.
2. Create the files you want to be in your egg.
3. Create a *setup.py* file.
4. Run.

```
python setup.py bdist_egg
```

We already have setuptools installed, so we'll go ahead and create the files we want in our egg:

```
$ cd /tmp
$ mkdir egg-example
$ cd egg-example
$ touch hello-egg.py
```

In this case, it will only contain an empty Python module named hello-egg.py.

Next, create the simplest possible *setup.py* file:

```
from setuptools import setup, find_packages
setup(
    name = "HelloWorld",
    version = "0.1",
    packages = find_packages(),
)
```

Now, we can create the egg:

```
$ python setup.py bdist_egg
running bdist_egg
running egg_info
creating HelloWorld.egg-info
writing HelloWorld.egg-info/PKG-INFO
writing top-level names to HelloWorld.egg-info/top_level.txt
writing dependency_links to HelloWorld.egg-info/dependency_links.txt
writing manifest file 'HelloWorld.egg-info/SOURCES.txt'
reading manifest file 'HelloWorld.egg-info/SOURCES.txt'
writing manifest file 'HelloWorld.egg-info/SOURCES.txt'
installing library code to build/bdist.macosx-10.5-i386/egg
running install_lib
warning: install_lib: 'build/lib' does not exist -- no Python modules to install
creating build
creating build/bdist.macosx-10.5-i386
creating build/bdist.macosx-10.5-i386/egg
creating build/bdist.macosx-10.5-i386/egg/EGG-INFO
copying HelloWorld.egg-info/PKG-INFO -> build/bdist.macosx-10.5-i386/egg/EGG-INFO
copying HelloWorld.egg-info/SOURCES.txt -> build/bdist.macosx-10.5-i386/egg/EGG-INFO
copying HelloWorld.egg-info/dependency_links.txt -> build/bdist.macosx-10.5-i386/egg/EGG-INFO
copying HelloWorld.egg-info/top_level.txt -> build/bdist.macosx-10.5-i386/egg/EGG-INFO
zip_safe flag not set; analyzing archive contents...
creating dist
creating 'dist/HelloWorld-0.1-py2.5.egg' and adding 'build/bdist.macosx-10.5-i386/egg' to it
removing 'build/bdist.macosx-10.5-i386/egg' (and everything under it)
$ ll
total 8
drwxr-xr-x  6 ngift  wheel  204 Mar 10 06:53 HelloWorld.egg-info
drwxr-xr-x  3 ngift  wheel  102 Mar 10 06:53 build
drwxr-xr-x  3 ngift  wheel  102 Mar 10 06:53 dist
-rw-r--r--  1 ngift  wheel    0 Mar 10 06:50 hello-egg.py
-rw-r--r--  1 ngift  wheel  131 Mar 10 06:52 setup.py
```

Install the egg:

```
$ sudo easy_install HelloWorld-0.1-py2.5.egg
sudo easy_install HelloWorld-0.1-py2.5.egg
Password:
Processing HelloWorld-0.1-py2.5.egg
Removing /Library/Python/2.5/site-packages/HelloWorld-0.1-py2.5.egg
Copying HelloWorld-0.1-py2.5.egg to /Library/Python/2.5/site-packages
Adding HelloWorld 0.1 to easy-install.pth file

Installed /Library/Python/2.5/site-packages/HelloWorld-0.1-py2.5.egg
Processing dependencies for HelloWorld==0.1
Finished processing dependencies for HelloWorld==0.1
```

As you can see, creating an egg is extremely simple. Because this egg was really a blank file, though, we'll create a Python script and go into building an egg in a little more detail.

Here is a very simple Python script that shows the files in a directory that are symlinks, where their corresponding real file is, and whether the real file exists or not:

```python
#!/usr/bin/env python

import os
import sys

def get_dir_tuple(filename, directory):
    abspath = os.path.join(directory, filename)
    realpath = os.path.realpath(abspath)
    exists = os.path.exists(abspath)
    return (filename, realpath, exists)

def get_links(directory):
    file_list = [get_dir_tuple(f, directory) for f in os.listdir(directory)
            if os.path.islink(os.path.join(directory, f))]
    return file_list

def main():
    if not len(sys.argv) == 2:
        print 'USAGE: %s directory' % sys.argv[0]
        sys.exit(1)
    directory = sys.argv[1]
    print get_links(directory)

if __name__ == '__main__':
    main()
```

Next, we'll create a setup.py that uses setuptools. This is another minimal *setup.py* file as in our previous example:

```python
from setuptools import setup, find_packages
setup(
    name = "symlinkator",
    version = "0.1",
    packages = find_packages(),
    entry_points = {
        'console_scripts': [
            'linkator = symlinkator.symlinkator:main',
```

```
            ],
        },
    )
```

This declares that name of the package is "symlinkator", that it is at version 0.1, and that setuptools will try to find any appropriate Python files to include. Just ignore the entry_points section for the moment.

Now, we'll build the egg by running python setup.py bdist_egg:

```
$ python setup.py bdist_egg
running bdist_egg
running egg_info
creating symlinkator.egg-info
writing symlinkator.egg-info/PKG-INFO
writing top-level names to symlinkator.egg-info/top_level.txt
writing dependency_links to symlinkator.egg-info/dependency_links.txt
writing manifest file 'symlinkator.egg-info/SOURCES.txt'
writing manifest file 'symlinkator.egg-info/SOURCES.txt'
installing library code to build/bdist.linux-x86_64/egg
running install_lib
warning: install_lib: 'build/lib' does not exist -- no Python modules to install
creating build
creating build/bdist.linux-x86_64
creating build/bdist.linux-x86_64/egg
creating build/bdist.linux-x86_64/egg/EGG-INFO
copying symlinkator.egg-info/PKG-INFO -> build/bdist.linux-x86_64/egg/EGG-INFO
copying symlinkator.egg-info/SOURCES.txt -> build/bdist.linux-x86_64/egg/EGG-INFO
copying symlinkator.egg-info/dependency_links.txt -> build/bdist.linux-x86_64/egg/EGG-INFO
copying symlinkator.egg-info/top_level.txt -> build/bdist.linux-x86_64/egg/EGG-INFO
zip_safe flag not set; analyzing archive contents...
creating dist
creating 'dist/symlinkator-0.1-py2.5.egg' and adding 'build/bdist.linux-x86_64/egg' to it
removing 'build/bdist.linux-x86_64/egg' (and everything under it)
```

Verify the egg contents. Let's go into the *dist* directory that was created and verify there is an egg located in there:

```
$ ls -l dist
total 4
-rw-r--r-- 1 jmjones jmjones 825 2008-05-03 15:34 symlinkator-0.1-py2.5.egg
```

Now, we'll install the egg:

```
$ easy_install dist/symlinkator-0.1-py2.5.egg
Processing symlinkator-0.1-py2.5.egg
....
Processing dependencies for symlinkator==0.1
Finished processing dependencies for symlinkator==0.1
```

Next, let's fire up IPython, import, and use our module:

```
In [1]: from symlinkator.symlinkator import get_links

In [2]: get_links('/home/jmjones/logs/')
Out[2]: [('fetchmail.log.old', '/home/jmjones/logs/fetchmail.log.3', False),
 ('fetchmail.log', '/home/jmjones/logs/fetchmail.log.0', True)]
```

Just in case you're interested, here is the directory that we ran the get_links() function
on:

```
$ ls -l ~/logs/
total 0
lrwxrwxrwx 1 jmjones jmjones 15 2008-05-03 15:11 fetchmail.log -> fetchmail.log.0
-rw-r--r-- 1 jmjones jmjones  0 2008-05-03 15:09 fetchmail.log.0
-rw-r--r-- 1 jmjones jmjones  0 2008-05-03 15:09 fetchmail.log.1
lrwxrwxrwx 1 jmjones jmjones 15 2008-05-03 15:11 fetchmail.log.old -> fetchmail.log.3
```

Entry Points and Console Scripts

From the setuptools documentation page:

> Entry points are used to support dynamic discovery of services or plugins provided by a
> project. See Dynamic Discovery of Services and Plugins for details and examples of the
> format of this argument. In addition, this keyword is used to support Automatic Script
> Creation.

The only kinds of entry points that we'll cover in this book are the console script variety.
setuptools will automatically create a console script for you given just a couple of pieces
of information that you place in your *setup.py*. Here is the relevant section from the
setup.py in the previous example:

```
entry_points = {
    'console_scripts': [
        'linkator = symlinkator.symlinkator:main',
    ],
},
```

In this example, we specified that we wanted to have a script named "linkator" and
that when the script was executed, we wanted it to call the main() function in the
symlinkator.symlinkator module. When we installed the egg, this linkator script was
placed in the same directory with our python binary:

```
#!/home/jmjones/local/python/scratch/bin/python
# EASY-INSTALL-ENTRY-SCRIPT: 'symlinkator==0.1','console_scripts','linkator'
__requires__ = 'symlinkator==0.1'
import sys
from pkg_resources import load_entry_point

sys.exit(
    load_entry_point('symlinkator==0.1', 'console_scripts', 'linkator')()
)
```

Everything that you see was generated by *setuptools*. It's really not important to understand everything that's in this script. Actually, it's probably not important at all to
understand *anything* in this script. The important thing to know is that when you define
a console_scripts entry point in your setup.py, setuptools will create a script that calls
your code into the place that you designated. And here is what happens when we call
this script in a comparable manner to calling it in a previous example:

```
$ linkator ~/logs/
[('fetchmail.log.old', '/home/jmjones/logs/fetchmail.log.3', False),
 ('fetchmail.log', '/home/jmjones/logs/fetchmail.log.0', True)]
```

There are some complex aspects to understand about entry points, but on a very high level, it is only important to know that you can use an entry point to "install" your script as a command-line tool in the user's path. In order to do this, you only need to follow the syntax listed above and define a function that runs your command-line tool.

Registering a Package with the Python Package Index

If you write a cool tool or useful module, naturally, you want to share it with other people. This is one of the most enjoyable parts of open source software development. Thankfully, it is a relatively simple process to upload a package to the Python Package Index.

The process is only slightly different from creating an egg. Two things to pay attention to are to remember to include a ReST, reStructuredText, formatted description in the long_description, and to provide a download_url value. We talked about ReST formatting in Chapter 4.

Although we discussed ReST formatting earlier, we should emphasize here that it is a good idea to format your documentation as ReST because it will be converted to HTML when it is uploaded to the cheeseshop. You can use the tool Aaron Hillegass created, ReSTless, to preview the formatted text to insure it is properly formatted while you preview it. One caveat to look out for is to make sure that you properly format your ReST. If you do not have properly formatted ReST, the text will display as plain text, and not HTML, when you upload your documentation.

See Example 9-2 for a look at a working **setup.py** for a command-line tool and library that Noah created.

Example 9-2. Sample setup.py for upload to Python Package Index

```python
#!/usr/bin/env python

# liten 0.1.4.2 -- deduplication command-line tool
#
# Author: Noah Gift
try:
    from setuptools import setup, find_packages
except ImportError:
    from ez_setup import use_setuptools
    use_setuptools()
    from setuptools import setup, find_packages
import os,sys

version = '0.1.4.2'
f = open(os.path.join(os.path.dirname(__file__), 'docs', 'index.txt'))
long_description = f.read().strip()
```

```
f.close()

setup(

        name='liten',
        version='0.1.4.2',
        description='a de-duplication command line tool',
        long_description=long_description,
        classifiers=[
                'Development Status :: 4 - Beta',
                'Intended Audience :: Developers',
                'License :: OSI Approved :: MIT License',
            ],
        author='Noah Gift',
        author_email='noah.gift@gmail.com',
        url='http://pypi.python.org/pypi/liten',
        download_url="http://code.google.com/p/liten/downloads/list",
        license='MIT',
        py_modules=['virtualenv'],
        zip_safe=False,
        py_modules=['liten'],
        entry_points="""
        [console_scripts]
        liten = liten:main
        """,
        )
```

Using this *setup.py* file, we can now "automatically" register a package with the Python
Package Index by issuing this command:

```
$ python setup.py register
running register
running egg_info
writing liten.egg-info/PKG-INFO
writing top-level names to liten.egg-info/top_level.txt
writing dependency_links to liten.egg-info/dependency_links.txt
writing entry points to liten.egg-info/entry_points.txt
writing manifest file 'liten.egg-info/SOURCES.txt'
Using PyPI login from /Users/ngift/.pypirc
Server response (200): OK
```

This `setup.py` adds some additional fields compared to the `symlinkator` example. Some
of the additional fields include `description`, `long_description`, `classifiers`, `author`,
and `download_url`. The entry point, as we discussed earlier, allows the tool to be run
from the command line and installed into the default scripts directory.

The `download_url` is critical because it tells `easy_install` where to search for your package. You can include a link to a page and `easy_install` is smart enough to find the
package or egg, but you can also explicitly create the link to an egg you created.

The `long_description` reuses documentation that exists in a */doc* relative directory that
was created with an *index.txt* file in it. The *index.txt* file is formatted as ReST, and then
the `setup.py` script reads that information in, and puts it into the field as it is registered
with the Python Package Index.

Where Can I Learn More About . . .

The following are important resources:

Easy install
 http://peak.telecommunity.com/DevCenter/EasyInstall

Python eggs
 http://peak.telecommunity.com/DevCenter/PythonEggs

The setuptools module
 http://peak.telecommunity.com/DevCenter/setuptools

The package resources module
 http://peak.telecommunity.com/DevCenter/PkgResources

Architectural overview of pkg_resources and Python eggs in general
 Architectural Overview of pkg_resources and Python Eggs in General

And don't forget the Python mailing list at *http://mail.python.org/pipermail/distutils-sig/*.

Distutils

As of the time of this writing, setuptools is the preferred way of creating packages and distributing them for many people, and it seems possible that parts of the setuptools library will make it into the standard library. That being said, it is still important to know how the distutils package works, what setuptools enhances, and what it doesn't.

When distutils has been used to create a package for distribution, the typical way to install the package will be to run:

```
python setup.py
install
```

Regarding building packages for distribution, we will be covering four topics:

- How to write a setup script, which is a *setup.py* file
- Basic configuration options in the *setup.py* file
- How to build a source distribution
- Creating binaries such as rpms, Solaris, pkgtool, and HP-UX swinstall

The best way to demonstrate how distutils works is to just jump in feet first.

Step 1: create some code. Let's use this simple script as an example to distribute:

```
#!/usr/bin/env python
#A simple python script we will package
#Distutils Example. Version 0.1

class DistutilsClass(object):
    """This class prints out a statement about itself."""
```

```
    def __init__(self):
        print "Hello, I am a distutils distributed script." \
            "All I do is print this message."

if __name__ == '__main__':
    DistutilsClass()
```

Step 2: make a *setup.py* in the same directory as your script.

```
#Installer for distutils example script

from distutils.core import setup

setup(name="distutils_example",
    version="0.1",
    description="A Completely Useless Script That Prints",
    author="Joe Blow",
    author_email = "joe.blow@pyatl.org",
    url = "http://www.pyatl.org")
```

Notice that we're passing setup() several keyword arguments that can later identify this package by this metadata. Please note this is a very simple example, as there are many more options, such as dealing with multiple dependencies, etc. We won't get into more advanced configurations, but we do recommend reading more about them in the official Python online documentation.

Step 3: create a distribution.

Now that we have a very basic setup.py script, we can create a source distribution package very easily by running this command in the same directory as your script, README and *setup.py* file:

```
python setup.py sdist
```

You will get the following output:

```
running sdist
        warning: sdist: manifest template 'MANIFEST.in' does not exist
          (using default file list)
        writing manifest file 'MANIFEST'
        creating distutils_example-0.1
        making hard links in distutils_example-0.1...
        hard linking README.txt distutils_example-0.1
        hard linking setup.py distutils_example-0.1
        creating dist
        tar -cf dist/distutils_example-0.1.tar distutils_example-0.1
        gzip -f9 dist/distutils_example-0.1.tar
        removing 'distutils_example-0.1' (and everything under it)
```

As you can tell from the output, now all someone has to do is unpack and install using:

```
python setup.py install
```

If you would like to build binaries, here are a few examples. Note that they rely on the underlying operating system to do the heavy lifting, so you cannot build an rpm on, say, OS X. With the plethora of virtualization products around, though, this shouldn't be a problem for you. Just keep a few virtual machines laying around that you can activate when you need to do builds.

To build an rpm:

```
python setup.py bdist_rpm
```

To build a Solaris pkgtool:

```
python setup.py bdist_pkgtool
```

To build a HP-UX swinstall:

```
python setup.py bdist_sdux
```

Finally, when you distribute the package you make, you may want to customize the installation directory when you get around to installing your package. Normally, the build and installation processes happen all at once, but you may want to select a customized build direction like the following:

```
python setup.py build --build-base=/mnt/python_src/ascript.py
```

When you actually run the `install` command, it copies everything in the *build* directory to an *installation* directory. By default, the *installation* directory is the *site-packages* directory in the Python environment in which you execute the command, but you can also specify a custom *installation* directory, such as an NFS mount point, as shown in the previous example.

Buildout

Buildout is a tool created by Jim Fulton of Zope Corporation to manage "building out" new applications. These applications can be Python programs or other programs, such as Apache. One of the main goals of Buildout is to allow buildouts to become repeatable across platforms. One of the author's first experiences using Buildout was to deploy a Plone 3.x site. Since then, he realized this was just the tip of the iceberg.

Buildout is one of the more buzz-worthy new package management tools that Python has to offer, as it allows complex applications that have complex dependencies to bootstrap themselves if they have a bootstrap.py and a config file. In the coming sections, we will separate our discussion into two pieces: using Buildout and developing with Buildout. We would also recommend you read the Buildout manual at *http://pypi.python.org/pypi/zc.buildout*, as it is an invaluable resource for the latest information about Buildout. In fact, this documentation is about as comprehensive as it gets for Buildout, and is a must-read for any Buildout user.

Jim Fulton

Jim Fulton is the creator and one of the maintainers of the Zope Object Database. Jim is also one of the creators of the Zope Object Publishing Environment and the CTO at Zope Corporation.

Using Buildout

Although many people that deal with Zope technologies are aware of Buildout, it has been a secret for the rest of the Python world. Buildout is the recommended mechanism by which Plone is deployed. If you are not familiar with Plone, it is an enterprise-grade content management system with a tremendous development community behind it. Plone used to be extremely complex to install until the invention of Buildout. Now Buildout makes Plone installation trivial.

What many people do not know is that you can use Buildout to manage a Python environment as well. Buildout is a very clever piece of software because it requires only two things:

- The latest copy of *bootstrap.py*. You can always download it here: *http://svn.zope.org/*checkout*/zc.buildout/trunk/bootstrap/bootstrap.py*.
- A *buildout.cfg* file, with the names of the "recipes" or "eggs" to install.

The best way to demonstrate Buildout is to use it to install something. Noah has written a de-duplication command-line tool called liten that is available from the central Python repository, PyPI. We are going to use Buildout to "bootstrap" a Python environment to run this tool.

Step 1: download the bootstrap.py script.

```
mkdir -p ~/src/buildout_demo
curl http://svn.zope.org/*checkout*/zc.buildout/trunk/
bootstrap/bootstrap.py > ~/src/buildout_demo/bootstrap.py
```

Step 2: define a simple *buildout.cfg*. As we stated earlier, Buildout requires a *build out.cfg* file to be present. If we tried to run the **bootstrap.py** script without the *build out.cfg* file, we would get the output below:

```
$ python bootstrap.py
While:
Initializing.
Error: Couldn't open /Users/ngift/src/buildout_demo/buildout.cfg
```

For example, we will create the configuration file shown in Example 9-3.

Example 9-3. Example Buildout configuration file

```
[buildout]
parts = mypython
[mypython]
recipe = zc.recipe.egg
interpreter = mypython
eggs = liten
```

If we save that file as `buildout.cfg` and then run the `bootstrap.py` script again, we will get the output shown in Example 9-4.

Example 9-4. Poking the buildout environment with a stick

```
$ python bootstrap.py
Creating directory '/Users/ngift/src/buildout_demo/bin'.
Creating directory '/Users/ngift/src/buildout_demo/parts'.
Creating directory '/Users/ngift/src/buildout_demo/eggs'.
Creating directory '/Users/ngift/src/buildout_demo/develop-eggs'.
Generated script '/Users/ngift/src/buildout_demo/bin/buildout'.
```

If we poke around these newly created directories, we will find executables, including a custom Python interpreter inside of the *bin* directory:

```
$ ls -l bin
total 24
-rwxr-xr-x  1 ngift  staff  362 Mar  4 22:17 buildout
-rwxr-xr-x  1 ngift  staff  651 Mar  4 22:23 mypython
```

Now that we finally have a Buildout tool installed, we can run it and our egg we defined earlier will work. See Example 9-5.

Example 9-5. Running Buildout and testing installation

```
$ bin/buildout
Getting distribution for 'zc.recipe.egg'.
Got zc.recipe.egg 1.0.0.
Installing mypython.
Getting distribution for 'liten'.
Got liten 0.1.3.
Generated script '/Users/ngift/src/buildout_demo/bin/liten'.
Generated interpreter '/Users/ngift/src/buildout_demo/bin/mypython'.
$ bin/mypython

>>>
$ ls -l bin
total 24
-rwxr-xr-x  1 ngift  staff  362 Mar  4 22:17 buildout
-rwxr-xr-x  1 ngift  staff  258 Mar  4 22:23 liten
-rwxr-xr-x  1 ngift  staff  651 Mar  4 22:23 mypython
$ bin/mypython

>>> import liten
```

Finally, because the "liten" was created with an entry point, which we discussed earlier in this chapter, the egg is able to automatically install a console script in addition to the module inside of the local Buildout *bin* directory. If we take a look at that, we will see the following output:

```
$ bin/liten
Usage: liten [starting directory] [options]

A command-line tool for detecting duplicates using md5 checksums.

Options:
--version              show program's version number and exit
-h, --help             show this help message and exit
-c, --config           Path to read in config file
-s SIZE, --size=SIZE   File Size Example:  10bytes, 10KB, 10MB,10GB,10TB, or
plain number defaults to MB (1 = 1MB)
-q, --quiet            Suppresses all STDOUT.
-r REPORT, --report=REPORT
Path to store duplication report. Default CWD
-t, --test             Runs doctest.
$ pwd
/Users/ngift/src/buildout_demo
```

That is a very powerful and simple example of how Buildout can be used to create an isolated environment and automatically deploy the correct dependencies for a project or environment. To really show the power of Buildout, though, we should look at another aspect of Buildout. Buildout has complete "control" of the directory in which it is run, and everytime that Buildout runs, it reads the *buildout.cfg* file to look for instructions. This means that if we remove the egg we listed, it will effectively remove the command-line tool and the library. See Example 9-6

Example 9-6. Stripped-down Buildout configuration file

```
[buildout]
parts =
```

Now, here is a rerunning of Buildout with the egg and interpreter removed. Note that Buildout has quite a few command-line options, and in this case, we are selecting -N, which will only modify changed files. Normally, Buildout will rebuild everything from scratch each time it is rerun.

```
$ bin/buildout -N
Uninstalling mypython.
```

When we look inside of the *bin* directory, the interpreter and the command-line tool are gone. The only item left is the actual Buildout command-line tool:

```
$ ls -l bin/
total 8
-rwxr-xr-x  1 ngift  staff  362 Mar  4 22:17 buildout
```

If we look inside of the eggs directory, though, the egg is installed but not activated. But we couldn't run it, as it doesn't have an interpreter:

```
$ ls -l eggs
total 640
drwxr-xr-x  7 ngift  staff      238 Mar  4 22:54 liten-0.1.3-py2.5.egg
-rw-r--r--  1 ngift  staff   324858 Feb 16 23:47 setuptools-0.6c8-py2.5.egg
drwxr-xr-x  5 ngift  staff      170 Mar  4 22:17 zc.buildout-1.0.0-py2.5.egg
drwxr-xr-x  4 ngift  staff      136 Mar  4 22:23 zc.recipe.egg-1.0.0-py2.5.egg
```

Developing with Buildout

Now that we have gone through a simple example of creating and destroying a Buildout-controlled environment, we can now go a step further and create a Buildout-controlled development environment.

One of the most common scenarios where Buildout is used is quite simple. A developer may work on an individual package that lives in version control. The developer then checks out her project into a top-level *src* directory. Inside of her *src* directory, she would then run Buildout as described earlier, with an example configuration file such as this:

```
[buildout]
develop = .
parts = test

[python]
recipe = zc.recipe.egg
interpreter = python
eggs = ${config:mypkgs}

[scripts]
recipe = zc.recipe.egg:scripts
eggs = ${config:mypkgs}

[test]
recipe = zc.recipe.testrunner
eggs = ${config:mypkgs}
```

virtualenv

"virtualenv is a tool to create isolated Python environments," according to the documentation on the Python Package Index page. The basic problem that virtualenv solves is to eliminate problems with conflicting packages. Often, one tool will require one version of a package, and another tool will require a different version of a package. This can create a dangerous scenario in which a production web application could be broken because someone "accidentally" modifies the global *site-packages* directory to run a different tool by upgrading a package.

Alternately, a developer may not have write access to a global *site-packages* directory, and can use virtualenv to keep a separate virtualenv that is isolated from the system Python. virtualenv is a great way to eliminate problems before they start, as it allows for the creation of new sandbox that can be, optionally, completely isolated from the global *site-packages* directory.

virtualenv can also "bootstrap" a virtual environment by allowing a developer to pre-populate a virtual environment with a custom environment. This is very similar to what Buildout does, although Buildout uses a declarative config file. We should note that Buildout and virtualenv both extensively use setuptools, of which Phillip J. Eby is the current maintainer.

So, how do you use virtualenv? The most straightforward approach is to use `easy_install` to install virtualenv:

```
sudo easy_install virtualenv
```

If you plan on using virtualenv with only one version of Python, this approach works quite well. If you have several versions of Python installed on your machine, such as Python 2.4, Python 2.5, Python 2.6, and perhaps Python 3000, and they share the same main *bin* directory, such as */usr/bin*, then an alternate approach could work best, as only one virtualenv script can be installed at a time in the same scripts directory.

One way to create several virtualenv scripts that work with multiple versions of Python is to just download the latest version of virtualenv and create an alias to each Python version. Here are the steps to do that:

1. curl *http://svn.colorstudy.com/virtualenv/trunk/virtualenv.py > virtualenv.py*

2. sudo cp *virtualenv.py /usr/local/bin/virtualenv.py*

3. Create two aliases in your Bash or zsh:

```
alias virtualenv-py24="/usr/bin/python2.4 /usr/local/bin/virtualenv.py"
alias virtualenv-py25="/usr/bin/python2.5 /usr/local/bin/virtualenv.py"
alias virtualenv-py26="/usr/bin/python2.6 /usr/local/bin/virtualenv.py"
```

With a multi-script environment behind us, we can go ahead and create several virtualenv containers for each version of Python we need to deal with. Here is an example of what that looks like.

Creating a Python2.4 virtual environment:

```
$ virtualenv-py24 /tmp/sandbox/py24ENV
New python executable in /tmp/sandbox/py24ENV/bin/python
Installing setuptools.................done.
$ /tmp/sandbox/py24ENV/bin/python
Python 2.4.4 (#1, Dec 24 2007, 15:02:49)
[GCC 4.0.1 (Apple Inc. build 5465)] on darwin
Type "help", "copyright", "credits" or "license" for more information.
>>>
$ ls /tmp/sandbox/py24ENV/
bin/  lib/
$ ls /tmp/sandbox/py24ENV/bin/
activate          easy_install*    easy_install-2.4*  python*        python2.4@
```

Creating a Python2.5 virtual environment:

```
$ virtualenv-py25 /tmp/sandbox/py25ENV
New python executable in /tmp/sandbox/py25ENV/bin/python
Installing setuptools.........................done.
$ /tmp/sandbox/py25ENV/bin/python
Python 2.5.1 (r251:54863, Jan 17 2008, 19:35:17)
[GCC 4.0.1 (Apple Inc. build 5465)] on darwin
Type "help", "copyright", "credits" or "license" for more information.
>>>
$ ls /tmp/sandbox/py25ENV/
bin/  lib/
$ ls /tmp/sandbox/py25ENV/bin/
activate          easy_install*    easy_install-2.5*  python*        python2.5@
```

If we look at the output of the commands, we can observe that virtualenv creates a relative bin directory and a relative *lib* directory. Inside the *bin* directory is a python interpretor that uses the *lib* directory as its own local *site-packages* directory. Another great feature is the prepopulated easy_install script that allows an easy_install of packages into the virtual environment.

Finally, it is important to take note that there are two ways to work with the virtual environment you create. You can always explicitly call the full path to a virtual environment:

```
$ /src/virtualenv-py24/bin/python2.4
```

Alternately, you can use the activate script located in the *bin* directory of your virtualenv to set your environment to use that "sandbox" without typing in a full path. This is an optional tool you can use, but it is not necessary, as you can always type in the full path to your virtualenv. Doug Hellmann, one of the reviewers for the book, created a clever hack you can find here: *http://www.doughellmann.com/projects/virtualenvwrapper/*. It uses activate with a Bash wrapper menu that let's you select which sandbox to work on at a time.

Creating a Custom Bootstrapped Virtual Environment

The release of virtualenv 1.0, which is current as of the writing of this book, includes support to create bootstrap scripts for virtualenv environments. One method of doing that is to call `virutalenv.create_bootstrap_script(text)`. What this does is create a bootstrap script, which is like virtualenv, but with additional features to extend option parsing, adjust_options, and use after_install hooks.

Let's go over how easy it is to create a custom bootstrap script that will install virtualenv and a custom set of eggs into a new environment. Going back to the liten package as an example, we can use virtualenv to create a brand new virtual environment and pre-populate it with liten. Example 9-7 shows exactly how to create a custom bootstrap script that installs liten.

Example 9-7. Bootstrap creator example

```
import virtualenv, textwrap
output = virtualenv.create_bootstrap_script(textwrap.dedent("""
import os, subprocess
def after_install(options, home_dir):
    etc = join(home_dir, 'etc')
    if not os.path.exists(etc):
        os.makedirs(etc)
    subprocess.call([join(home_dir, 'bin', 'easy_install'),
                    'liten'])
"""))
f = open('liten-bootstrap.py', 'w').write(output)
```

This example was adapted from the virtualenv documentation, and the last two lines are the important lines to pay attention to:

```
    subprocess.call([join(home_dir, 'bin', 'easy_install'),
    'liten'])
"""))
f = open('liten-bootstrap.py', 'w').write(output)
```

In a nutshell, this tells our `after_install` function to write a new file in the current working directory called *liten-bootstrap.py* and then include a custom `easy_install` of the module liten. It is important to note that this snippet of code will create a *bootstrap.py*, and then this *bootstrap.py* file will need to be run. After running this script, we will have a *liten-bootstrap.py* file that can be distributed to a developer or end user.

If we run `liten-bootstrap.py` without any options, we get the following output:

```
$ python liten-bootstrap.py
You must provide a DEST_DIR
Usage: liten-bootstrap.py [OPTIONS] DEST_DIR

Options:
  --version           show program's version number and exit
  -h, --help          show this help message and exit
  -v, --verbose       Increase verbosity
  -q, --quiet         Decrease verbosity
  --clear             Clear out the non-root install and start from scratch
  --no-site-packages  Don't give access to the global site-packages dir to the
                      virtual environment
```

When we actually run this tool with a destination directory, we get this output:

```
$ python liten-bootstrap.py  --no-site-packages /tmp/liten-ENV
New python executable in /tmp/liten-ENV/bin/python
Installing setuptools..........................done.
Searching for liten
Best match: liten 0.1.3
Processing liten-0.1.3-py2.5.egg
Adding liten 0.1.3 to easy-install.pth file
Installing liten script to /tmp/liten-ENV/bin

Using /Library/Python/2.5/site-packages/liten-0.1.3-py2.5.egg
Processing dependencies for liten
Finished processing dependencies for liten
```

Our clever bootstrap script automatically creates an environment with our module. So, if we run the full path to the virtualenv on our the liten tool, we get the following:

```
$ /tmp/liten-ENV/bin/liten
Usage: liten [starting directory] [options]

A command-line tool for detecting duplicates using md5 checksums.

Options:
--version            show program's version number and exit
-h, --help           show this help message and exit
-c, --config         Path to read in config file
-s SIZE, --size=SIZE File Size Example:  10bytes, 10KB, 10MB,10GB,10TB, or
plain number defaults to MB (1 = 1MB)
-q, --quiet          Suppresses all STDOUT.
-r REPORT, --report=REPORT
Path to store duplication report. Default CWD
-t, --test           Runs doctest.
```

This is a great trick to know about, as it allows a completely isolated and bootstrapped virtual environment.

We hope it is clear from this section on virtualenv that one of its core strengths is how simple it is to use and understand. More than anything, virtualenv respects the sacred rule of KISS, and that alone is reason enough to consider using it to help manage isolated development environments. Be sure to visit the virtualenv mailing list at *http://groups.google.com/group/python-virtualenv/* if you have more questions about it.

EPM Package Manager

Because EPM creates native packages for each operating system, it will need to be installed on each "build" system. Due to the incredible advances in virtualization in the past few years, it is trivial to get a few build virtual machines set up. I created a small cluster of virtual machines running in the equivalent of Red Hat run level init 3, with a minimal allocation of RAM, to test out the code examples in this book.

A coworker and contributor to EPM first introduced me to what EPM can do. I was looking for a tool that would allow me to create operating system-specific software packages for a tool I had developed, and he mentioned EPM. After reading through some of the online documentation at *http://www.epmhome.org/epm-book.html*, I was pleasantly suprised at how painless the process was. In this section, we are going to walk through the steps involved to create a software package ready for installation on multiple platforms: Ubuntu, OS X, Red Hat, Solaris, and FreeBSD. These steps can easily be applied to other systems that EPM supports, such as AIX or HP-UX.

Before we jump into the tutorial, here is a little background on EPM. According to the official documentation for EPM, it was designed from the beginning to build a binary software distribution using a common software specification format. Because of this design goal, the same distribution files work for all operating systems and all distribution formats.

EPM Package Manager Requirements and Installation

EPM requires only a Bourne type shell, a C compiler, the make program and gzip. These utilities are easily obtained on almost every *nix system, if they are not already installed. After downloading the source for EPM, it is necessary to run the following:

```
./configure
make
make install
```

Creating a Hello World Command-Line Tool to Distribute

To get started with building packages for almost every *nix operating system made, we need something to actually distribute. In the spirit of tradition, we are going to create a simple command-line tool called `hello_epm.py`. See Example 9-8.

Example 9-8. Hello EPM command-line tool

```python
#!/usr/bin/env python

import optparse

def main():
  p = optparse.OptionParser()
  p.add_option('--os', '-o', default="*NIX")
  options, arguments = p.parse_args()
  print 'Hello EPM, I like to make packages on %s' % options.os

if __name__ == '__main__':
  main()
```

If we run this tool, we get the following output:

```
$ python hello_epm.py
Hello EPM, I like to make packages on *NIX
```

```
$ python hello_epm.py --os RedHat
Hello EPM, I like to make packages on RedHat
```

Creating Platform-Specific Packages with EPM

The "basics," are so simple that you may wonder why you never used EPM to package cross-platform software before. EPM reads a "list" file(s) that describe your software package. Comments begin with a # character, directives begin with a % character, variables start with a $ character, and finally, file, directory, init script, and symlink lines start with a letter.

It is possible to create a generic cross-platform install script as well as platform-specific packages. We will focus on creating vendor package files. The next step to creating platform-specific packages is to create a manifest or "list" that describes our package. Example 9-9 is a template we used to create packages for our hello_epm command-line tool. It is general enough that you could get away with changing it slightly to create your own tools.

Example 9-9. "List" template for EPM

```
#EPM List File Can Be Used To Create Package For Any Of These Vendor Platforms
#epm -f format foo bar.list ENTER
#The format option can be one of the following keywords:

#aix - AIX software packages.
#bsd - FreeBSD, NetBSD, or OpenBSD software packages.
#depot or swinstall - HP-UX software packages.
#dpkg - Debian software packages.
#inst or tardist - IRIX software packages.
#native - "Native" software packages (RPM, INST, DEPOT, PKG, etc.) for the platform.
#osx - MacOS X software packages.
#pkg - Solaris software packages.
#portable - Portable software packages (default).
#rpm - Red Hat software packages.
#setld - Tru64 (setld) software packages.
#slackware - Slackware software packages.


# Product Information Section

%product hello_epm
%copyright 2008 Py4SA
%vendor O'Reilly
%license COPYING
%readme README
%description Command Line Hello World Tool
%version 0.1

# Autoconfiguration Variables

$prefix=/usr
$exec_prefix=/usr
```

```
$bindir=${exec_prefix}/bin
$datadir=/usr/share
$docdir=${datadir}/doc/
$libdir=/usr/lib
$mandir=/usr/share/man
$srcdir=.

# Executables

%system all
f 0555 root sys ${bindir}/hello_epm hello_epm.py

# Documentation

%subpackage documentation
f 0444 root sys ${docdir}/README $srcdir/README
f 0444 root sys ${docdir}/COPYING $srcdir/COPYING
f 0444 root sys ${docdir}/hello_epm.html $srcdir/doc/hello_epm.html

# Man pages

%subpackage man
%description Man pages for hello_epm
f 0444 root sys ${mandir}/man1/hello_epm.1 $srcdir/doc/hello_epm.man
```

If we examine this file, which we will call *hello_epm.list*, you will notice that we define the $srcdir variable as the current working directory. In order to create packages on any platform, we now just need to create the following in our current working directory: a *README* file, a *COPYING* file, a *doc/hello_epm.html* file, and a *doc/hello_epm.man* file, and our script hello_epm.py has to be in this same directory.

If we wanted to "cheat" for our hello_epm.py tool, and just place blank files in our packaging directory, we could do this:

```
$ pwd
/tmp/release/hello_epm
$ touch README
$ touch COPYING
$ mkdir doc
$ touch doc/hello_epm.html
$ touch doc/hello_epm.man
```

Looking inside of our directory, we have this layout:

```
$ ls -lR
total 16
-rw-r--r--  1 ngift  wheel     0 Mar 10 04:45 COPYING
-rw-r--r--  1 ngift  wheel     0 Mar 10 04:45 README
drwxr-xr-x  4 ngift  wheel   136 Mar 10 04:45 doc
-rw-r--r--  1 ngift  wheel  1495 Mar 10 04:44 hello_epm.list
-rw-r--r--@ 1 ngift  wheel   278 Mar 10 04:10 hello_epm.py

./doc:
total 0
```

```
-rw-r--r--  1 ngift  wheel  0 Mar 10 04:45 hello_epm.html
-rw-r--r--  1 ngift  wheel  0 Mar 10 04:45 hello_epm.man
```

Making the Package

Now, we have a directory with a "list" file that contains generic directives that will work on any platform EPM supports. All that is left is to run the epm -f command appended with what platform we are on and the name of our list file. Example 9-10 shows what it looks like on OS X.

Example 9-10. Creating a native OS X installer with EPM

```
$ epm -f osx hello_epm hello_epm.list
epm: Product names should only contain letters and numbers!
^C
$ epm -f osx helloEPM hello_epm.list
$ ll
total 16
-rw-r--r--  1 ngift  wheel     0 Mar 10 04:45 COPYING
-rw-r--r--  1 ngift  wheel     0 Mar 10 04:45 README
drwxr-xr-x  4 ngift  wheel   136 Mar 10 04:45 doc
-rw-r--r--  1 ngift  wheel  1495 Mar 10 04:44 hello_epm.list
-rw-r--r--@ 1 ngift  wheel   278 Mar 10 04:10 hello_epm.py
drwxrwxrwx  6 ngift  staff   204 Mar 10 04:52 macosx-10.5-intel
```

Notice the warning when the package name had an underscore in it. As a result, we renamed the package without an underscore and ran it again. It then creates a *macosx-10.5-intel* directory that contains the following.

```
$ ls -la macosx-10.5-intel
total 56
drwxrwxrwx  4 ngift  staff    136 Mar 10 04:54 .
drwxr-xr-x  8 ngift  wheel    272 Mar 10 04:54 ..
-rw-r--r--@ 1 ngift  staff  23329 Mar 10 04:54 helloEPM-0.1-macosx-10.5-intel.dmg
drwxr-xr-x  3 ngift  wheel    102 Mar 10 04:54 helloEPM.mpkg
```

This is convenient, as it makes both a .dmg image archive that is native to OS X and contains our installer and the native OS X installer.

If we run the installer, we will notice that OS X will install our blank man pages and documentation and show our blank license file. Finally, it places our tool exactly where we told it to and creates the custom name we gave it the following:

```
$ which hello_epm
/usr/bin/hello_epm
$ hello_epm
Hello EPM, I like to make packages on *NIX
$ hello_epm -h
Usage: hello_epm [options]

Options:
-h, --help      show this help message and exit
```

```
-o OS, --os=OS
$
```

EPM Summary: It Really Is That Easy

If we `scp -r the /tmp/release/hello_epm` to a Red Hat, Ubuntu, or Solaris machine, we can run the exact same command, except with the platform-specific name, and it will "just work." In Chapter 8, we examined how to create a build farm using this technique so that you can instantly create cross-platform packages by running a script. Please note that all of this source code is available for download along with the example package created. You should be able to slightly modify it and create your own cross-platform packages in minutes.

There are quite a few additional advanced features that EPM has to offer, but going into those is beyond the scope of this book. If you are curious about creating packages that handle dependencies, run pre- and post-install scripts, etc., then you owe it to yourself to read EPM's official documentation, which covers all of these scenarios and more.

## CHAPTER 10

Processes and Concurrency

Introduction

Dealing with processes as a Unix/Linux systems administrator is a fact of life. You need to know about startup scripts, run levels, daemons, cron jobs, long-running processes, concurrency, and a host of other issues. Fortunately, Python makes dealing with processes quite easy. Since Python 2.4, Subprocess has been the one-stop shop module that allows you to spawn new processes and talk to standard input, standard output, and standard error. While talking to a processes is one aspect of dealing with processes, it is also import to understand how to deploy and manage long-running processes as well.

Subprocess

With Python 2.4 came subprocess, which takes the place of several older modules: `os.system`, `os.spawn`, `os.popen`, and `popen2` commands. Subprocess is a revolutionary change for systems administrators and developers who need to deal with processes and "shelling out." It is now a one-stop shop for many things dealing with processes and it may eventually include the ability to manage a flock of processes.

Subprocess might just be the single most important module for a systems administrator, as it is the unified API to "shelling out." Subprocess is responsible for the following things in Python: spawning new processes connecting to standard input, connecting to standard output, connecting to error streams, and listening to return codes.

To whet your appetite, let's use the KISS principle (Keep It Simple Stupid), and do the absolute simplest possible thing we can with Subprocess and make a trivial system call. See Example 10-1.

Example 10-1. Simplest possible use of Subprocess

```
In [4]: subprocess.call('df -k', shell=True)
Filesystem    1024-blocks      Used Available Capacity  Mounted on
/dev/disk0s2     97349872 80043824  17050048     83%    /
```

```
devfs                    106        106        0    100%    /dev
fdesc                      1          1        0    100%    /dev
map -hosts                 0          0        0    100%    /net
map auto_home              0          0        0    100%    /home
Out[4]: 0
```

Using that same simple syntax it is possible to include shell variables as well. Example 10-2 is an example of finding out the summary of the space used in our home directory.

Example 10-2. Summary of disk usage

```
In [7]: subprocess.call('du -hs $HOME', shell=True)
28G     /Users/ngift
Out[7]: 0
```

One interesting trick to point out with Subprocess is the ability to suppress standard out. Many times, someone is just interested in running a system call, but is not concerned about the stdout. In these cases, it is often desirable to suprocess the stdout of `subprocess.call`. Fortunately, there is a very easy way to do this. See Example 10-3.

Example 10-3. Suppressing stdout of subprocess.call

```
In [3]: import subprocess

In [4]: ret = subprocess.call("ping -c 1 10.0.1.1",
                              shell=True,
                              stdout=open('/dev/null', 'w'),
                              stderr=subprocess.STDOUT)
```

There are a few things to point out about these two examples and subprocess.call in general. You typically use subprocess.call when you do not care about the ouptut of the shell command and you just want it to run. If you need to capture the output of a command, then you will want to use **subprocess.Popen**. There is another sizable difference between **subprocess.call** and **subprocess.Popen**. **Subprocess.call** will block waiting for a response, while **subprocess.Popen** will not.

Using Return Codes with Subprocess

One interesting thing to note about subprocess.call is that you can use return codes to determine the success of your command. If you have experience with programming in C or Bash, you will be quite at home with return codes. The phrases "exit code" and "return code" are often used interchangeably to describe the status code of a system process.

Every process will have a return code when it exits, and the status of the return code can be used to determine what actions a program should take. Generally, if a program exits with a code of anything but zero, it is an error. The obvious use of a return code for a developer is to determine that if a process it needs to use return with an exit code of anything but zero, then it was a failure. The not-so-obvious use of return codes has many interesting possibilities. There are special return codes for a program not being found, a program not being executable, and a program being terminated by Ctrl-C. We will explore the use of these return codes in Python programs in this section.

Let's look at a list of common return codes with special meaning:

0

Success

1

General errors

2

Misuse of shell built-ins

126

Command invoked cannot execute

127

Command not found

128

Invalid argument to exit

Fatal error signal "n"

130

Script terminated by Ctrl-C 255 Exit status out of range

The most useful scenario where this may come into play is with the use of return codes 0 and 1, which generally signifies success or failure of a command you just ran. Let's take a look at some common examples of this with subprocess.call. See Example 10-4.

Example 10-4. Failure return code with subprocess.call

```
In [16]: subprocess.call("ls /foo", shell=True)
ls: /foo: No such file or directory
Out[16]: 1
```

Because that directory did not exist, we received a return code of 1 for failure. We can also capture the return code and use it to write conditional statements. See Example 10-5.

Example 10-5. Conditional statements based on return code true/false with subprocess.call

```
In [25]: ret = subprocess.call("ls /foo", shell=True)
ls: /foo: No such file or directory

In [26]: if ret == 0:
   ....:     print "success"
   ....: else:
   ....:     print "failure"
   ....:
```

```
....:
failure
```

Here is an example of a "command not found" return code, which is 127. This might be a useful way to write a tool that attempted to run several similar shell commands based on what was available. You might first try to run rsync, but if you get a return code of 127, then you would move on to scp -r. See Example 10-6.

Example 10-6. Conditional statements based on return code 127 with subprocess.call

```
In [28]: subprocess.call("rsync /foo /bar", shell=True)
/bin/sh: rsync: command not found
Out[28]: 127
```

Let's take the previous example and make it less abstract. Often, when writing cross-platform code that needs to run on a variety of *nix boxes, you may find yourself in a situation in which you need to accomplish something that requires a different system program depending on which OS the program is run. HP-UX, AIX, Solars, FreeBSD, and Red Hat could each have a slightly different utility that does what you want. A program could listen to the return code of the first program it attemps to call via subprocess and if return code 127 is given, then the next command could be tried, etc.

Unfortunately, exit codes can vary from OS to OS, so if you are writing a cross-platform script, you may want to only rely a zero or nonzero exit code. To give you an example, this is an exit code on Solaris 10 for the exact same command we ran earlier on Red Hat Enterprise Linux 5:

```
ash-3.00# python
Python 2.4.4 (#1, Jan  9 2007, 23:31:33) [C] on sunos5
Type "help", "copyright", "credits" or "license" for more information.
>>> import subprocess
>>> subprocess.call("rsync", shell=True)
    /bin/sh: rsync: not found
    1
```

We could still use a specific exit code, but we might first want to determine what the operating system is. After we have determined the operating system, then we could check for the platform-specific command's existence. If you find yourself writing this type of code, then it is a good idea to become intimately familiar with the platform module. The process module is talked about in detail in Chapter 8, so you can refer to that chapter for more information.

Let's look at Example 10-7 to see how to use the platform module interactively in IPython to determine what to pass to subprocess.call.

Example 10-7. Using platform and Subprocess module to determine command execution on Solaris 10

```
In [1]: import platform
In [2]: import subprocess
In [3]: platform?

        Namespace:      Interactive
```

```
        File:          /usr/lib/python2.4/platform.py
        Docstring:
        This module tries to retrieve as much platform-identifying data as
        possible. It makes this information available via function APIs.

        If called from the command line, it prints the platform
        information concatenated as single string to stdout. The output
        format is useable as part of a filename.


In [4]: if platform.system() == 'SunOS':
   ....:     print "yes"
   ....:
yes

In [5]: if platform.release() == '5.10':
   ....:     print "yes"
   ....:
yes

In [6]: if platform.system() == 'SunOS':
   ...:     ret = subprocess.call('cp /tmp/foo.txt /tmp/bar.txt', shell=True)
   ...:     if ret == 0:
   ...:         print "Success, the copy was made on %s %s " % (platform.system(),
               platform.release())
   ...:
Success, the copy was made on SunOS 5.10
```

As you can see, using the platform module with `subprocess.call` can be an effective weapon in writing cross-platform code. Please refer to Chapter 8 for detailed information on using the platform module to write cross-platform *nix code. See Example 10-8.

Example 10-8. Capturing standard out with Subprocess

```
In [1]: import subprocess

In [2]: p = subprocess.Popen("df -h", shell=True, stdout=subprocess.PIPE)

In [3]: out = p.stdout.readlines()

In [4]: for line in out:
   ...:     print line.strip()
   ...:
   ...:
Filesystem      Size   Used  Avail Capacity  Mounted on
/dev/disk0s2    93Gi   78Gi   15Gi    85%    /
devfs          107Ki  107Ki    0Bi   100%    /dev
fdesc          1.0Ki  1.0Ki    0Bi   100%    /dev
map -hosts       0Bi    0Bi    0Bi   100%    /net
map auto_home    0Bi    0Bi    0Bi   100%    /home
```

Note that `readlines()` returns a list with newline characters. We had to use `line.strip()` to remove the newlines. Subprocess also has the ability to communicate with stdin and stdout to create pipes. Here is a simple example of communicating to the standard input of a process. One interesting thing we can do with Python that would be horrendous in Bash is to create a piping factory. With a trivial few lines of code, we have arbitrary commands that get created and printed depending on the number of arguments. See Example 10-9.

Example 10-9. Subprocess piping factory

```
def multi(*args):
    for cmd in args:
        p = subprocess.Popen(cmd, shell=True, stdout = subprocess.PIPE)
        out = p.stdout.read()
        print out
```

Here is an example of this simple function in action:

```
In [28]: multi("df -h", "ls -l /tmp", "tail /var/log/system.log")
Filesystem      Size   Used  Avail Capacity  Mounted on
/dev/disk0s2    93Gi   80Gi   13Gi    87%    /
devfs          107Ki  107Ki   0Bi    100%    /dev
fdesc          1.0Ki  1.0Ki   0Bi    100%    /dev
map -hosts       0Bi    0Bi   0Bi    100%    /net
map auto_home    0Bi    0Bi   0Bi    100%    /home

lrwxr-xr-x@ 1 root   admin  11 Nov 24 23:37 /tmp -> private/tmp


Feb 21 07:18:50 dhcp126 /usr/sbin/ocspd[65145]: starting
Feb 21 07:19:09 dhcp126 login[65151]: USER_PROCESS: 65151 ttys000
Feb 21 07:41:05 dhcp126 login[65197]: USER_PROCESS: 65197 ttys001
Feb 21 07:44:24 dhcp126 login[65229]: USER_PROCESS: 65229 ttys002
```

Due to the power of python and *args, we can arbitrarily run commands using our function as a factory. Each command gets popped off a list starting at the beginning due to the `args.pop(0)` syntax. If we used `args.pop()`, it would have popped the arguments in reverse order. Since this may be confusing, we can also write the same command factory function using a simple iteration for loop:

```
def multi(*args):
    for cmd in args:
        p = subprocess.Popen(cmd, shell=True, stdout = subprocess.PIPE)
        out = p.stdout.read()
        print out
```

Sysadmins quite frequently need to run a sequence of commands, so creating a module that simplifies this process could make quite a bit of sense. Let's take a look at how we could do that with a simple example of inheritance. See Example 10-10.

Example 10-10. Creating a module around Subprocess

```
#!/usr/bin/env python
from subprocess import call
import time
import sys
```

```
"""Subtube is module that simplifies and automates some aspects of subprocess"""

class BaseArgs(object):
"""Base Argument Class that handles keyword argument parsing"""

def __init__(self, *args, **kwargs):
    self.args = args
    self.kwargs = kwargs
    if self.kwargs.has_key("delay"):
        self.delay = self.kwargs["delay"]
    else:
        self.delay = 0
    if self.kwargs.has_key("verbose"):
        self.verbose = self.kwargs["verbose"]
    else:
        self.verbose = False

def run (self):
    """You must implement a run method"""
    raise NotImplementedError

    class Runner(BaseArgs):
        """Simplifies subprocess call and runs call over a sequence of commands

        Runner takes N positional arguments, and optionally:

        [optional keyword parameters]
        delay=1, for time delay in seconds
        verbose=True for verbose output

        Usage:

        cmd = Runner("ls -l", "df -h", verbose=True, delay=3)
        cmd.run()

        """
def run(self):
    for cmd in self.args:
        if self.verbose:
            print "Running %s with delay=%s" % (cmd, self.delay)
        time.sleep(self.delay)
        call(cmd, shell=True)
```

Let's take a look at how we would actually use our newly created module:

```
In [8]: from subtube import Runner
In [9]: r = Runner("df -h", "du -h /tmp")

In [10]: r.run()
Filesystem      Size   Used  Avail Capacity  Mounted on
/dev/disk0s2    93Gi   80Gi   13Gi     87%   /
devfs          108Ki  108Ki    0Bi    100%   /dev
fdesc          1.0Ki  1.0Ki    0Bi    100%   /dev
map -hosts       0Bi    0Bi    0Bi    100%   /net
map auto_home    0Bi    0Bi    0Bi    100%   /home
4.0K     /tmp
```

```
In [11]: r = Runner("df -h", "du -h /tmp", verbose=True)

In [12]: r.run()
Running df -h with delay=0
Filesystem      Size   Used  Avail Capacity  Mounted on
/dev/disk0s2    93Gi   80Gi   13Gi    87%    /
devfs          108Ki  108Ki    0Bi   100%    /dev
fdesc          1.0Ki  1.0Ki    0Bi   100%    /dev
map -hosts       0Bi    0Bi    0Bi   100%    /net
map auto_home    0Bi    0Bi    0Bi   100%    /home
Running du -h /tmp with delay=0
4.0K    /tmp
```

If we had ssh keys set up on all of our systems, we could easily code something like this:

```
machines = ['homer', 'marge','lisa', 'bart']
for machine in machines:
    r = Runner("ssh " + machine + "df -h", "ssh " + machine + "du -h /tmp")
    r.run()
```

This is a crude example of a remote command runner, but the idea is a good one, because the Red Hat Emerging Technology group has a project that facilitates wholesale scripting of large clusters of machines in Python. According to the Func website, "Here's an interesting and contrived example—rebooting all systems that are running httpd. It's contrived, yes, but it's also very simple, thanks to Func." We got into more detailed use of Func in Chapter 8, and we covered a home-brew "dispatching" system that works on any *nix platform.

```
results = fc.Client("*").service.status("httpd")
for (host, returns) in results.iteritems():
if returns == 0:
fc.Client(host).reboot.reboot()
```

Because subprocess is a unified API for "shelling out," we can quite easily write to stdin. In Example 10-11, we will tell the word count utility to listen to standard in, and then we will write a string of characters for word count to process.

Example 10-11. Communicating to standard in with Subprocess

```
In [35]: p = subprocess.Popen("wc -c", shell=True, stdin=subprocess.PIPE)
In [36]: p.communicate("charactersinword")
    16
```

The equivalent Bash is the following:

```
> echo charactersinword | wc -c
```

Let's emulate Bash this time and redirect a file to the standard input. First, we need to write something to a file, so let's do that with the new Python 2.6 syntax. Remember that if you are using Python 2.5, you must you the future import idiom:

```
In [5]: from __future__ import with_statement
```

```
In [6]: with open('temp.txt', 'w') as file:
   ...:     file.write('charactersinword')
```

We can reopen the file the classic way and read the file in as a string assigned to f:

```
In [7]: file = open('temp.txt')
```

```
In [8]: f = file.read()
```

Then we "redirect" the file output to our waiting process:

```
In [9]: p = subprocess.Popen("wc -c", shell=True, stdin=subprocess.PIPE)
```

```
In [10]: p.communicate(f)
```

```
In [11]: p.communicate(f)
16
```

In Bash, this would be equivalent to the following sequence of commands:

```
% echo charactersinword > temp.txt
% wc -c < temp.txt
16
```

Next, let's take a look at actually piping several commands together as we would do in a typical shell scenario. Let's take a look at a series of commands piped together in Bash and then the same series of commands piped together in Python. A realistic example that we encounter quite often is when dealing with logfiles. In Example 10-12, we are looking for the successful logins to the screensaver on a Macintosh laptop.

Example 10-12. Chaining commands with Subprocess

In Bash here is a simple chain:

```
[ngift@Macintosh-6][H:10014][J:0]> cat /etc/passwd | grep 0:0 | cut -d ':' -f 7
/bin/sh
```

Here is the same chain in Python:

```
In [7]: p1 = subprocess.Popen("cat /etc/passwd", shell=True, stdout=subprocess.PIPE)
In [8]: p2 = subprocess.Popen("grep 0:0", shell=True, stdin=p1.stdout, stdout=subprocess.PIPE)
In [9]: p3 = subprocess.Popen("cut -d ': ' -f 7", shell=True, stdin=p2.stdout,
   stdout=subprocess.PIPE)
```

```
In [10]: print p3.stdout.read()
/bin/sh
```

Just because we can do something using subprocess piping, it doesn't mean we have to. In the previous example, we grabbed the shell of the root user by piping a series of commands. Python has a built-in module that does this for us, so it is important to know that sometimes you don't even need to use Subprocess; Python might have a built-in module that does the work for you. Many things you might want to do in the shell, such as tar or zip, Python can also do. It is always a good idea to see if Python has a built-in equivalent if you find yourself doing a very complex shell pipeline using Subprocess. See Example 10-13.

Example 10-13. Using pwd, the password database module instead of Subprocess

```
In [1]: import pwd

In [2]: pwd.getpwnam('root')
Out[2]: ('root', '********', 0, 0, 'System Administrator', '/var/root', '/bin/sh')

In [3]: shell = pwd.getpwnam('root')[-1]

In [4]: shell
Out[4]: '/bin/sh'
```

Subprocess can also handle sending input and receiving output at the same time, and also listening to standard error. Let's take a look at an example of that.

Note that inside of IPython we use the "ed upper.py" feature to automatically switch to Vim when we want to write a snippet of code that may block such as the one in Example 10-14.

Example 10-14. Sending input and receiving output and standard error

```
import subprocess

p = subprocess.Popen("tr a-z A-Z", shell=True,stdin=subprocess.PIPE,
stdout=subprocess.PIPE)
output, error = p.communicate("translatetoupper")
print output
```

So when we exit Vim inside of IPython, it automatically runs this snippet of code and we get the following:

```
done. Executing edited code...
TRANSLATETOUPPER
```

Using Supervisor to Manage Processes

As a sysadmin, you often need to manage and deal with processes. When the web developers find out that their sysadmin is a Python expert, they are going to be very excited because many Python web frameworks do not offer an elegant way to temporarily manage long-running processes. Supervisor can help these situations by managing how a long process is controlled and ensuring it starts back up in the case of a reboot of the system.

Supervisor does quite a bit more than just help web applications get deployed; it has much more general applications. Supervisor can act as cross-platform controller to manage and interact with processes. It can start, stop, and restart other programs on a *nix system. It can also restart crashed processes, which can come in quite handy. The coauthor of Supervisor, Chris McDonough, tells us that it can also help manage "bad" processes, too. This could include processes that consume too much memory or hog the CPU, for example. Supervisor does remote control via XML-RPC XML-RPC Interface Extensions Event Notification System.

Most *nix systems administrators will mainly be concerned with "supervisord," which is the daemon program that runs designed programs as child processes, and "supervisorctl," which is a client program that can view the logs and control the processes from a unified session. There is a web interface as well, but well, this is a book on *nix, so let's move right along.

As of this writing, the latest version of Supervisor is 3.0.x. The latest version of the manual can always be found at *http://supervisord.org/manual/current/*. Installing Supervisor is a piece of cake, thanks to the fact that you can easy_install it. Assuming you have used virtualenv to create a virtual Python installation directory, you can use the following command to easy_install supervisor:

```
bin/easy_install supervisor
```

This will install Supervisor into your *bin* directory. If you did an easy_install to your system Python, then it will be installed in something like */usr/local/bin*, or your system scripts directory.

The next step to getting a very basic Supervisor daemon running is to create a very simple script that prints, sleeps for 10 seconds, and then dies. This is the exact opposite of a long-running process, but it shows one of the more powerful aspects of Supervisor, the ability to auto-restart and daemonize a program. Now, we can simply echo out a *supervisord.conf* file somewhere by using a special supervisor command called echo_supervisord_conf. In this example, we will just echo this out to */etc/supervisord.conf*. It is good to note that the Supervisor config file can live anywhere, as the supervisord daemon can be run with an option to specify the location of a config file.

```
echo_supervisord_conf > /etc/supervisord.conf
```

With those few basic steps out of the way, we are ready to create a very simple example of a process that will die after a few seconds. We will use the upervisor autostart feature to keep this process alive. See Example 10-15.

Example 10-15. Simple example of Supervisor restarting a dying process

```
#!/usr/bin/env python
import time
print "Daemon runs for 3 seconds, then dies"
time.sleep(3)
print "Daemons dies"
```

As we mentioned earlier, in order to actually run a child program inside of supervisord, we need to edit the configuration file, and add our application. Let's go ahead and add a couple lines to */etc/supervisord.conf*:

```
[program:daemon]
command=/root/daemon.py                ; the program (relative uses PATH, can take args)
autorestart=true                   ; retstart at unexpected quit (default: true)
```

Now, we can start supervisord and then use the **supervisorectl** to watch and start the process:

```
[root@localhost]~# supervisord
[root@localhost]~# supervisorctl
daemon                          RUNNING    pid 32243, uptime 0:00:02
supervisor>
```

At this point, we can run the help command to see what options are available for supervisorctl:

```
supervisor> help

Documented commands (type help topic):
========================================
EOF    exit  maintail  quit    restart  start  stop  version
clear  help  open      reload  shutdown status tail
```

Next, let's start our process which we called daemon in the config file and then tail it to watch it while it dies, then reawakens magically, in an almost Frankenstein-like way...mwahahaha. It's alive, then dead, and then alive again.

```
supervisor> stop daemon
daemon: stopped
supervisor> start daemon
daemon: started
```

And for the final part in our play, we can interactively tail the stdout of this program:

```
supervisor> tail -f daemon
== Press Ctrl-C to exit ==
    for 3 seconds, then die
    I just died
    I will run for 3 seconds, then die
```

Using Screen to Manage Processes

An alternate approach to manage long-running processes is to use the GNU screen application. As a sysadmin, if you do not use screen, it is worth knowing even if you will not be managing Python programs with it. One of the core features of screen that makes it so useful is its ability to allow you to detach from a long-running process and come back to it. This is so useful, we would consider it an essential Unix skill to know.

Let's take a look at a typical scenario in which we want to detach from a long-running web application such as trac. There are a few ways to configure trac, but one of the most simple is to just detach from the standalone trac process with screen.

All that is necessary to run a process is screen the append screen to the front of the long-running process, Ctrl-A, and then Ctrl-D to detach. To reattach to that process, you just need to type in screen and then press Ctrl-A again.

In Example 10-16, we tell tracd to run within screen. Once the process starts, we can then simply detach using Ctrl-A, then Ctrl-D, if we ever want to reattach.

Example 10-16. Running Python processes in screen

```
screen python2.4 /usr/bin/tracd --hostname=trac.example.com --port 8888
  -r --single-env --auth=*
,/home/noahgift/trac-instance/conf/password,tracadminaccount /home/example/trac-instance/
```

If I ever need to reattach I can run:

```
[root@cent ~]# screen -r
There are several suitable screens on:
4797.pts-0.cent    (Detached)
24145.pts-0.cent    (Detached)
Type "screen [-d] -r [pid.]tty.host" to resume one of them.
```

This approach might not be the best to use in a production environment, but while doing development work, or for personal use, it certainly has its advantages.

Threads in Python

Threads could be described as a necessary evil to some people, although many people dislike threads, to solve many problems that require dealing with multiple things at once. Threads are different than processes because they all run inside of the same process and share state and memory. That is both the thread's greatest advantage and disadvantage. The advantage is that you can create a data structure that all threads can access without creating an IPC, or interprocess communication mechanism.

There are also hidden complexities in dealing with threads. Often, a trivial program of just a few dozens lines of code can become extremely complex with the introduction of threads. Threads are difficult to debug without adding extensive tracing and even then it is complex, as the output of the tracing can become confusing and overwhelming. While one of the authors was writing an SNMP discovery system that discovered data centers, the sheer magnitude of threads that needed to be spawned was very difficult to handle.

There are strategies to deal with threads, however, and often implementing a robust tracing library is one of them. That said, they can become a very handy tool in solving a complex problem.

For systems administrators, knowing some of the basics of programming with threads may be useful. Here are some of the ways that threads are useful for everyday sysadmin tasks: autodiscovering a network, fetching multiple web pages at the same time, stress-testing a server, and performing network-related tasks.

In keeping with our KISS theme, let's use one of the most basic threading examples possible. It is good to note that threading a module requires an understanding of object-oriented programming. This can be a bit of a challenge, and if you have not had much, or any, exposure to object-oriented programming (OOP), then this example may be somewhat confusing. We would recommend picking up a copy of Mark Lutz's *Learning Python* (O'Reilly) to understand some of the basics of OOP, although you can also refer to our Introduction and practice some of the techniques there. Ultimately, practicing OOP programming is the best way to learn it.

Because this book is about pragmatic Python, let's get right into a threading example using the simplest possible threading example we could think of. In this simple threading script, we inherit from threading.Thread, set a global count variable, and then override the run method for threading. Finally, we launch five threads that explicitly print their number.

In many ways, this example is overly simplistic and has a bad design because we are using a global count so that multiple threads can share state. Often, it is much better to use queues with threads, as they take care of the complexity of dealing with shared state for you. See Example 10-17.

Example 10-17. KISS example of threading

```
#subtly bad design because of shared state
import threading
import time
count = 1
class KissThread(threading.Thread):
    def run(self):
        global count
        print "Thread # %s:  Pretending to do stuff" % count
        count += 1
        time.sleep(2)
        print "done with stuff"
    for t in range(5):
        KissThread().start()


[ngift@Macintosh-6][H:10464][J:0]> python thread1.py
Thread # 1:  Pretending to do stuff
Thread # 2:  Pretending to do stuff
Thread # 3:  Pretending to do stuff
Thread # 4:  Pretending to do stuff
Thread # 5:  Pretending to do stuff
done with stuff
done with stuff
done with stuff
done with stuff
done with stuff


    #common.py
    import subprocess
    import time
```

```
IP_LIST = [ 'google.com',
  'yahoo.com',
  'yelp.com',
  'amazon.com',
  'freebase.com',
  'clearink.com',
  'ironport.com' ]

cmd_stub = 'ping -c 5 %s'

def do_ping(addr):
  print time.asctime(), "DOING PING FOR", addr
  cmd = cmd_stub % (addr,)
  return subprocess.Popen(cmd, shell=True, stdout=subprocess.PIPE)

from common import IP_LIST, do_ping
import time

z = []
#for i in range(0, len(IP_LIST)):
for ip in IP_LIST:
  p = do_ping(ip)
  z.append((p, ip))

for p, ip in z:
  print time.asctime(), "WAITING FOR", ip
  p.wait()
  print time.asctime(), ip, "RETURNED", p.returncode

jmjones@dinkgutsy:thread_discuss$ python nothread.py
Sat Apr 19 06:45:43 2008 DOING PING FOR google.com
Sat Apr 19 06:45:43 2008 DOING PING FOR yahoo.com
Sat Apr 19 06:45:43 2008 DOING PING FOR yelp.com
Sat Apr 19 06:45:43 2008 DOING PING FOR amazon.com
Sat Apr 19 06:45:43 2008 DOING PING FOR freebase.com
Sat Apr 19 06:45:43 2008 DOING PING FOR clearink.com
Sat Apr 19 06:45:43 2008 DOING PING FOR ironport.com
Sat Apr 19 06:45:43 2008 WAITING FOR google.com
Sat Apr 19 06:45:47 2008 google.com RETURNED 0
Sat Apr 19 06:45:47 2008 WAITING FOR yahoo.com
Sat Apr 19 06:45:47 2008 yahoo.com RETURNED 0
Sat Apr 19 06:45:47 2008 WAITING FOR yelp.com
Sat Apr 19 06:45:47 2008 yelp.com RETURNED 0
Sat Apr 19 06:45:47 2008 WAITING FOR amazon.com
Sat Apr 19 06:45:57 2008 amazon.com RETURNED 1
Sat Apr 19 06:45:57 2008 WAITING FOR freebase.com
Sat Apr 19 06:45:57 2008 freebase.com RETURNED 0
Sat Apr 19 06:45:57 2008 WAITING FOR clearink.com
Sat Apr 19 06:45:57 2008 clearink.com RETURNED 0
Sat Apr 19 06:45:57 2008 WAITING FOR ironport.com
Sat Apr 19 06:46:58 2008 ironport.com RETURNED 0
```

As a disclaimer for the following threading examples, note that they are somewhat complex examples, because the same thing can be done using subprocess.Popen. subprocess.Popen is a great choice if you need to launch a bunch of processes and then wait for a response. If you need to communicate with each process, then using subprocess.Popen with a thread would be appropriate. The point in showing multiple examples is to highlight that concurrency is often full of choices with trade-offs. It is often difficult to say one model fits all, whether it be threads, or processes, or asynchronous libraries such as stackless or twisted. The following is the most efficient way to ping a large pool of IP addresses.

Now that we have the equivalent of Hello World out of the way for threading, let's actually do something a real systems administrator would appreciate. Let's take our example and slightly modify it to create a small script to ping a network for responses. This is a starter kit for a general network tool. See Example 10-18.

Example 10-18. Threaded ping sweep

```python
#!/usr/bin/env python
from threading import Thread
import subprocess
from Queue import Queue

num_threads = 3
queue = Queue()
ips = ["10.0.1.1", "10.0.1.3", "10.0.1.11", "10.0.1.51"]
def pinger(i, q):
    """Pings subnet"""
    while True:
        ip = q.get()
        print "Thread %s: Pinging %s" % (i, ip)
        ret = subprocess.call("ping -c 1 %s" % ip,
                              shell=True,
                              stdout=open('/dev/null', 'w'),
                              stderr=subprocess.STDOUT)
        if ret == 0:
            print "%s: is alive" % ip
        else:
            print "%s: did not respond" % ip
        q.task_done()

for i in range(num_threads):

    worker = Thread(target=pinger, args=(i, queue))
    worker.setDaemon(True)
    worker.start()

for ip in ips:
    queue.put(ip)

print "Main Thread Waiting"
```

```
queue.join()
print "Done"
```

When we run this reasonably simple piece of code, we get this output:

```
[ngift@Macintosh-6][H:10432][J:0]# python ping_thread_basic.py
Thread 0: Pinging 10.0.1.1
Thread 1: Pinging 10.0.1.3
Thread 2: Pinging 10.0.1.11
Main Thread Waiting
10.0.1.1: is alive
Thread 0: Pinging 10.0.1.51
10.0.1.3: is alive
10.0.1.51: is alive
10.0.1.11: did not respond
Done
```

This example deserves to be broken down into understandable pieces, but first a little explanation is in order. Using threads to develop a ping sweep of a subnet is about as good of an example of using threads as it gets. A "normal" Python program that did not use threads would take up to N * (average response time per ping). There are two ping states: a response state and a timeout state. A typical network would be a mixture of responses and timeouts.

This means that if you wrote a ping sweep application that sequentially examined a Class C network with 254 addresses, it could take up to 254 * (~ 3 seconds). That comes out to 12.7 minutes. If you use threads, we can reduce that to a handful of seconds. That is why threads are important for network programming. Now, let's take this one step further and think about a realistic environment. How many subnets exist in a typical data center? 20? 30? 50? Obviously, this sequential program becomes un-realistic very quickly, and threads are an ideal match.

Now, we can revisit our simple script and look at some of the implementation details. The first thing to examine are the modules that were imported. The two to look at in particular are threading and queue. As we mentioned in the very first example, using threading without queues makes it more complex than many people can realistically handle. It is a much better idea to always use the queuing module if you find you need to use threads. Why? Because the queue module also alleviates the need to explicitly protect data with mutexes because the queue itself is already protected internally by a mutex.

Imagine you are a farmer/scientist living in the Middle Ages. You have noticed that a group of crows, commonly referred to as a "murder," (please consult Wikipedia for the reasons why), attack your crops in groups of 20 or more.

Because these crows are quite smart, it is almost impossible to scare them all away by throwing rocks, as you can throw, at most, a rock every 3 seconds, and the group of crows numbers, at times, up to 50. To scare away all of the crows, it can take up to several minutes, at least, by which time significant damage is done to your crops. As a student of math and science, you understand that the solution to this problem is simple.

You need to create a queue of rocks in a basket, and then allocate several workers to grab rocks out of this basket and throw them at the crows all at once.

Using this new strategy, if you allocated 30 workers to pull rocks from the basket and throw rocks at the crows, you could throw a rock at 50 crows in less than 10 seconds. This is the basic formula for threads and queuing in Python as well. You give a pool of workers something to do, and when the queue is empty, the job is over.

Queues act as a way to delegate a task to a "pool" of workers in a centralized manner. One of the most important parts of our simple program is the join(). If we look at the docstring, we see that queue.join() states the following:

```
Namespace:    Interactive
File:         /System/Library/Frameworks/Python.framework/Versions/2.5/lib/python2.5/
   Queue.py
Definition:   Queue.Queue.join(self)
Docstring:
Blocks until all items in the Queue have been gotten and processed.

The count of unfinished tasks goes up whenever an item is added to the
queue. The count goes down whenever a consumer thread calls task_done()
to indicate the item was retrieved and all work on it is complete.

When the count of unfinished tasks drops to zero, join() unblocks.
```

A join is a way to control the main thread from exiting the program before the other threads get a chance to finish working on items in a queue. To go back to our farmer metaphor, it would be like the farmer dropping his basket of rocks and leaving while the workers lined up ready to throw rocks. In our example, if we comment out the queue.join() line, we can see the negative repercussions of our actions: First, we comment out the queue.join line:

```
print "Main Thread Waiting"
#By commenting out the join, the main program exits before threads have a chance
   to run
#queue.join()
print "Done"
```

Next, we watch our nice script barf. See Example 10-19.

Example 10-19. Example of main thread exiting before worker threads

```
[ngift@Macintosh-6][H:10189][J:0]# python ping_thread_basic.py
Main Thread Waiting
Done
Unhandled exception in thread started by
Error in sys.excepthook:

Original exception was:
```

With that background theory on threads and queue out of the way, here is the walk-through of that code step by step. In this portion, we hardcode values that would normally be passed into a more generic program. The num_threads is the number of worker threads, the queue is an instance of queue, and finally, the ips, are a list of IP addresses that we will eventually place into a queue:

```
num_threads = 3
queue = Queue()
ips = ["10.0.1.1", "10.0.1.3", "10.0.1.11", "10.0.1.51"]
```

This is the function that does all of the work in the program. This function is run by each thread everytime an "ip" is pulled from the queue. Notice that a new IP address is popped off a stack just like it is in a list. Doing this allows us to take an item until the queue is empty. Finally, notice that q.task_done() is called at the end of this while loop; this is significant because it tells the join() that it has completed what it pulled from the queue. Or, in plain English, it says the job is done. Let's look at the docstring for Queue.Queue.task_done:

```
File:       /System/Library/Frameworks/Python.framework/Versions/2.5/lib/python2.5/
    Queue.py
Definition:    Queue.Queue.task_done(self)
Docstring:
Indicate that a formerly enqueued task is complete.

Used by Queue consumer threads. For each get() used to fetch a task,
a subsequent call to task_done() tells the queue that the processing
on the task is complete.

If a join() is currently blocking, it will resume when all items
have been processed (meaning that a task_done() call was received
for every item that had been put() into the queue).

Raises a ValueError if called more times than there were items
placed in the queue.
```

From the docstring, we can see that there is a relationship between q.get(), q.task_done(), and finally, q.join(). It is almost like a start, a middle, and an end to a story:

```
def pinger(i, q):
    """Pings subnet"""
    while True:
        ip = q.get()
        print "Thread %s: Pinging %s" % (i, ip)
        ret = subprocess.call("ping -c 1 %s" % ip,
                        shell=True,
                        stdout=open('/dev/null', 'w'),
                        stderr=subprocess.STDOUT)
        if ret == 0:
            print "%s: is alive" % ip
        else:
            print "%s: did not respond" % ip
        q.task_done()
```

If we look below, we are using a simple for loop as a controller that is orchestrating the spawning of a thread pool. Notice that this thread pool will just sit and "block," or wait, until something is placed in the queue. It is not until the next section that anything even happens.

There is one subtle suprise lurking in our program that will be sure to catch you off guard. Notice the use of the `setDaemon(True)`. If this is not set before the start method is called, our program will hang indefinitely.

The reason is fairly subtle, and that is because a program will only exit if daemon threads are running. You may have noticed that in the pinger function, we used an infinite loop. Since threads never die, it's imperative to declare them as daemon threads. To see this happen, just comment out the `worker.start()` line and see what happens. To cut to the chase, the program will hang around indefinitely without the setting of the threads to a daemonic flag. You should test this out for yourself, as it will take away part of the magic of the process:

```
for i in range(num_threads):
    worker = Thread(target=pinger, args=(i, queue))
    worker.setDaemon(True)
    worker.start()
```

By this point in our program, we have an angry pool of three threads waiting to do our bidding. They just need to have items placed in their queue, as that sends a signal to our threads to grab an item and do what we told it, in this case, ping an IP address:

```
for ip in ips:
    queue.put(ip)
```

Finally, this one critical line sandwiched in the middle of two print statements is what ultimately has control of the program. Calling `join` on a queue, as we discussed earlier, will cause the main thread of the program to wait until the queue is empty. This is why threads and queue are like chocolate and peanut butter. Each is great alone, but together, they make an especially tasty treat.

```
print "Main Thread Waiting"
queue.join()
print "Done"
```

To really understand threads and queues, we need to take our example a step further and create another thread pool and another queue. In our first example, we ping a list of IP addresses that a thread pool grabs from a queue. In this next example, we will have our first pool of threads place valid IP addresses that respond to a ping into a second queue.

Next, our second pool of threads will take the IP addresses from the first queue and then perform an arping and return the IP address along with the Mac address if it can find it. Let's see how this looks. See Example 10-20.

Example 10-20. Multiple queues with multiple thread pools

```
#!/usr/bin/env python
#This requires Python2.5 or greater
from threading import Thread
```

```python
import subprocess
from Queue import Queue
import re

num_ping_threads = 3
num_arp_threads = 3
in_queue = Queue()
out_queue = Queue()
ips = ["10.0.1.1", "10.0.1.3", "10.0.1.11", "10.0.1.51"]

def pinger(i, iq, oq):
    """Pings subnet"""
    while True:
        ip = iq.get()
        print "Thread %s: Pinging %s" % (i, ip)
        ret = subprocess.call("ping -c 1 %s" % ip,
                        shell=True,
                        stdout=open('/dev/null', 'w'),
                        stderr=subprocess.STDOUT)
        if ret == 0:
            #print "%s: is alive" % ip
            #place valid ip address in next queue
            oq.put(ip)
        else:
            print "%s: did not respond" % ip
        iq.task_done()

def arping(i, oq):
    """grabs a valid IP address from a queue and gets macaddr"""
    while True:
        ip = oq.get()
        p = subprocess.Popen("arping -c 1 %s" % ip,
                        shell=True,
                        stdout=subprocess.PIPE)
        out = p.stdout.read()

        #match and extract mac address from stdout
        result = out.split()
        pattern = re.compile(":")
        macaddr = None
        for item in result:
            if re.search(pattern, item):
                macaddr = item
        print "IP Address: %s | Mac Address: %s " % (ip, macaddr)
        oq.task_done()

#Place ip addresses into in queue
for ip in ips:
    in_queue.put(ip)

#spawn pool of ping threads
for i in range(num_ping_threads):

    worker = Thread(target=pinger, args=(i, in_queue, out_queue))
    worker.setDaemon(True)
```

```
    worker.start()

#spawn pool of arping threads
for i in range(num_arp_threads):

    worker = Thread(target=arping, args=(i, out_queue))
    worker.setDaemon(True)
    worker.start()

print "Main Thread Waiting"
#ensures that program does not exit until both queues have been emptied
in_queue.join()
out_queue.join()

print "Done"
```

If we run this code, here is what the output looks like:

```
python2.5 ping_thread_basic_2.py
Main Thread Waiting
Thread 0: Pinging 10.0.1.1
Thread 1: Pinging 10.0.1.3
Thread 2: Pinging 10.0.1.11
Thread 0: Pinging 10.0.1.51
IP Address: 10.0.1.1  | Mac Address: [00:00:00:00:00:01]
IP Address: 10.0.1.51 | Mac Address: [00:00:00:80:E8:02]
IP Address: 10.0.1.3  | Mac Address: [00:00:00:07:E4:03]
10.0.1.11: did not respond
Done
```

To implement this solution, we only slightly extended the behavior of our first example by adding another pool of threads and queue. This is an important technique to have in your own personal toolkit, as using the queue module makes using threads a lot easier and safer. Arguably, it could even be called necessary.

Timed Delay of Threads with threading.Timer

Python has another threading feature that comes in handy for systems administration tasks. It is quite trivial to run the timed execution of a function inside of a thread by using threading.Timer. Example 10-21 is contrived.

Example 10-21. Thread timer

```
#!/usr/bin/env python
from threading import Timer
import sys
import time
import copy

#simple error handling
if len(sys.argv) != 2:
        print "Must enter an interval"
        sys.exit(1)
```

```
#our function that we will run
def hello():
    print "Hello, I just got called after a %s sec delay" % call_time

#we spawn our time delayed thread here
delay = sys.argv[1]
call_time = copy.copy(delay)     #we copy the delay to use later
t = Timer(int(delay), hello)
t.start()

#we validate that we are not blocked, and that the main program continues
print "waiting %s seconds to run function" % delay
for x in range(int(delay)):
    print "Main program is still running for %s more sec" % delay
    delay = int(delay) - 1
    time.sleep(1)
```

And if we run this code, we can see that the main thread, or program, continues to run, while a timed delay has been triggered for our function:

```
[ngift@Macintosh-6][H:10468][J:0]# python thread_timer.py 5
waiting 5 seconds to run function
Main program is still running for 5 more sec
Main program is still running for 4 more sec
Main program is still running for 3 more sec
Main program is still running for 2 more sec
Main program is still running for 1 more sec
Hello, I just got called after a 5 sec delay
```

Threaded Event Handler

Because this is a book about systems administration, let's use our previous technique for a realistic application. In this example, we take our delayed thread trick and mix in an event loop that watches two directories for changes in filenames. We could get really sophisticated and examine file modification times, but in the spirit of keeping examples simple, we will look at how this event loop looks for a registered event, and if the event is triggered, then an action method is called in a delayed thread.

This module could be abstracted quite easily into a more generic tool, but for now, Example 10-22 is hardcoded to keep two directories in sync if they fall out of sync by using rsync -av --delete in a delayed background thread.

Example 10-22. Threaded directory synchronization tool

```
#!/usr/bin/env python
from threading import Timer
import sys
import time
import copy
import os
from subprocess import call

class EventLoopDelaySpawn(object):
```

```python
    """An Event Loop Class That Spawns a Method in a Delayed Thread"""

    def __init__(self, poll=10,
                       wait=1,
                       verbose=True,
                       dir1="/tmp/dir1",
                       dir2="/tmp/dir2"):

        self.poll = int(poll)
        self.wait = int(wait)
        self.verbose = verbose
        self.dir1 = dir1
        self.dir2 = dir2

    def poller(self):
        """Creates Poll Interval"""
        time.sleep(self.poll)
        if self.verbose:
            print "Polling at %s sec interval" % self.poll

    def action(self):
        if self.verbose:
            print "waiting %s seconds to run Action" % self.wait
        ret = call("rsync -av --delete %s/ %s" % (self.dir1, self.dir2), shell=True)

    def eventHandler(self):
        #if two directories contain same file names
        if os.listdir(self.dir1) != os.listdir(self.dir2):
            print os.listdir(self.dir1)
            t = Timer((self.wait), self.action)
            t.start()
            if self.verbose:
                print "Event Registered"
        else:
            if self.verbose:
                print "No Event Registered"

    def run(self):
        """Runs an event loop with a delayed action method"""
        try:
            while True:
                self.eventHandler()
                self.poller()

        except Exception, err:
            print "Error: %s " % err

        finally:
            sys.exit(0)

E = EventLoopDelaySpawn()
E.run()
```

The observant reader may be thinking that the delay is not strictly necessary, and this is true. The delay can create some added benefit, however. If you add a delay for, say, five seconds, you could tell the thread to cancel if you discovered another event, such as if your master directory was accidentally deleted. A thread delay is a great mechanism to create conditional future operations that can still be canceled.

Processes

Threads are not the only way to deal with concurrency in Python. In fact, processes have some advantages to threads in that they will scale to multiple processors, unlike threads in Python. Because of the GIL, or global interpreter lock, only one thread can truly run at one time, and it is limited to a single processor. However, to make heavy use of the CPU with Python code, threads are not a good option. In such cases, it's better to use separate processes.

If a problem requires the use of multiple processors, then processes are a fine choice. Additionally, there are many libraries that just will not work with threads. For example, the current Net-SNMP library for Python is synchronous, so writing concurrent code requires the use of forked processes.

While threads share global state, processes are completely independent, and communication with a process requires a bit more effort. Talking to processes through pipes can be a little difficult; fortunately, however, there is a processing library that we will discuss in great detail here. There has been some talk of integrating the processing library into the standard library in Python, so it would be useful to understand.

In an earlier note, we mentioned an alternate method of using `subprocess.Popen` to spawn multiple processes. For many situations, this an excellent and very simple choice to execute code in parallel. If you refer to Chapter 13, you can take a look at an example of where we did this in creating a tool that spawned many dd processes.

Processing Module

So what is this processing module we have hinted at, anyway? As of the printing of this book, "processing is a package for the Python language which supports the spawning of processes using the API of the standard library's threading module..." One of the great things about the processing module is that it maps to the threading API, more or less. This means that you don't have to learn a new API to fork processes instead of threads. Visit *http://pypi.python.org/pypi/processing* to find out more about the processing module.

As we mentioned earlier, things are never simple with concurrency. This example could be considered inefficient as well, because we could have just used subprocess.Popen, instead of forking with the processing module, and then running subprocess.call. In the context of a larger application, however, there are some benefits to using the queue type API, and as such, it serves as a reasonable comparison to the threading example earlier. There is some talk of merging the processing module into Subprocess, as Subprocess currently lacks the ability to manage a flock of processes like the processing module does. This request was made in the original PEP, or Python Enhancement Proposal, for Subprocess: *http://www.python.org/dev/peps/pep-0324/.*

Now that we have some background on the processing module, let's take a look at Example 10-23.

Example 10-23. Introduction to processing module

```python
#!/usr/bin/env python
from processing import Process, Queue
import time

def f(q):
    x = q.get()
    print "Process number %s, sleeps for %s seconds" % (x,x)
    time.sleep(x)
    print "Process number %s finished" % x
q = Queue()

for i in range(10):
    q.put(i)
    i = Process(target=f, args=[q])
    i.start()

print "main process joins on queue"
i.join()
print "Main Program finished"
```

If we look at the output, we see the following:

```
[ngift@Macintosh-7][H:11199][J:0]# python processing1.py
Process number 0, sleeps for 0 seconds
Process number 0 finished
Process number 1, sleeps for 1 seconds
Process number 2, sleeps for 2 seconds
Process number 3, sleeps for 3 seconds
Process number 4, sleeps for 4 seconds
main process joins on queue
Process number 5, sleeps for 5 seconds
Process number 6, sleeps for 6 seconds
Process number 8, sleeps for 8 seconds
Process number 7, sleeps for 7 seconds
Process number 9, sleeps for 9 seconds
```

```
Process number 1 finished
Process number 2 finished
Process number 3 finished
Process number 4 finished
Process number 5 finished
Process number 6 finished
Process number 7 finished
Process number 8 finished
Process number 9 finished
Main Program finished
```

All this program does is tell each process to sleep as long as the number of the processes. As you can see, it is a clean and straightforward API.

Now that we have the equivalent of a Hello World out of the way for the processing module, we can do something more interesting. If you remember in the threading section, we wrote a simple threaded subnet discovery script. Because the processing API is very similar to the threading API, we can implement an almost identical script using processes instead of threads. See Example 10-24.

Example 10-24. Processed-based ping sweep

```python
#!/usr/bin/env python
from processing import Process, Queue, Pool
import time
import subprocess
from IPy import IP
import sys

q = Queue()
ips = IP("10.0.1.0/24")
def f(i,q):
    while True:
        if q.empty():
            sys.exit()
        print "Process Number: %s" % i
        ip = q.get()
        ret = subprocess.call("ping -c 1 %s" % ip,
                        shell=True,
                        stdout=open('/dev/null', 'w'),
                        stderr=subprocess.STDOUT)
        if ret == 0:
            print "%s: is alive" % ip
        else:
            print "Process Number: %s didn't find a response for %s " % (i, ip)

for ip in ips:
    q.put(ip)

#q.put("192.168.1.1")

for i in range(50):
    p = Process(target=f, args=[i,q])
    p.start()
```

```
print "main process joins on queue"
p.join()
print "Main Program finished"
```

This code looks remarkably similar to the threaded code we reviewed earlier. If we take a look at the output, we will see something similar as well:

```
[snip]
10.0.1.255: is alive
Process Number: 48 didn't find a response for 10.0.1.216
Process Number: 47 didn't find a response for 10.0.1.217
Process Number: 49 didn't find a response for 10.0.1.218
Process Number: 46 didn't find a response for 10.0.1.219
Main Program finished
[snip]
[ngift@Macintosh-7][H:11205][J:0]#
```

This snippet of code bears some explanation. Even though the API is similar, it is slightly different. Notice that each process runs inside of a infinite loop, grabbing items from the queue. In order to tell the processes to "go away" with the processing module, we create a conditional statement that looks at whether the queue is empty. Each of the 50 threads first checks to see if the queue is empty, and if it is, then it "poisons" itself, by running sys.exit.

If the queue still has things in it, then the process happily grabs the item, in this case, an IP address, and goes along with the job it was assigned, in this case, pinging the IP address. The main program uses a join, just like we do in a threading script, and joins on the queue until it is empty. After all of the worker processes die and the queue is empty, the next print statement gets run, stating the program is finished.

With an API as simple to use as the processing module, forking instead of threading is a relative no-brainer. In Chapter 7, we discussed a practical implementation of using the processing module with Net-SNMP, which has synchronous bindings to Python.

Scheduling Python Processes

Now that we have covered the gamut of ways to deal with processes in Python, we should talk about ways to schedule these processes. Using good old-fashioned cron is highly suitable for running processes in Python.

One of the nice new features of cron in many POSIX systems is the advent of scheduled directories. This is the only way we use cron anymore, as it is very convenient to just drop a python script in one of the four default directories: */etc/cron.daily*, */etc/cron.hour ly*, */etc/cron.monthly*, and */etc/cron.weekly*.

Quite a few sysadmins have, at one point in their life, written the good-old-fashioned disk usage email. You place a Bash script in */etc/cron.daily* and it looks something like this:

```
df -h | mail -s "Nightly Disk Usage Report" staff@example.com
```

You then put that script in */etc/cron.daily/diskusage.sh* and the email looks something like this.

```
From:      guru-python-sysadmin@example.com
Subject:     Nightly Disk Usage Report
Date:      February 24, 2029 10:18:57 PM EST
To:      staff@example.com

Filesystem            Size  Used Avail Use% Mounted on
/dev/hda3             72G   16G   52G  24% /
/dev/hda1             99M   20M   75M  21% /boot
tmpfs               1010M    0 1010M   0% /dev/shm
```

There is a better way than this. Even cron jobs can benefit from Python scripts instead of Bash or Perl. In fact, cron and Python go quite well together. Let's take our Bash example and "Pythonize" it. See Example 10-25.

Example 10-25. Cron-based disk report email Python

```python
import smtplib
import subprocess
import string

p = subprocess.Popen("df -h", shell=True, stdout=subprocess.PIPE)
MSG = p.stdout.read()
FROM = "guru-python-sysadmin@example.com"
TO = "staff@example.com"
SUBJECT = "Nightly Disk Usage Report"
msg = string.join((
    "From: %s" % FROM,
    "To: %s" % TO,
    "Subject: %s" % SUBJECT,
    "",
    MSG), "\r\n")
server = smtplib.SMTP('localhost')
server.sendmail(FROM, TO, msg)
server.quit()
```

This is a trivial recipe to create an automated cron-based disk report, but for many tasks, it should work just fine. Here is a walk through of what this handful of Python does. First, we use subprocess.Popen to read the stdout of df. Next, we create variables for From, To, and Subject. Then, we join those strings together to create the message. That is the most difficult part of the script. Finally, we set the outgoing smtp mail server to use localhost, and then pass the variables we set earlier into server.sendmail().

A typical way to use this script would be to simply place it in */etc/cron.daily/night ly_disk_report.py*.

If you are new to Python, you may want to use this script as boilerplate code to get something fun working rather quickly. In Chapter 4, we went into even greater detail on creating email messages, so you should refer to that chapter for more advice.

daemonizer

Dealing with daemons is a given for anyone who has spent more than a cursory amount of time on Unix. Daemons do everything from handling requests to sending files to a printer (such as lpd), fielding HTTP requests, and serving up files (such as Apache's httpd).

So, what is a daemon? A daemon is often thought of as a background task that doesn't have a controlling terminal. If you are familiar with Unix job control, you may think that running a command with an & at the end of it will make it a daemon. Or perhaps starting a process and then hitting Ctrl-z and then issuing the bg command will make a daemon. Both of these will background the process, but neither of them breaks the process free from your shell process and disassociates them from the controlling terminal (probably of your shell process as well). So, these are the three signs of a daemon: running in the background, being dislocated from the process that started it, and having no controlling terminal. Backgrounding a process with normal shell job control will only accomplish the first of these.

Following is a piece of code that defines a function named daemonize() that causes the calling code to become a daemon in the sense that we discussed in the previous paragraph. This function was extracted from the "Forking a Daemon Process on Unix" recipe in David Ascher's *Python Cookbook*, Second Edition, pages 388–389 (O'Reilly). This code follows pretty closely to the steps that Richard Stevens laid out in his book *UNIX Network Programming: The Sockets Networking API* (O'Reilly) for the "proper" way of daemonizing a process. For anyone not familiar with the Stevens book, it is typically regarded as *the* reference for Unix network programming as well as how to make a daemon process under Unix. See Example 10-26.

Example 10-26. Daemonize function

```
import sys, os
def daemonize (stdin='/dev/null', stdout='/dev/null', stderr='/dev/null'):
    # Perform first fork.
    try:
        pid = os.fork( )
        if pid > 0:
            sys.exit(0) # Exit first parent.
    except OSError, e:
        sys.stderr.write("fork #1 failed: (%d) %s\n" % (e.errno, e.strerror))
        sys.exit(1)
    # Decouple from parent environment.
    os.chdir("/")
    os.umask(0)
    os.setsid( )
    # Perform second fork.
    try:
        pid = os.fork( )
        if pid > 0:
            sys.exit(0) # Exit second parent.
    except OSError, e:
```

```
        sys.stderr.write("fork #2 failed: (%d) %s\n" % (e.errno, e.strerror))
        sys.exit(1)
    # The process is now daemonized, redirect standard file descriptors.
    for f in sys.stdout, sys.stderr: f.flush( )
    si = file(stdin, 'r')
    so = file(stdout, 'a+')
    se = file(stderr, 'a+', 0)
    os.dup2(si.fileno( ), sys.stdin.fileno( ))
    os.dup2(so.fileno( ), sys.stdout.fileno( ))
    os.dup2(se.fileno( ), sys.stderr.fileno( ))
```

The first thing that this code does is to fork() a process. fork()ing makes a copy of the running process where the copy is considered the "child" process and the original is considered the "parent" process. When the child process forks off, the parent is free to exit. We check for what the pid is after the fork. If the pid is positive, it means that we're in the parent process. If you have never fork()ed a child process, this may seem a bit odd to you. After the call to os.fork() completes, there will be two copies of the same process running. Both then check the return code of the fork() call, which returns 0 in the child and the process ID in the parent. Whichever process has a non-zero return code, which will only be the parent, exits. If an exception occurs at this point, the process exits. If you called this script from an interactive shell (such as Bash), you would now have your prompt back because the process you started would have just terminated. But the child process of the process you started (i.e., the grandchild process) lives on.

The next three things the process does is to change directory to / (os.chdir("/"), set its umask to 0 (os.umask(0), and create a new session (os.setsid()). Changing directory to / puts the daemon process in a directory that will always exist. An added benefit of changing to / is that your long-running process won't tie up your ability to unmount a filesystem if it happens to be in a directory of a filesystem you are trying to unmount. The next thing that the process does is to change its file mode creation mask to most permissive. If the daemon needs to create files with group-read and group-write permissions, an inherited mask with more restrictive permissions might have ill effects. The last of these three actions (os.setsid()) is perhaps the least familiar to most people. The setsid call does a number of things. First, it causes the process to become a session leader of a new session. Next, it causes the process to become a process group leader of a new process group. Finally, and perhaps most important for the purposes of daemonization, it causes the process to have no controlling terminal. The fact that it has no controlling terminal means that the process cannot fall victim to unintentional (or even intentional) job control actions from some terminal. This is important to having an uninterrupted, long-running process like a daemon.

But the fun doesn't stop there. After the call to os.setsid(), there is another forking that takes place. The first fork and setsid set the stage for this second fork; they detach from any controlling terminal and set the process as a session leader. Another fork means that the resulting process cannot be a session leader. This means that the process cannot acquire a controlling terminal. This second fork is not necessary, but is more of a precaution. Without the final `fork`, the only way that the process could acquire a controlling terminal is if it directly opened a terminal device without using a `O_NOCTTY` flag.

The last thing that happens here is some file cleanup and readjustment. Standard output and error (`sys.stdout` and `sys.stderr`) are flushed. This ensures that information intended for those streams actually make it there. This function allows the caller to specify files for `stdin`, `stdout`, and `stderr`. The defaults for all three are `/dev/null`. This code takes either the user specified or default `stdin`, `stdout`, and `stderr` and sets the process's standard input, output, and error to these files, respectively.

So, how do you use this daemonizer? Assuming the daemonizer code is in a module named `daemonize.py`, Example 10-27 is a sample script to use it.

Example 10-27. Using a daemonizer

```
from daemonize import daemonize
import time
import sys

def mod_5_watcher():
    start_time = time.time()
    end_time = start_time + 20
    while time.time() < end_time:
        now = time.time()
        if int(now) % 5 == 0:
            sys.stderr.write('Mod 5 at %s\n' % now)
        else:
            sys.stdout.write('No mod 5 at %s\n' % now)
        time.sleep(1)

if __name__ == '__main__':
    daemonize(stdout='/tmp/stdout.log', stderr='/tmp/stderr.log')
    mod_5_watcher()
```

This script first daemonizes and specifies that */tmp/stdout.log* should be used for standard output and */tmp/stderr.log* should be used for standard error. It then watches the time for the next 20 seconds, sleeping 1 second in between checking the time. If the time, denoted in seconds, is divisible by five, we write to standard error. If the time is not divisible by five, we write to standard output. Since the process is using */tmp/stdout.log* for standard output and */tmp/stderr.log* for standard error, we should be able to see the results in those files after running this example.

After running this script, we immediately saw a new prompt silently appear:

```
jmjones@dinkgutsy:code$ python use_daemonize.py
jmjones@dinkgutsy:code$
```

And here are the result files from running the example:

```
jmjones@dinkgutsy:code$ cat /tmp/stdout.log
No mod 5 at 1207272453.18
No mod 5 at 1207272454.18
```

```
No mod 5 at 1207272456.18
No mod 5 at 1207272457.19
No mod 5 at 1207272458.19
No mod 5 at 1207272459.19
No mod 5 at 1207272461.2
No mod 5 at 1207272462.2
No mod 5 at 1207272463.2
No mod 5 at 1207272464.2
No mod 5 at 1207272466.2
No mod 5 at 1207272467.2
No mod 5 at 1207272468.2
No mod 5 at 1207272469.2
No mod 5 at 1207272471.2
No mod 5 at 1207272472.2
jmjones@dinkgutsy:code$ cat /tmp/stderr.log
Mod 5 at 1207272455.18
Mod 5 at 1207272460.2
Mod 5 at 1207272465.2
Mod 5 at 1207272470.2
```

This is a really simple example of writing a daemon, but hopefully it gets the basic concepts across. You could use this daemonizer to write directory watchers, network monitors, network servers, or anything else you can imagine that runs for a long (or unspecified amount of) time.

Summary

Hopefully, this chapter demonstrated just how mature and powerful Python is at dealing with processes. Python has an elegant and sophisticated threading API, but it is always good to remember about the GIL. If you are I/O bound, then often this is not an issue, but if you require multiple processors, then using processes is a good choice. Some people think processes are better than using threads even if the GIL did not exist. The main reason for this is that debugging threaded code can be a nightmare.

Finally, it would be a good idea to get familiar with the Subprocess module if you are not already. Subprocess is a one-stop shop for dealing with, well, subprocesses.

## CHAPTER 11

Building GUIs

When informed people consider the duties of a system administrator, building GUI applications probably does not come to mind at all. However, there are times when you will *need* to build a GUI application, or by building a GUI app your life will be easier than if you didn't. We're using GUI in the broad sense here to mean both traditional GUI applications using toolkits such as GTK and QT, as well as web-based applications.

This chapter will focus on PyGTK, curses, and the Django web framework. We'll start off with the basics of GUI building, then move on to creating a fairly simple application using PyGTK, then the same app using curses and Django. Finally, we'll show you how Django can, with very little code, work as a fairly polished frontend to a database.

GUI Building Theory

When you write a console utility, you often expect it to run and complete without user intervention. This is definitely the case when scripts are run from cron and at, anyway. But when you write a GUI utility, you expect that a user will have to provide some input in order to make things happen and exercise your utility. Think for a moment about your experiences with GUI applications such as web browsers, email clients, and word processors. You *run* the application somehow. The application performs some sort of initialization, perhaps loading some configuration and putting itself into some known state. But then, in general, the application just waits for the user to do something. Of course, there are examples of applications executing seemingly on their own, such as Firefox automatically checking for updates without the explicit request or consent of the user, but that's another story.

What is the application waiting for? How does it know what to do when the user does something? The application is waiting for an *event* to happen. An event is just something that happens within the application, specifically to one of the GUI components such as a button being pressed or a checkbox being selected. And the application "knows" what to do when these events happen because the programmer associated certain events with certain pieces of code. The "pieces of code" that are associated with certain events, are referred to as *event handlers*. One of the jobs of a GUI toolkit is to call the right event handler when the associated event occurs. To be a little more precise, the GUI toolkit provides an "event loop" that quietly loops around, waits for events to happen, and when they do, it handles them appropriately.

Behavior is event driven. When you code your GUI application, you decide how you want your application to behave when a user does certain things. You set up event handlers that the GUI toolkit calls when the user triggers events.

That describes the behavior of an application, but what about the form? Meaning, how do you get the buttons, text fields, labels, and checkboxes on an application? The answer to this question can vary a bit. There may be a GUI builder for the GUI toolkit that you choose. A GUI builder lays out the various components such as buttons, labels, checkboxes, etc. for a GUI application. For example, if you are working on a Mac and choose to write a Cocoa app, Interface Builder is available to lay the GUI components out for you. Or, if you are using PyGTK on Linux, you can use Glade. Or, if you are using PyQT, you can use QT Designer.

GUI builders can be helpful, but sometimes you may want more control of your GUI than the builder offers. In those cases, it is not difficult to lay out a GUI "by hand" by writing a little code. In PyGTK, each type of GUI component corresponds to a Python class. For example, a window is an object of the class `gtk.Window`. And a button is an object of the class `gtk.Button`. In order to create a simple GUI app that has a window and a button, you instantiate objects of classes `gtk.Window` and `gtk.Button` and add the button to the window. If you want the button to do something when it is clicked, you have to specify an event handler for the "clicked" event for the button.

Building a Simple PyGTK App

We'll create a simple piece of code which uses the already-mentioned `gtk.Window` and `gtk.Button` classes. Following is a simple GUI application that doesn't do anything useful except show some of the basic tenets of GUI programming.

Before being able to run this example or write your own PyGTK app, you'll have to install PyGTK. This is pretty simple if you're running a relatively modern Linux distribution. It even looks pretty easy for Windows. If you're running Ubuntu, it should already be installed. If there isn't a binary distribution for your platform, you can expect pain. See Example 11-1.

Example 11-1. Simple PyGTK application with one window and one button

```
#!/usr/bin/env python

import pygtk
import gtk
import time

class SimpleButtonApp(object):
```

```python
"""This is a simple PyGTK app that has one window and one button.
When the button is clicked, it updates the button's label with the current time.
"""

    def __init__(self):
        #the main window of the application
        self.window = gtk.Window(gtk.WINDOW_TOPLEVEL)

        #this is how you "register" an event handler. Basically, this
        #tells the gtk main loop to call self.quit() when the window "emits"
        #the "destroy" signal.
        self.window.connect("destroy", self.quit)

        #a button labeled "Click Me"
        self.button = gtk.Button("Click Me")

        #another registration of an event handler. This time, when the
        #button "emits" the "clicked" signal, the 'update_button_label'
        #method will get called.
        self.button.connect("clicked", self.update_button_label, None)

        #The window is a container. The "add" method puts the button
        #inside the window.
        self.window.add(self.button)

        #This call makes the button visible, but it won't become visible
        #until its container becomes visible as well.
        self.button.show()

        #Makes the container visible
        self.window.show()

    def update_button_label(self, widget, data=None):
        """set the button label to the current time

        This is the handler method for the 'clicked' event of the button
        """
        self.button.set_label(time.asctime())

    def quit(self, widget, data=None):
        """stop the main gtk event loop

        When you close the main window, it will go away, but if you don't
        tell the gtk main event loop to stop running, the application will
        continue to run even though it will look like nothing is really
        happening.
        """
        gtk.main_quit()


    def main(self):
        """start the gtk main event loop"""
        gtk.main()

if __name__ == "__main__":
```

```
s = SimpleButtonApp()
s.main()
```

The first thing you probably noticed in this example is that the main class inherits from `object` rather than some GTK class. Creating a GUI application in PyGTK is not necessarily an object-oriented exercise. You will certainly have to instantiate objects, but you don't have to create your own custom classes. However, for anything more than a trivial example such as what we are creating, we strongly recommend creating your own custom class. The main benefit to creating your own class for a GUI application is that all your GUI components (windows, buttons, checkboxes) wind up all attached to the same object, which allows easy access to those components from elsewhere in the application.

Since we chose to create a custom class, the first place to look to start understanding what is going on is in the constructor (the `__init__()` method). In fact, in this example, you can see what is going on by focusing on the constructor. This example is pretty well commented, so we won't duplicate an explanation of everything here, but we will give a recap. We created two GUI objects: a `gtk.Window` and a `gtk.Button`. We put the button in the window, since the window is a container object. We also created event handlers for the window and the button for the `destroy` and `clicked` events, respectively. If you run this code, it will display a window with a button labeled "Click Me." Every time you click the button, it will update the button's label with the current time. Figures 11-1 and 11-2 are screenshots of the application before and after clicking the button.

Figure 11-1. Simple PyGTK app—before clicking the button

Figure 11-2. Simple PyGTK app—after clicking the button

Building an Apache Log Viewer Using PyGTK

Now that we have covered the basics of GUI building in general and of using PyGTK specifically, the following is an example of building something a little more useful with PyGTK; we're going to walk through creating an Apache logfile viewer. The functionality we are going to include in this application is as follows:

- Select and open specified logfile
- View line number, remote host, status, and bytes sent at a glance
- Sort loglines by line number, remote host, status, or bytes sent

This example builds on the Apache log parsing code that we wrote in Chapter 3. Example 11-2 is the source code for the logfile viewer.

Example 11-2. PyGTK Apache log viewer

```python
#!/usr/bin/env python

import gtk
from apache_log_parser_regex import dictify_logline

class ApacheLogViewer(object):
    """Apache log file viewer which sorts on various pieces of data"""

    def __init__(self):
        #the main window of the application
        self.window = gtk.Window(gtk.WINDOW_TOPLEVEL)
        self.window.set_size_request(640, 480)
        self.window.maximize()

        #stop event loop on window destroy
        self.window.connect("destroy", self.quit)

        #a VBox is a container that holds other GUI objects primarily for layout
        self.outer_vbox = gtk.VBox()

        #toolbar which contains the open and quit buttons
        self.toolbar = gtk.Toolbar()

        #create open and quit buttons and icons
        #add buttons to toolbar
        #associate buttons with correct handlers
        open_icon = gtk.Image()
        quit_icon = gtk.Image()
        open_icon.set_from_stock(gtk.STOCK_OPEN, gtk.ICON_SIZE_LARGE_TOOLBAR)
        quit_icon.set_from_stock(gtk.STOCK_QUIT, gtk.ICON_SIZE_LARGE_TOOLBAR)
        self.open_button = gtk.ToolButton(icon_widget=open_icon)
        self.quit_button = gtk.ToolButton(icon_widget=quit_icon)
        self.open_button.connect("clicked", self.show_file_chooser)
        self.quit_button.connect("clicked", self.quit)
        self.toolbar.insert(self.open_button, 0)
        self.toolbar.insert(self.quit_button, 1)

        #a control to select which file to open
        self.file_chooser = gtk.FileChooserWidget()
        self.file_chooser.connect("file_activated", self.load_logfile)

        #a ListStore holds data that is tied to a list view
        #this ListStore will store tabular data of the form:
        #line_numer, remote_host, status, bytes_sent, logline
        self.loglines_store = gtk.ListStore(int, str, str, int, str)
```

```
        #associate the tree with the data...
        self.loglines_tree - gtk.TreeView(model=self.loglines_store)
        #...and set up the proper columns for it
        self.add_column(self.loglines_tree, 'Line Number', 0)
        self.add_column(self.loglines_tree, 'Remote Host', 1)
        self.add_column(self.loglines_tree, 'Status', 2)
        self.add_column(self.loglines_tree, 'Bytes Sent', 3)
        self.add_column(self.loglines_tree, 'Logline', 4)

        #make the area that holds the apache log scrollable
        self.loglines_window = gtk.ScrolledWindow()

        #pack things together
        self.window.add(self.outer_vbox)
        self.outer_vbox.pack_start(self.toolbar, False, False)
        self.outer_vbox.pack_start(self.file_chooser)
        self.outer_vbox.pack_start(self.loglines_window)
        self.loglines_window.add(self.loglines_tree)

        #make everything visible
        self.window.show_all()
        #but specifically hide the file chooser
        self.file_chooser.hide()

    def add_column(self, tree_view, title, columnId, sortable=True):
        column = gtk.TreeViewColumn(title, gtk.CellRendererText() , text=columnId)
        column.set_resizable(True)
        column.set_sort_column_id(columnId)
        tree_view.append_column(column)

    def show_file_chooser(self, widget, data=None):
        """make the file chooser dialog visible"""
        self.file_chooser.show()

    def load_logfile(self, widget, data=None):
        """load logfile data into tree view"""
        filename = widget.get_filename()
        print "FILE-->", filename
        self.file_chooser.hide()
        self.loglines_store.clear()
        logfile = open(filename, 'r')
        for i, line in enumerate(logfile):
            line_dict = dictify_logline(line)
            self.loglines_store.append([i + 1, line_dict['remote_host'],
                    line_dict['status'], int(line_dict['bytes_sent']), line])
        logfile.close()

    def quit(self, widget, data=None):
        """stop the main gtk event loop"""
        gtk.main_quit()


    def main(self):
        """start the gtk main event loop"""
```

```
        gtk.main()

if __name__ == "__main__":
    l = ApacheLogViewer()
    l.main()
```

In the PyGTK Apache Log Viewer example, the main class, `ApacheLogViewer`, only derives from `object`. There is nothing special about our main object; it just happens to be where we are hanging all of the pieces and actions of the GUI.

Next, and jumping to the `__init__()` method, we create a window object. Something a little different about this example from the previous, "simple" example is that we specify sizing requirements for this window. We initially specify that this window should be displayed at 640×480 and then specify that it should be maximized. Setting the sizing parameters twice was intentional. 640×480 is a reasonable starting, so this isn't a bad default. While 640×480 is a fine size, bigger is better, so we maximized the window. It turns out that setting 640×480 (or some other size of your preference) first is probably a good practice. According to the PyGTK documentation, the window manager may not honor the `maximize()` request. Also, the user can unmaximize the window after it is maximized, so you may want to specify the size when it is unmaximized.

After creating and sizing the window, we create a `VBox`. This is a "vertical box," which is simply a container object. GTK has the concept of using vertical (`VBox`) and horizontal (`HBox`) boxes for laying out widgets on a window. The idea behind these boxes is that you "pack" them with widgets relative either to their beginning (which is the top for `VBoxes` and left for `HBoxes`) or their end. If you don't know what a widget is, it's simply a GUI component such as a button or text box. By using these boxes, you can lay out the widgets on a window pretty much any way you can imagine. Since boxes are containers, they can contain other boxes, so feel free to pack one box into another.

After adding the `VBox` to the window, we add the toolbar and tool buttons. The toolbar itself is another container and provides methods for adding components to itself. We create the icons for the buttons, create the buttons, and attach the event handlers to the buttons. Finally, we add the buttons to the toolbar. Just as with `pack_start()` on `VBox`, we use `insert()` on the `ToolBar` to add widgets.

Next, we create a file chooser widget that we use to navigate to the logfile to process and then associate it with an event handler. This part is very straightforward, but we will readdress it in a moment.

After creating the file chooser, we create the list component that will contain the loglines. This component comes in two pieces: the data piece (which is a `ListStore`), and the piece you interact with (which is a `TreeView`). We create the data piece first by defining what data types we want in which columns. Next, we create the display component and associate the data component with it.

After creating the list component, we create one final container, a scrollable window, and then pack everything together. We pack the toolbar, file chooser, and the scrollable window into the VBox we created earlier. We put the list piece, which will contain the loglines, into the scrollable window so that if there are more than a handful of lines, we can scroll through them.

Finally, we make things visible and invisible. We make the main window visible with the show_all() call. This call also makes all children visible. Given how we have created this GUI application, we want the file chooser to be invisible until we click the "open" button. So, we make the file chooser control invisible when it is created.

When you launch this application, you can see that it meets our initial requirements. We are able to select and open specified logfiles. Each of the line number, remote host, status, and bytes pieces of data have their own columns in the list control, so we can easily surmise those pieces of data just by glancing at each line. And, we can sort on any of those columns by simply clicking on the corresponding column header.

Building an Apache Log Viewer Using Curses

curses is a library that facilitates the creation of interactive text-based applications. Unlike GUI toolkits, curses does not follow an event handling and callback approach. You are responsible for getting input from the user and then doing something with it, whereas in GTK, the widget handles getting input from the user and the toolkit calls a handler function when an event occurs. Another difference between curses and GUI toolkits is that with GUI toolkits you are adding widgets to some container and letting the toolkit deal with drawing and refreshing the screen. With curses, you are typically painting text directly on the screen.

Example 11-3 is the Apache log viewer again, implemented using the curses module from the Python Standard Library.

Example 11-3. curses Apache log viewer

```
#!/usr/bin/env python

"""
curses based Apache log viewer

Usage:

    curses_log_viewer.py logfile

This will start an interactive, keyboard driven log viewing application. Here
are what the various key presses do:

    u/d   - scroll up/down
    t     - go to the top of the log file
    q     - quit
    b/h/s - sort by bytes/hostname/status
```

```
      r      - restore to initial sort order

"""

import curses
from apache_log_parser_regex import dictify_logline
import sys
import operator

class CursesLogViewer(object):
    def __init__(self, logfile=None):
        self.screen = curses.initscr()
        self.curr_topline = 0
        self.logfile = logfile
        self.loglines = []

    def page_up(self):
        self.curr_topline = self.curr_topline - (2 * curses.LINES)
        if self.curr_topline < 0:
            self.curr_topline = 0
        self.draw_loglines()

    def page_down(self):
        self.draw_loglines()

    def top(self):
        self.curr_topline = 0
        self.draw_loglines()

    def sortby(self, field):
        #self.loglines = sorted(self.loglines, key=operator.itemgetter(field))
        self.loglines.sort(key=operator.itemgetter(field))
        self.top()

    def set_logfile(self, logfile):
        self.logfile = logfile
        self.load_loglines()

    def load_loglines(self):
        self.loglines = []
        logfile = open(self.logfile, 'r')
        for i, line in enumerate(logfile):
            line_dict = dictify_logline(line)
            self.loglines.append((i + 1, line_dict['remote_host'],
                line_dict['status'], int(line_dict['bytes_sent']), line.rstrip()))
        logfile.close()
        self.draw_loglines()

    def draw_loglines(self):
        self.screen.clear()
        status_col = 4
        bytes_col = 6
        remote_host_col = 16
        status_start = 0
        bytes_start = 4
```

```
                remote_host_start = 10
                line_start = 26
                logline_cols - curses.COLS - status_col - bytes_col - remote_host_col - 1
                for i in range(curses.LINES):
                    c = self.curr_topline
                    try:
                        curr_line = self.loglines[c]
                    except IndexError:
                        break
                    self.screen.addstr(i, status_start, str(curr_line[2]))
                    self.screen.addstr(i, bytes_start, str(curr_line[3]))
                    self.screen.addstr(i, remote_host_start, str(curr_line[1]))
                    #self.screen.addstr(i, line_start, str(curr_line[4])[logline_cols])
                    self.screen.addstr(i, line_start, str(curr_line[4]), logline_cols)
                    self.curr_topline += 1
                self.screen.refresh()

        def main_loop(self, stdscr):
            stdscr.clear()
            self.load_loglines()
            while True:
                c = self.screen.getch()
                try:
                    c = chr(c)
                except ValueError:
                    continue
                if c == 'd':
                    self.page_down()
                elif c == 'u':
                    self.page_up()
                elif c == 't':
                    self.top()
                elif c == 'b':
                    self.sortby(3)
                elif c == 'h':
                    self.sortby(1)
                elif c == 's':
                    self.sortby(2)
                elif c == 'r':
                    self.sortby(0)
                elif c == 'q':
                    break

if __name__ == '__main__':
    infile = sys.argv[1]
    c = CursesLogViewer(infile)
    curses.wrapper(c.main_loop)
```

In Example 11-3, we created a single class, CursesLogViewer, in order to structure our code. In the constructor, we create a curses screen and initialize a few variables. We instantiate CursesLogViewer in the "main" of our program and pass in the logfile that we want to view. We could have set an option in the application for browsing to a file and selecting it, but it would have been considerably more effort than the file browser in the PyGTK implementation of the log viewer. Besides, since users will be at a shell to run this application, it won't be abnormal to expect them to navigate to the file from the command line and pass it in as they start the application. After instantiating Curse sLogViewer, we pass its main_loop() method to the curses function wrapper(). The curses function wrapper() sets the terminal to a state that makes it ready for a curses application to use it, calls the function, then sets the terminal back to normal before returning.

The main_loop() method acts as a rudimentary event loop. It sits waiting for a user to enter input at the keyboard. When a user enters input, the loop dispatches the proper method (or at least to the proper behavior). Pressing the u or d keys will scroll up or down, respectively, by calling the page_up() or page_down() methods, respectively. The page_down() method simply calls draw_loglines(), which paints the loglines on the terminal, starting with the current top line. As each line is drawn to the screen, the current top line moves to the next log line. Since draw_loglines() only draws as many loglines as will fit on the screen, the next time it is called, it will start drawing the next log line on the top line of the screen. So, repeatedly calling draw_loglines() will have the visual effect of scrolling down through a logfile. The page_up() method will set the current top line two pages up and then redraw the loglines by calling draw_log lines(). This has the visual effect of scrolling up through a logfile. The reason that we set the current top line two pages up in page_up() is that when we draw a page, the current top line is really at the bottom of the screen. This is really set this way in anticipation of scrolling down.

The next class of behavior for our application is sorting. We have built functionality in to sort by hostname, status, and number of bytes sent in a request. Invoking any of the sort behaviors results in a call to sortby(). The sortby() method sorts the loglines list for our CursesLogViewer object on the specified field, and then calls the top() method. The top() method sets the current top line to the first line in the loglines list, and then draws the next page of loglines (which will be the first page).

The final event handler for our application is quit. The quit method simply breaks out of the "event loop" and lets the main_loop() method return to the curses wrapper() function for further terminal cleanup.

While the number of lines of code for the PyGTK app and the curses app are comparable, the curses app felt like more work. Perhaps it was having to create our own event loop. Or perhaps it was having to, in a sense, create our own widgets. Or perhaps it was "painting" text directly on the terminal screen that made it feel like more work. However, there are times when knowing how to put together a curses app will benefit you.

Figure 11-3 shows the curses log viewer sorting records by bytes transferred.

One improvement we could have made on this application is the ability to reverse the sort order of whichever sort method is currently active. This would be a very simple change to make, but we'll leave that to the reader. Another improvement would be to

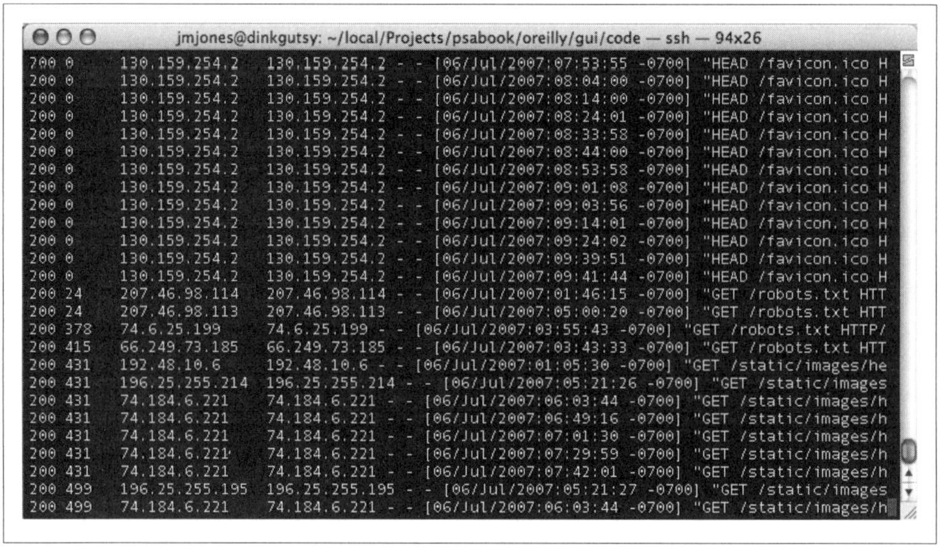

Figure 11-3. Apache log listing

view the entire contents of a log line as we scroll past it. This should also be a moderately simple change to make, but we'll leave it as an exercise for the reader as well.

Web Applications

To say that the Web is huge is an understatement. The Web is teeming with applications that people rely on daily. Why are there so many applications available on the Web? First, a web application is potentially universally accessible. This means that when a web application is deployed, anyone with access to it can just point their browser at a URL and use it. Users don't have to download and install anything except for the browser (which they likely already have installed) unless you are using browser plug-ins like Flash. The primary appeal of this point is for the user. Second, web applications are potentially unilaterally upgradeable for the whole user base. This means that one party (the owner of the application) can upgrade the entire user base without the other party (the user) having to do anything. This is really only true when you are not relying on features that may not be in the user's current environment. For example, if your upgrade relies on a feature in a newer version of Flash than what the current user base is required to install, this benefit may fly right out the window. But, when it works, this point is appealing to both parties, although the users are less likely to be as conscious of it. Third, the browser is pretty much a universal deployment platform. There are some cross-browser compatibility issues, but for the most part, if you are not using special plug-ins, a web application that works in one browser on one operating system will mostly work in another browser on another operating system. This point is appealing to both parties as well. Just a little more work on the development side will get the application working in multiple browser environments. And the user enjoys using the application where he chooses.

So how is this relevant for you as a system administrator? All the reasons that we have posited regarding building GUIs in general apply to building web applications. One benefit of web applications for system administrators is that the web application can have access to the filesystem and process table of the machine on which it runs. This particular property of web applications makes a web application an excellent solution for system, application, and user monitoring and reporting mechanisms. And that class of problems is in the domain of the system administrator.

Hopefully, you can see the benefit, though it may be useful for you only occasionally, of building a web application for yourself or your users. But what can you use to build a web application? Since this is a book on Python, we will, of course, recommend a Python solution. But which one? One of the criticisms of Python is that it has as many different web application frameworks as a year has days. At the moment, the four dominant choices are TurboGears, Django, Pylons, and Zope. Each of these four has its own benefits, but we felt that Django fit the subject of this book particularly well.

Django

Django is a full-stack web application framework. It contains a templating system, database connectivity by way of an object-relational mapper, and, of course, Python itself for writing the logic pieces of the application. Related to being a "full stack" framework, Django also follows a Model-View-Template (MVT) approach. This Model-View-Template approach is similar, if not identical, to a common approach called Model-View-Controller (MVC). Both are ways of developing applications so that the pieces of the application are not unnecessarily comingled. The database code is separated into an area referred to in both approaches as the "model." The business logic is separated into an area referred to as the "view" in MVT and the "controller" in MVC. And the presentation is separated into an area referred to as the "template" in MVT and the "view" in MVC.

Apache Log Viewer Application

In the following example, which consists of several pieces of code, we will create another implementation of the Apache log viewer similar to the PyGTK implementation. Since we are going to be opening logfiles to allow a user to view and sort them, we really won't need a database, so this example is devoid of any database connectivity. Before we walk through the example code, we will show you how to set up a project and application in Django.

You can download the Django code from *http://www.djangoproject.com/*. At the time of this writing, the latest release was 0.96. The recommended version to install, however, is from the development trunk. Once you've downloaded it, just install with the normal `python setup.py install` command. After installation, you will have the Django libraries in your *site-packages* directory and a script `django-admin.py` in your *scripts* directory. Typically, on *nix systems, the *scripts* directory will be the same directory that your `python` executable file lives in.

After installing Django, you need to create a project and an application. Projects contain one or more applications. They also act as the center for configuration for the overall web application (not to be confused with the Django application) that you are building. Django applications are smaller pieces of functionality that can be reused in different projects. For our Apache log viewing application, we created a project called "dj_apache" by running `django-admin.py startproject dj_apache`. This step created a directory and a handful of files. Example 11-4 is a tree view of the new project.

Example 11-4. Tree view of a Django project

```
jmjones@dinkbuntu:~/code$ tree dj_apache
dj_apache
|-- __init__.py
|-- manage.py
|-- settings.py
`-- urls.py

0 directories, 4 files
```

Now that we have a project, we can give it an application. We first navigate into the *dj_apache* directory, and then create an application with `django-admin.py startapp logview`. This will create a *logview* directory in our *dj_apache* directory and a few files. Example 11-5 is a tree view of all the files and directories we now have.

Example 11-5. Tree view of a Django application

```
jmjones@dinkbuntu:~/tmp$ tree dj_apache/
dj_apache/
|-- __init__.py
|-- logview
|   |-- __init__.py
|   |-- models.py
|   `-- views.py
|-- manage.py
|-- settings.py
`-- urls.py
```

You can see that the application directory (`logview`) contains `models.py` and `views.py`. Django follows the MVT convention, so these files help break the overall application up into its corresponding components. The file `models.py` contains the database layout, so it falls into the model component of the MVT acronym. The `views.py` contains the logic behind the application, so it falls into the view component of the acronym.

That leaves us without the template component of the acronym. The template component contains the presentation layer of the overall application. There are a few ways we can get Django to see our templates, but for Example 11-6, we will create a *templates* directory under the *logview* directory.

Example 11-6. Adding a templates directory

```
jmjones@dinkbuntu:~/code$ mkdir dj_apache/logview/templates
jmjones@dinkbuntu:~/code$ tree dj_apache/
dj_apache/
|-- __init__.py
|-- logview
|   |-- __init__.py
|   |-- models.py
|   |-- templates
|   `-- views.py
|-- manage.py
|-- settings.py
`-- urls.py

2 directories, 7 files
```

Now, we are ready to start fleshing out the application. The first thing we will do is decide how we want our URLs to work. This is a pretty basic application, so the URLs will be pretty straightforward. We want to list the logfiles and view them. Since our functionality is so simple and limited, we will let "/" list the logfiles to open and "/viewlog/some_sort_method/some_log_file" view the specified logfile using the specified sort method. In order to associate a URL with some activity, we have to update the *urls.py* file in the project top-level directory. Example 11-7 is the `urls.py` for our log viewer application.

Example 11-7. Django URL config (urls.py)

```
from django.conf.urls.defaults import *

urlpatterns = patterns('',
    (r'^$', 'dj_apache.logview.views.list_files'),
    (r'^viewlog/(?P<sortmethod>.*?)/(?P<filename>.*?)/$',
        'dj_apache.logview.views.view_log'),
)
```

The URL config file is pretty clear and fairly simple to figure out. This config file relies heavily on regular expressions to map URLs that match a given regular expression to a view function that exactly matches a string. We are mapping the URL "/" to the function "dj_apache.logview.views.list_files". We are also mapping all URLs matching the regular expression '^viewlog/(?P<sortmethod>.*?)/(?P<filename>.*?)/$' to the view function "dj_apache.logview.views.view_log". When a browser connects to a Django application and sends a request for a certain resource, Django looks through `urls.py` for an item whose regular expression matches the URL, then dispatches the request to the matching view function.

The source file in Example 11-8 contains both of the view functions for this application along with a utility function.

Example 11-8. Django view module (views.py)

```
# Create your views here.

from django.shortcuts import render_to_response

import os
from apache_log_parser_regex import dictify_logline
import operator

log_dir = '/var/log/apache2'

def get_log_dict(logline):
    l = dictify_logline(logline)
    try:
        l['bytes_sent'] = int(l['bytes_sent'])
    except ValueError:
        bytes_sent = 0
    l['logline'] = logline
    return l

def list_files(request):
    file_list = [f for f in os.listdir(log_dir) if
                 os.path.isfile(os.path.join(log_dir, f))]
    return render_to_response('list_files.html', {'file_list': file_list})

def view_log(request, sortmethod, filename):
    logfile = open(os.path.join(log_dir, filename), 'r')
    loglines = [get_log_dict(l) for l in logfile]
    logfile.close()
    try:
        loglines.sort(key=operator.itemgetter(sortmethod))
    except KeyError:
        pass
    return render_to_response('view_logfile.html', {'loglines': loglines,
                                                     'filename': filename})
```

The list_files() function lists all files in the directory specified by log_dir and passes that list to the list_files.html template. That's really all that happens in list_files(). This function is configurable by changing the value of log_dir. Another option for configuring this is to put the log directory in the database somehow. If we put the value of the log directory in the database, we could change the value without having to restart the application.

The view_log() function accepts as arguments the sort method and the logfile name. Both of these parameters were extracted from the URL by way of regular expression in the *urls.py* file. We named the regular expression groups for the sort method and file-name in urls.py, but we didn't have to. Arguments are passed into the view function from the URL in the same sequence that they are found in their respective groups. It is good practice, though, to use named groups in the URL regular expression so you can easily tell what parameters you are extracting from a URL as well as what a URL should look like.

The `view_log()` function opens the logfile whose filename comes in from the URL. It then uses the Apache log parsing library from earlier examples to convert each log line into a tuple in the format of `status`, `remote host`, `bytes_sent`, and the log line itself. Then `view_log()` sorts the list of tuples based on the sort method that was passed in from the URL. Finally, `view_log()` passes this list into the `view_logfile.html` template for formatting.

The only thing left is to create the templates that we have told the view functions to render to. In Django, templates can inherit from other templates, thereby improving code reuse and making it simple to establish a uniform look and feel among pages. The first template we'll build is a template the two other templates will inherit from. This template will set a common look and feel for the other two templates in the application. That's why we are starting with it. This is `base.html`. See Example 11-9.

Example 11-9. Django base template (base.html)

```
<html>
    <head>
        <title>{% block title %}Apache Logviewer - File Listing{% endblock %}</title>
    </head>
    <body>
        <div><a href="/">Log Directory</a></div>
        {% block content %}Empty Content Block{% endblock %}
    </body>
</html>
```

This is a very simple base template. It is perhaps the simplest HTML page you can get. The only items of interest are the two "block" sections: "content" and "title." When you define a "block" section in a parent template, a child template can override the parent block with its own content. This allows you to set default content on a part of a page and allow the child template to override that default. The "title" block allows the child pages to set a value which will show up in their page's `title` tag. The "content" block is a common convention for updating the "main" section of a page while allowing the rest of the page to remain unchanged.

Example 11-10 is a template that will simply list the files in the specified directory.

Example 11-10. Django file listing template (list_files.html)

```
{% extends "base.html" %}

{% block title %}Apache Logviewer - File Listing{% endblock %}

{% block content %}
<ul>
{% for f in file_list %}
  <li><a href="/viewlog/linesort/{{ f }}/" >{{ f }}</a></li>
{% endfor %}
</ul>
{% endblock %}
```

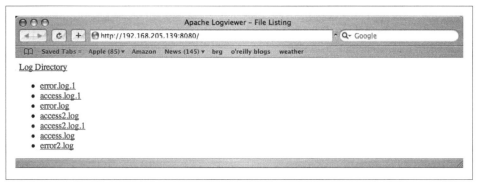

Figure 11-4. Apache log listing

Figure 11-4 shows what the file listing page looks like.

In this template, we state that we are extending "base.html." This allows us to get everything defined in "base.html" and plug in code into any defined code blocks and override their behavior. We do exactly that with the "title" and "content" blocks. In the "content" block, we loop over a variable `file_list` that was passed into the template. For each item in `file_list`, we create a link that will result in opening and parsing the logfile.

The template in Example 11-11 is responsible for creating the pages that the link in the previous Example 11-10 takes the user to. It displays the detail of the specified logfile.

Example 11-11. Django file listing template (view_log file.html)

```
{% extends "base.html" %}

{% block title %}Apache Logviewer - File Viewer{% endblock %}

{% block content %}
<table border="1">
    <tr>
        <td><a href="/viewlog/status/{{ filename }}/">Status</a></td>
        <td><a href="/viewlog/remote_host/{{ filename }}/">Remote Host</a></td>
        <td><a href="/viewlog/bytes_sent/{{ filename }}/">Bytes Sent</a></td>
        <td><a href="/viewlog/linesort/{{ filename }}/">Line</a></td>
    </tr>
{% for l in loglines %}
    <tr>
        <td>{{ l.status }}</td>
        <td>{{ l.remote_host }}</td>
        <td>{{ l.bytes_sent }}</td>
        <td><pre>{{ l.logline }}</pre></td>
    </tr>
{% endfor %}
</table>
{% endblock %}
```

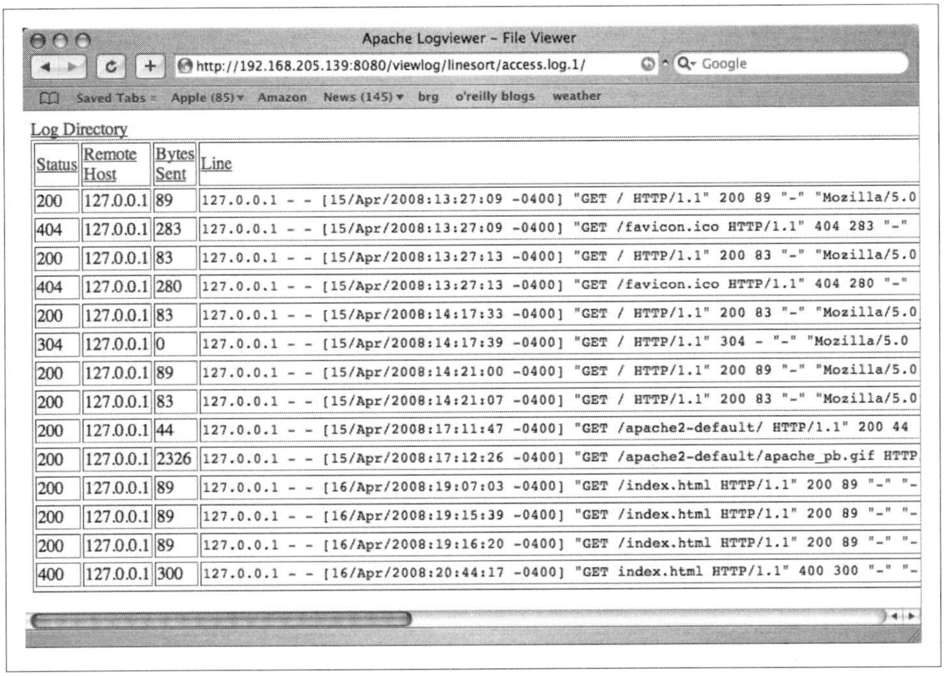

Figure 11-5. Django Apache log viewer—line order

The template in Example 11-11 inherits from the base template mentioned earlier and creates a table in the "content" area. The table header details the contents of each column: status, remote host, bytes sent, and the log line itself. In addition to detailing the column contents, the header allows users to specify how to sort the logfile. For example, if a user clicks on the "Bytes Sent" column header (which is simply a link), the page will reload and the code in the view will sort the loglines by the "bytes sent" column. Clicking on any column header except for "Line" will sort the loglines by that column in ascending order. Clicking on "Line" will put the loglines back in their original order.

Figure 11-5 shows the application viewed in Line order, and Figure 11-6 shows the application viewed in Bytes Sent order.

This was a very simple web application built using Django. And actually, this is a pretty atypical application as well. Most Django applications are going to be connected to a database of some sort. Improvements that could have been made include sorting all fields in reverse order, filtering loglines based on a specific status code or remote host, filtering loglines based on greater than or less than criteria for bytes sent, combining filters with one another, and putting AJAXy touches on it. Rather than walking through any of those improvements, we'll just leave that as an exercise for the willing reader.

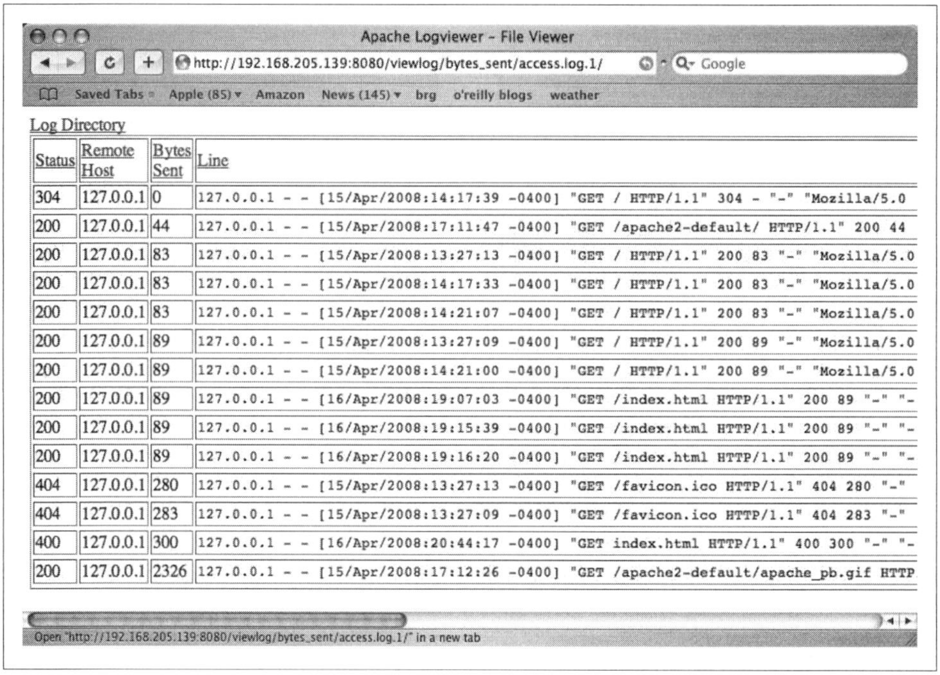

Status	Remote Host	Bytes Sent	Line
304	127.0.0.1	0	127.0.0.1 - - [15/Apr/2008:14:17:39 -0400] "GET / HTTP/1.1" 304 - "-" "Mozilla/5.0
200	127.0.0.1	44	127.0.0.1 - - [15/Apr/2008:17:11:47 -0400] "GET /apache2-default/ HTTP/1.1" 200 44
200	127.0.0.1	83	127.0.0.1 - - [15/Apr/2008:13:27:13 -0400] "GET / HTTP/1.1" 200 83 "-" "Mozilla/5.0
200	127.0.0.1	83	127.0.0.1 - - [15/Apr/2008:14:17:33 -0400] "GET / HTTP/1.1" 200 83 "-" "Mozilla/5.0
200	127.0.0.1	83	127.0.0.1 - - [15/Apr/2008:14:21:07 -0400] "GET / HTTP/1.1" 200 83 "-" "Mozilla/5.0
200	127.0.0.1	89	127.0.0.1 - - [15/Apr/2008:13:27:09 -0400] "GET / HTTP/1.1" 200 89 "-" "Mozilla/5.0
200	127.0.0.1	89	127.0.0.1 - - [15/Apr/2008:14:21:00 -0400] "GET / HTTP/1.1" 200 89 "-" "Mozilla/5.0
200	127.0.0.1	89	127.0.0.1 - - [16/Apr/2008:19:07:03 -0400] "GET /index.html HTTP/1.1" 200 89 "-" "-
200	127.0.0.1	89	127.0.0.1 - - [16/Apr/2008:19:15:39 -0400] "GET /index.html HTTP/1.1" 200 89 "-" "-
200	127.0.0.1	89	127.0.0.1 - - [16/Apr/2008:19:16:20 -0400] "GET /index.html HTTP/1.1" 200 89 "-" "-
404	127.0.0.1	280	127.0.0.1 - - [15/Apr/2008:13:27:13 -0400] "GET /favicon.ico HTTP/1.1" 404 280 "-"
404	127.0.0.1	283	127.0.0.1 - - [15/Apr/2008:13:27:09 -0400] "GET /favicon.ico HTTP/1.1" 404 283 "-"
400	127.0.0.1	300	127.0.0.1 - - [16/Apr/2008:20:44:17 -0400] "GET index.html HTTP/1.1" 400 300 "-" "-
200	127.0.0.1	2326	127.0.0.1 - - [15/Apr/2008:17:12:26 -0400] "GET /apache2-default/apache_pb.gif HTTP

Figure 11-6. Django Apache log viewer—bytes sent order

Simple Database Application

We mentioned that the previous Django example varied from the norm of Django applications in that it did not use a database. While the following example will be more in line with how people are using Django, the focus will be slightly different. When people build a Django application that connects to a database, they often write templates to display data from a database, as well as forms to validate and process user input. This example will show how to create a database model using Django's object-relational mappers and how to write templates and views to display that data, but the data entry will rely on Django's built-in admin interface. The purpose of taking this approach is to show you how quickly and easily you can put together a database with a usable frontend to enter and maintain the data.

The application that we are going to walk through creating is an inventory management app for computer systems. Specifically, this application is geared to allow you to add computers to the database with a description of the computer, associate IP addresses with it, state what services are running on it, detail what hardware constitutes the server, and more.

We'll follow the same steps to create this Django project and application as in the previous Django example. Following are the commands to create the project and the application using the django-admin command-line tool:

```
jmjones@dinkbuntu:~/code$ django-admin startproject sysmanage
jmjones@dinkbuntu:~/code$ cd sysmanage
jmjones@dinkbuntu:~/code/sysmanage$ django-admin startapp inventory
jmjones@dinkbuntu:~/code/sysmanage$
```

This created the same sort of directory structure as our Django-based Apache log viewer. Following is a tree view of the directories and files that were created:

```
jmjones@dinkbuntu:~/code/sysmanage$ cd ../
jmjones@dinkbuntu:~/code$ tree sysmanage/
sysmanage/
|-- __init__.py
|-- inventory
|   |-- __init__.py
|   |-- models.py
|   `-- views.py
|-- manage.py
|-- settings.py
`-- urls.py
```

After creating the project and app, we need to configure the database we want to connect to. SQLite is a great option, especially if you are testing or developing an app and not rolling it out to production. If more than a few people were going to be hitting the application, we would recommend considering a more robust database such as PostgreSQL. In order to configure the application to use a SQLite database, we change a couple of lines in the *settings.py* file in the project main directory. Here are the lines we change to configure the database:

```
DATABASE_ENGINE = 'sqlite3'
DATABASE_NAME = os.path.join(os.path.dirname(__file__), 'dev.db')
```

We set "sqlite3" as our database engine. The line configuring the location of the database (the `DATABASE_NAME` option) does something worth noting. Rather than specifying an absolute path to the database file, we configure the database such that it will always be in the same directory as the *settings.py* file. `__file__` holds the absolute path to the *settings.py* file. Calling `os.path.dirname(__file__)` gives us the directory that the *settings.py* file is in. Passing the directory that the file is in and the name of the database file we want to create to `os.path.join()` will give us the absolute path of the database file that is resilient to the application living in different directories. This is a useful idiom to get into the habit of using for your settings files.

In addition to configuring our database, we need to include the Django admin interface and our inventory application among the applications for this project. Here is the relevant portion of the *settings.py* file:

```
INSTALLED_APPS = (
    'django.contrib.admin',
    'django.contrib.auth',
    'django.contrib.contenttypes',
    'django.contrib.sessions',
    'django.contrib.sites',
    'sysmanage.inventory',
)
```

We added the `django.contrib.admin` and `sysmanage.inventory` to the list of installed apps. This means that when we tell Django to create the database for us, it will create tables for all included projects.

Next, we will change the URL mapping so that the this project includes the admin interface. Here is the relevant line from the URL config file:

```
# Uncomment this for admin:
    (r'^admin/', include('django.contrib.admin.urls')),
```

The tool that created the urls.py created it with a line to include the admin interface, but the line needs to be uncommented. You can see that we have simply removed the # character from the beginning of the line to include the admin URLs config file.

Now that we have configured a database, added the admin and inventory applications, and added the admin interface to the URLs config file, we are ready to start defining the database schema. In Django, each application has its own schema definition. In each application directory, "inventory" in this case, there is a file named *models.py* that contains definitions for the tables and columns that your application will use. With Django, as well as many other web frameworks that rely on ORMs, it is possible to create and use a database without having to write a single SQL expression. Django's ORM turns classes into tables and class attributes into columns on those tables. For example, following is a piece of code that defines a table definition in the configured database (this piece of code is part of the larger example that we'll get into shortly):

```
class HardwareComponent(models.Model):
    manufacturer = models.CharField(max_length=50)
    #types include video card, network card...
    type = models.CharField(max_length=50)
    model = models.CharField(max_length=50, blank=True, null=True)
    vendor_part_number = models.CharField(max_length=50, blank=True, null=True)
    description = models.TextField(blank=True, null=True)
```

Notice that the `HardwareComponent` class inherits from a Django model class. This means that the `HardwareComponent` class is of the `Model` type and will behave appropriately. We have given our hardware component a number of attributes: `manufacturer`, `type`, `model`, `vendor_part_number`, and `description`. Those attributes are coming from Django. Not that Django supplies some listing of hardware manufacturers, but it does provide the `CharField` type.

This class definition in the `inventory` application will create an `inventory_hardwarecom ponent` table with six columns: id, manufacturer, type, model, vendor_part_number, and description. This mostly corresponds with the class definition for the ORM. Actually, it *consistently* corresponds to the class definition for the ORM. When you define a model class, Django will create a corresponding table the name of which is the application name (lowercased), followed by an underscore, followed by the lowercased class name. Also, if you do not specify otherwise, Django will create an `id` column on your table that will act as the primary key. Following is the SQL table creation code that corresponds to the `HardwareComponent` model:

```
CREATE TABLE "inventory_hardwarecomponent" (
    "id" integer NOT NULL PRIMARY KEY,
    "manufacturer" varchar(50) NOT NULL,
    "type" varchar(50) NOT NULL,
    "model" varchar(50) NULL,
    "vendor_part_number" varchar(50) NULL,
    "description" text NULL
)
```

If you ever want to see the SQL that Django uses to create your database, simply run, in your project directory, `python manage.py sql myapp`, where `myapp` corresponds to the name of your application.

Now that you have been exposed to Django's ORM, we'll walk through creating the database model for our system inventory application. Example 11-12 is the `model.py` for the inventory application.

Example 11-12. Database layout (models.py)

```python
from django.db import models

# Create your models here.

class OperatingSystem(models.Model):
    name = models.CharField(max_length=50)
    description = models.TextField(blank=True, null=True)

    def __str__(self):
        return self.name

    class Admin:
        pass

class Service(models.Model):
    name = models.CharField(max_length=50)
    description = models.TextField(blank=True, null=True)

    def __str__(self):
        return self.name

    class Admin:
        pass

class HardwareComponent(models.Model):
    manufacturer = models.CharField(max_length=50)
    #types include video card, network card...
    type = models.CharField(max_length=50)
    model = models.CharField(max_length=50, blank=True, null=True)
    vendor_part_number = models.CharField(max_length=50, blank=True, null=True)
    description = models.TextField(blank=True, null=True)

    def __str__(self):
        return self.manufacturer

    class Admin:
```

```
        pass

class Server(models.Model):
    name = models.CharField(max_length=50)
    description = models.TextField(blank=True, null=True)
    os = models.ForeignKey(OperatingSystem)
    services = models.ManyToManyField(Service)
    hardware_component = models.ManyToManyField(HardwareComponent)

    def __str__(self):
        return self.name

    class Admin:
        pass

class IPAddress(models.Model):
    address = models.TextField(blank=True, null=True)
    server = models.ForeignKey(Server)

    def __str__(self):
        return self.address

    class Admin:
        pass
```

We defined five classes for our model: OperatingSystem, Service, HardwareComponent, Server, and IPAddress. The OperatingSystem class will allow us to define, as needed, different operating systems for the servers in which we are taking inventory. We defined this class with a name and description attribute, which is all we really need. It would be better to create an OperatingSystemVendor class and link to it from the OperatingSys tem class, but in the interest of simplicity and explicability, we will leave the vendor relation out of it. Each server will have one operating system. We will show you that relationship when we get to the Server.

The Service class allows us to list all potential services that can run on a server. Examples include Apache web server, Postfix mail server, Bind DNS server, and OpenSSH server. As with the OperatingSystem class, this class holds a name and a description attribute. Each server may have many services. We will show you how these classes relate to one another in the Server class.

The HardwareComponent class represents a list of all hardware components that our servers may contain. This will only be interesting if you have either added hardware to the system your vendor supplied you with or if you built your own server from individual components. We defined five attributes for HardwareComponent: manufacturer, type, model, vendor_part_number, and description. As with the vendor for Operating System, we could have created other classes for the hardware manufacturer and type and created relationships to them. But, again, for the sake of simplicity, we chose not to create those relationships.

The Server class is the heart of this inventory system. Each Server instance is a single server that we are tracking. Server is where we tie everything together by establishing relationships to the three previous classes. First of all, we have given each Server a name and description attribute. These are identical to the attributes that we have given the other classes. In order to link to the other classes, we had to specify what kind of relationship Server had to them. Each Server will have only one operating system, so we created a foreign key relationship to OperatingSystem. As virtualization becomes more common, this type of relationship will make less sense, but for now, it serves its purpose. A server may have many services running on it and each type of service may run on many servers, so we created a many to many relationship between Server and Service. Likewise, each server may have many hardware components and each type of hardware component may exist on multiple servers. Therefore, we created another many to many relationship from Server to HardwareComponent.

Finally, IPAddress is a listing of all IP addresses on all servers that we are tracking. We listed this model last to emphasize the relationship that IP addresses have with servers. We gave IPAddress one attribute and one relationship. The address is the attribute and should by convention be in the *XXX.XXX.XXX.XXX* format. We created a foreign key relationship from IPAddress to Server because one IP address should belong to only one server. Yes, again, this is simplistic, but it serves the purpose of demonstrating how to establish relationships between data components in Django.

Now we are ready to create the sqlite database file. Running python manage.py syncdb in your project directory will create any uncreated tables for all applications you included in your *settings.py* file. It will also prompt you to create a superuser if it creates the auth tables. Following is the (truncated) output from running python manage.py syncdb:

```
jmjones@dinkbuntu:~/code/sysmanage$ python manage.py syncdb
Creating table django_admin_log
Creating table auth_message
. . .
Creating many-to-many tables for Server model
Adding permission 'log entry | Can add log entry'
Adding permission 'log entry | Can change log entry'
Adding permission 'log entry | Can delete log entry'

You just installed Django's auth system, which means you don't have any
superusers defined.
Would you like to create one now? (yes/no): yes
Username (Leave blank to use 'jmjones'): E-mail address: none@none.com
Password:
Password (again): Superuser created successfully.
Adding permission 'message | Can add message'
. . .
Adding permission 'service | Can change service'
Adding permission 'service | Can delete service'
Adding permission 'server | Can add server'
Adding permission 'server | Can change server'
Adding permission 'server | Can delete server'
```

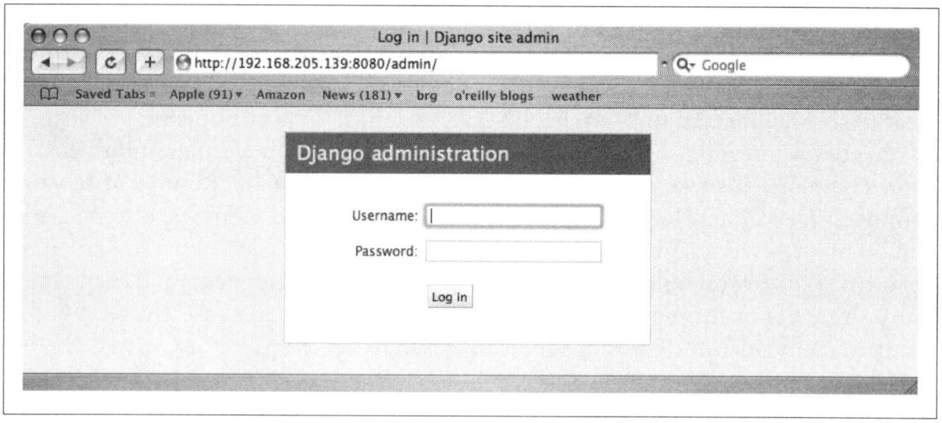

Figure 11-7. Django admin login

We are now ready to start the Django development server and explore the admin interface. Following is the command to start the Django development server and the output that command generates:

```
jmjones@dinkbuntu:~/code/sysmanage$ python manage.py runserver 0.0.0.0:8080
Validating models...
0 errors found

Django version 0.97-pre-SVN-unknown, using settings 'sysmanage.settings'
Development server is running at http://0.0.0.0:8080/
Quit the server with CONTROL-C.
```

Figure 11-7 shows the login form. Once we log in, we can add servers, hardware, operating systems, and the like. Figure 11-8 shows the Django admin main page and Figure 11-9 shows the "add hardware" form. There is benefit to having a database tool to store and display your data in a consistent, simple, usable manner. Django does a fantastic job of providing a simple, usable interface to a set of data. And if that is all that it did, it would be a useful tool. But that's just the start of what Django can do. If you can think of a way that a browser can display data, you can very likely get Django to do it. And it is typically not very difficult.

For example, if we wanted one page with every type of operating system, hardware component, service, etc., we could do it. And if we wanted to be able to click on each one of those individual items and display a page containing nothing but servers with those individual characteristics, we could do that, too. And if we wanted to be able to click on each one of those servers in the list and have it display detailed information about the server, we could do that as well. Actually, let's do that. We'll use those "suggestions" for requirements that we will go by for this application.

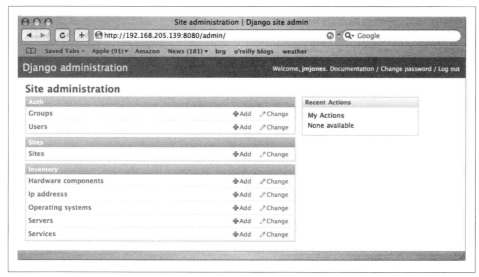

Figure 11-8. Django admin main page

First, Example 11-13 is an updated *urls.py*.

Example 11-13. URL mapping (urls.py)

```
from django.conf.urls.defaults import *

urlpatterns = patterns('',
    # Example:
    # (r'^sysmanage/', include('sysmanage.foo.urls')),

    # Uncomment this for admin:
    (r'^admin/', include('django.contrib.admin.urls')),
    (r'^$', 'sysmanage.inventory.views.main'),
    (r'^categorized/(?P<category>.*?)/(?P<category_id>.*?)/$',
            'sysmanage.inventory.views.categorized'),
    (r'^server_detail/(?P<server_id>.*?)/$',
            'sysmanage.inventory.views.server_detail'),
)
```

We added three new lines mapping non-admin URLs to functions. There is really nothing different to see here from what was in the Apache log viewer app. We are mapping regular expressions of URLs to functions and using a little bit of regular expression groupings as well.

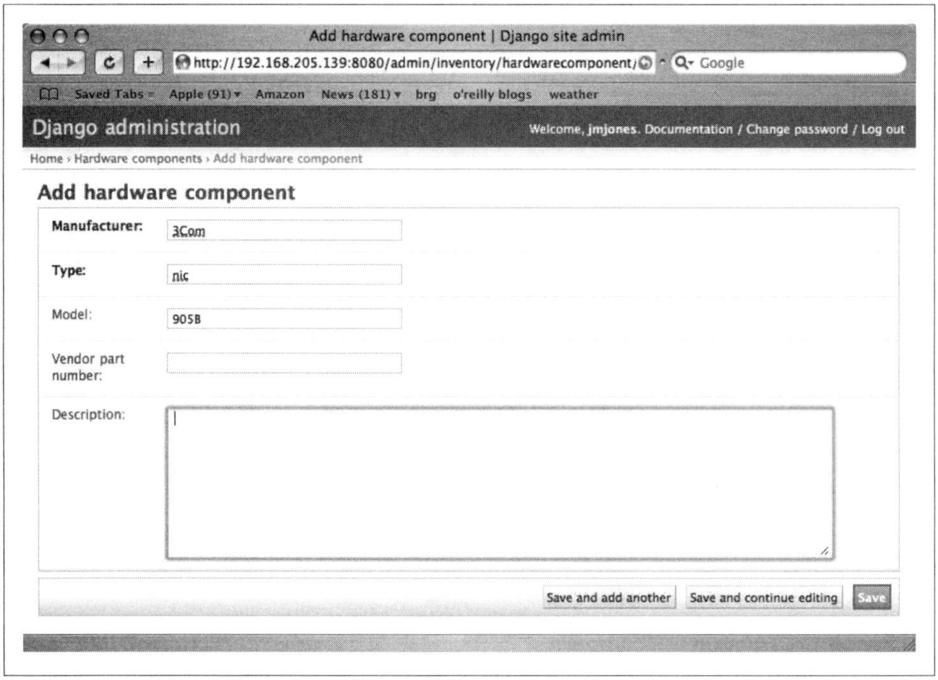

Figure 11-9. Django admin add hardware component

The next thing we will do is to add functions to the **views** module that we declared in the URL mapping file. Example 11-14 is the **views** module.

Example 11-14. Inventory views (views.py)

```python
# Create your views here.

from django.shortcuts import render_to_response
import models

def main(request):
    os_list = models.OperatingSystem.objects.all()
    svc_list = models.Service.objects.all()
    hardware_list = models.HardwareComponent.objects.all()
    return render_to_response('main.html', {'os_list': os_list,
            'svc_list': svc_list, 'hardware_list': hardware_list})

def categorized(request, category, category_id):
    category_dict = {'os': 'Operating System',
        'svc': 'Service', 'hw': 'Hardware'}
    if category == 'os':
        server_list = models.Server.objects.filter(os__exact=category_id)
        category_name = models.OperatingSystem.objects.get(id=category_id)
    elif category == 'svc':
        server_list = \
            models.Server.objects.filter(services__exact=category_id)
```

```
            category_name = models.Service.objects.get(id=category_id)
        elif category == 'hw':
            server_list = \
                models.Server.objects.filter(hardware_component__exact=category_id)
            category_name = models.HardwareComponent.objects.get(id=category_id)
        else:
            server_list = []
        return render_to_response('categorized.html', {'server_list': server_list,
            'category': category_dict[category], 'category_name': category_name})

def server_detail(request, server_id):
    server = models.Server.objects.get(id=server_id)
    return render_to_response('server_detail.html', {'server': server})
```

Just as we added three URL mappings to the *urls.py* file, so we also added three functions to the *views.py* file. The first is `main()`. This function simply takes a list of all the different OSes, hardware components, and services and passes them into the main.html template.

In Example 11-14, we created a *templates* directory in the application folder. We will do the same thing here:

```
jmjones@dinkbuntu:~/code/sysmanage/inventory$ mkdir templates
jmjones@dinkbuntu:~/code/sysmanage/inventory$
```

Example 11-15 is the "main.html" template that the `main()` view function is passing data into.

Example 11-15. Main Template (main.html)

```
{% extends "base.html" %}

{% block title %}Server Inventory Category View{% endblock %}

{% block content %}
<div>
    <h2>Operating Systems</h2>
    <ul>
    {% for o in os_list %}
      <li><a href="/categorized/os/{{ o.id }}/" >{{ o.name }}</a></li>
    {% endfor %}
    </ul>
</div>
<div>
    <h2>Services</h2>
    <ul>
    {% for s in svc_list %}
      <li><a href="/categorized/svc/{{ s.id }}/" >{{ s.name }}</a></li>
    {% endfor %}
    </ul>
</div>
<div>
    <h2>Hardware Components</h2>
    <ul>
    {% for h in hardware_list %}
```

```
        <li><a href="/categorized/hw/{{ h.id }}/" >{{ h.manufacturer }}</a></li>
        {% endfor %}
        </ul>
</div>
{% endblock %}
```

This template is pretty straightforward. It divides up the page into three parts, one for each category that we want to see. For each category, it itemizes the entries that the category has along with a link to see all servers that have the specified category item.

When a user clicks on one of those links, it will take them to the next view function, `categorized()`.

The main template passes a category (being one of `os` for `Operating System`, `hw` for `Hardware Component`, and `svc` for `Service`) and a category ID (i.e., the specific component that the user clicked on, such as "3Com 905b Network Card") into the `categorized()` view function. The `categorized()` function takes these arguments and retrieves a list of all servers from the database that have the selected component. After querying the database for the proper information, the `categorized()` function passes its information on to the "categorized.html" template. Example 11-16 shows the contents of the "categorized.html" template.

Example 11-16. Categorized Template (categorized.html)

```
{% extends "base.html" %}

{% block title %}Server List{% endblock %}

{% block content %}
<h1>{{ category }}::{{ category_name }}</h1>
<div>
        <ul>
        {% for s in server_list %}
          <li><a href="/server_detail/{{ s.id }}/" >{{ s.name }}</a></li>
        {% endfor %}
        </ul>
</div>
{% endblock %}
```

The "categorized.html" template displays a list of all the servers that `categorized()` passed in to it.

The user can then click on a link to individual servers, which will take her to the `server_detail()` view function. The `server_detail()` view function takes a server id parameter, retrieves data about that server from the database, and passes that data on to the "server_detail.html" template.

The "server_detail.html" template shown in Example 11-17 is perhaps the longest of the templates, but it is very simple. Its job is to display the individual pieces of data for the server, such as what OS the server is running, what pieces of hardware the server has, what services are running on the server, and what IP addresses the server has.

Example 11-17. Server detail template (server_detail.html)

```
{% extends "base.html" %}

{% block title %}Server Detail{% endblock %}

{% block content %}
<div>
    Name: {{ server.name }}
</div>
<div>
    Description: {{ server.description }}
</div>
<div>
    OS: {{ server.os.name }}
</div>
<div>
    <div>Services:</div>
    <ul>
    {% for service in server.services.all %}
        <li>{{ service.name }}</li>
    {% endfor %}
    </ul>
</div>
<div>
    <div>Hardware:</div>
    <ul>
    {% for hw in server.hardware_component.all %}
        <li>{{ hw.manufacturer }} {{ hw.type }} {{ hw.model }}</li>
    {% endfor %}
    </ul>
</div>
<div>
    <div>IP Addresses:</div>
    <ul>
    {% for ip in server.ipaddress_set.all %}
        <li>{{ ip.address }}</li>
    {% endfor %}
    </ul>
</div>
{% endblock %}
```

And that is an example of how to build a pretty simple database application using Django. The admin interface provides a friendly means of populating the database and with just a few more lines of code, we were able to create custom views of sorting and navigating the data, as shown in Figures 11-10, 11-11, and 11-12.

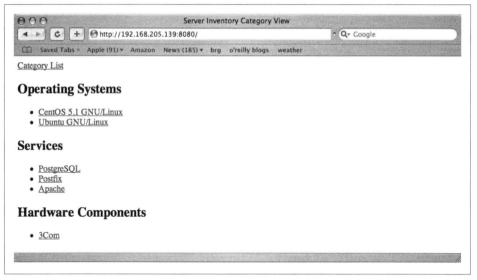

Figure 11-10. System management application main page

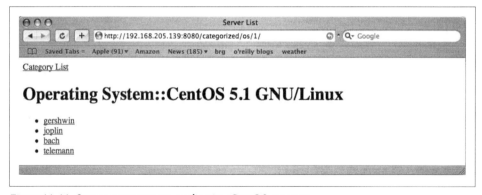

Figure 11-11. System management application CentOS category

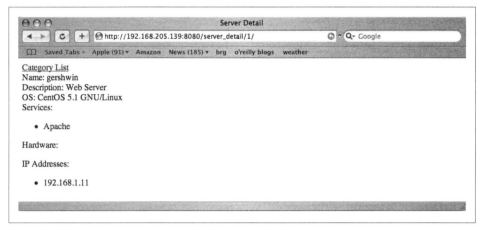

Figure 11-12. System management application server detail

Conclusion

While building GUI applications doesn't seem to fit the traditional responsibilities of a system administrator, it can prove to be an invaluable skill. Sometimes, you may *need* to build some simple application for one of your users. Other times, you may *need* to build a simple application for yourself. Still other times, you may realize that you *don't need* it, but it might make some task go along just a little bit more smoothly. Once you're comfortable building GUI applications, you may be surprised at how often you find yourself building them.

## CHAPTER 12

Data Persistence

Data persistence, in a simple, generic sense, is saving data for later use. This implies that the data, once saved for later, will survive if the process that saved it terminates. This is typically accomplished by converting the data to some format and then writing that data to disk. Sometimes, the format is human readable, such as XML or YAML. Other times, the format is not usable directly by humans, such as a Berkeley DB file (bdb) or a SQLite database.

What kind of data might you need to save for later? Perhaps you have a script that keeps track of the last modified date of the files in a directory and you need to run it occasionally to see which files have changed since the last time you ran it. The data about the files is something you want to save for later, where later is the next time you run the script. You could store this data in some kind of persistent data file. In another scenario, you have one machine that has potential network issues and you decide to run a script every 15 minutes to see how quickly it pings a number of other machines on the network. You could store the ping times in a persistent data file for later use. Later in this case has more to do with when you plan on examining the data, rather than when the program that gathered the data needs access to it.

We will be breaking this discussion of serialization into two categories: simple and relational.

Simple Serialization

There are a number of ways of storing data to disk for later use. We are calling "simple serialization" the process of saving data to disk without saving the relationships between the pieces of data. We'll discuss the difference between simple and relational in the relational section.

Pickle

The first, and perhaps the most basic "simple serialization" mechanism for Python is the standard library `pickle` module. If you think of pickling in the agricultural or culinary sense, the idea is to preserve a food item, put it into a jar, and use it later. The culinary concept translates nicely to what happens with the `pickle` module. With the `pickle` module, you take an object, write it to disk, exit your Python process, come back later, start your Python process again, read your object back from disk, and then interact with it.

What can you pickle? Here is a list taken from the Python Standard Library documentation on pickle that lists types of objects that are pickleable:

- None, true, and false
- Integers, long integers, floating-point numbers, complex numbers
- Normal and Unicode strings
- Tuples, lists, sets, and dictionaries containing only pickleable objects
- Functions defined at the top level of a module
- Built-in functions defined at the top level of a module
- Classes that are defined at the top level of a module
- Instances of such classes whose __dict__ or __setstate__( ) is pickleable

Here is how to serialize your object to disk using the `pickle` module:

```
In [1]: import pickle

In [2]: some_dict = {'a': 1, 'b': 2}

In [3]: pickle_file = open('some_dict.pkl', 'w')

In [4]: pickle.dump(some_dict, pickle_file)

In [5]: pickle_file.close()
```

And here is what the `pickled` file looks like:

```
jmjones@dinkgutsy:~$ ls -l some_dict.pkl
-rw-r--r-- 1 jmjones jmjones 30 2008-01-20 07:13 some_dict.pkl
jmjones@dinkgutsy:~$ cat some_dict.pkl
(dp0
S'a'
p1
I1
sS'b'
p2
I2
```

You could learn the pickle file format and create one manually, but we wouldn't recommend it.

Here is how to unpickle a pickle file:

```
In [1]: import pickle

In [2]: pickle_file = open('some_dict.pkl', 'r')
```

```
In [3]: another_name_for_some_dict = pickle.load(pickle_file)

In [4]: another_name_for_some_dict
Out[4]: {'a': 1, 'b': 2}
```

Notice that we didn't name the object that we unpickled the same thing that we named it before it was pickled. Remember that a name is just a way of referring to an object.

It's interesting to note that there need not be a one-to-one relationship between your objects and your pickle files. You can dump as many objects to a single pickle file as you have hard drive space for or your filesystem allows, whichever comes first. Here is an example of dumping a number of **dictionary** objects to a single pickle file:

```
In [1]: list_of_dicts = [{str(i): i} for i in range(5)]

In [2]: list_of_dicts
Out[2]: [{'0': 0}, {'1': 1}, {'2': 2}, {'3': 3}, {'4': 4}]

In [3]: import pickle

In [4]: pickle_file = open('list_of_dicts.pkl', 'w')

In [5]: for d in list_of_dicts:
   ...:     pickle.dump(d, pickle_file)
   ...:
   ...:

In [6]: pickle_file.close()
```

We created a list of dictionaries, created a writable file object, iterated over the list of dictionaries, and serialized each one to the pickle file. Notice that this is the exact same method that we used to write one object to a pickle file in an earlier example, only without the iterating and the multiple **dump()** calls.

Here is an example of unpickling and printing the objects from the pickle file that contains multiple objects:

```
In [1]: import pickle

In [2]: pickle_file = open('list_of_dicts.pkl', 'r')

In [3]: while 1:
   ...:     try:
   ...:         print pickle.load(pickle_file)
   ...:     except EOFError:
   ...:         print "EOF Error"
   ...:         break
   ...:
   ...:
{'0': 0}
{'1': 1}
{'2': 2}
{'3': 3}
```

```
{'4': 4}
EOF Error
```

We created a readable file object pointing at the file created in the previous example and kept trying to load a `pickle` object from the file until we hit an `EOFError`. You can see that the dictionaries that we got out of the pickle file are the same (and in the same order) as the files we stuffed into the pickle file.

Not only can we `pickle` simple built-in types of objects, but we can also `pickle` objects of types that we ourselves have created. Here is a module that we'll use for the next two examples. This module contains a custom class that we'll be pickling and unpickling:

```python
#!/usr/bin/env python

class MyClass(object):
    def __init__(self):
        self.data = []
    def __str__(self):
        return "Custom Class MyClass Data:: %s" % str(self.data)
    def add_item(self, item):
        self.data.append(item)
```

Here is a module that imports the module with the custom class and `pickles` a custom object:

```python
#!/usr/bin/env python

import pickle
import custom_class

my_obj = custom_class.MyClass()
my_obj.add_item(1)
my_obj.add_item(2)
my_obj.add_item(3)

pickle_file = open('custom_class.pkl', 'w')
pickle.dump(my_obj, pickle_file)
pickle_file.close()
```

In this example, we imported the module with the custom class, instantiated an object from the custom class, added a few items to the object, then serialized it. Running this module gives no resulting output.

Here is a module that imports the module with the custom class and then loads the custom object from the pickle file:

```python
#!/usr/bin/env python

import pickle
import custom_class

pickle_file = open('custom_class.pkl', 'r')
my_obj = pickle.load(pickle_file)
```

```
    print my_obj
    pickle_file.close()
```

Here is the output from running the unpickling file:

```
jmjones@dinkgutsy:~/code$ python custom_class_unpickle.py
Custom Class MyClass Data:: [1, 2, 3]
```

It is not necessary for the unpickling code to explicitly import the custom class you are unpickling. However, it is necessary for the unpickling code to be able to find the module that the custom class is in. Following is a module that doesn't import the custom class module:

```
#!/usr/bin/env python

import pickle
##import custom_class ##commented out import of custom class

pickle_file = open('custom_class.pkl', 'r')
my_obj = pickle.load(pickle_file)
print my_obj
pickle_file.close()
```

Here is the output from running the nonimporting module:

```
jmjones@dinkgutsy:~/code$ python custom_class_unpickle_noimport.py
Custom Class MyClass Data:: [1, 2, 3]
```

And here is the output from running the same module after copying it (and the pickle file) to another directory and running from there:

```
jmjones@dinkgutsy:~/code/cantfind$ python custom_class_unpickle_noimport.py
Traceback (most recent call last):
  File "custom_class_unpickle_noimport.py", line 7, in <module>
    my_obj = pickle.load(pickle_file)
  File "/usr/lib/python2.5/pickle.py", line 1370, in load
    return Unpickler(file).load()
  File "/usr/lib/python2.5/pickle.py", line 858, in load
    dispatch[key](self)
  File "/usr/lib/python2.5/pickle.py", line 1090, in load_global
    klass = self.find_class(module, name)
  File "/usr/lib/python2.5/pickle.py", line 1124, in find_class
    __import__(module)
ImportError: No module named custom_class
```

The last line of this traceback shows an import error because pickle failed to load our custom module. Pickle will try to find the module that your custom class is in and import it so that it can return you an object of the same type as you initially pickled.

All of the previous examples on pickle work fine, but there is an option that we haven't mentioned yet. pickle uses the default protocol when pickling an object-like pickle.dump(object_to_pickle, pickle_file). The protocol is the format specification for how the file is serialized. The default protocol uses the almost human readable format that we showed earlier. Another protocol choice is a binary format. You may want to consider using the binary protocol if you notice that pickling your objects is taking a substantial amount of time. Here is a comparison of using the default protocol and the binary protocol:

```
In [1]: import pickle

In [2]: default_pickle_file = open('default.pkl', 'w')

In [3]: binary_pickle_file = open('binary.pkl', 'wb')

In [4]: d = {'a': 1}

In [5]: pickle.dump(d, default_pickle_file)

In [6]: pickle.dump(d, binary_pickle_file, -1)

In [7]: default_pickle_file.close()

In [8]: binary_pickle_file.close()
```

The first pickle file we created (named *default.pkl*) will contain the pickle data in its default nearly human-readable format. The second pickle file we created (named *binary.pkl*) will contain the pickle data in a binary format. Notice that we opened *default.pkl* in normal **write** mode ('w'), but we opened *binary.pkl* in binary **writable** mode ('wb'). The only difference between the call to dump between these objects is the call to the binary dump has one more argument: a -1 that signifies that the "highest" protocol, which currently is a binary protocol, will be used.

Here is a hex dump of the binary pickle file:

```
jmjones@dinkgutsy:~/code$ hexcat binary.pkl
00000000 - 80 02 7d 71  00 55 01 61  71 01 4b 01  73 2e          ..}q.U.aq.K.s.
```

And here is a hex dump of the default pickle file:

```
jmjones@dinkgutsy:~/code$ hexcat default.pkl
00000000 - 28 64 70 30  0a 53 27 61  27 0a 70 31  0a 49 31 0a  (dp0.S'a'.p1.I1.
00000010 - 73 2e                                               s.
```

That is really unnecessary since we can just cat it out and will be able to read the contents of the file. Here are the plain contents of the default pickle file:

```
jmjones@dinkgutsy:~/code$ cat default.pkl
(dp0
S'a'
p1
I1
s.
```

cPickle

In the Python Standard Library, there is another implementation of the Pickle library that you should consider using. It is called cPickle. As the name implies, cPickle was implemented in C. As with our suggestion regarding using binary files, if you notice

---

that pickling your objects is taking a while, you may want to consider trying the cPickle module. The syntax is identical for cPickle as for "regular" pickle.

shelve

Another persistence option is the shelve module. shelve provides an easy, usable interface to object persistence that simplifies multiple object persistence. By that we mean storing multiple objects in the same persistent object store and then easily getting them back. Storing objects in the shelve persistent data store is similar to simply using a Python dictionary. Here is an example of opening a shelve file, serializing data to it, then reopening it and accessing its contents:

```
In [1]: import shelve

In [2]: d = shelve.open('example.s')

In [3]: d
Out[3]: {}

In [4]: d['key'] = 'some value'

In [5]: d.close()

In [6]: d2 = shelve.open('example.s')

In [7]: d2
Out[7]: {'key': 'some value'}
```

One difference between using shelve and using a plain dictionary is that you create a shelve object by using shelve.open() rather than instantiating the dict class or using curly braces ({}). Another difference is that with shelve, when you are done with your data, you need to call close() on the shelve object.

Shelve has a couple of tricky points. We already mentioned the first: you have to call close() when you are done with the operation you are working on. If you don't close() your shelve object, any changes you made to it won't be persisted. Following is an example of losing your changes by not closing your shelve object. First, we'll just create and persist our shelve object and exit IPython:

```
In [1]: import shelve

In [2]: d = shelve.open('lossy.s')

In [3]: d['key'] = 'this is a key that will persist'

In [4]: d
Out[4]: {'key': 'this is a key that will persist'}

In [5]: d.close()

In [6]:
Do you really want to exit ([y]/n)?
```

Next, we'll start IPython again, open the same shelve file, create another item, and exit without explicitly closing the shelve object:

```
In [1]: import shelve

In [2]: d = shelve.open('lossy.s')

In [3]: d
Out[3]: {'key': 'this is a key that will persist'}

In [4]: d['another_key'] = 'this is an entry that will not persist'

In [5]:
Do you really want to exit ([y]/n)?
```

Now, we'll start IPython again, reopen the same shelve file, and see what we have:

```
In [1]: import shelve

In [2]: d = shelve.open('lossy.s')

In [3]: d
Out[3]: {'key': 'this is a key that will persist'}
```

So, make sure you close() any shelve objects that you have changed and whose data you would like to save.

Another tricky area is around changing mutable objects. Remember that mutable objects are objects whose value can be changed without having to reassign the value to the variable. Here, we create a shelve object, create a key that contains a mutable object (in this case, a list), change the mutable object, then close the shelve object:

```
In [1]: import shelve

In [2]: d = shelve.open('mutable_lossy.s')

In [3]: d['key'] = []

In [4]: d['key'].append(1)

In [5]: d.close()

In [6]:
Do you really want to exit ([y]/n)?
```

Since we called close() on the shelve object, we might expect that the value for 'key' is the list [1]. But we would be wrong. Here is the result of opening the previous shelve file and deserializing it:

```
In [1]: import shelve

In [2]: d = shelve.open('mutable_lossy.s')

In [3]: d
Out[3]: {'key': []}
```

This isn't odd or unexpected behavior at all. In fact, it's in the shelve documentation. The problem is that inline changes to persistent objects aren't picked up by default. But there are a couple of ways to work around this behavior. One is specific and targeted, and the other is broad and all-encompassing. First, in the specific/targeted approach, you can just reassign to the shelve object like this:

```
In [1]: import shelve

In [2]: d = shelve.open('mutable_nonlossy.s')

In [3]: d['key'] = []

In [4]: temp_list = d['key']

In [5]: temp_list.append(1)

In [6]: d['key'] = temp_list

In [7]: d.close()

In [8]:
Do you really want to exit ([y]/n)?
```

When we deserialize our shelved object, here is what we get:

```
In [1]: import shelve

In [2]: d = shelve.open('mutable_nonlossy.s')

In [3]: d
Out[3]: {'key': [1]}
```

The list that we created and appended to has been preserved.

Next, the broad and all-encompassing approach: changing the writeback flag for the shelve object. The only parameter we demonstrated passing in to shelve.open() was the filename of the shelve file. There are a few other options, one of which is the writeback flag. If the writeback flag is set to True, any entries of the shelve object that have been accessed are cached in memory and then persisted when close() is called on the shelve object. This can be useful for the case of dealing with mutable objects, but it does have a trade-off. Since the accessed objects will all be cached and then persisted upon close (whether changed or not), memory usage and file sync time will grow proportionately to the number of objects you are accessing on the shelve object. So, if you have a large number of objects you are accessing on a shelve object, you may want to consider not setting the writeback flag to True.

In this next example, we will set the writeback flag to True and manipulate a list inline without reassigning it to the shelve object:

```
In [1]: import shelve

In [2]: d = shelve.open('mutable_nonlossy.s', writeback=True)
```

```
In [3]: d['key'] = []

In [4]: d['key'].append(1)

In [5]: d.close()

In [6]:
Do you really want to exit ([y]/n)?
```

Now, let's see if our change was persisted.

```
In [1]: import shelve

In [2]: d = shelve.open('mutable_nonlossy.s')

In [3]: d
Out[3]: {'key': [1]}
```

It was persisted as we hoped it would be.

Shelve offers an easy way to work with persistent data. There are a couple of gotchas along the way, but overall, it's a useful module.

YAML

Depending on who you ask, YAML stands for "YAML ain't markup language" or "yet another markup language." Either way, it is a data format that is often used to store, retrieve, and update pieces of data in a plain text layout. This data is often hierarchical. Probably the easiest way to start working with YAML in Python is to easy_install PyYAML. But why use YAML when you have to install it and pickle is built-in? There are two attractive reasons for choosing YAML over pickle. These two reasons don't make YAML the right choice in all situations, but for certain cases, it can make a lot of sense. First, YAML is human-readable. The syntax feels similar to a config file. If you have cases where editing a config file is a good option, YAML may be a good choice for you. Second, YAML parsers have been implemented in many other languages. If you need to get data between a Python application and an application written in another language, YAML can be a good intermediary solution.

Once you easy_install PyYAML, you can serialize and deserialize YAML data. Here is an example of serializing a simple dictionary:

```
In [1]: import yaml

In [2]: yaml_file = open('test.yaml', 'w')

In [3]: d = {'foo': 'a', 'bar': 'b', 'bam': [1, 2,3]}

In [4]: yaml.dump(d, yaml_file, default_flow_style=False)

In [5]: yaml_file.close()
```

This example is pretty easy to follow, but let's walk through it anyway. The first thing we do is import the YAML module (named yaml). Next, we create a writable file that we will later use to store the YAML in. Next, we create a dictionary (named d) that contains the data that we want to serialize. Then, we serialize the dictionary (named d) using the dump() function from the yaml module. The parameters that we pass to dump() are the dictionary that we are serializing, the YAML output file, and a parameter that tells the YAML library to write the output in block style rather than the default style, pieces of which look like a string conversion of the data object that we are serializing.

Here is what the YAML file looks like:

```
jmjones@dinkgutsy:~/code$ cat test.yaml
bam:
- 1
- 2
- 3
bar: b
foo: a
```

If we want to deserialize the file, we perform the inverse operations as what we performed in the dump() example. Here is how we get the data back out of the YAML file:

```
In [1]: import yaml

In [2]: yaml_file = open('test.yaml', 'r')

In [3]: yaml.load(yaml_file)
Out[3]: {'bam': [1, 2, 3], 'bar': 'b', 'foo': 'a'}
```

As with the dump() example, we first have to import the YAML module (yaml). Next we create a YAML file. This time, we create a readable file object from the YAML file on disk. Finally, we call the load() function from the yaml module. load() then returns back a dictionary that is equivalent to the input dictionary.

When using the yaml module, you will probably find yourself cyclically creating data, dumping it to disk, then loading it back up, and so on.

You may not need to dump your YAML data out to a human-readable format, so let's walk through serializing the same dictionary from the previous example in non-block mode. Here is how to dump the same dictionary as before in nonblock mode:

```
In [1]: import yaml

In [2]: yaml_file = open('nonblock.yaml', 'w')

In [3]: d = {'foo': 'a', 'bar': 'b', 'bam': [1, 2,3]}

In [4]: yaml.dump(d, yaml_file)

In [5]: yaml_file.close()
```

Here is what the YAML file looks like: jmjones@dinkgutsy:~/code$ cat nonblock.yaml
bam: [1, 2, 3] bar: b foo: a. This looks pretty similar to the block-mode format except
for the list value for bam. The differences appear when there is some level of nesting and
some array-like data structure like a list or dictionary. Let's compare a couple of examples to show those differences. But before we do, it will be easier to walk through
these examples if we don't have to keep showing the output of catting the YAML files.
The file argument in the dump() function of the yaml module is optional. (Actually, the
PyYAML documentation refers to the "file" object as a "stream" object, but doesn't
really matter much.) If you leave out the "file" or "stream" argument, dump() will write
the serialized object to standard out. So, in the following example, we will leave out
the file object and print out the YAML results.

Here is a comparison of a few data structures using the block style serialization and
non-block style serialization. The examples that have default_flow_style use the block
formatting and the examples that don't have default_flow_style do not use the block
formatting:

```
In [1]: import yaml

In [2]: d = {'first': {'second': {'third': {'fourth': 'a'}}}}

In [3]: print yaml.dump(d, default_flow_style=False)
first:
  second:
    third:
      fourth: a


In [4]: print yaml.dump(d)
first:
  second:
    third: {fourth: a}


In [5]: d2 = [{'a': 'a'}, {'b': 'b'}, {'c': 'c'}]

In [6]: print yaml.dump(d2, default_flow_style=False)
- a: a
- b: b
- c: c


In [7]: print yaml.dump(d2)
- {a: a}
- {b: b}
- {c: c}


In [8]: d3 = [{'a': 'a'}, {'b': 'b'}, {'c': [1, 2, 3, 4, 5]}]

In [9]: print yaml.dump(d3, default_flow_style=False)
- a: a
```

```
    - b: b
    - c:
      - 1
      - 2
      - 3
      - 4
      - 5


In [10]: print yaml.dump(d3)
- {a: a}
- {b: b}
- c: [1, 2, 3, 4, 5]
```

What if you want to serialize a custom class? The yaml module behaves nearly identically
to the pickle regarding custom classes. The following example will even use the same
custom_class module that we used in the pickle custom_class example.

Here is a Python module that imports the custom_class module, creates an object from
MyClass, adds some items to the object, and then serializes it:

```
#!/usr/bin/env python

import yaml
import custom_class

my_obj = custom_class.MyClass()
my_obj.add_item(1)
my_obj.add_item(2)
my_obj.add_item(3)

yaml_file = open('custom_class.yaml', 'w')
yaml.dump(my_obj, yaml_file)
yaml_file.close()
```

When we run the previous module, here is the output we see:

```
jmjones@dinkgutsy:~/code$ python custom_class_yaml.py
jmjones@dinkgutsy:~/code$
```

Nothing. That means that everthing went well.

Here is the inverse of the previous module:

```
#!/usr/bin/env python

import yaml
import custom_class

yaml_file = open('custom_class.yaml', 'r')
my_obj = yaml.load(yaml_file)
print my_obj
yaml_file.close()
```

This script imports the `yaml` and `custom_class` modules, creates a readable `file` object from the YAML file created previously, `load`s the YAML file into an object, and prints the object.

When we run it, we see the following:

```
jmjones@dinkgutsy:~/code$ python custom_class_unyaml.py
Custom Class MyClass Data:: [1, 2, 3]
```

This is identical to the output from the unpickling example that we ran earlier in this chapter, so the behavior is what we would expect to see.

ZODB

Another option for serializing data is Zope's ZODB module. ZODB stands for "Zope Object Database." Simple usage of ZODB feels pretty similar to serializing to pickle or YAML, but ZODB has the ability to grow with your needs. For example, if you need atomicity in your operations, ZODB provides transactions. And if you need a more scalable persistent store, you can use ZEO, Zope's distributed object store.

ZODB could have possibly gone into the "relational persistence" section rather than the "simple persistence" section. However, this object database doesn't exactly fit the mold of what we've come to recognize as a relational database over the years even though you can easily establish relationships among objects. Also, we're only displaying some of the more basic features of ZODB, so in our examples, it looks more like `shelve` than a relational database. So, we decided to keep ZODB in the "simple persistence" section.

Regarding installation of ZODB, it is as simple of a matter as doing `easy_install ZODB3`. The ZODB module has a number of dependencies but `easy_install` resolves them well, downloads everything it needs, and installs them.

For an example of simple use of ZODB, we'll create a ZODB storage object and add a dictionary and a list to it. Here is the code for serializing the dictionary and list:

```python
#!/usr/bin/env python

import ZODB
import ZODB.FileStorage
import transaction

filestorage = ZODB.FileStorage.FileStorage('zodb_filestorage.db')
db = ZODB.DB(filestorage)
conn = db.open()

root = conn.root()
root['list'] = ['this', 'is', 'a', 'list']
root['dict'] = {'this': 'is', 'a': 'dictionary'}

transaction.commit()
conn.close()
```

ZODB requires a couple more lines of code to start working with it than we've seen with pickle or YAML, but once you have a persistent store created and initialized, usage is pretty similar to the other options. This example is pretty self-explanatory, especially given the other examples of data persistence. But we'll walk through it quickly, anyway.

First, we import a couple of ZODB modules, namely ZODB, ZODB.FileStorage, and transaction. (We'll engage in just a little hair splitting at this point. Providing a module for import that does not contain an identifying prefix seems awkward. It seems to us that the transaction module that we import above should be prefixed by ZODB. Regardless, this is how it is, so you'll just want to be aware of that. Now we'll move on.) Next, we create a FileStorage object by specifying the database file to use for it. Then, we create a DB object and connect it to the FileStorage object. Then we open() the database object and get root node of it. From there, we can update the root object with our data structures, which we do with an impromptu list and dictionary. We then commit the changes we have made with transaction.commit() and then close the database connection with conn.close().

Once you've created a ZODB data storage container (such as the file storage object in this example) and have committed some data to it, you may want to get that data back out. Here is an example of opening the same database up, but reading the data rather than writing it:

```
#!/usr/bin/env python

import ZODB
import ZODB.FileStorage

filestorage = ZODB.FileStorage.FileStorage('zodb_filestorage.db')
db = ZODB.DB(filestorage)
conn = db.open()

root = conn.root()
print root.items()

conn.close()
```

And if we run this code after running the code that populates the database, here is the output we would see:

```
jmjones@dinkgutsy:~/code$ python zodb_read.py
No handlers could be found for logger "ZODB.FileStorage"
[('list', ['this', 'is', 'a', 'list']), ('dict', {'this': 'is', 'a': 'dictionary'})]
```

Just as we've shown how to serialize custom classes for other data persistence frameworks, we'll show how to do so with ZODB. We will diverge, however, from using the same MyClass example (and we'll explain why later). Just as with the other frameworks, you just define a class, create an object from it, and then tell the serialization engine to save it to disk. Here is the custom class that we'll be using this time:

```
#!/usr/bin/env python
```

```
import persistent

class OutOfFunds(Exception):
    pass

class Account(persistent.Persistent):
    def __init__(self, name, starting_balance=0):
        self.name = name
        self.balance = starting_balance
    def __str__(self):
        return "Account %s, balance %s" % (self.name, self.balance)
    def __repr__(self):
        return "Account %s, balance %s" % (self.name, self.balance)
    def deposit(self, amount):
        self.balance += amount
        return self.balance
    def withdraw(self, amount):
        if amount > self.balance:
            raise OutOfFunds
        self.balance -= amount
        return self.balance
```

This is a very simple account class for managing financial funds. We defined an OutOfFunds exception that we will explain later. The Account class subclasses persistent.Persistent. (Regarding persistent, we could go into the same rant about the propriety of providing a meaningful prefix to a module that people are going to be using. How does a glance at this code inform the reader that ZODB code is being used here? It doesn't. But we won't go into that rant again.) Subclassing from persistent.Persistent does some magic behind the scenes to make it easier for ZODB to serialize this data. In the class definition, we created custom __str__ and __repr__ string converters. You'll get to see those in action later. We also created deposit() and withdraw() methods. Both methods update the object attribute balance positively or negatively, depending on which method was called. The withdraw() method checks if there is enough money in the balance attribute before it subtracts funds. If there is not enough money in balance, the withdraw() method will raise the OutOfFunds exception that we mentioned earlier. Both deposit() and withdraw return the resulting balance after either adding or subtracting funds.

Here is a bit of code that will serialize the custom class that we just walked through:

```
#!/usr/bin/env python

import ZODB
import ZODB.FileStorage
import transaction
import custom_class_zodb

filestorage = ZODB.FileStorage.FileStorage('zodb_filestorage.db')
db = ZODB.DB(filestorage)
conn = db.open()

root = conn.root()
```

```
noah = custom_class_zodb.Account('noah', 1000)
print noah
root['noah'] = noah
jeremy = custom_class_zodb.Account('jeremy', 1000)
print jeremy
root['jeremy'] = jeremy

transaction.commit()
conn.close()
```

This example is nearly identical to the previous ZODB example in which we serialized a dictionary and a list. However, we are importing our own module, creating two objects from a custom class, and serializing those two objects to the ZODB database. Those two objects are a noah account and a jeremy account, both of which are created with a balance of 1000 (presumably $1,000.00 USD, but we didn't identify any currency units).

Here is this example's output:

```
jmjones@dinkgutsy:~/code$ python zodb_custom_class.py
Account noah, balance 1000
Account jeremy, balance 1000
```

And if we run the module that displays the contents of a ZODB database, here is what we see:

```
jmjones@dinkgutsy:~/code$ python zodb_read.py
No handlers could be found for logger "ZODB.FileStorage"
[('jeremy', Account jeremy, balance 1000), ('noah', Account noah, balance 1000)]
```

Our code not only created the objects as we expected, but it also saved them to disk for later use.

How do we open the database up and change data for different accounts? This code would be pretty useless if it didn't allow us to do that. Here is a piece of code that will open the database previously created and transfer 300 (presumably dollars) from the noah account to the jeremy account:

```
#!/usr/bin/env python

import ZODB
import ZODB.FileStorage
import transaction
import custom_class_zodb

filestorage = ZODB.FileStorage.FileStorage('zodb_filestorage.db')
db = ZODB.DB(filestorage)
conn = db.open()

root = conn.root()
noah = root['noah']
print "BEFORE WITHDRAWAL"
print "================="
print noah
```

```
jeremy = root['jeremy']
print jeremy
print "-----------------"

transaction.begin()
noah.withdraw(300)
jeremy.deposit(300)
transaction.commit()

print "AFTER WITHDRAWAL"
print "================"
print noah
print jeremy
print "---------------"

conn.close()
```

Here is the output from running this script:

```
jmjones@dinkgutsy:~/code$ python zodb_withdraw_1.py
BEFORE WITHDRAWAL
=================
Account noah, balance 1000
Account jeremy, balance 1000
-----------------
AFTER WITHDRAWAL
================
Account noah, balance 700
Account jeremy, balance 1300
---------------
```

And if we run our ZODB database printint script, we can see if the data was saved:

```
jmjones@dinkgutsy:~/code$ python zodb_read.py
[('jeremy', Account jeremy, balance 1300), ('noah', Account noah, balance 700)]
```

The noah account went from 1000 to 700 and the jeremy account went from 1000 to 1300.

The reason that we wanted to diverge from the MyClass custom class example was to show a little bit about transactions. One of the canonical examples for demonstrating how transactions work is with a bank account. If you want to be able to ensure that funds are successfully transfered from one account to another without losing or gaining funds, transactions are probably the first approach to look at. Here is a code example that uses transactions in a loop in order to show that no money is lost:

```
#!/usr/bin/env python

import ZODB
import ZODB.FileStorage
import transaction
import custom_class_zodb

filestorage = ZODB.FileStorage.FileStorage('zodb_filestorage.db')
db = ZODB.DB(filestorage)
```

```
conn = db.open()

root = conn.root()
noah = root['noah']
print "BEFORE TRANSFER"
print "================"
print noah
jeremy = root['jeremy']
print jeremy
print "----------------"

while True:
    try:
        transaction.begin()
        jeremy.deposit(300)
        noah.withdraw(300)
        transaction.commit()
    except custom_class_zodb.OutOfFunds:
        print "OutOfFunds Error"
        print "Current account information:"
        print noah
        print jeremy
        transaction.abort()
        break

print "AFTER TRANSFER"
print "=============="
print noah
print jeremy
print "---------------"

conn.close()
```

This is a slight modification of the previous transfer script. Instead of only transferring once, it transfers 300 from the noah account to the jeremy account until there isn't enough money left to transfer. At the point that there are insufficient funds to transfer, it will print out a notice that an exception has occurred and the current account information. It will then abort() the transaction and break from the loop. The script also prints account information before and after the transaction loop. If the transactions worked, both the before and after account details should total 2000, since both accounts started with 1000 each.

Here is a result of running the script:

```
jmjones@dinkgutsy:~/code$ python zodb_withdraw_2.py
BEFORE TRANSFER
===============
Account noah, balance 700
Account jeremy, balance 1300
------------------
OutOfFunds Error
Current account information:
Account noah, balance 100
Account jeremy, balance 2200
```

```
AFTER TRANSFER
==============
Account noah, balance 100
Account jeremy, balance 1900
----------------
```

In the "before" snapshot, noah has 700 and jeremy has 1300 for a total of 2000. When the OutOfFunds exception occurs, noah has 100 and jeremy has 2200 for a total of 2300. In the "after" snapshot, noah has 100 and jeremy has 1900 for a total of 2000. So during the exception, before the `transaction.abort()`, there was an additional 300 that would have been unexplained. But aborting the transaction fixed that problem.

ZODB feels like a solution between the simple and the relational. It is straightforward in its approach. An object that you serialize to disk corresponds to an object in memory both before serialization and after deserialization. But, it has some advanced features like transactions. ZODB is an option worth considering if you want the straightforwardness of simple object mapping, but you may need to grow into more advanced features later.

In summary of simple persistence, sometimes all you need is to simply save and store Python objects for later use. All the options we laid out here are excellent. Each one has its strengths and weaknesses. If you need this at some point, you will have to investigate which one will work best for you and your project.

Relational Serialization

Sometimes simple serialization isn't enough. Sometimes you need the power of relational analysis. Relational serialization refers to either serializing Python objects and relationally connecting them with other Python objects or storing relational data (for example, in a relational database) and providing a Python object-like interface to that data.

SQLite

Sometimes it's helpful to store and deal with data in a more structured and relational way. What we're talking about here is the family of information stores referred to as relational databases, or RDBMSs. We assume that you have used a relational database such as MySQL, PostgreSQL, or Oracle before. If so, you should have no problem with this section.

According to the SQLite website, SQLite "is a software library that implements a self-contained, serverless, zero-configuration, transactional SQL database engine." So what does all that mean? Rather than the database running in a separate server process from your code, the database engine runs in the same process as your code and you access it as a library. The data lives in a file rather than in multiple directories scattered across multiple filesystems. And rather than having to configure which hostname, port, username, password, etc. to connect to, you just point your code at the database file that the SQLite library creates. This statement also means that SQLite is a fairly featureful database. In a nutshell, the statement identifies two main benefits of using SQLite: it's easy to use and it will do much of the same work that a "real" database will do. Another benefit is that it is ubiquitous. Most major operating systems and programming languages offer support for SQLite.

Now that you know why you may want to consider using it, let's look at how to use it. We pulled the following table definitions from the Django example in Chapter 11. Assume we have a file named *inventory.sql* that contains the following data:

```sql
BEGIN;
CREATE TABLE "inventory_ipaddress" (
    "id" integer NOT NULL PRIMARY KEY,
    "address" text NULL,
    "server_id" integer NOT NULL
)
;
CREATE TABLE "inventory_hardwarecomponent" (
    "id" integer NOT NULL PRIMARY KEY,
    "manufacturer" varchar(50) NOT NULL,
    "type" varchar(50) NOT NULL,
    "model" varchar(50) NULL,
    "vendor_part_number" varchar(50) NULL,
    "description" text NULL
)
;
CREATE TABLE "inventory_operatingsystem" (
    "id" integer NOT NULL PRIMARY KEY,
    "name" varchar(50) NOT NULL,
    "description" text NULL
)
;
CREATE TABLE "inventory_service" (
    "id" integer NOT NULL PRIMARY KEY,
    "name" varchar(50) NOT NULL,
    "description" text NULL
)
;
CREATE TABLE "inventory_server" (
    "id" integer NOT NULL PRIMARY KEY,
    "name" varchar(50) NOT NULL,
    "description" text NULL,
    "os_id" integer NOT NULL REFERENCES "inventory_operatingsystem" ("id")
)
;
CREATE TABLE "inventory_server_services" (
    "id" integer NOT NULL PRIMARY KEY,
    "server_id" integer NOT NULL REFERENCES "inventory_server" ("id"),
    "service_id" integer NOT NULL REFERENCES "inventory_service" ("id"),
    UNIQUE ("server_id", "service_id")
)
;
CREATE TABLE "inventory_server_hardware_component" (
```

```
"id" integer NOT NULL PRIMARY KEY,
"server_id" integer NOT NULL REFERENCES "inventory_server" ("id"),
"hardwarecomponent_id" integer
   NOT NULL REFERENCES "inventory_hardwarecomponent" ("id"),
UNIQUE ("server_id", "hardwarecomponent_id")
)
;
COMMIT;
```

We can create a SQLite database with the following command-line argument:

```
jmjones@dinkgutsy:~/code$ sqlite3 inventory.db < inventory.sql
```

Assuming, of course, that you have SQLite installed. With Ubuntu and Debian systems, installing is as easy as `apt-get install sqlite3`. On Red Hat systems, all you have to do is yum `install sqlite`. For other distributions of Linux that may not have it installed, other UNIXes, or for Windows, you can download source and precompiled binaries at *http://www.sqlite.org/download.html*.

Assuming you have SQLite installed and have a database created, we'll proceed with "connecting" to the database and populating it with some data. Here is all it takes to connect to a SQLite database:

```
In [1]: import sqlite3

In [2]: conn = sqlite3.connect('inventory.db')
```

All we had to do was import the SQLite library and then call `connect()` on the `sqlite3` module. `Connect()` returns a connection object, which we referred to as `conn` and which we will use in the remainder of the example. Next, we execute a query on the connection object to insert data into the database:

```
In [3]: cursor = conn.execute("insert into inventory_operatingsystem (name,
description) values ('Linux', '2.0.34 kernel');")
```

The `execute()` method returns a database cursor object, so we decided to refer to it as `cursor`. Notice that we only provided values for the `name` and `description` fields and left out a value for the `id` field, which is the primary key. We'll see in a moment what value it gets populated with. Since this is an insert rather than a select, we would not expect a result set from the query, so we'll just look at the cursor and fetch any results it may be holding:

```
In [4]: cursor.fetchall()
Out[4]: []
```

Nothing, as we expected. Now, we'll commit and move on:

```
In [5]: conn.commit()

In [6]:
```

Really, we shouldn't have to commit this insert. We would expect this change to flush when we close the database connection at the latest. But it never hurts to explicitly `commit()` a change when you know that you want it committed.

Now that we can create and populate a database using SQLite, let's get that data back out. First, we'll fire up an IPython prompt, import sqlite3, and create a connection to our database file:

```
In [1]: import sqlite3
```

```
In [2]: conn = sqlite3.connect('inventory.db')
```

Now, we'll execute a select query and get a cursor to the results:

```
In [3]: cursor = conn.execute('select * from inventory_operatingsystem;')
```

Finally, we'll fetch the results from the cursor:

```
In [4]: cursor.fetchall()
Out[4]: [(1, u'Linux', u'2.0.34 kernel')]
```

This is the data that we plugged in above. Both the name and the description fields are unicode. And the id field is populated with an integer. Typically, when you insert data into a database and do not specify a value for the primary key, the database will populate it for you and automatically increment the value with the next unique value for that field.

Now that you are familiar with the basic methods of dealing with a SQLite database, doing joins, updating data, and doing more complex things becomes mostly an academic exercise. SQLite is a great format in which to store data, especially if the data is only going to be accessed by one script at a time, or only a few users at a time. In other words, the format is great for fairly small uses. However, the interface that the sqlite3 module provides is arcane.

Storm ORM

While a plain SQL interface to a database is all you really need to retrieve, update, insert, and delete data from a database, it is often convenient to have access to the data without diverting from the simplicity of Python. A trend regarding database access over the last few years has been to create an object-oriented representation of the data that is stored within a database. This trend is called an Object-RelationalMapping (or ORM). An ORM is different from merely providing an object-oriented interface to the database. In an ORM, an object in the programming language can correspond to a single row for a single table of a database. Tables connected with a foreign key relationship can even be accessed as an attribute of that object.

Storm is an ORM that was recently released as open source by Canonical, the company responsible for the creation of the Ubuntu distribution of Linux. Storm is a relative newcomer to the database arena for Python, but it has already developed a noticeable following and we expect it to become one of the front-running Python ORMs.

We will now use Storm to access the data in the database defined earlier in the "SQLite" section. The first thing we have to do is to create a mapping to the tables of which we are interested. Since we've already accessed the `inventory_operatingsystem` table and added an entry to it, we'll continue accessing only that table. Here is what a mapping in Storm looks like:

```
import storm.locals

class OperatingSystem(object):
    __storm_table__ = 'inventory_operatingsystem'
    id = storm.locals.Int(primary=True)
    name = storm.locals.Unicode()
    description = storm.locals.Unicode()
```

This is a pretty normal class definition. There doesn't appear to be weird, magical things going on. There is no subclass other than the built-in `object` type. There are a number of class-level attributes being defined. The one slightly odd-looking thing is the class attribute of `__storm_table__`. This lets Storm know which table that objects of this type should be accessing. While it seems pretty simple, straightforward, and non-magical, there is at least a little bit of magic in the mix. For example, the `name` attribute is mapped to the `name` column of the `inventory_operatingsystem` table and the `description` attribute is mapped to the `description` column of the `inventory_operatingsystem` table. How? Magic. Any attribute that you assign to a Storm mapping class is automatically mapped to a column that shares its name in the table designated by the `__storm_table__` attribute.

What if you don't want the `description` attribute of your object mapped to the `description` column? Simple. Pass in a `name` keyword argument to the `storm.locals.Type` that you are using. For example, changing the `description` attribute to this: `dsc = storm.locals.Unicode(name='description')` connects `OperatingSystem` objects to the same columns (namely, `name` and `description`). However, rather than referring to the description as `mapped_object.description`, you would refer to it as `mapped_object.dsc`.

Now that we have a mapping of a Python class to a database table, let's add another row to the database. To go along with our ancient Linux distribution with a 2.0.34 kernel, we'll add Windows 3.1.1 to the operating system table:

```
import storm.locals
import storm_model
import os

operating_system = storm_model.OperatingSystem()
operating_system.name = u'Windows'
operating_system.description = u'3.1.1'

db = storm.locals.create_database('sqlite:///%s' % os.path.join(os.getcwd(),
    'inventory.db'))

store = storm.locals.Store(db)
store.add(operating_system)
store.commit()
```

In this example, we imported the `storm.locals`, `storm_model`, and `os` modules. Then, we instantiated an `OperatingSystem` object and assigned values to the `name` and `description` attributes. (Notice that we used unicode values for these attributes.) Then we created a database object by calling the `create_database()` function and passing it the path to our SQLite database file, *inventory.db*. While you might think that the database object is what we would use to add data to the database, it isn't, at least not directly. We first had to create a `Store` object by passing the database into its constructor. After we did that, we were able to add the `operating_system` object to the `store` object. Finally, we called `commit()` on the `store` to finalize the addition of this `operating_system` to the database.

We also want to see that the data we inserted does in fact find its way into the database. Since this is a SQLite database, we could just use the `sqlite3` command-line tool. If we did that, we would have less reason to write code to retrieve data from the database using Storm. So, here is a simple utility to retrieve all records from the `inventory_oper` `atingsystem` table and print it out (albeit in rather ugly fashion):

```
import storm.locals
import storm_model
import os

db = storm.locals.create_database('sqlite:///%s' % os.path.join(os.getcwd(),
    'inventory.db'))

store = storm.locals.Store(db)

for o in store.find(storm_model.OperatingSystem):
    print o.id, o.name, o.description
```

The first several lines of code in this example are strikingly similar to the first several lines of the previous example. Part of the reason for that is that we copied and pasted the code from one file to the other. Never mind that, though. The bigger reason is that both examples require some common setup steps before they can "talk" to the database. We have the same import statements here as in the previous example. We have a `db` object that was returned from the `create_database()` function. We have a `store` object created by passing the `db` object to the `Store` constructor. But now, rather than adding an object to the store, we're calling the `find()` method of the `store` object. This particular call to `find()` (i.e., `store.find(storm_model.OperatingSystem)`) returns a result set of all `storm_model.OperatingSystem` objects. Because we mapped the `OperatingSys` `tem` class to the `inventory_operatingsystem` table, Storm will look up all the relevant records in the `inventory_operatingsystem` table and create `OperatingSystem` objects from them. For each `OperatingSystem` object, we print out the `id`, `name`, and `descrip` `tion` attributes. These attributes map to the column values in the database that share the same names for each record.

We should have one record already in the database from the earlier example in the "SQLite" section. Let's see what happens when we run the retrieve script. We would expect it to display one record even though that record was not inserted using the Storm library:

```
jmjones@dinkgutsy:~/code$ python storm_retrieve_os.py
1 Linux 2.0.34 kernel
```

This is exactly what we expected to happen. Now, what happens when we run the add script and then the retrieve script? It should show the old entry that was in the database from earlier (the 2.0.34 Linux kernel) as well as the newly inserted entry (Windows 3.1.1):

```
jmjones@dinkgutsy:~/code$ python storm_add_os.py
jmjones@dinkgutsy:~/code$ python storm_retrieve_os.py
1 Linux 2.0.34 kernel
2 Windows 3.1.1
```

Again, this was exactly what we expected.

But what if we want to filter the data? Supposed we only want to see operating system entries that started with the string "Lin." Here is a piece of code to do just that:

```
import storm.locals
import storm_model
import os

db = storm.locals.create_database('sqlite:///%s' % os.path.join(os.getcwd(),
  'inventory.db'))

store = storm.locals.Store(db)

for o in store.find(storm_model.OperatingSystem,
  storm_model.OperatingSystem.name.like(u'Lin%')):
    print o.id, o.name, o.description
```

This example is identical to the previous example that uses `store.find()` except that this one passes in a second parameter to `store.find()`: a search criteria. `Store.find(storm_model.OperatingSystem,storm_model.OperatingSys tem.name.like(u'Lin%'))` tells Storm to look for all `OperatingSystem` objects that have a name that starts with the unicode value `Lin`. For each value that is in the result set, we print it out identically to the previous example.

And when you run it, you will see something like this:

```
jmjones@dinkgutsy:~/code$ python storm_retrieve_os_filter.py
1 Linux 2.0.34 kernel
```

This database still has the "Windows 3.1.1" entry, but it was filtered out because "Windows" does not begin with "Lin."

SQLAlchemy ORM

While Storm is gaining an audience and building a community, SQLAlchemy appears to be the dominate ORM in Python at the moment. Its approach is similar to that of

Storm. That could probably be better said as, "Storm's approach is similar to that of SQLAlchemy," since SQLAlchemy was first. Regardless, we'll walk through the same inventory_operatingsystem example for SQLAlchemy that we finished for Storm.

Here is the table and object definition for the inventory_operatingsystem table:

```python
#!/usr/bin/env python

import os
from sqlalchemy import create_engine
from sqlalchemy import Table, Column, Integer, Text, VARCHAR, MetaData
from sqlalchemy.orm import mapper
from sqlalchemy.orm import sessionmaker

engine = create_engine('sqlite:///%s' % os.path.join(os.getcwd(),
        'inventory.db'))

metadata = MetaData()
os_table = Table('inventory_operatingsystem', metadata,
    Column('id', Integer, primary_key=True),
    Column('name', VARCHAR(50)),
    Column('description', Text()),
)

class OperatingSystem(object):
    def __init__(self, name, description):
        self.name = name
        self.description = description

    def __repr__(self):
        return "<OperatingSystem('%s','%s')>" % (self.name, self.description)

mapper(OperatingSystem, os_table)
Session = sessionmaker(bind=engine, autoflush=True, transactional=True)
session = Session()
```

The biggest difference between our Storm and SQLAlchemy example table definition code is that SQLAlchemy uses an additional class other than the table class and then maps the two together.

Now that we have a definition of our table, we can write a piece of code to query all records from that table:

```python
#!/usr/bin/env python

from sqlalchemy_inventory_definition import session, OperatingSystem

for os in session.query(OperatingSystem):
    print os
```

And if we run it now, after populating some data from the previous examples, we'll see this:

```
$ python sqlalchemy_inventory_query_all.py <OperatingSystem('Linux','2.0.34 kernel')>
<OperatingSystem('Windows','3.1.1')>
</OperatingSystem></OperatingSystem>
```

If we want to create another record, we can easily do so by just instantiating an OperatingSystem object and adding it to the session:

```
#!/usr/bin/env python

from sqlalchemy_inventory_definition import session, OperatingSystem

ubuntu_710 = OperatingSystem(name='Linux', description='2.6.22-14 kernel')
session.save(ubuntu_710)
session.commit()
```

That will add another Linux kernel to the table, this time a more current kernel. Running our query all script again gives us this output:

```
$ python sqlalchemy_inventory_query_all.py
<OperatingSystem('Linux','2.0.34 kernel')>
<OperatingSystem('Windows','3.1.1')>
<OperatingSystem('Linux','2.6.22-14 kernel')>
```

Filtering results is pretty simple in SQLAlchemy as well. For example, if we wanted to filter out all the OperatingSystems whose names start with "Lin," we could write a script like this:

```
#!/usr/bin/env python

from sqlalchemy_inventory_definition import session, OperatingSystem

for os in session.query(OperatingSystem).filter(OperatingSystem.name.like('Lin%')):
    print os
```

And we would see output like this:

```
$ python sqlalchemy_inventory_query_filter.py
<OperatingSystem('Linux','2.0.34 kernel')>
<OperatingSystem('Linux','2.6.22-14 kernel')>
```

This was just a brief overview of what SQLAlchemy can do. For more information on using SQLAlchemy, visit the website at *http://www.sqlalchemy.org/*. Or you can check out *Essential SQLAlchemy* by Rick Copeland (O'Reilly).

Summary

In this chapter, we addressed a number of different tools that allow you to store your data for later use. Sometimes you'll need something simple and lightweight like the `pickle` module. Other times, you'll need something more full-featured like the SQLAlchemy ORM. As we've shown, with Python, you have plenty of options from very simple to complex and powerful.

## CHAPTER 13

Command Line

Introduction

The command line has a special relationship with the sysadmin. No other tool carries the same level of significance or prestige as the command line. A complete mastery of the art of the command line is a rite of passage for most systems administrators. Many sysadmins think less of other sysadmins that use a "GUI" and call GUI administration a crutch. This may not be completely fair, but it is a commonly held belief for true mastery of the art of system's administration.

For the longest time, Unix systems embraced the philosophy that the command line interface (CLI) was far superior to any GUI that could be developed. In a recent turn of events, it seems like Microsoft has also gotten back to its roots. Jeffrey Snover, architect of Windows Powershell, said, "It was a mistake to think that GUIs ever would, could, or even should, eliminate CLIs."

Even Windows, which has had the poorest CLI of any modern OS for decades, now recognizes the value of the CLI in its current Windows PowerShell implementation. We will not be covering Windows in this book, but it is a very interesting fact that cements just how important mastering the command line and command-line tool creation really is.

There is more to the story, though, than just mastering prebuilt Unix command-line tools. To really become a master at the command line, you need to create your own tools, and this may be the sole reason you picked up this book in the first place. Don't worry, this chapter won't dissapoint you. After finishing it, you will be a master of creating command-line tools in Python.

It was a purposeful decision to make the last chapter of the book focus on creating command-line tools. The reason for this was to first expose you to a wide assortment of techniques in Python, and then to finally teach you how to harness all of these skills to summon your full power to create command-line tool masterpieces.

Basic Standard Input Usage

The simplest possible introduction to creating a command-line tool revolves around knowing that the **sys** module is able to process command-line arguments via **sys.argv**. Example 13-1 shows quite possibly the simplest command-line tool.

Example 13-1. sysargv.py

```
#!/usr/bin/env python

import sys
print sys.argv
```

These two lines of code return to standard out, whatever you type on the command line after executing the command:

```
./sysargv.py
```

```
['./sysargv.py']
```

and

```
./sysargv.py foo
```

returns to standard out

```
['./sysargv.py', 'test']
```

and

```
./sysargv.py foo bad for you
```

returns to standard out

```
['./sysargv.py', 'foo', 'bad', 'for', 'you']
```

Let's be a little more specific and slightly change the code to count the number of command-line arguments in Example 13-2.

Example 13-2. sysargv.py

```
#!/usr/bin/env python
import sys

#Python indexes start at Zero, so let's not count the command itself which is
#sys.argv[0]

num_arguments = len(sys.argv) - 1
print sys.argv, "You typed in ", num_arguments, "arguments"
```

You might be thinking, "Wow, this is pretty easy, all I have to do now is reference **sys.argv** arguments by number and write some logic to connect them." Well, you're right, it is pretty easy to do that. Let's add some features to our command-line application. One final thing we can do is send an error message to standard out if there are no arguments passed to the command line. See Example 13-3.

Example 13-3. sysargv-step2.py

```
#!/usr/bin/env python
import sys

num_arguments = len(sys.argv) - 1

#If there are no arguments to the command, send a message to standard error.
if num_arguments == 0:
        sys.stderr.write('Hey, type in an option silly\n')

else:
        print sys.argv, "You typed in ", num_arguments, "arguments"
```

Using sys.argv to create command-line tools is quick and dirty but is often the wrong choice. The Python Standard Library includes the optparse module, which handles all of the messy and uncomfortable parts of creating a quality command-line tool. Even for tiny "throwaway" tools, it is a better choice to use optparse than sys.argv, as often "throwaway" tools have a habit of growing into production tools. In the coming sections, we will explore why, but the short answer is that a good option parsing module handles the edge cases for you.

Introduction to Optparse

As we mentioned in the previous section, even small scripts can benefit from using optparse to handle option handling. A fun way to get started with optparse is to code up a "Hello World" example that handles options and arguments. Example 13-4 is our Hello World example.

Example 13-4. Hello World optparse

```
#!/usr/bin/env python
import optparse

def main():
    p = optparse.OptionParser()
    p.add_option('--sysadmin', '-s', default="BOFH")
    options, arguments = p.parse_args()
    print 'Hello, %s' % options.sysadmin

if __name__ == '__main__':
    main()
```

When we run this, we the get the following different kinds of outputs:

```
$ python hello_world_optparse.py
Hello, BOFH

$ python hello_world_optparse.py --sysadmin Noah
Hello, Noah

$ python hello_world_optparse.py --s Jeremy
Hello, Jeremy
```

```
$ python hello_world_optparse.py --infinity Noah
Usage: hello_world_optparse.py [options]

hello_world_optparse.py: error: no such option: --infinity
```

In our small script, we saw that we could set both short -s, and long --sysadmin options, as well as default values. Finally, we saw the power of the built-in error handling that optparse delivers when we wrongly entered an option, readability, that did not exist for Perl.

Simple Optparse Usage Patterns

No Options Usage Pattern

In the previous section, we mentioned that even for small scripts optparse can be useful. Example 13-5 is a simple optparse usage pattern in which we don't even take options but still take advantage of the power of optparse.

Example 13-5. ls command clone

```python
#!/usr/bin/env python
import optparse
import os

def main():
    p = optparse.OptionParser(description="Python  'ls' command clone",
                              prog="pyls",
                              version="0.1a",
                              usage="%prog [directory]")
    options, arguments = p.parse_args()
    if len(arguments) == 1:
        path = arguments[0]
        for filename in os.listdir(path):
            print filename
    else:
        p.print_help()
if __name__ == '__main__':
    main()
```

In this example, we reimplement the ls command in Python, except we only take an argument, the path to perform the ls on. We don't even use options, but can still utilize the power of optparse, by relying on it to handle the flow of our program. First we provide some implementation deals this time when we make an instance of optparse, and add a usage value that instructs the potential user of our tool how to execute it properly. Next, we check to make sure the number of arguments is exactly one; if there are more or less arguments than one, we use the built-in help message p.print_help() to display the instructions on how to use the tool again. Here is what it looks like when run correctly first by running it against our current directory or ".":

```
$ python no_options.py .
.svn
hello_world_optparse.py
no_options.py
```

Next we look at what happens when we don't enter any options:

```
$ python no_options.py
Usage: pyls [directory]

Python 'ls' command clone

Options:
--version   show program's version number and exit
-h, --help  show this help message and exit
```

What is interesting about this is we defined this behavior with the `p.print_help()` call if the arguments were not exactly one. This is exactly the same as if we entered `--help`:

```
$ python no_options.py --help
Usage: pyls [directory]

Python 'ls' command clone

Options:
--version   show program's version number and exit
-h, --help  show this help message and exit
```

And because we defined a `--version` option, we can see that output as well:

```
$ python no_options.py --version
0.1a
```

In this example, `optparse` was helpful even on simple "throwaway" scripts that you might be tempted to toss.

True/False Usage Pattern

Using an option to set a `True` or `False` statement in your program is quite useful. The classic example of this involves setting both a `--quiet`, which supresses all standard out, and a `--verbose`, which triggers extra output. Example 13-6 is what this looks like.

Example 13-6. Adding and subtracting verbosity

```
#!/usr/bin/env python
import optparse
import os

def main():
    p = optparse.OptionParser(description="Python 'ls' command clone",
                              prog="pyls",
                              version="0.1a",
                              usage="%prog [directory]")
    p.add_option("--verbose", "-v", action="store_true",
                 help="Enables Verbose Output",default=False)
```

```
        options, arguments = p.parse_args()
        if len(arguments) == 1:
            if options.verbose:
                print "Verbose Mode Enabled"
            path = arguments[0]
            for filename in os.listdir(path):
                if options.verbose:
                    print "Filename: %s " % filename
                elif options.quiet:
                    pass
                else:
                    print filename
        else:
            p.print_help()
if __name__ == '__main__':
    main()
```

By using a --verbose, we have effectively set levels of verbosity for stdout. Let's take a look at each level of verbosity in action. First, here is the normal way:

```
$ python true_false.py /tmp
.aksusb
alm.log
amt.log
authTokenData
FLEXnet
helloworld
hsperfdata_ngift
ics10003
ics12158
ics13342
icssuis501
MobileSync.lock.f9e26440fe5adbb6bc42d7bf8f87c1e5fc61a7fe
summary.txt
```

Next, here is our --verbose mode:

```
$ python true_false.py --verbose /tmp
Verbose Mode Enabled
Filename: .aksusb
Filename: alm.log
Filename: amt.log
Filename: authTokenData
Filename: FLEXnet
Filename: helloworld
Filename: hsperfdata_ngift
Filename: ics10003
Filename: ics12158
Filename: ics13342
Filename: icssuis501
Filename: MobileSync.lock.f9e26440fe5adbb6bc42d7bf8f87c1e5fc61a7fe
Filename: summary.txt
```

When we set the --verbose option, it makes options.verbose become True, and as a result, our conditional statement gets executed that prints "Filename:" in front of the actual filename. Notice in our script that we set `default=False` and `action="store_true"`, this effectively says in English, by default be `False`, but if someone specifies this `--option`, set the option value to become `True`. This is the essence of using `True/False` options with `optparse`.

Counting Options Usage Pattern

In a typical Unix command-line tool, for example, `tcpdump`, if you specify `-vvv`, you will get extra verbose output as opposed to just using `-v` or `-vv`. You can do the same thing with `optparse` by adding a count for each time an option is specified. For example, if you wanted to add the same level of verbosity in your tool, it would look like Example 13-7.

Example 13-7. Counting Options Usage pattern

```python
#!/usr/bin/env python
import optparse
import os

def main():
    p = optparse.OptionParser(description="Python 'ls' command clone",
                              prog="pyls",
                              version="0.1a",
                              usage="%prog [directory]")
    p.add_option("-v", action="count", dest="verbose")
    options, arguments = p.parse_args()
    if len(arguments) == 1:
        if options.verbose:
            print "Verbose Mode Enabled at Level: %s" % options.verbose
        path = arguments[0]
        for filename in os.listdir(path):
            if options.verbose == 1:
                print "Filename: %s " % filename
            elif options.verbose ==2 :
                fullpath = os.path.join(path,filename)
                print "Filename: %s | Byte Size: %s" % (filename,
                                          os.path.getsize(fullpath))
            else:
                print filename
    else:
        p.print_help()
if __name__ == '__main__':
    main()
```

By using an auto-incremented count design pattern, we can make sure of just one option, yet do three different things. The first time we call `-v`, it sets `options.verbose` to 1, and if we use `--v` it sets `options.verbose` to 2. In our actual program, with no options we just print out the filename, with `-v` we print out the word Filename with the filename, and then finally, whew, with `-vv` we print out the byte size as well as the filename. This is our output with `-vv` specified:

```
$ python verbosity_levels_count.py -vv /tmp
Verbose Mode Enabled at Level: 2
Filename: .aksusb | Byte Size: 0
Filename: alm.log | Byte Size: 1403
Filename: amt.log | Byte Size: 3038
Filename: authTokenData | Byte Size: 32
Filename: FLEXnet | Byte Size: 170
Filename: helloworld | Byte Size: 170
Filename: hsperfdata_ngift | Byte Size: 102
Filename: ics10003 | Byte Size: 0
Filename: ics12158 | Byte Size: 0
Filename: ics13342 | Byte Size: 0
Filename: ics14183 | Byte Size: 0
Filename: icssuis501 | Byte Size: 0
Filename: MobileSync.lock.f9e26440fe5adbb6bc42d7bf8f87c1e5fc61a7fe | Byte Size: 0
Filename: summary.txt | Byte Size: 382
```

Choices Usage Pattern

Sometimes it's just easier to present a few choices for an option. In our last example, we created options for --verbose and --quiet, but we could also just make them choices that get selected from a --chatty option. Using our previous example, Example 13-8 is what it looks like when it is reworked to use options.

Example 13-8. Choices Usage pattern

```python
#!/usr/bin/env python
import optparse
import os

def main():
    p = optparse.OptionParser(description="Python 'ls' command clone",
                              prog="pyls",
                              version="0.1a",
                              usage="%prog [directory]")
    p.add_option("--chatty", "-c", action="store", type="choice",
                 dest="chatty",
                 choices=["normal", "verbose", "quiet"],
                 default="normal")
    options, arguments = p.parse_args()
    print options
    if len(arguments) == 1:
        if options.chatty == "verbose":
            print "Verbose Mode Enabled"
        path = arguments[0]
        for filename in os.listdir(path):
            if options.chatty == "verbose":
                print "Filename: %s " % filename
            elif options.chatty == "quiet":
                pass
            else:
                print filename
    else:
        p.print_help()
```

```
if __name__ == '__main__':
    main()
```

If we run this command without an option like we did in the previous example, we get this error:

```
$ python choices.py --chatty
Usage: pyls [directory]

pyls: error: --chatty option requires an argument
```

And if we give the wrong argument to the option, we get another error that tells us the available options:

```
$ python choices.py --chatty=nuclear /tmp
Usage: pyls [directory]

pyls: error: option --chatty: invalid choice: 'nuclear' (choose from 'normal',
    'verbose', 'quiet')
```

One of the handy aspects of using choices is that it prevents relying on the user to enter the correct argument for your command. The user can only select from choices you have determined. Finally, here is what the command looks like when run correctly:

```
$ python choices.py --chatty=verbose /tmp
{'chatty': 'verbose'}
Verbose Mode Enabled
Filename: .aksusb
Filename: alm.log
Filename: amt.log
Filename: authTokenData
Filename: FLEXnet
Filename: helloworld
Filename: hsperfdata_ngift
Filename: ics10003
Filename: ics12158
Filename: ics13342
Filename: ics14183
Filename: icssuis501
Filename: MobileSync.lock.f9e26440fe5adbb6bc42d7bf8f87c1e5fc61a7fe
Filename: summary.txt
```

If you notice, the output at the top has "chatty" as the key and "verbose" as the value. In our example above, we put a print statement for options to show you what they look like to our program. Finally, here is one final example of using --chatty with a quiet choice:

```
$ python choices.py --chatty=quiet /tmp
{'chatty': 'quiet'}
```

Option with Multiple Arguments Usage Pattern

By default, an option with **optparse** can only take one argument, but it is possible to set the number to something else. Example 13-9 is a contrived example in which we make a version 1s that displays the output of two directories at once.

Example 13-9. Listing of two directories

```python
#!/usr/bin/env python
import optparse
import os

def main():
    p = optparse.OptionParser(description="Lists contents of two directories",
                              prog="pymultils",
                              version="0.1a",
                              usage="%prog [--dir dir1 dir2]")
    p.add_option("--dir", action="store", dest="dir", nargs=2)
    options, arguments = p.parse_args()
    if options.dir:
        for dir in options.dir:
            print "Listing of %s:\n" % dir
            for filename in os.listdir(dir):
                print filename
    else:
        p.print_help()
if __name__ == '__main__':
    main()
```

If we look at the output of this command with the only argument for the **--dir** option, we get this error:

```
[ngift@Macintosh-8][H:10238][J:0]# python multiple_option_args.py --dir /tmp ⌐
Usage: pymultils [--dir dir1 dir2]

pymultils: error: --dir option requires 2 arguments
```

With the correct number of arguments for our **--dir** option, we get this:

```
pymultils: error: --dir option requires 2 arguments
[ngift@Macintosh-8][H:10239][J:0]# python multiple_option_args.py --dir /tmp
    /Users/ngift/Music
Listing of /tmp:

.aksusb
FLEXnet
helloworld
hsperfdata_ngift
ics10003
ics12158
ics13342
ics14183
ics15392
icssuis501
MobileSync.lock.f9e26440fe5adbb6bc42d7bf8f87c1e5fc61a7fe
```

```
summary.txt
Listing of /Users/ngift/Music:

.DS_Store
.localized
iTunes
```

Unix Mashups: Integrating Shell Commands into Python Command-Line Tools

In Chapter 10, we looked at many of the common ways to use the subprocess module. Creating new command-line tools by either wrapping existing command-line tools with Python and changing their API, or mixing one or more Unix command-line tools with Python offers an interesting approach to examine. It is trivial to wrap an existing command-line tool with Python and change the behavior to meet your specific needs. You may choose to integrate a configuration file that holds some of the arguments for some of the options you use, or you may choose to create defaults for others. Regardless of the requirement, you can use subprocess and optparse to change a native Unix tools behavior without much trouble.

Alternately, mixing a command-line tool with pure Python can lead to interesting tools that are not easily created in C or Bash. How about mixing the dd command with threads and queues, tcpdump with Python's regular expression library, or perhaps a customized version of rsync? These Unix 2.0 "mashups" are very similar to their Web 2.0 cousins. By mixing Python with Unix tools, new ideas are created, and problems are solved in different ways. In this section, we explore some of these techniques.

Kudzu Usage Pattern: Wrapping a Tool in Python

Sometimes you find yourself using a command-line tool that isn't exactly what you want it to be. It might require too many options, or the argument order is reversed from the way you want to use it. With Python, it is trivial to change the behavior of a tool and make it do whatever you really want it to do. We like to call this the "Kudzu" design pattern. If you are not familiar with Kudzu, it was a fast-growing vine imported from Japan to the southern United States. Kudzu often engulfs and surrounds natural habit and creates an alternate landscape. With Python, you can do the same to your Unix environment if you so choose.

For this example, we are going to wrap the snmpdf command with Python to simplify its use. First let's take a look at what it looks like when we run snmpdf normally:

```
[ngift@Macintosh-8][H:10285][J:0]# snmpdf -c public -v 2c example.com
Description          size (kB)           Used       Available  Used%
Memory Buffers        2067636          249560         1818076    12%
Real Memory           2067636         1990704           76932    96%
Swap Space            1012084              64         1012020     0%
/                    74594112        17420740        57173372    23%
```

/sys	0	0	0	0%
/boot	101086	20041	81045	19%

If you are not familiar with the snmpdf, it is meant to be run remotely on a system that has SNMP enabled and configured to allow access to the disk section of the MIB tree. Often, command-line tools that deal with the SNMP protocol have many options, which make them difficult to use. To be fair, the tool creators had to design something that would work with SNMP versions 1, 2, and 3, plus a whole assortment of other issues. What if you don't care about this, though, and you are a very lazy person. You want to make your own "Kudzu" version of snmpdf that takes only a machine as an argument. Sure, we can do that; Example 13-10 is what it looks like.

 Often, when you wrap a Unix tool in Python to alter the behavior of the tool, it becomes more lines of code than if you altered it with Bash. Ultimately, though, we feel this is a win because it allows you to use the richer Python toolset to extend this tool as you see fit. In addition, you can test this code the same way you test the rest of the tools you write, so often this extra code is the right way to go for the long haul.

Example 13-10. Wrapping SNMPDF command with Python

```python
#!/usr/bin/env python
import optparse
from subprocess import call

def main():
    p = optparse.OptionParser(description="Python wrapped snmpdf command",
                              prog="pysnmpdf",
                              version="0.1a",
                              usage="%prog machine")
    p.add_option("-c", "--community", help="snmp community string")
    p.add_option("-V", "--Version", help="snmp version to use")
    p.set_defaults(community="public",Version="2c")
    options, arguments = p.parse_args()
    SNMPDF = "snmpdf"
    if len(arguments) == 1:
        machine = arguments[0]
        #Our new snmpdf action
        call([SNMPDF, "-c", options.community, "-v",options.Version, machine])
    else:
        p.print_help()
if __name__ == '__main__':
    main()
```

This script runs in at about twenty lines of code, yet it makes our life much easier. Using some of the magic of optparse to help us, we created options that had default arguments that matched out needs. For example, we set a SNMP version option to be version 2 by default, as we know our data center uses only version 2 right now. We also set the community string to "public," because that is what it is set to in our research and development lab, for example. One of the nice things about doing it with optparse and not a hardcoded script is that we have the flexibility to change our options without changing the script.

Notice that the default arguments were set using the set_defaults method, which allows us to set all defaults for a command-line tool in one spot. Also, notice the use of subprocess.call. We embedded the old options, such as -c, and then wrapped the new values that come in from optparse, or options.community in this case, to fill things in. Hopefully, this technique highlights some of the "Kudzu" power of Python to engulf a tool and change it to meet our needs.

Hybrid Kudzu Design Pattern: Wrapping a Tool in Python, and Then Changing the Behavior

In our last example, we made snmpdf quite a bit easier to use, but we didn't change the basic behavior of the tool. The output of both tools was identical. Another approach we can use is to not only engulf a Unix tool, but to then change the basic behavior of the tool with Python as well.

In the next example, we use Python's generators in a functional programming style to filter the results of our snmpdf command to search for critical information, and then append a "CRITICAL" flag to it. Example 13-11 shows what it looks like.

Example 13-11. Altering the SNMPDF command with generators

```python
#!/usr/bin/env python
import optparse
from subprocess import Popen, PIPE
import re

def main():
    p = optparse.OptionParser(description="Python wrapped snmpdf command",
                              prog="pysnmpdf",
                              version="0.1a",
                              usage="%prog machine")
    p.add_option("-c", "--community", help="snmp community string")
    p.add_option("-V", "--Version", help="snmp version to use")
    p.set_defaults(community="public",Version="2c")
    options, arguments = p.parse_args()
    SNMPDF = "snmpdf"
    if len(arguments) == 1:
        machine = arguments[0]

        #We create a nested generator function
        def parse():
            """Returns generator object with line from snmpdf"""
            ps = Popen([SNMPDF, "-c", options.community,
                        "-v",options.Version, machine],
                        stdout=PIPE, stderr=PIPE)
            return ps.stdout

        #Generator Pipeline To Search For Critical Items
```

```
        pattern = "9[0-9]%"
        outline = (line.split() for line in parse()) #remove carriage returns
        flag = (" ".join(row) for row in outline if re.search(pattern, row[-1]))
        #patt search, join strings in list if match
        for line in flag: print "%s CRITICAL" % line
        #Sample Return Value
        #Real Memory 2067636 1974120 93516 95% CRITICAL

    else:
        p.print_help()
if __name__ == '__main__':
    main()
```

If we run our new "altered" version of snmpdf we get this output on test machine:

```
[ngift@Macintosh-8][H:10486][J:0]# python snmpdf_alter.py localhost
Real Memory 2067636 1977208 90428 95% CRITICAL
```

We now have a completely different script that will only generate output if a value in snmpdf is 90 percent or higher, which we have signified as critical. We could run this in a cron job nightly against a few hundred machines, and then send an email if there is a return value from our script. Alternately, we could extend this script a little further and search for usage levels of 80 percent, 70 percent, and generate warnings if they reach those levels as well. It would also be trivial to integrate this with Google App Engine, for example, so that you could create a web application that monitors the disk usage in an infrastructure.

In looking at the code itself, there are a few things to point out that make it different than our previous example. The first difference is the use of subprocess.Popen instead of using subprocess.call. If you find yourself wanting to parse the output of a Unix command-line tool, then subprocess.Popen is what you want to do. Note also, that we used stdout.readlines(), which returns a list instead of a string. This is important later on when we take this output and funnel it through a series of generator expressions.

In the Generator pipeline section, we funnel our generator objects into two expressions to find a match for the critical search criteria we set. As we stated before, we could easily add a couple more generator lines similar to the flag expression, to get results for thresholds in 70 percent and 80 percent ranges.

This tool is perhaps more complex than you would want to implement into a production tool. A better idea might be to break it down into several smaller generic pieces that you import. That being said, it works to illustrate our example.

Hybrid Kudzu Design Pattern: Wrapping a Unix Tool in Python to Spawn Processes

Our last example was reasonably cool, but another interesting way to change the behavior of existing Unix tools is to make them spawn multiple copies in an efficient way. Sure, it is a little freaky, but hey, sometimes you need to be creative to get your job done. This is one of the parts of being a sysadmin that is fun, sometimes you have to do crazy things to solve a problem in production.

In the data chapter, we created a test script that created image files using the dd command running in parallel. Well, let's take that idea and run with it, and make a permanent command-line tool we can reuse over and over again. At the very least, we will have something to hammer disk I/O time when we are testing a new file server. See Example 13-12.

Example 13-12. Multi dd command

```python
from subprocess import Popen, PIPE
import optparse
import sys

class ImageFile():
    """Created Image Files Using dd"""
    def __init__(self, num=None, size=None, dest=None):
        self.num = num
        self.size = size
        self.dest = dest

    def createImage(self):
        """creates N 10mb identical image files"""
        value = "%sMB " % str(self.size/1024)
        for i in range(self.num):
            try:
                cmd = "dd if=/dev/zero of=%s/file.%s bs=1024 count=%s"\
                    % (self.dest,i,self.size)
                Popen(cmd, shell=True, stdout=PIPE)
            except Exception, err:
                sys.stderr.write(err)

    def controller(self):
        """Spawn Many dd Commands"""
        p = optparse.OptionParser(description="Launches Many dd",
                                  prog="Many dd",
                                  version="0.1",
                                  usage="%prog [options] dest")
        p.add_option('-n', '--number', help='set many dd',
                     type=int)
        p.add_option('-s', '--size', help='size of image in bytes',
                     type=int)
        p.set_defaults(number=10,
                       size=10240)
        options, arguments = p.parse_args()
        if len(arguments) == 1:
```

```
        self.dest = arguments[0]
        self.size = options.size
        self.num = options.number
        #runs dd commands
        self.createImage()

def main():
    start = ImageFile()
    start.controller()

if __name__ == "__main__":
    main()
```

Now if we run our multi dd command, we can set the byte size of the file, the path, and the total number of files/processes. Here is what it looks like:

```
$ ./subprocess_dd.py /tmp/
$ 10240+0 records in
10240+0 records out
10485760 bytes transferred in 1.353665 secs (7746199 bytes/sec)
10240+0 records in
10240+0 records out
10485760 bytes transferred in 1.793615 secs (5846160 bytes/sec)
10240+0 records in
10240+0 records out
10485760 bytes transferred in 2.664616 secs (3935186 bytes/sec)

...output supressed for space....
```

One immediate use for this hybrid tool would be in testing the disk I/O performance of a high-speed Fibre SAN, or NAS device. With a bit of work, you could add hooks for generation of PDF reports, and email the results. It would be good to point out that the same thing could be accomplished with threads as well, if threads seemed to fit the problem you needed to solve.

Integrating Configuration Files

Integrating a configuration file into a command-line tool can make all the difference in terms of usability and future customization. It is a bit odd to talk about usability and the command line, because often it is only brought up for GUI or web tools. This is unfortunate, as a command-line tool deserves the same attention to usability that a GUI tool does.

A configuration file can also be a useful way to centralize the way a command-line tool runs on multiple machines. The configuration file could be shared out via an NFS mount, and then hundreds of machines could read this configuration file from a generic command-line tool you created. Alternately, you may have some sort of configuration management system in place, and you could distribute configuration files to tools you created as well.

The Python Standard Library has an excellent module, ConfigParser, for reading and writing configuration files using the *.ini* syntax. It turns out that the .ini format is a nice medium to read and write simple configuration data, without having to resort to XML, and without locking the person editing the file into knowing the Python language. Please refer to the previous chapter for a more detailed look at using the ConfigParser module as well.

Be sure that you do not get in the habit of depending on the order of items in the config file. Interally, the ConfigParser module uses a dictionary, and as such you will need to refer to it in this way to correctly obtain a mapping.

To get started with integrating configuration files into a command-line tool, we are going to create a "hello world" configuration file. Name the file *hello_config.ini* and paste this inside:

```
[Section A]
phrase=Config
```

Now that we have a simple config file, we can integrate this into our previous Hello World command-line tool in Example 13-13.

Example 13-13. Hello config file command-line tool

```
#!/usr/bin/env python
import optparse
import ConfigParser

def readConfig(file="hello_config.ini"):
    Config = ConfigParser.ConfigParser()
    Config.read(file)
    sections = Config.sections()
    for section in sections:
        #uncomment line below to see how this config file is parsed
        #print Config.items(section)
        phrase = Config.items(section)[0][1]
        return phrase

def main():
    p = optparse.OptionParser()
    p.add_option('--sysadmin', '-s')
    p.add_option('--config', '-c', action="store_true")
    p.set_defaults(sysadmin="BOFH")

    options, arguments = p.parse_args()
    if options.config:
        options.sysadmin = readConfig()
    print 'Hello, %s' % options.sysadmin

if __name__ == '__main__':
    main()
```

If we run this tool without any options, we get a default value of BOFH just like the original "hello world" program:

```
[ngift@Macintosh-8][H:10543][J:0]# python hello_config_oplparse.py
Hello, BOFH
```

If we select --config file, though, we parse our configuration file and get this response:

```
[ngift@Macintosh-8][H:10545][J:0]# python hello_config_optparse.py --config
Hello, Config
```

Most of the time you will probably want to set a default path for a --config option and allow someone to customize the location where the file gets read. You can do that as follows instead of just storing the option to be default_true:

```
p.add_option('--config', '-c',
help='Path to read in config file')
```

If this was a bigger, and actually useful program, we could turn it over to someone without knowledge of Python. It would allow them to customize it by changing the value to parser=Config to be something else without having to touch the code. Even if they do have knowledge of Python, though, it is often nice to not have to enter the same options over and over on the command line, yet keep the tool flexible.

Summary

The standard library Optparse and ConfigParser modules are very easy to work with and have been around for quite some time, so they should be available on most systems you run into. If you find yourself needing to write a lot of command-line tools, it might be worth exploring on your own some of the advanced abilities of optparse, such as using callbacks and extending optparse itself. You also might be interested in looking at a few related modules that do not appear in the standard library such as: CommandLineApp (*http://www.doughellmann.com/projects/CommandLineApp/*), Argparse (*http://pypi.python.org/pypi/argparse*), and ConfigObj (*http://pypi.python.org/pypi/ConfigObj*).

## CHAPTER 14

Pragmatic Examples

Managing DNS with Python

Managing a DNS server is a fairly straightforward task compared to, say, an Apache configuration file. The real problem that afflicts data centers and web hosting providers, though, is performing programatic large-scale DNS changes. It turns out that Python does quite a good job in this regard with a module called dnspython. Note there is also also another DNS module named PyDNS, but we will be covering dnspython.

Make sure you refer to the official documentation: *http://www.dnspython.org/*. There is also a great article on using dnspython here: *http://vallista.idyll.org/~grig/articles/*.

To get started using dnspython, you will only need to do an easy_install as the package is listed in the Python Package Index.

```
ngift@Macintosh-8][H:10048][J:0]# sudo easy_install dnspython
Password:
Searching for dnspython
Reading http://pypi.python.org/simple/dnspython/
[output supressed]
```

Next, we explore the module with IPython, like many other things in the book. In this example, we get the A and MX records for *oreilly.com*:

```
In [1]: import dns.resolver
In [2]: ip = dns.resolver.query("oreilly.com","A")
In [3]: mail = dns.resolver.query("oreilly.com","MX")
In [4]: for i,p in ip,mail:
....:       print i,p
....:
....:
208.201.239.37 208.201.239.36
20 smtp1.oreilly.com. 20 smtp2.oreilly.com.
```

In Example 14-1, we assign the "A" record results to ip and the "MX" records to mail. The "A" results are on top, and the "MX" records are on the bottom. Now that we have some idea how it works, let's write a script that collects the "A" records of a collection of hosts.

Example 14-1. Query a group of hosts

```
import dns.resolver

hosts = ["oreilly.com", "yahoo.com", "google.com", "microsoft.com", "cnn.com"]

def query(host_list=hosts):
    collection = []
    for host in host_list:
        ip = dns.resolver.query(host,"A")
        for i in ip:
            collection.append(str(i))
    return collection

if __name__ == "__main__":
    for arec in query():
        print arec
```

If we run this script, we get all of the "A" records for these hosts, and it looks like this:

```
[ngift@Macintosh-8][H:10046][J:0]# python query_dns.py
208.201.239.37
208.201.239.36
216.109.112.135
66.94.234.13
64.233.167.99
64.233.187.99
72.14.207.99
207.46.197.32
207.46.232.182
64.236.29.120
64.236.16.20
64.236.16.52
64.236.24.12
```

One obvious problem this solves is programmatically testing whether all of your hosts have the correct "A" record that you have on file.

There is quite a bit more that dnspython can do: it can manage DNS zones and perform more complex queries than what we described here. If you are interested in seeing even more examples, please see the URLs referenced earlier.

Using LDAP with OpenLDAP, Active Directory, and More with Python

LDAP is a buzzword at most corporations, and one of the authors even runs an LDAP database to manage his home network. If you are not familiar with LDAP, it stands for Lightweight Directory Access Protocol. One of the best definitions we have heard of LDAP comes from Wikipedia, "an application protocal for querying and modifying directory services running over TCP/IP." One example of a service is authentication, which is by far the most popular use for the protocol. Examples of directory dervers that support the LDAP protocol are Open Directory, Open LDAP, Red Hat Directory Server, and Active Directory. The python-ldap API suports communication with both OpenLDAP and Active Directory.

There is a Python API to LDAP called python-ldap, and it includes in its API support an object-oriented wrapper with OpenLDAP 2.x. There is also support for other LDAP-related items, including processing LDIF files and LDAPv3. To get started, you will need to download the package from the python-ldap sourceforge project here: *http://python-ldap.sourceforge.net/download.shtml.*

After you install python-ldap, you will want to first explore the library in IPython. Here is what an interactive session looks like in which we perform both a succesful bind to a public ldap server and then an unsuccesful bind. Getting into the specifics of setting up and configuring LDAP is beyond the scope of this book, but we can start testing the python-ldap API using the University of Michigan's public LDAP server.

```
In [1]: import ldap

In [2]: l = ldap.open("ldap.itd.umich.edu")

In [3]: l.simple_bind()
Out[3]: 1
```

That simple bind tells us we are successful, but let's look at a failure and see what that looks like as well:

```
In [5]: try:
   ....:     l = ldap.open("127.0.0.1")
   ....: except Exception,err:
   ....:     print err
   ....:
   ....:

In [6]: l.simple_bind()
---------------------------------------------------------------
SERVER_DOWN                              Traceback (most recent call last)

/root/&lt;ipython console>

/usr/lib/python2.4/site-packages/ldap/ldapobject.py in simple_bind(self, who, cred,
   serverctrls, clientctrls)
   167     simple_bind([who='' [,cred='']]) -> int
   168     """
--> 169     return self._ldap_call(self._l.simple_bind,who,cred,EncodeControlTuples
   (serverctrls),EncodeControlTuples(clientctrls))
   170
   171   def simple_bind_s(self,who='',cred='',serverctrls=None,clientctrls=None):

/usr/lib/python2.4/site-packages/ldap/ldapobject.py in _ldap_call(self, func, *args,
   **kwargs)
    92     try:
    93       try:
--->  94         result = func(*args,**kwargs)
    95       finally:
```

```
  96             self._ldap_object_lock.release()

SERVER_DOWN: {'desc': "Can't contact LDAP server"}
```

As we can see, in this example, there is not an LDAP server running, and our code blew up.

Importing an LDIF File

Making a simple bind to a public LDAP directory is not very useful to help you get your job done. Here is an example of doing an asynchronous LDIF import:

```
import ldap
import ldap.modlist as modlist

ldif = "somefile.ldif"
def create():
    l = ldap.initialize("ldaps://localhost:636/")
    l.simple_bind_s("cn=manager,dc=example,dc=com","secret")
    dn="cn=root,dc=example,dc=com"
    rec = {}
    rec['objectclass'] = ['top','organizationalRole','simpleSecurityObject']
    rec['cn'] = 'root'
    rec['userPassword'] = 'SecretHash'
    rec['description'] = 'User object for replication using slurpd'
    ldif = modlist.addModlist(attrs)
    l.add_s(dn,ldif)
    l.unbind_s()
```

Going over this example, we initialize to a local LDAP server first, then create an object class that will map to the LDAP database when we do a mass asynchronous import of an LDIF file. Note that l.add_s is what shows us that we are making an ansynchronous call to the API.

These are the basics for using Python and LDAP together, but you should refer to the resources given at the beginning of the chapter for further information about using python-ldap. Specifically, there are examples that detail LDAPv3; Create, Read, Update, Delete (CRUD); and more.

One final thing to mention is that there is a tool aptly named web2ldap, and it is a Python, web-based frontend for LDAP by the same author of python-ldap. You might consider trying it out as well as an alternative to some of the other web-based management solutions for LDAP. Go to *http://www.web2ldap.de/* for the official documentation. It is highly structured around LDAPv3 support.

Apache Log Reporting

Currently, Apache is the web server for approximately 50 percent of the domains on the Internet. The following example is intended to show you an approach for reporting on your Apache logfiles. This example will focus only on one aspect of the information available in your Apache logs, but you should be able to take this approach and apply it to any type of data that is contained in those logs. This approach will also scale well to large data files as well as large numbers of files.

In Chapter 3, we gave a couple of examples of parsing an Apache web server log to extract some information from it. In this example, we'll reuse the modules we wrote for Chapter 3 to show how to generate a human-readable report from one or more logfiles. In addition to handling all of the logfiles that you specify separately, you can tell this script to consolidate the logfiles together and generate one single report. Example 14-2 shows the code for the script.

Example 14-2. Consolidated Apache logfile reporting

```python
#!/usr/bin/env python

from optparse import OptionParser

def open_files(files):
    for f in files:
        yield (f, open(f))

def combine_lines(files):
    for f, f_obj in files:
        for line in f_obj:
            yield line

def obfuscate_ipaddr(addr):
    return ".".join(str((int(n) / 10) * 10) for n in addr.split('.'))

if __name__ == '__main__':
    parser = OptionParser()
    parser.add_option("-c", "--consolidate", dest="consolidate", default=False,
        action='store_true', help="consolidate log files")
    parser.add_option("-r", "--regex", dest="regex", default=False,
        action='store_true', help="use regex parser")

    (options, args) = parser.parse_args()
    logfiles = args

    if options.regex:
        from apache_log_parser_regex import generate_log_report
    else:
        from apache_log_parser_split import generate_log_report

    opened_files = open_files(logfiles)

    if options.consolidate:
        opened_files = (('CONSOLIDATED', combine_lines(opened_files)),)

    for filename, file_obj in opened_files:
        print "*" * 60
        print filename
        print "-" * 60
        print "%-20s%s" % ("IP ADDRESS", "BYTES TRANSFERRED")
```

```
print "-" * 60
report_dict = generate_log_report(file_obj)
for ip_addr, bytes in report_dict.items():
    print "%-20s%s" % (obfuscate_ipaddr(ip_addr), sum(bytes))
print "=" * 60
```

At the top of the script, we define two functions: open_files() and combine_lines().
Later in the script, both of these functions allow us later to use some mild generator-
chaining to simplify the code just a bit. open_files() is a generator function that takes
a list (actually, any iterator) of filenames. For each of those filenames, it yields a tuple
of the filename and a corresponding open file object. combine_lines() takes an iterable
of open file objects as its only argument. It iterates over the file objects with a for loop.
For each of those files, it iterates over the lines in the file. And it yields each line that
it iterates over. The iterable that we get from combine_lines() is comparable to how
file objects are commonly used: iterating over the lines of the file.

Next, we use optparse to parse the command-line arguments from the user. We're only
accepting two arguments, both of them Boolean: consolidate logfiles and use regular
expression library. The consolidate option tells the script to treat all the files as one
file. In a sense, we wind up concatenating the files together if this option is passed in.
But we'll get to that momentarily. The regex option tells the script to use the regular
expression library that we wrote in Chapter 3 rather than the "split" library. Both should
offer identical functionality, but the "split" library is faster.

Next, we check whether the regex flag was passed in. If it was, we use the regex module.
If not, we use the split module. We really included this flag and import condition to
compare the performance of the two libraries. But, we'll get to the running and performance of this script later.

Then, we call open_files() on our list of file names passed in by the user. As we've
already mentioned, open_files() is a generator function and yields file objects from
the list of filenames that we pass in to it. This means that it doesn't actually open the
file until it yields it back to us. Now that we have an iterable of open file objects, we
can do a couple of things with it. We can either iterate over all of the files that we have
generated and report on each file, or we can somehow combine the logfiles together
and report on them as one file. This is where the combine_lines() function comes in.
If the user passed in the "consolidate" flag, the "files" that will be iterated over are
actually just a single file-like object: a generator of all the lines in all the files.

So, whether it is a real or combined file, we pass each file to the appropriate
generate_log_report() function, which then returns a dictionary of IP addresses and
bytes sent to that IP. For each file, we print out some section breaking strings and
formatted strings containing the results of generate_log_report(). The output for a run
on a single 28 KB logfile looks like this:

```
*************************************************************
access.log
-------------------------------------------------------------
```

```
IP ADDRESS            BYTES TRANSFERRED
-------------------------------------------------------------

190.40.10.0           17479
200.80.230.0          45346
200.40.90.110         8276
130.150.250.0         0
70.0.10.140           2115
70.180.0.220          76992
200.40.90.110         23860
190.20.250.190        499
190.20.250.210        431
60.210.40.20          27681
60.240.70.180         20976
70.0.20.120           1265
190.20.250.210        4268
190.50.200.210        4268
60.100.200.230        0
70.0.20.190           378
190.20.250.250        5936
=============================================================
```

The output for three logfiles (actually, the same logfile three times with the same log
data duplicated over and over) looks like this:

```
*************************************************************
access.log
-------------------------------------------------------------
IP ADDRESS            BYTES TRANSFERRED
-------------------------------------------------------------

190.40.10.0           17479
200.80.230.0          45346
<snip>
70.0.20.190           378
190.20.250.250        5936
=============================================================
*************************************************************
access_big.log
-------------------------------------------------------------
IP ADDRESS            BYTES TRANSFERRED
-------------------------------------------------------------

190.40.10.0           1747900
200.80.230.0          4534600
<snip>
70.0.20.190           37800
190.20.250.250        593600
=============================================================
*************************************************************
access_bigger.log
-------------------------------------------------------------
IP ADDRESS            BYTES TRANSFERRED
-------------------------------------------------------------

190.40.10.0           699160000
200.80.230.0          1813840000
<snip>
70.0.20.190           15120000
```

```
190.20.250.250        237440000
============================================================
```

And the output of all three consolidated together looks like this:

```
************************************************************
CONSOLIDATED
------------------------------------------------------------
IP ADDRESS              BYTES TRANSFERRED
------------------------------------------------------------
190.40.10.0            700925379
200.80.230.0           1818419946
<snip>
190.20.250.250         238039536
============================================================
```

So, how well does this script perform? And what does memory consumption look like? All benchmarks in this section were run on an Ubuntu Gutsy server with an AMD Athlon 64 X2 5400+ 2.8 GHz, 2 GB of RAM, and a Seagate Barracuda 7200 RPM SATA drive. And we were using a roughly 1 GB file:

```
jmjones@ezr:/data/logs$ ls -l access*log
-rw-r--r-- 1 jmjones jmjones 1157080000 2008-04-18 12:46 access_bigger.log
```

Here are the run times.

```
$ time python summarize_logfiles.py --regex access_bigger.log
************************************************************
access_bigger.log
------------------------------------------------------------
IP ADDRESS              BYTES TRANSFERRED
------------------------------------------------------------
190.40.10.0            699160000
<snip>
190.20.250.250         237440000
============================================================

real    0m46.296s
user    0m45.547s
sys     0m0.744s

jmjones@ezr:/data/logs$ time python summarize_logfiles.py access_bigger.log
************************************************************
access_bigger.log
------------------------------------------------------------
IP ADDRESS              BYTES TRANSFERRED
------------------------------------------------------------
190.40.10.0            699160000
<snip>
190.20.250.250         237440000
============================================================

real    0m34.261s
user    0m33.354s
sys     0m0.896s
```

For the regular expression version of the data extraction library, it took about 46 seconds. For the version that uses string.split(), it took about 34 seconds. But memory usage was abysmal. It ran up to about 130 MB of memory. The reason for this is that the generate_log_report() keeps a list of bytes transferred for each IP address in the logfile. So, the larger the file, the more memory this script will consume. But we can do something about that. Here is a less memory-hungry version of the parsing library:

```python
#!/usr/bin/env python

def dictify_logline(line):
    '''return a dictionary of the pertinent pieces of an apache combined log file

    Currently, the only fields we are interested in are remote host and bytes sent,
    but we are putting status in there just for good measure.
    '''
    split_line = line.split()
    return {'remote_host': split_line[0],
            'status': split_line[8],
            'bytes_sent': split_line[9],
    }

def generate_log_report(logfile):
    '''return a dictionary of format remote_host=>[list of bytes sent]

    This function takes a file object, iterates through all the lines in the file,
    and generates a report of the number of bytes transferred to each remote host
    for each hit on the webserver.
    '''
    report_dict = {}
    for line in logfile:
        line_dict = dictify_logline(line)
        host = line_dict['remote_host']
        #print line_dict
        try:
            bytes_sent = int(line_dict['bytes_sent'])
        except ValueError:
            ##totally disregard anything we don't understand
            continue
        report_dict[host] = report_dict.setdefault(host, 0) + bytes_sent
    return report_dict
```

Basically, this one tallies the bytes_sent as it goes rather than making the calling function tally it. Here is a slightly modified summarize_logfiles script with a new option to import the less memory-hungry version of the library:

```python
#!/usr/bin/env python

from optparse import OptionParser

def open_files(files):
    for f in files:
        yield (f, open(f))

def combine_lines(files):
```

```
        for f, f_obj in files:
            for line in f_obj:
                yield line

    def obfuscate_ipaddr(addr):
        return ".".join(str((int(n) / 10) * 10) for n in addr.split('.'))

    if __name__ == '__main__':
        parser = OptionParser()
        parser.add_option("-c", "--consolidate", dest="consolidate", default=False,
            action='store_true', help="consolidate log files")
        parser.add_option("-r", "--regex", dest="regex", default=False,
            action='store_true', help="use regex parser")
        parser.add_option("-m", "--mem", dest="mem", default=False,
            action='store_true', help="use mem parser")

        (options, args) = parser.parse_args()
        logfiles = args

        if options.regex:
            from apache_log_parser_regex import generate_log_report
        elif options.mem:
            from apache_log_parser_split_mem import generate_log_report
        else:
            from apache_log_parser_split import generate_log_report

        opened_files = open_files(logfiles)

        if options.consolidate:
            opened_files = (('CONSOLIDATED', combine_lines(opened_files)),)

        for filename, file_obj in opened_files:
            print "*" * 60
            print filename
            print "-" * 60
            print "%-20s%s" % ("IP ADDRESS", "BYTES TRANSFERRED")
            print "-" * 60
            report_dict = generate_log_report(file_obj)
            for ip_addr, bytes in report_dict.items():
                if options.mem:
                    print "%-20s%s" % (obfuscate_ipaddr(ip_addr), bytes)
                else:
                    print "%-20s%s" % (obfuscate_ipaddr(ip_addr), sum(bytes))
            print "=" * 60
```

And this actually wound up being a bit faster than the more memory-hungry version:

```
jmjones@ezr:/data/logs$ time ./summarize_logfiles_mem.py --mem access_bigger.log
************************************************************
access_bigger.log
---------------------------------------------------------------
IP ADDRESS          BYTES TRANSFERRED
---------------------------------------------------------------
190.40.10.0         699160000
<snip>
190.20.250.250      237440000
```

```
======================================================================
real    0m30.508s
user    0m29.866s
sys     0m0.636s
```

Memory consumption held steady at about 4 MB for the duration of this run. This script will handle about 2 GB of logfiles per minute. Theoretically, the file sizes could be indefinite and memory wouldn't grow like it did with the previous version. However, since this is using a dictionary and each key is a unique IP address, the memory usage will grow with unique IP addresses. If memory consumption becomes a problem, however, you could swap out the dictionary with a persistent database, either relational or even a Berkeley DB.

FTP Mirror

This next example shows how to connect to an FTP server and recursively retrieve all the files on that server starting with some user-specified directory. It also allows you to remove each file after you have retrieved it. You may be wondering, "What is the point of this script? Doesn't rsync handle all of that?" And the answer is, "Yes, it does." However, what if rsync is not installed on the server you are working on and you aren't permitted to install it? (This is unlikely for you as a sysadmin, but it happens.) Or, what if you don't have SSH or rsync access to the server you're trying to pull from? It helps to have an alternative. Here is the source code for the mirror script:

```python
#!/usr/bin/env python

import ftplib
import os

class FTPSync(object):
    def __init__(self, host, username, password, ftp_base_dir,
                            local_base_dir, delete=False):
        self.host = host
        self.username = username
        self.password = password
        self.ftp_base_dir = ftp_base_dir
        self.local_base_dir = local_base_dir
        self.delete = delete

        self.conn = ftplib.FTP(host, username, password)
        self.conn.cwd(ftp_base_dir)
        try:
            os.makedirs(local_base_dir)
        except OSError:
            pass
        os.chdir(local_base_dir)
    def get_dirs_files(self):
        dir_res = []
        self.conn.dir('.', dir_res.append)
        files = [f.split(None, 8)[-1] for f in dir_res if f.startswith('-')]
```

```
        dirs = [f.split(None, 8)[-1] for f in dir_res if f.startswith('d')]
        return (files, dirs)
    def walk(self, next_dir):
        print "Walking to", next_dir
        self.conn.cwd(next_dir)
        try:
            os.mkdir(next_dir)
        except OSError:
            pass
        os.chdir(next_dir)

        ftp_curr_dir = self.conn.pwd()
        local_curr_dir = os.getcwd()

        files, dirs = self.get_dirs_files()
        print "FILES:", files
        print "DIRS:", dirs
        for f in files:
            print next_dir, ':', f
            outf = open(f, 'wb')
            try:
                self.conn.retrbinary('RETR %s' % f, outf.write)
            finally:
                outf.close()
            if self.delete:
                print "Deleting", f
                self.conn.delete(f)
        for d in dirs:
            os.chdir(local_curr_dir)
            self.conn.cwd(ftp_curr_dir)
            self.walk(d)

    def run(self):
        self.walk('.')


if __name__ == '__main__':
    from optparse import OptionParser
    parser = OptionParser()
    parser.add_option("-o", "--host", dest="host",
        action='store', help="FTP host")
    parser.add_option("-u", "--username", dest="username",
        action='store', help="FTP username")
    parser.add_option("-p", "--password", dest="password",
        action='store', help="FTP password")
    parser.add_option("-r", "--remote_dir", dest="remote_dir",
        action='store', help="FTP remote starting directory")
    parser.add_option("-l", "--local_dir", dest="local_dir",
        action='store', help="Local starting directory")
    parser.add_option("-d", "--delete", dest="delete", default=False,
        action='store_true', help="use regex parser")

    (options, args) = parser.parse_args()
    f = FTPSync(options.host, options.username, options.password,
```

```
                options.remote_dir, options.local_dir, options.delete)
    f.run()
```

This script was a little easier to write by using a class. The constructor takes a number of parameters. To connect and log in, you have to pass it host, username, and password. To get to the appropriate places on the remote server and your local server, you have to pass in ftp_base_dir and local_base_dir. delete is just a flag that specifies whether to delete the file from the remote server once you've downloaded it—you can see in the constructor that we set the default value for this to False.

Once we set these values that we received as object attributes, we connect to the specified FTP server and log in. Then, we change to the specified start directory on the server and change to the start directory on the local machine. Before actually changing into the local start directory, we first try to create it. If it exists, we'll get an OSError exception, which we ignore.

We have three additional methods defined: get_dirs_files(), walk(), and run(). get_dirs_files() determines which files in the current directory are files and which are directories. (By the way, this is expected to only work on Unix servers.) It figures out which are files and which are directories by doing a directory listing looking at the first character of each line of the listing. If the character is d, then it is a directory. If the character is -, then it is a file. This means that we won't follow symlinks nor deal with block devices.

The next method that we defined is walk(). This method is where the bulk of the work happens. The walk() method takes a single argument: the next directory to visit. Before we go any further, we'll mention that this is a recursive function. We intend for it to call itself. If any directory contains other directories, they will be walked into. The code in the walk() method first changes directory on the FTP server to the specified directory. Then we change into the directory on the local server, creating it if necessary. Then we store our current positions on both the FTP server and locally into the variables ftp_curr_dir and local_curr_dir for use later. Next, we get the files and directories in this directory from our get_dirs_files() method that we've already mentioned. For each of the files in the directory, we retrieve them using the retrbinary() FTP method. We also delete the file if the delete flag was passed in. Next, we change directory to the current directories on the FTP server and FTP server and call walk() to walk into those lower directories. The reason that we change into the current directory again is so that when lower walk() calls return, we can come back up to where we are.

The final method that we defined is run(). run() is simply a convenience method. Calling run() simply calls walk() and passes it the current FTP directory.

We have some very basic error and exception handling in this script. First, we don't check all the command-line arguments and make sure that at least host, username, and password are passed in. The script will blow up quickly if those aren't specified. Also, we don't try to download a file again if an exception happened. Instead, if something causes a download to fail, we're going to get an exception. The program will terminate in that case. If the script terminates in the middle of a download, the next time you start it up, the script will begin downloading the file again. The upside to this is that it won't delete a file it has only partially downloaded.

Callbacks

The concept of callbacks and passing functions around may be foreign to you. If so, it is definitely worth digging into so that you understand it well enough to use it, or at the very least, understand what is going on when you see it being used. In Python, functions are "first class," which means that you can pass them around and treat them as objects—because they really are objects. See Example A-1.

Example A-1. Showing functions as first class

```
In [1]: def foo():
   ...:         print foo
   ...:
   ...:

In [2]: foo
Out[2]: <function foo at 0x1233270>

In [3]: type(foo)
Out[3]: <type 'function'>

In [4]: dir(foo)
Out[4]:
['__call__',
 '__class__',
 '__delattr__',
 '__dict__',
 '__doc__',
 '__get__',
 '__getattribute__',
 '__hash__',
 '__init__',
 '__module__',
 '__name__',
 '__new__',
 '__reduce__',
 '__reduce_ex__',
 '__repr__',
 '__setattr__',
 '__str__',
```

```
'func_closure',
'func_code',
'func_defaults',
'func_dict',
'func_doc',
'func_globals',
'func_name']
```

Simply referring to a function, such as foo in the previous example, does not call it. Referring to a function's name lets you get at any attributes the function has and to even refer to the function by a different name later. See Example A-2.

Example A-2. Referring to functions by name

```
In [1]: def foo():
   ...:     """this is a docstring"""
   ...:     print "IN FUNCTION FOO"
   ...:
   ...:

In [2]: foo
Out[2]: <function foo at 0x8319534>

In [3]: foo.__doc__
Out[3]: 'this is a docstring'

In [4]: bar = foo

In [5]: bar
Out[5]: <function foo at 0x8319534>

In [6]: bar.__doc__
Out[6]: 'this is a docstring'

In [7]: foo.a = 1

In [8]: bar.a
Out[8]: 1

In [9]: foo()
IN FUNCTION FOO

In [10]: bar()
IN FUNCTION FOO
```

We created a new function foo so that it contained a docstring. We then stated that bar was going to point to the function foo that we just created. In Python, what you usually think of as variables are typically just names that point at (or refer to) some object. The process of associating a name with an object is called "name binding." So, when we created the function foo, we really created a function object and then bound the name foo to that new function. Using the IPython prompt to see the basic information it can tell us about foo, it reported back that it was a foo function. Interestingly, it said the same thing about the name bar, namely that it was a foo function. We set an attribute a on the function named foo and were able to access it from bar. And, calling both foo and bar produced the same result.

One of the places in this book that we use callbacks is in the chapter on networking, Chapter 5. Passing functions around as in the FTP example in that chapter allows for runtime dynamism and code-time flexibility and can even improve code reuse. Even if you don't think you'll ever use it, it's a thought process worth putting in your brain's catalog.

Index

Symbols

.py files (see wrappers)

\ (backslash)

    escape sequences, list of, 73

$ (dollar sign)

    for shell execute variables, 36

! (exclamation point)

    for shell execute, 36

    !! for shell execute, 37

%-TAB, 31

? (question mark) for help, 12, 31

    to obtain object information, 54

    to search for objects, 56

    ?? to obtain object information, 54

' (quotation mark, single)

    creating strings with, 72

" (quotation marks, double)

    creating strings with, 72

_ (underscore)

    for results history, 62–64

    __ (in variable names), 38

    __ object, 57

    ___ object, 57

"magic" functions, 34

    (see also specific function)

A

Active Directory, using with Python, 406–408

active version of package, changing, 264

alias function, 34–35, 64

alias table, 37, 38

Amazon Web services (Boto), 247

Apache config file, hacking (example), 97–100

Apache log reporting, 408–415

Apache Log Viewer, building (example)

    with curses library, 330–334

    with Django, 335–341

    with PyGTK, 326–330

Apache logfile, parsing (example), 110–116

appscript project, 241

archiving data, 199–204

    examining TAR file contents, 201–204

ARP protocol, 221

asr utility, 242

attachments (email), sending, 143

attrib attribute (Element object), 118

authentication

    when installing eggs, 265

authentication (SMTP), 142

automated information gathering, 123–126

    receiving email, 125–126

automatically re-imaging routines, 242

automation, with IPython shell, 64–69

B

background threading, 211

backslash (\)

    escape sequences, list of, 73

backups, 177

    examining TAR file contents, 201–204

bar charts, creating, 137

Bash, Python versus, 2

Bayer, Michael, 385

Bicking, Ian, 280

blocks of code, editing, 29

bookmark command, 41

bookmarks

    navigating to bookmarked directories, 40

We'd like to hear your suggestions for improving our indexes. Send email to *index@oreilly.com*.

About the Authors

Noah Gift has an M.A. in CIS from California State University, Los Angeles, a B.S. in nutritional science from California Polytechnic San Luis Obispo, is an Apple and LPI certified sysadmin, and has worked at companies such as Caltech, Disney Feature Animation, Sony Imageworks, and Turner Studios.

In his free time, he enjoys hanging out with his wife, Leah, and their son, Liam, playing the piano, and exercising religiously.

Jeremy M. Jones is a software engineer who works for Predictix. His weapon of choice is Python, but he has done some shell, plenty of Perl, a touch of Java, is currently learning C#, and finds functional programming languages (especially OCaml) fascinating.

He is the author of the open source projects Munkware, a multiproducer/multiconsumer, transactional, and persistent queuing mechanism; ediplex, an EDI (electronic data interchange) parsing engine; and podgrabber, a podcast downloader. All three projects were written in the Python language.

Jeremy spends his spare time enjoying his family and doing a little writing. He lives in Conyers, Georgia (just east of Atlanta) with his wife, Debra, two children, Zane and Justus, and a lab named Genevieve (how Madelinesque).

Opinions and views expressed by Jeremy are his own and not those of Predictix.

Colophon

The image on the cover of *Python for Unix and Linux System Administration* is a boa constrictor (*boa constrictor*). Found throughout South and Central America and some islands in the Caribbean, boa constrictors are non-venomous snakes that can thrive in a wide array of environments, from deserts to open savannas and wet tropical forests, but they prefer arid terrain over wet surroundings. They are both terrestrial and arboreal, but as they get older, they tend to spend more time on the ground.

Boa constrictors have very unique markings that include diamond- and oval-like patterns. Their scales change colors depending on their habitat, allowing them to hide from the forest-dwelling animals that hunt them.

In the wild, boa constrictors thrive on small- to medium-size rodents, lizards, bats, birds, mongooses, squirrels, and have even been known to feast on other mammals as large as ocelots. Being cold-blooded and slow moving, boas can go up to a week without eating after capturing large prey. They are solitary and nocturnal hunters, with heat-sensitive pads on their heads to help them hunt. Particularly fond of bats, boas will hang in trees and from the mouths of caves waiting for them to fly by, then they can grab the bats with their mouths. Not surprisingly, boa constrictors kill by constriction. The snake wraps its body around its prey in coils, tightening its grip each time the victim breathes out, eventually suffocating it to death.

Boas are a common attraction in zoos, and they are even relatively common pets. In fact, thousands of dollars are made every year importing them into the U.S. In South America, they are revered as "destroyers of rodents" and are often domesticated for that reason. Boa constrictors grow quite tame in captivity and can live there as such for 20–30 years. Hunted for the exotic pet trade and their decorative markings, some boa constrictors are endangered and have protected status.

Boa constrictors are seasonal breeders. To attract males, females emit a scent from their cloacas, which is the chamber into which the intestinal and urogenital tracts discharge. Fertilization happens internally, and females can give birth to up to 60 live babies at one time. Significantly smaller than their anaconda cousins, newborn boas average 2 feet in length and can grow up to 13 feet long and weigh more than 100 pounds. Found in South America, the largest boa constrictor on record was 18 feet!

The cover image is a 19th-century engraving from the Dover Pictorial Archive. The cover font is Adobe ITC Garamond. The text font is Linotype Birka; the heading font is Adobe Myriad Condensed; and the code font is LucasFont's TheSansMonoCondensed.

Related Titles from O'Reilly

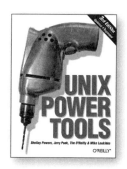

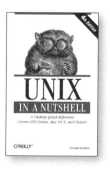

Unix Administration

Classic Shell Scripting

DNS and BIND, *5th Edition*

DNS & BIND Cookbook

Essential System
Administration, *3rd Edition*

Essential System Administration
Pocket Reference

Postfix: The Definitive Guide

qmail

sendmail, *4th Edition*

sendmail Cookbook

System Performance Tuning,
2nd Edition

Unix Basics

bash Cookbook

GNU Emacs Pocket Reference

Learning GNU Emacs,
3rd Edition

Learning the bash Shell,
3rd Edition

Learning the Korn Shell,
2nd Edition

Learning the Unix Operating
System, *5th Edition*

Learning the vi Editor,
6th Edition

sed & awk Pocket Reference,
2nd Edition

sed & awk, *2nd Edition*

Unix in a Nutshell, *4th Edition*

Using csh & tcsh

Unix Tools

BSD Hacks

CVS Pocket Reference,
2nd Edition

Effective awk Programming,
3rd Edition

Essential CVS, *2nd Edition*

GDB Pocket Reference

lex & yacc, *2nd Edition*

Managing Projects with GNU
make, *3rd Edition*

Practical PostgreSQL

The Complete FreeBSD,
4th Edition

Unix Power Tools, *3rd edition*

Version Control with
Subversion

O'REILLY®

Our books are available at most retail and online bookstores.

To order direct: 1-800-998-9938 • *order@oreilly.com* • *www.oreilly.com*

Online editions of most O'Reilly titles are available by subscription at *safari.oreilly.com*